*Electronic
Engineering*

Wiley International Edition

Electronic
Engineering

SECOND EDITION

Charles L. Alley & Kenneth W. Atwood

UNIVERSITY OF UTAH, ELECTRICAL ENGINEERING DEPARTMENT

JOHN WILEY & SONS, INC. NEW YORK LONDON SYDNEY

TOPPAN COMPANY, LTD.,   Tokyo, Japan

Library of Congress Catalog Card Number: 66-16128
Printed in Japan
By TOPPAN PRINTING COMPANY. LTD.

To Mildred and Ruth
whose patience and understanding
made this book possible.

Preface

The rapidly changing field of electronics requires a continual re-evaluation of the content of an electronics textbook. Also, improved methods of presenting familiar subjects are constantly being sought by a resourceful teacher. For these reasons, we felt that a new edition would be very beneficial to those teachers who strive to keep their material up to date. Also, the practicing engineer requires reference material which is current.

Great assistance in planning this second edition was given by the publisher, who mailed questionnaires to a large number of users of the first edition. Criticism of the first edition and recommendations for the second edition were solicited and generously given. We are deeply indebted to these many contributors for their response and excellent suggestions. Although it was impossible to incorporate all of these suggestions into a single volume, the second edition does incorporate a great number of these recommendations. In addition, the publisher obtained outstanding reviews of the revised material, which resulted in a considerable improvement of the text. To all of those who have given their time to this cause, we express our heartfelt thanks.

The major changes in the second edition include the following ones.

1. IEEE standard notation has been adopted.
2. Some of the newer devices such as field-effect transistors and unijunction transistors have been included.
3. A new chapter on cascaded amplifiers and noise has been included.
4. Emphasis on the semiconductor devices has been increased.
5. Chapter 16 on pulse applications has been completely rewritten and major changes have been made in most of the remaining chapters in order to achieve the aforementioned goals.

6. A large number of problems have been rewritten and many new comprehensive problems have been added.

7. By deleting some of the less important material and improving the efficiency of presentation, the second edition is not substantially longer than the first edition.

The new material in this second edition has been presented to Electrical Engineering classes at the University of Utah with gratifying results. We are indebted to these students for their helpful suggestions. We also thank John P. Stringham for designing the nomograph given in Fig. 3.39. The secretarial staff of the Electrical Engineering Department under the able direction of Mrs. Joyce Hansen and Mrs. Marian Swenson have been unusually helpful and cooperative in the preparation of the manuscript.

We hope you enjoy this new edition.

CHARLES L. ALLEY
KENNETH W. ATWOOD

Preface

TO THE FIRST EDITION

The recent development of semiconductor devices necessitated the addition of one or more courses to an already crowded curriculum in Electrical Engineering. In teaching the tube and transistor courses, we observed that there was much duplication of both basic theory and applications. At about this same time, the *s*-domain or complex frequency concept was introduced into the basic circuits courses. The students expressed disappointment that this powerful tool was not utilized in the electronic circuits courses also. Therefore, we concluded not only that a unified treatment of tube and semiconductor theory was needed, but also that the complex frequency concept should be used for electronic circuit analysis. The *complete response* of a system could then be obtained rather than the restricted steady-state response. A unified treatment of system response to a variety of input signals (such as pulses, step functions, sinusoids, etc.) could be achieved, as well as a unification of the tube and semiconductor devices. With these objectives in mind, we wrote notes which were used in teaching electronics at the University of Utah. These notes were used and continually revised for four years before the first edition of *Electronic Engineering* was published.

As a means of achieving the foregoing objectives, sufficient semiconductor theory is given to provide an adequate understanding of both semiconductor and electron tube devices. In general, the basic ideas are approached from the point of view of semiconductors. Then, with very slight modification, concepts are extended to include the electron-tube devices. This broadened application provides better insight into the behavior of both semiconductors and electron tubes than is normally acquired when each is treated separately. Electron-tube applications are

ix

considered first, only when this approach provides easier understanding.

The use of the complex frequency domain leads logically to the use of the root-locus technique for analyzing feedback circuits. This approach to feedback problems, which provides improved design criteria and visualization, is used in the discussion of oscillators and negative feedback amplifiers.

The material is organized to provide a consistent development of ideas from the basic physical principles of the device to the more complex circuit applications. The organization was chosen to provide maximum ease of understanding rather than sophistication of presentation.

To gain maximum understanding of the material in this book, the student should have a good foundation in alternating current circuits, calculus, and the Laplace transformation. However, since the s-domain concept is not used in the first six chapters, the study of circuits and mathematics could parallel the study of this book. By accepting some of the derived formulas on faith and by using a few transformations in a cookbook manner, the essential goals can be achieved by students who have had no transformation theory and whose mathematical background is otherwise less than ideal.

Chapter 1 provides a background in electric and magnetic fields. This chapter may be omitted if the reader has an adequate knowledge of these topics.

Chapter 2 furnishes the proper background in semiconductor theory. If this material has been studied elsewhere, Chapter 2 may also be omitted.

Chapters 3 to 6 present the principles of operation and methods of analysis of typical semiconductor and electron-tube devices. Both graphical analysis and equivalent circuits are stressed.

Chapters 7 to 9 discuss cascaded small-signal amplifiers. In these chapters, the s-domain equivalent circuits are used to predict the response of typical circuit configurations to various types of excitation.

Chapters 10 to 13 treat large-signal amplifiers, negative feedback, and oscillators.

Chapters 14 and 15 present the basic principles of modulation and detection. Typical circuits are also included. These chapters could be omitted without loss of continuity.

Chapter 16 deals with electronic devices used as switches. Topics such as saturation resistance and storage time, which are important in the switching mode, are discussed in this chapter. Typical applications such as multivibrators are also included.

Chapter 17 discusses electronic-power supplies, both regulated and unregulated. Either Chapters 16 or 17 could be studied in any sequence following Chapter 10.

An instructor's manual will be provided with problem solutions and answers as well as a set of suggested laboratory experiments. A transistor manual and a tube manual should supplement the text. In addition, a study of the root-locus method from a suitable text such as *Introduction to Feedback Systems* by L. Dale Harris (John Wiley and Sons) would be desirable. However, acceptable root-locus plots can be made by following the rules in Appendix II.

We are indebted to the students and staff of the Electrical Engineering Department of the University of Utah for the many helpful suggestions offered during the revision period. We are especially appreciative of the suggestions and comments given by L. Dale Harris and James E. Dalley of the Electrical Engineering Department staff. We are also indebted to Mrs. Joyce Hansen for the helpful suggestions and supervision of the preparation of the manuscript.

CHARLES L. ALLEY
KENNETH W. ATWOOD

Contents

xiii

List of Symbols

A Constant (may have subscripts)

A Angstrom $= 10^{-10}$ m

A Area in square meters

a The turns ratio of a transformer

a A constant (may have subscripts)

a Acceleration in m/sec^2

α Forward current gain parameter of a common base transistor (also h_{fb})

α_0 The low frequency current gain factor

α' A current gain parameter related to α by Eq. 4.42

$\alpha*$ The low collector voltage current gain factor

B Constant

B Magnetic field intensity in webers/m^2

B The bandwidth of a single-stage amplifier

B_n The bandwidth of an n-stage amplifier

b Ratio of actual coupling to critical or transitional coupling

b A constant (may have subscripts)

β Current amplification factor (same as h_{fe})

β Feedback factor

C Capacitance in farads (may have subscripts)

C A constant (may have subscripts)

C Centigrade

c Velocity of light ($2.998 \ldots \times 10^8$ m/sec)

γ Carrier transport factor

D Diffusion constant

D_f Distortion with feedback

D_n	Diffusion constant of electrons
D_0	Open loop distortion (no feedback)
D_p	Diffusion constant of holes
d	Length or distance
d	Differential operator
db	Decibels
Δ	A very small finite amount
δ	Internal collector efficiency
δ_i	The interacting parameter
E	Energy in ergs
e	Base of the natural logarithm
$\mathscr{E}$	Electric field intensity in v/m
ϵ	Permittivity ($\epsilon_r \epsilon_v$)
ϵ_r	Dielectric constant
ϵ_v	Dielectric constant of free space ($8.855 \ldots \times 10^{-12}$ f/m)
F	The spot noise figure
F	Force in newtons
F_a	The figure of merit for an amplifier
f	Frequency in cycles/sec or Hertz
f	Abbreviation for farads
$f(W)$	Fermi-Dirac distribution function
f_τ	The frequency at which the common emitter current gain is one
ζ	The damping ratio of a pair of complex poles
G	Giga or 10^9
G_A	The total gain of a multistage amplifier
G_i	Current gain
G_v	Voltage gain
G_p	Power gain
GB	The gain-bandwidth product
g	Weight in grams
g	Conductance in mhos $= 1/r$
g_m	Transconductance of a vacuum tube
g_{m2}	Transconductance of the screen grid in a vacuum tube
g_{m2p}	Transconductance which indicates the effect the screen grid potential has on the plate current
g_0	The quiescent value of g_m
g_c	The conversion transconductance of a device
H	Scale factor
Hz	Hertz or cycles per second

h Planck's Constant $(6.625 \times 10^{-34}$ j sec)

h The abbreviation for henries

h_i Input impedance of a device (a second subscript indicates common element in configuration)

h_r Reverse voltage amplification factor of a device (may have second subscripts)

h_f Forward current gain of a device (may have second subscript)

h_o Output admittance of a device (may have second subscript)

ϕ_τ Thermal resistance (may have additional subscripts)

I Current

I_I Injection current

I_S Saturation current

I_o The reverse current of a diode at 300°K

I_{c_O} Current in the collector circuit due to thermally generated carriers

$\overline{i_n}$ The rms noise current

To differentiate the various currents and voltages associated with tubes and transistors, the following notation is used:

I_B A capital letter with a capital subscript is used to denote the quiescent element current.

I_b A capital letter with a lower-case subscript is used to denote the rms value of the sinusoidal component of current through a given element. This same symbol is also used to denote the s-domain current through a given element.

i_B A lower-case letter with a capital subscript is used to denote the total instantaneous current through a given element.

i_b A lower-case letter with a lower-case subscript is used to denote the instantaneous time-varying component of current through a given element.

The subscript letter indicates the particular element which is involved. Thus, B (as used in the foregoing examples) denotes the base of a transistor; C denotes the transistor collector; E denotes the transistor emitter; G denotes the grid of a tube. (A second subscript consisting of a number may be used to differentiate between grids in a multi-grid tube); K denotes the tube cathode; P denotes the tube plate; I denotes the input current to a circuit and O denotes the circuit output current.

J Current density in amperes/meter²

J_n Current density due to electron motion

J_p Current density due to hole motion

J_I Injection current density

J_S Saturation current density

     $(-1)^{\frac{1}{2}}$

K Reference gain of an amplifier

K Kilo or 10^3

K_A Reference gain of a multistage amplifier

k	Coefficient of coupling
K	Constant (may have subscripts)
°K	Degrees kelvin
k	Boltzmann's Constant 1.38×10^{-23} j/°K
k	The coefficient of coupling of a coil
k_c	The critical coupling of a coil
k_g	Kilograms
L	Inductance in henries
L	Length or distance
L_n	The length of the depletion region in n-material
L_p	The length of the depletion region in p-material
l	Length or distance
l	Mean-free path in the X direction of an electron
l_p	Mean-free path in the X direction of a hole
ln	The natural logarithm of a number
log	The logarithm to the base 10 of a number
M	Mutual inductance
M	Meg or 10^6
M	The modulation index (may have subscripts to indicate the type of modulation)
m	Mass in kilograms
m	Milli or 10^{-3}
m_0	The mass of a body at rest
$m_e{}^*$	The effective mass of an electron
$m_p{}^*$	The effective mass of a hole
μ	Micro or 10^{-6}
μ	Charge mobility
μ	Voltage amplification factor of a tube
N	Number
N_a	Acceptor atom density
N_c	The density of states in the conduction band
N_d	Donor atom density
N_L	Number of electrons which cross a reference plane to the left in time t
N_R	Number of electrons which cross a reference plane to the right in time t
N_s	Number of states/unit volume
N_x	Total number of electrons which cross the reference surface in time t
n	An integer number
n	Nano or 10^{-9}
n	Number of electrons/unit volume
n	The turns of a coil
n_n	Number of electrons/unit volume in n-type material

n_p	Number of electrons/unit volume in p-type material
n_t	The total number of electrons which cross the reference surface/second
η	Efficiency (may have subscripts)
η	The voltage dividing parameter of a unijunction transistor
ω	Radian frequency $= 2\pi f$ (may have subscripts)
P	Power in watts
P_d	The power dissipated in a device
P_i	The input power
P_o	The output power
p	Instantaneous power in watts
p	Number of holes/unit volume
p_n	Number of holes/unit volume in n-type material
p_o	A reference density of holes
p_p	Number of holes/unit volume in p-type material
π	A mathematical constant (3.1416 . . .)
Q	The figure of merit for a coil or a tuned circuit
Q	The charge on a body in coulombs
Q	The quiescent operating point of a device
Q_0	The unloaded Q of a circuit
q	The charge on an electron (16.019 . . . $\times$ 10^{-20} coulombs)
R	Resistance in ohms
R_{sh}	The total shunt resistance in a circuit
Re	The abbreviation for "real part of"
R_{cs}	The collector saturation resistance
r	Radius in meters
r_f	Diode forward resistance
r_b	Diode reverse resistance
r_p	Dynamic plate resistance
r_P	Static plate resistance
r_{g2}	Dynamic resistance of screen grid in a vacuum tube
ρ	Charge density in coulombs/m^3
S	Switch (may have subscript)
S_I	The collector current stability factor
s	Distance in meters. Complex frequency ($\sigma + j\omega$)
σ	Conductivity
T	Temperature in °K
T	The time for one period of a periodic function
T_0	A reference temperature usually room temperature (300°K)

T_A The ambient temperature

T_j Junction temperature

T_r The rise time of an amplifier

t Time in seconds

t_r The rise time of a transistor

t_f The fall time of a transistor

t_s The storage time of a transistor

t_d The delay time of a transistor

$\bar{t}$ The time for one mean-free path

τ Time constant (may have subscript)

τ The carrier lifetime in a semiconductor

τ_x The excess base charge lifetime

V The potential difference in volts

V_{ho} The potential difference across a *p-n* junction with no external battery

V_h The potential difference across a *p-n* junction with an external battery

V_{BB} Transistor base bias supply voltage

V_{CC} Transistor collector bias supply voltage

V_{GG} Vacuum tube control grid bias supply voltage

V_{KK} Vacuum tube cathode supply voltage

V_{PP} Vacuum tube plate supply voltage

v The velocity in meters/sec

$\bar{v}_n$ The rms noise voltage

$\bar{v}_n$ The mean thermal velocity of electrons

v_p The mean thermal velocity of holes

Tube and transistor voltages use the same convention as noted for currents.

W Energy or work in joules

W_a The energy level of the acceptor holes

W_{cn} Energy at the lowest value in the conduction band in *n*-type material

W_{cp} Energy at the lowest value of the conduction band in *p*-type material

W_c The lowest energy level in the conduction band

W_d The energy level of the donor electrons

W_f Energy of the Fermi-level

W_v The highest energy level in the valence band

W_g The energy width of the forbidden band

W_w The work function of the cathode surface

w Base width of a transistor

x Distance along one axis

Y Admittance in mhos

Z Impedance in ohms

*Electronic
Engineering*

1

Electron Ballistics

1.1 PROPERTIES OF AN ELECTRON

Certain properties of an electron are well known. The mass of an electron, which is 9.1066×10^{-31} kg, is the lightest known finite[1] particle of matter. The charge on an electron is 1.6019×10^{-19} coulombs. This charge is the smallest known unit of electrical charge. In addition, certain effects of an electron can be seen. For example, the path of an electron under certain conditions can be seen with the aid of a cloud chamber; permanent records of some electron paths can be obtained by using photographic emulsions or plates. Moreover, certain materials emit scintillations of visible light when struck by an electron. Hence it is possible to see the actual point of impact of electrons. Since electrons obey certain basic laws, their behavior can be predicted and controlled quite accurately. In fact, the entire science of electricity and electronics is based on man's ability to predict and control the movements of electrons.

Some properties of an electron are not known. For example, the exact size, shape, and color are all unknown. In fact, since the size of an electron

---

[1] Some "particles" (i.e., photons and neutrinos) are assumed to have zero rest mass. No measurable mass has been found to date for these particles.

1

is so much smaller than the wavelengths of visible light, it may not be proper to associate color with a particle of this size.

Other properties of an electron are somewhat paradoxical. As an example, an electron acts as if it were a small particle in some experiments; whereas in other experiments, electrons act as if they were waves. The nature of the experiment determines which property will be the more pronounced. However, as far as the electrical engineer is concerned, the electron *usually* behaves as if it were a small particle of matter.

1.2 BEHAVIOR OF AN ELECTRON IN AN ELECTRIC FIELD

A basic law of physics states that the force on an object is equal to the time rate of change in momentum of the object. If the electron is assumed to be a small charged particle, this law can be written[2] as

$$\mathbf{F} = \frac{d(m\mathbf{v})}{dt} \tag{1.1}$$

where $\mathbf{F}$ = the force, newtons
  m = the mass, kg
  $\mathbf{v}$ = the velocity, m/sec

Now, if the mass is assumed to be constant,[3] Eq. 1.1 can be reduced to the familiar form

$$\mathbf{F} = m\frac{d\mathbf{v}}{dt} = m\mathbf{a} \tag{1.2}$$

where $\mathbf{a}$ is the acceleration in m/sec². The equation for the electrostatic force on a charged body in an electric field is

$$\mathbf{F} = Q\mathscr{E} \tag{1.3}$$

where Q is the charge on the body in coulombs and $\mathscr{E}$ is the electric field intensity at the position of the charge in volts per meter. A combination of Eqs. 1.2 and 1.3 gives

$$Q\mathscr{E} = m\mathbf{a} \tag{1.4}$$

Since acceleration is the time rate of change of velocity, Eq. 1.4 can be written as

$$\frac{Q\mathscr{E}}{m} = \frac{d\mathbf{v}}{dt} \tag{1.5}$$

---

[2] A symbol set in boldface type indicates a vector quantity.
[3] The more general case where mass is not a constant will be treated later in this section.

or

$$\mathbf{v} = \int \frac{Q\mathscr{E}}{m}\, dt \qquad (1.6)$$

where $\mathbf{v}$ is the velocity in m/sec. Equation 1.6 will apply in all cases when mass is constant. The importance of this generality can be realized if we note that in some cases the electric field and perhaps even the charge are each a function of time. However, a simpler equation can be found if the charged body is in a uniform electric field that does not change appreciably while the electron is in this field. This condition does not restrict the use of this simpler equation to fields which do not change with time. Because of its small mass and relatively large charge, the electron travels at very high velocities. Consequently, as long as the $\mathscr{E}$ field does not change appreciably during the time an electron is in the field, the approximate formula will be valid. Under these conditions, the $\mathscr{E}$ term of the equation may be treated as a constant. If the charge on the charged body is constant, and if the mass is assumed to be constant, Eq. 1.6 becomes

$$\mathbf{v} = \frac{Q\mathscr{E}}{m} \int dt \qquad (1.7)$$

or

$$\mathbf{v} = \frac{Q\mathscr{E}}{m} t + \mathbf{v}_0 \qquad (1.8)$$

where $\mathbf{v}_0$ is the constant of integration and in this case is the initial velocity of the charged body at time $t = 0$.

Velocity is the time rate of change of distance, so Eq. 1.8 can be written as

$$\frac{d\mathbf{s}}{dt} = \frac{Q\mathscr{E}t}{m} + \mathbf{v}_0 \qquad (1.9)$$

or

$$\mathbf{s} = \int \frac{Q\mathscr{E}t}{m}\, dt + \int \mathbf{v}_0\, dt \qquad (1.10)$$

where $\mathbf{s}$ is the distance in meters. Again, assuming Q, $\mathscr{E}$, and m are constant, Eq. 1.10 becomes

$$\mathbf{s} = \frac{Q\mathscr{E}}{2m} t^2 + \mathbf{v}_0 t + \mathbf{s}_0 \qquad (1.11)$$

where $\mathbf{s}_0$ is the constant of integration or initial displacement at time $t = 0$.

Equations 1.4, 1.8, and 1.11 are very similar to the three corresponding equations for a body of mass m in a gravitational field. $Q\mathscr{E}$ assumes the role of the gravitational force.[4] As a consequence, a charged body in an electric field "falls" like a body in a gravitational field.

When a charged body falls through an electric field, the charged body loses potential energy as it gains kinetic energy. From the law of conservation of energy, the kinetic energy gained is equal to the potential energy lost. Then

$$QV = \tfrac{1}{2}mv^2 \tag{1.12}$$

or

$$v = \left(\frac{2QV}{m}\right)^{\frac{1}{2}} \tag{1.13}$$

where Q = the charge on the charged body, coulombs

v = the velocity, m/sec, after falling through a potential difference V

V = the potential difference through which the charged body has fallen, volts

m = the mass of the body, kg.

This equation will, of course, hold for any charged particle. If the numerical values for Q and m are substituted into Eq. 1.13, the equation for an electron becomes

$$v = 5.93 \times 10^5 (V)^{\frac{1}{2}} \text{ m/sec} \tag{1.14}$$

It is interesting to note in passing that if an electron has fallen through only 3×10^{-7} v, the electron will be traveling at approximately the speed of sound in air at sea level. The very large velocities encountered in work with electrons can thus be visualized.

PROB. 1.1. What will be the speed in miles per hour of an electron which has been accelerated through 10 v? How does this compare with 18,000 mph which is required to place a satellite into orbit?

The foregoing equations are based on the assumption that the mass of the charged particles remained constant. However, when large velocities are encountered, the mass of an object changes. The manner in which the mass changes is now considered.

From Eq. 1.1,

$$F = \frac{d(mv)}{dt} \tag{1.1}$$

If mass is assumed to be constant, Eq. 1.2 results. However, if mass is

---

[4] In the foregoing derivation, the effect of gravity was ignored. Since the electrostatic force on an electron is usually very much greater than the gravitational force, very little error is introduced by ignoring the gravitational force. If large bodies with small charges are considered, both gravitational and electrostatic forces must be considered.

not assumed to be constant, Eq. 1.1 must be written as

$$F = m\frac{dv}{dt} + v\frac{dm}{dt} \tag{1.15}$$

Also, force multiplied by distance in this derivation is equal to kinetic energy W. Consequently, Eq. 1.15 can be modified to

$$dW = F\,ds = m\frac{dv}{dt}\,ds + v\frac{dm}{dt}\,ds \tag{1.16}$$

Furthermore, since ds/dt is equal to v, Eq. 1.16 can be written as

$$dW = mv\,dv + v^2\,dm \tag{1.17}$$

Einstein has shown that mass and energy are related by the equation

$$E = c^2 m \tag{1.18}$$

where E is the total energy, including mass energy, and c is the velocity of light (2.998×10^8 m/sec). The derivative of Eq. 1.18 may be taken to yield

$$dE = c^2\,dm \tag{1.19}$$

This change of energy (dE) is equal to the dW in Eq. 1.17. If this value of energy (dE) is substituted into Eq. 1.17,

$$c^2\,dm = mv\,dv + v^2\,dm$$

or

$$(c^2 - v^2)\,dm = mv\,dv \tag{1.20}$$

This equation can be rearranged to yield

$$\frac{dm}{m} = \frac{v}{c^2 - v^2}\,dv \tag{1.21}$$

If the mass of the object is m_0 when the velocity is zero, the mass m at velocity v can be found by integrating Eq. 1.21 as shown below.

$$\int_{m_0}^{m} \frac{1}{m}\,dm = -\frac{1}{2}\int_{0}^{v} \frac{-2v}{c^2 - v^2}\,dv \tag{1.22}$$

Carrying out the integration,

$$\ln m - \ln m_0 = -\tfrac{1}{2}\ln(c^2 - v^2) + \tfrac{1}{2}\ln c^2 \tag{1.23}$$

which can be written as

$$\ln m = \ln\left(\frac{m_0 c}{(c^2 - v^2)^{1/2}}\right) \tag{1.24}$$

or

$$m = \frac{m_0}{[1 - v^2/c^2]^{\frac{1}{2}}} \tag{1.25}$$

The relationship between mass and velocity has now been achieved. Other useful equations may be established by inserting the value of m from Eq. 1.25 into Eq. 1.17. Then,

$$dW = F\,ds = \frac{m_0 v}{[1 - (v^2/c^2)]^{\frac{1}{2}}}\,dv + v^2\,d\left\{\frac{m_0}{[1 - (v^2/c^2)]^{\frac{1}{2}}}\right\} \tag{1.26}$$

However, F is given in Eq. 1.3 as $Q\mathscr{E}$ hence, Eq. 1.26 can be written as

$$Q\mathscr{E}\,ds = \frac{m_0 c v}{(c^2 - v^2)^{\frac{1}{2}}}\,dv + v^2\,\frac{m_0 c v}{(c^2 - v^2)^{\frac{3}{2}}}\,dv \tag{1.27}$$

When the integral is taken of both sides of the equation,

$$Q\int_0^s \mathscr{E}\,ds = m_0 c\int_0^v \frac{v}{(c^2 - v^2)^{\frac{1}{2}}}\,dv + m_0 c\int_0^v \frac{v^3}{(c^2 - v^2)^{\frac{3}{2}}}\,dv \tag{1.28}$$

Since $\int_0^s \mathscr{E}\,ds$ is the voltage V through which the charged particle has fallen, Eq. 1.28 becomes

$$QV = m_0 c\left[-(c^2 - v^2)^{\frac{1}{2}}\right]_0^v + m_0 c\left[2(c^2 - v^2)^{\frac{1}{2}} + \frac{v^2}{(c^2 - v^2)^{\frac{1}{2}}}\right]_0^v \tag{1.29}$$

which reduces to

$$QV = m_0 c^2\left[\frac{1}{\left(1 - \frac{v^2}{c^2}\right)^{\frac{1}{2}}} - 1\right] \tag{1.30}$$

or

$$QV = (m - m_0)c^2$$

Equation 1.30 can be solved for v. After some manipulation,

$$v = c\left[1 - \frac{1}{\left(1 + V\dfrac{Q}{m_0 c^2}\right)^2}\right]^{\frac{1}{2}} \tag{1.31}$$

When the numerical values for c, Q, and m_0 are inserted in Eq. 1.31, the velocity of an electron is

$$v = c\left[1 - \frac{1}{(1 + 1.966 \times 10^{-6}V)^2}\right]^{\frac{1}{2}} \text{ m/sec} \tag{1.32}$$

This value of v can be inserted into Eq. 1.25 to yield

$$m = m_0(1 + 1.966 \times 10^{-6}V) \tag{1.33}$$

A plot of velocity vs electron energy[5] is shown in Fig. 1.1. Figure 1.1 may be divided into three regions. Region 1 extends from 0 to about 40,000 ev. In this region, m is approximately equal to m_0 and Eq. 1.14 yields the velocity. In region 2, both mass and velocity change simultaneously. This region 2 extends from about 40,000 electron volts to

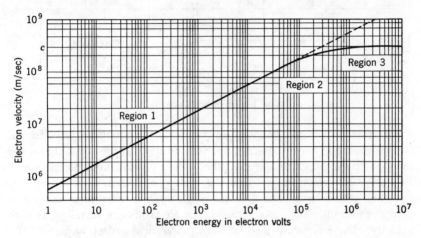

Fig. 1.1. Velocity vs energy of an electron as found from Eq. 1.32.

approximately 3,000,000 electron volts. Equations 1.25 or 1.33 must be used to determine the mass, and Eq. 1.32 can be used to find the velocity in region 2. Region 3 extends from 3,000,000 electron volts upward. In region 3, the velocity is almost equal to the velocity of light and the mass can be calculated from Eq. 1.33. Of course, Eqs. 1.32 and 1.33 are applicable in any region, but accurate values are quite difficult to evaluate in region 1.

PROB. 1.2. What is the velocity and mass of an electron which has been accelerated through 10,000 v? *Answer: $v = 5.93 \times 10^7$ m/sec $m = 1.02 m_0$.*

PROB. 1.3. Repeat Prob. 1.2 for 200,000 v.

PROB. 1.4. What velocity must an electron have in order to exhibit a mass equal to the mass of a proton at rest? What potential must this electron have fallen through in order to achieve this velocity?

Mass of a proton = 1832 mass of an electron. *Answer: $V = 9.32 \times 10^8$ volts $v = 2.997 \times 10^8$ m/sec.*

PROB. 1.5. If an electron is converted into energy, how much energy does the electron represent? How much energy is represented by a mass of one gram?

[5] This electron energy is shown as electron-volts where an electron volt is the amount of energy an electron receives when accelerated through one volt.

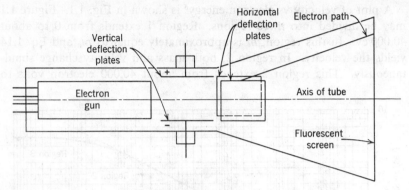

Fig. 1.2. A cathode-ray tube.

An example will help us visualize the use of the equations just derived. In this example, a cathode-ray tube will be used. Figure 1.2 shows the principal parts of a cathode ray tube; while typical tubes are shown in Fig. 1.3. The electron gun (see Fig. 1.4) produces a narrow beam of electrons which have been accelerated through a potential difference of several thousand volts. As a result, the electrons are traveling at high velocity. These electrons pass between the vertical deflection plates. If a potential difference exists between these deflection plates, the electrons will

Fig. 1.3. Typical cathode-ray tubes.

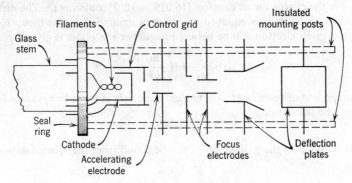

Fig. 1.4. A typical electron gun.

be attracted toward the positive plate and repelled by the negative plate. Thus, the beam of electrons is deflected from the axis of the tube an amount proportional to the voltage difference between the deflection plates. Two sets of deflection plates are provided to obtain both vertical and horizontal deflection of the beam. After being deflected, the electron beam continues on and impinges on a fluorescent screen, which emits visible light when struck by an electron. The cathode-ray tube thus allows the visual examination of a voltage waveform.

Example 1.1. A cathode-ray tube has the dimensions as shown in Fig. 1.5. The electrons (in the electron beam) have been accelerated through a voltage V_x when they enter the space between the deflection plates. The velocity in the x direction (along the axis of the tube) is, therefore,

$$v_x = \left(\frac{2qV_x}{m}\right)^{1/2} \tag{1.34}$$

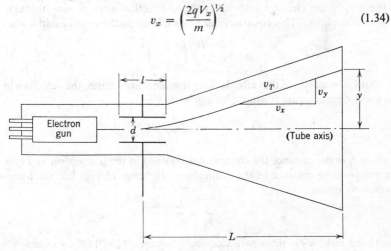

Fig. 1.5. Configuration for Example 1.1.

where q is the charge on an electron (16.019×10^{-10} coulombs).[6] The distance traveled by an electron is equal to the velocity multiplied by the time. Hence, the time a given electron will be between the deflection plates is given by

$$t = \frac{l}{v_x} = l\left(\frac{m}{2qV_x}\right)^{\frac{1}{2}}$$

The component of velocity at right angles to the axis of the tube v_y can be found by using the relationship

$$v_y = a_y t$$

The acceleration in the y direction a_y can be found from the relationship

$$F_y = ma_y$$

But the force in the y direction is

$$F_y = -q\mathscr{E}_y$$

The electric field intensity can be found from

$$-\mathscr{E}_y = \frac{V_y}{d}$$

where d is the distance between the deflection plates in meters and V_y is the potential difference between the vertical deflection plates. This relationship assumes the electric field between the deflecting plates to be constant. This is a good approximation if the dimensions of the plates are large in comparison with the distance between them. When the foregoing substitutions are made for a_y and t, the formula for v_y becomes

$$v_y = \frac{qV_y l}{md}\left(\frac{m}{2qV_x}\right)^{\frac{1}{2}}$$

where v_y is the electron velocity in the y direction after passing through the deflection plates. This equation can be simplified to the relationship

$$v_y = \frac{lV_y}{d}\left(\frac{q}{2mV_x}\right)^{\frac{1}{2}} \tag{1.35}$$

Now, if we assume that after leaving the deflection plates, the velocities in the x and y directions are constant, we can write

$$\frac{l_y}{v_y} = \frac{l_x}{v_x}$$

where l_y is the distance the electron has traveled in the y direction and l_x is the corresponding distance in the x direction. In terms of Fig. 1.5, the foregoing equation becomes

$$\frac{y}{v_y} = \frac{L}{v_x}$$

[6] Most cathode-ray tubes have accelerating voltages, V_x of 18,000 v or less. Consequently, the mass can be assumed to be constant.

or

$$y = L\frac{v_y}{v_x} \tag{1.36}$$

where L and y are defined in Fig. 1.5. When the equalities of v_x and v_y (Eq. 1.34 and Eq. 1.35) are substituted into this equation

$$y = L\frac{\dfrac{lV_y}{d}\left(\dfrac{q}{2mV_x}\right)^{\frac{1}{2}}}{\left(\dfrac{2qV_x}{m}\right)^{\frac{1}{2}}}$$

or

$$y = \frac{LlV_y}{2dV_x} \tag{1.37}$$

This equation is approximate, since certain simplifications were made in the derivation. For example, the fringing effect of the flux field at the edges of the plates was ignored. When this fringing is included, the equation is about the same as Eq. 1.37, except l is slightly longer than the deflection plates.

The reader may question the validity of Eq. 1.36, which infers that the electron has no velocity in the y direction until the electron reaches the center of the deflection plates. On reaching the center of the deflection plates, however, the electron suddenly acquires the full velocity v_y. This of course, is certainly not the way the electron would behave. The electron actually follows a parabolic path while between the two deflection plates. However, if tangents are drawn to the parabolic curve where this curve enters and leaves the area between the two deflection plates, these tangents will intersect at the center of the deflection plates as shown in Fig. 1.5. There is, therefore, no error introduced due to the simplification of Eq. 1.36.

PROB. 1.6. The sensitivity of a cathode-ray tube is defined as the ratio of deflection distance (of the electron beam on the screen) to the deflecting voltage applied to the deflection plates. What is the sensitivity in cm/v of the cathode-ray tube shown in Fig. 1.5 if $d = 1$ cm, $l = 4$ cm, and $L = 10$ in.? Assume the screen is at the same potential as the point where the electron leaves the area between the deflection plates. The electron has been accelerated through 2000 v when it enters the space between the deflection plates. *Answer: 0.0254 cm/volt.*

PROB. 1.7. How far from the axis of the tube in Prob. 1.6 will an electron be when striking the screen if a potential of 10 v is applied between the deflection plates? If a particle with the same charge as an electron but with a mass 800 times as large as an electron is used in this tube, how far from the axis of the tube will this particle strike? (Assume 10 v between deflection plates.) Explain. What would be the effect of increasing the charge by a factor of 10?

The derivation of Eq. 1.37 is based on the premise that v_x is constant. This condition is true only if the potential of the fluorescent screen is the same as the potential of the deflection plate field at the point of exit of the electrons. If the potential of the screen is different from the potential of the field at the point of exit from the deflection plates, the situation becomes quite complicated. Fortunately, an approximate relationship can be found quite easily. If we assume that the potential varies linearly from the center of the deflection plates to the screen, then the average value of v_x becomes important. In this case

$$v_{av} = \frac{v_{x1} + v_{x2}}{2} \tag{1.38}$$

Now v_{x1} is the velocity v_x in the original equation (Eq. 1.34) and will have the value

$$v_{x1} = \left(\frac{2qV_x}{m}\right)^{\frac{1}{2}} \tag{1.39}$$

where V_x is again the potential through which the electrons have been accelerated when they enter the area between the deflection plates. The velocity v_{x2} is the velocity of the electrons when they strike the screen. This velocity is given by the equation

$$v_{x2} = \left(\frac{2qV_s}{m}\right)^{\frac{1}{2}} \tag{1.40}$$

where V_s is the potential difference between the cathode of the electron gun and the screen of the tube. Perhaps it is well to note here that the velocity of an electron is determined completely by the potential difference through which this electron has fallen. Consequently, an electron which started from a cathode at zero potential and was accelerated to a velocity corresponding to a potential of 100 v will have exactly the same velocity as an electron that started at zero potential, was accelerated to a velocity corresponding to a potential of 100,000 v, and then decelerated back to a velocity corresponding to 100 v above the cathode. The history of the electron is therefore not important. All we need to know to determine the speed of this electron is the potential at which the electron started (usually this is the potential of the cathode) and the potential in which the electron finds itself at a given instant.

When Eqs. 1.39 and 1.40 are substituted back into Eq. 1.38, v_{av} becomes

$$v_{av} = \frac{\left(\frac{2q}{m}V_x\right)^{\frac{1}{2}} + \left(\frac{2q}{m}V_s\right)^{\frac{1}{2}}}{2} \tag{1.41}$$

Now, if this value is substituted back into Eq. 1.36 in place of v_x and Eq. 1.35 is substituted in place of v_y, then

$$y = \frac{LlV_y}{d[V_x + (V_x V_s)^{1/2}]} \qquad (1.42)$$

This equation is much more useful than Eq. 1.37 because V_x is usually not equal to V_s. Notice that Eq. 1.42 reduces to Eq. 1.37 if $V_x = V_s$. Equation 1.42 will, of course, be meaningless if V_s is equal to zero or is less than zero, because the electrons will never strike the screen.

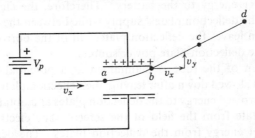

Fig. 1.6. Action of an electron in passing through a set of deflection plates.

The electron in the foregoing example appears to have gained some energy in being deflected. The source of this energy, however, is not very obvious. To explain the energy relations in a cathode-ray tube, refer to Fig. 1.6. Assume that no electrons are in the vicinity of the deflection plates. A certain charge distribution will then be on the deflection plates due to the battery V_p. An electron is then injected into the area between the plates with a velocity v_x which is parallel to the axis of the tube. At the point of injection, the electron is in position a of Fig. 1.6. As the electron proceeds, it is repelled by the negative plate and attracted to the positive plate. Therefore, when the electron leaves the deflection plate area, it will be in position b of Fig. 1.6. There has been no force in the x direction, so v_x is constant. However, the electron now has a velocity in the y direction because of the field between the two deflection plates. Hence, the electron has more kinetic energy at point b than at point a. However, the electron is closer to the positive plate at point b than at point a. As a result of the electron being nearer to the positive plate, the charge on the two plates is redistributed. In this new condition, more positive charge appears on the positive plate, and more negative charge is on the negative plate. This movement of charge constitutes a flow of current through the battery in such a direction that energy is taken from the battery. This energy that is taken from the battery is coupled through the electric field to the electron in the space between the two plates.

As the electron leaves the area between the deflection plates, however, another action takes place. The electron at point b of Fig. 1.6 is much nearer the positive plate than the negative plate. As a result, the electron experiences a decelerating force due to the positive plate and an accelerating force from the negative plate. But, since the decelerating force is greater than the accelerating force, the electron is slowed down. Also, as the electron gets farther from the plates, the charge on the plates will return to the charge distribution which existed before the electron entered the field, causing the current that flows (due to the change of charge distribution) to deliver energy to the battery. Therefore, the electron *borrows* energy from the deflection plates' supply while between these plates. But, as the electron leaves the deflection plates, all of the borrowed energy is restored to the deflection-plate power source.

If the screen of the tube is maintained at a potential such that the electron is not slowed down after leaving the deflection plates, the electron returns its borrowed energy to the deflection plates and obtains new energy at the same rate from the field of the screen. The electron, therefore, obtains *no* net energy from the deflection plates. The deflection plates do change the *direction* of travel of the electron, however.

The previous work assumed that the electric field remains essentially constant as a given electron travels through the field. As already noted, this condition is met in practical situations except when the rate of change of the electric field is very fast. However, if the electric field changes very rapidly, the voltage between the deflection plates will be different when the electron leaves the deflection plate area than when this electron entered the area. The electron can then acquire a net energy from the field of the deflection plates. The source supplying energy to the deflection plates must be capable of furnishing this energy. This loss of driving energy causes difficult problems when frequencies in the microwave band (several thousand megacycles) are being used.

PROB. 1.8. How far from the axis of the tube (Fig. 1.7) will the electron strike the face of the tube?
  Potential of cathode $= -2000$ v
  Potential of plate 1 $= +10$ v
  Potential of plate 2 $= -10$ v
  Potential of final electrode in electron gun $= 0$ v
  Potential of screen $= +2000$ v. *Answer: $y = 0.311$ cm.*

PROB. 1.9. Repeat Prob. 1.8 with a screen potential of 0 v. Does this condition cause the tube to be more or less sensitive? Explain.

PROB. 1.10. When the voltage difference between two deflection plates becomes large enough, the electron beam will strike one of the deflection plates. At what deflection plate voltage does this condition occur in the tube of Prob. 1.8? *Answer: $V_y = 445$ volts.*

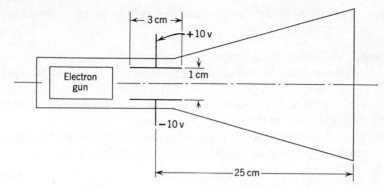

Fig. 1.7. Configuration for Probs. 1.8, 1.9, and 1.10.

PROB. 1.11. How much time is required for an electron to pass between two deflection plates 3 cm long? Assume that the electron has been accelerated through a potential V_x of 2000 v before entering the area between the deflection plates. If a signal of $20 \sin 2\pi 10^6 t$ is applied to the deflection plates, what is the maximum voltage change which can occur while the electron is between the deflection plates?

1.3 BEHAVIOR OF AN ELECTRON IN A MAGNETIC FIELD

An electron in a magnetic field experiences a force only if the electron has a component of velocity at right angles to the flux lines of the magnetic field. This principle is illustrated in Fig. 1.8. The component of velocity v_x which is perpendicular to the flux lines B_z produces the force F_y. A velocity in the $+y$ direction produces a force in the $-x$ direction. However, a velocity in the z direction (parallel to the magnetic force) produces no

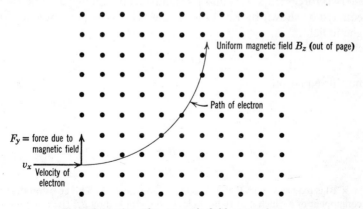

Fig. 1.8. Action of a magnetic field on an electron.

force. The magnitude of the force can be found from the relationship

$$F_y = B_z q v_x \tag{1.43}$$

where F_y = force in the y direction in newtons.

B_z = magnetic flux density in the z direction in webers per square meter.

q = charge on the electron (16.019×10^{-20} coulombs).

v_x = velocity in the x direction in m/sec.

Similar relationships can be derived for forces in the x and z directions. A general expression can be written in vector form[7] as

$$\mathbf{F} = Q(\mathbf{v} \times \mathbf{B}) \tag{1.44}$$

where Q is the charge on any charged body and includes the sign of the charge. $\mathbf{F}$, $\mathbf{v}$, and $\mathbf{B}$ are vector quantities for force, velocity, and magnetic flux.

The force is always at right angles to the velocity (Fig. 1.8). In addition, this force is constant for a constant velocity and constant magnetic flux. Under these conditions, the path of an electron will be circular. The force due to Eq. 1.44 is tending to pull the electron toward the center of the circle. In contrast, the centrifugal force of the electron tends to pull the electron away from the center of the circle. This centrifugal force is equal to

$$F = \frac{mv^2}{r} \tag{1.45}$$

where F = the force, newtons

m = the mass of electron, kg

v = the velocity of electron, m/sec

r = the radius of curvature of the electron path, m

These two forces (Eqs. 1.44 and 1.45) must be in equilibrium and thus can be equated as shown by Eq. 1.46. If the velocity is perpendicular to the magnetic field,

$$Bqv = \frac{mv^2}{r} \tag{1.46}$$

From this equation,

$$r = \frac{mv}{Bq} \tag{1.47}$$

or

$$v = \frac{Bqr}{m} \tag{1.48}$$

---

[7] ($\mathbf{v} \times \mathbf{B}$) is read as $\mathbf{v}$ cross $\mathbf{B}$ and does *not* mean $\mathbf{v}$ times $\mathbf{B}$. This cross product means the component of v which is at right angles to B multiplied by B. The resultant force is at right angles to both the component of v (which is at right angles to B) and to B.

In making one complete circle, the electron travels a distance s as given below.

$$s = 2\pi r \qquad (1.49)$$

The time required to make a complete circle T is given by

$$T = \frac{s}{v} \qquad (1.50)$$

When the values of s and v from Eqs. 1.49 and 1.48 are substituted into Eq. 1.50,

$$T = \frac{2\pi r m}{Bqr}$$

or

$$T = \frac{2\pi m}{Bq} \qquad (1.51)$$

For an electron, m and q are constants (for velocity $\ll$ speed of light), so the time for one circle is dependent only on the magnetic flux density. When the values for the charge and mass of an electron are substituted into Eq. 1.51,

$$T = \frac{35.5}{B} \times 10^{-12} \sec \qquad (1.52)$$

Magnetic fields are used in many applications. For example, magnetic deflection of electron beams in cathode-ray tubes (especially in television receivers) is widely used. Also, magnetic fields can be used for focusing electron beams, and they are even used in the generation of microwave frequencies. Furthermore, charged particles are accelerated to very high velocities by "cyclotrons." This latter application will be considered as an example of the use of magnetic fields.

A cyclotron is constructed as shown in Fig. 1.9. Two hollow D-shaped conductors are arranged as shown. An electron emitter or gun is located inside the hollow D's and very near the center of the cyclotron. A uniform magnetic flux is maintained throughout the area of each D. Finally, a high voltage a-c source is connected between the two D's. Now, assume a *group* of electrons is emitted from the electron gun just as D no. 1 is maximum positive and D no. 2 is maximum negative. These electrons are accelerated into the D no. 1 space. Since the electrons now have a velocity, they will be deflected into a circular path as shown in Fig. 1.9. If the frequency of the a-c supply is correct, the electrons will arrive at the gap between the two D's (position b) just when D no. 2 is maximum positive and D no. 1 is maximum negative. The electrons will again be accelerated between the two D's. Since the electrons will now have a higher velocity than they had from *a* to *b*, the radius of the electron path will be greater. Similarly, the electrons will arrive at point *c* just in time to be accelerated again. The electrons continue this action for many cycles. Each time the electrons cross the gap between the *D*'s, an increase of velocity and radius of the path results. When the velocity is sufficiently high, the electrons are removed from the magnetic field and travel in a straight line to the desired target. Since a group of electrons can be released once each cycle,

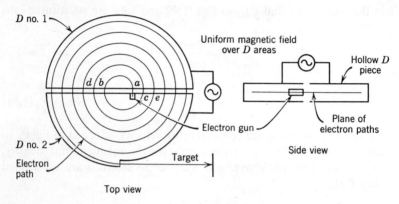

Fig. 1.9. A simplified cyclotron.

the output of a cyclotron is a periodic pulse of high-velocity particles. Whereas the foregoing analysis has used an electron as the charged particle, most cyclotrons are used to accelerate protons, hydrogen nuclei, or other large particles. However, the analysis is the same.

Example 1.2. A cyclotron has the configuration shown in Fig. 1.9. The maximum voltage from the a-c source is V_m. If mass is assumed to be constant, the electrons will have a velocity of

$$v = 5.93 \times 10^5 (V_m)^{1/2} \text{ m/sec} \qquad (1.14)$$

after the first passage through the gap. From Eq. 1.46

$$r = \frac{mv}{Bq} = 3.37 \times 10^{-6} \frac{(V_m)^{1/2}}{B} \text{ meters} \qquad (1.53)$$

In the curve from *b* to *c* (Fig. 1.9), the velocity will be

$$v = 5.93 \times 10^5 (2V_m)^{1/2}$$

and the radius of the path will be

$$r = 3.37 \times 10^{-6} \frac{(2V_m)^{1/2}}{B}$$

In general, the velocity after passing through the gap n times is

$$v_n = 5.93 \times 10^5 (nV_m)^{\frac{1}{2}} \tag{1.54}$$

and the radius of the path for this velocity will be

$$r = 3.37 \times 10^{-6} \frac{(nV_m)^{\frac{1}{2}}}{B} \tag{1.55}$$

The frequency of the high voltage source can be found by noting

$$T = \frac{35.5}{B} \times 10^{-12} \text{ sec} \tag{1.52}$$

and,

$$f = \frac{1}{T} = \frac{B}{35.5} \times 10^{12} \text{ cycles/sec} \tag{1.56}$$

Cyclotrons of the type just described are used only for accelerations up to about 0.1 of the velocity of light. When greater accelerations are required, the change of mass must be considered. As noted in Eq. 1.51, the period becomes longer as the mass increases. Some cyclotrons have been built which are frequency modulated (the frequency is changed) to allow for the change of mass. At the time a given group of electrons (or other particles) leaves the emitter (or particle source) the frequency of the high voltage oscillator is high. As the mass of the particles increases, the frequency of the oscillator decreases. The given group of particles, therefore, always arrives at the gap between the D's just as the field is a maximum.

PROB. 1.12. (a) How many times must an electron pass through the gap of a cyclotron before achieving a velocity of 0.1 times the velocity of light? Assume the high voltage oscillator produces 1000 v peak. (b) How many times must a hydrogen ion (composed of one proton) pass through the gap of this cyclotron before achieving a velocity 0.1 times the velocity of light?

PROB. 1.13. (a) If the magnetic field strength of Prob. 1.12 is 1.53×10^{-2} webers/m², how large must the D's be to accommodate the largest radius path? (b) To what frequency should the oscillator be set? *Answer: d = 40.8 m, f = 2.34 × 10⁵ cps.*

PROB. 1.14. A cyclotron is to be designed to furnish electrons with an energy of 1,000,000 ev. A high voltage oscillator with an output of 10,000 v is to be used. Use a magnetic flux density of 1.5×10^{-2} webers/m². (a) Find the size of D required. (b) What is the frequency of the oscillator at the start of an electron bunch? (c) What is the frequency of the oscillator at the time the electrons leave the D? (d) How many bunches per second can this cyclotron produce? (Assume the frequency changes at a linear rate.)

PROB. 1.15. A magnetic field exists as shown in the sketch of Fig. 1.10. Two electrons enter this field at point A with a velocity of 10^7 m/sec. The velocity of electron a has the direction shown where $\alpha = \frac{1}{2}°$. The velocity of electron b has the direction shown where $\beta = 1°$. (a) How far from A will electron a again

Fig. 1.10. Configuration for Prob. 1.15.

cross the axis? (*Hint:* Break the velocity of the electron *a* into two components, one component parallel to the magnetic flux lines and one component perpendicular to the magnetic flux lines.) (*b*) What path will electron *a* follow? (*c*) How far from *A* will electron *b* again cross the axis? (*d*) What use does this problem suggest for magnetic fields?

1.4 BEHAVIOR OF AN ELECTRON IN A COMBINATION ELECTRIC AND MAGNETIC FIELD

When an electron is in an area that contains both an electric and a magnetic field, the force on the electron is the vector sum of the force due to the electric field and the force due to the magnetic field. These forces may either tend to reinforce each other or tend to cancel each other, depending on their respective directions.

It is possible for one force to completely cancel another force. Such a condition is shown in Fig. 1.11. The magnitude of the force due to the electric field, F_E, can be found from Eq. 1.3.

$$F_E = Q\mathscr{E} \tag{1.57}$$

The magnitude of the force due to the magnetic field, F_M, can be found from Eq. 1.43.

$$F_M = BQv \tag{1.58}$$

If these two forces are equal and opposite in direction, the electron will

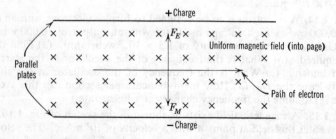

Fig. 1.11. Cancellation of force due to an electric field by a magnetic field.

continue in a straight line. The two forces can be equated to give

$$Q\mathscr{E} = BQv$$

or

$$\frac{\mathscr{E}}{B} = v \qquad (1.59)$$

where $\mathscr{E}$ = the electric field intensity in v/m

B = the magnetic flux density in webers/m²

v = the velocity of the electron in m/sec

If the velocity of a charged particle is less than this v, the particle will be pulled toward the positive plate. In this case, F_E is greater than F_M. If the velocity of the charged particle is greater than v as given by Eq. 1.59, the particle will be forced toward the negative plate. This type of configuration is known as a velocity filter. Only particles with a given velocity will be passed; all other particles will be captured by the two plates. A filter of this type may be used on a cyclotron to remove the particles in the outermost orbit from the magnetic field.

PROB. 1.16. Design a velocity filter to remove electrons from the cyclotron of Prob. 1.13. The spacing between plates must be 1 cm. What voltage must be applied to these plates? *Answer: V = 4590 volts.*

PROB. 1.17. Repeat Prob. 1.16 for the cyclotron of Prob. 1.14.

PROB. 1.18. An electron enters the space between two deflection plates with a velocity of 13.27×10^6 m/sec. If the configuration of the deflection plates is as given in Fig. 1.12, how far from the input end of the deflection plate will the electron strike the deflection plate?

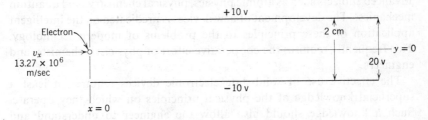

Fig. 1.12. The configuration for Prob. 1.18.

PROB. 1.19. How far will the electron of Fig. 1.12 have traveled in the y direction when it has traveled 10 cm in the x direction?

2

Semiconductors

Modern engineering must be based on an understanding of the basic physical properties and processes of materials. A thorough understanding of engineering materials may be obtained only from a serious study of advanced subjects such as atomic physics, physical chemistry, and quantum mechanics. The development of new devices is predicated on the intelligent application of these principles to the problems of modern technology. This frequently requires the cooperative effort of physicists, chemists, and engineers.

The effective use of solid-state electronic devices requires at least a superficial knowledge of the physical principles on which they operate. Such a knowledge should also allow the engineer to understand and effectively use the many devices which will almost certainly be developed in the future.

The purpose of this chapter is to present some of the physical principles of semiconductor material. The treatment will, of necessity, be superficial, since a thorough treatment is clearly beyond the scope of this book. It is hoped, however, that the reader will acquire some mental images and basic relationships which are sufficiently correct to permit him to intelligently use the available devices. Consequently, physical models will be used at the expense of mathematical rigor in an effort to make the otherwise intangible principles somewhat concrete. For example, the Bohr model of the atom will be used in favor of the quantum theory because the particle theory of matter is easier to visualize than its wave nature. Models and analogies will be borrowed frequently from the literature. An attempt will be made to give proper credit, but this will not always be possible because the original sources may be unknown or the evolutionary modifications of the original may make it impractical, if not impossible, to give the deserved credit to all the contributors.

2.1 ATOMIC MODELS

The Bohr model of the atom places an orderly arrangement of electrons in elliptical orbits around a nucleus of protons and neutrons. This concept was contributed primarily by Bohr during the early part of this century. The theories developed from this model agreed so well with experimental evidence that the measuring instruments and techniques of that period were unable to detect any difference between the predicted and actual behavior of matter. However, as the measuring instruments and techniques improved, it became evident that discrepancies existed.

The discovery and investigation of the photoelectric effect provided convincing evidence that light has a dual nature. Some effects, such as diffraction, can be explained only on the premise that light behaves as a wave. Other phenomena, such as the mechanism of photo emission, can be explained only on the basis that light consists of bundles of energy or particles known as photons. Later it was shown by Davisson and Germer, by the use of diffraction techniques, that electrons in motion also have the properties of a wave. This rather startling discovery led DeBroglie, Schrodinger, and others to the development of a wave theory for all matter. This wave mechanics or quantum mechanics eliminates certain discrepancies inherent in the Bohr model. An atomic model which accurately represents the wave mechanics concept is difficult to visualize, however, because the particles are not so discrete and well defined. For example, probability densities which are dependent on boundary conditions replace the solid charged satellites of the Bohr model. For this reason, the Bohr model will be used, as stated previously, to aid the visualization of the basic principles.

The Bohr model diagrams of a few atoms of interest are shown in Fig. 2.1. The simplest atom is hydrogen which has one planetary electron and a nucleus consisting of one proton. The tetravalent atoms are of considerable interest to the semiconductor industry. The simplest of these is carbon, which has six planetary electrons and six protons in the nucleus.

The two electrons nearest the nucleus form what is known as a "closed shell." That is, only two electrons can be accommodated at that energy level. The four outer electrons are known as valence electrons and they determine the chemical activity of the material. These valence electrons were originally thought to occupy the same energy level. However, closer investigation has revealed that the valence shell is split into at least two levels, with two electrons in the lower level or subgroup. The outer level

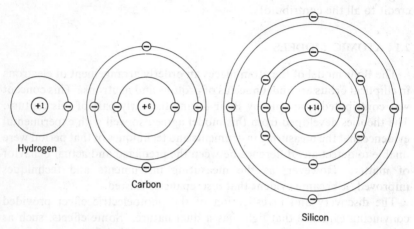

Fig. 2.1. Bohr model diagrams of a few atoms.

would require four additional electrons to fill the shell. This behavior may be observed from the silicon diagram which, like carbon, has four valence electrons but has a filled shell between the inner shell and the valence shell. Silicon's chemical properties are similar to those of carbon. Another element in this group is germanium, which has thirty-two orbital electrons including four valence electrons. Germanium has two filled shells between the valence electrons and the inner shell.

The energy of the orbital electrons may be determined from the laws of mechanics. The hydrogen atom will be used as an example. If the single orbital electron is removed to infinity, the atom is said to be ionized. The electron at infinity is considered to be at rest and to have a potential energy equal to zero. This is an arbitrary choice of reference for potential energy, but it is a convenient and widely accepted one. If the electron is given a very slight nudge in the direction of the nucleus, the electron will travel toward the nucleus and will be accelerated by the electrostatic force

$$F = \frac{q^2}{4\pi\epsilon r^2}$$

(2.1)

where ϵ is the permittivity and r is the distance between the charges. The potential energy at any given point is the work required to bring the charge from the reference to the point in question. If the point is a specific distance r from the nucleus and the reference is at $r = \infty$, then the potential energy is

$$W_p = \int_\infty^r \frac{q^2}{4\pi\epsilon_v r^2} \, dr = -\frac{q^2}{4\pi\epsilon_v r} \tag{2.2}$$

where ϵ_v is the permittivity of free space. The negative sign indicates that the potential energy of the electron decreases as it moves toward the nucleus. In contrast, the kinetic energy increases as the electron moves toward the nucleus because the electron is being accelerated by the force. As noted in Chapter 1, the electron can be considered as "falling" toward the nucleus because of the similarity to a mass falling in a gravitational field.

If the electron has any component of velocity or force normal to the radial direction r, the electron will go into an elliptical or circular orbit around the nucleus. For mathematical simplicity, it will be assumed that the orbit will be circular with radius r. In order to have equilibrium, the electrostatic force between the electron and nucleus must be equal to the centrifugal force.

$$F = \frac{q^2}{4\pi\epsilon_v r^2} = \frac{mv^2}{r} \tag{2.3}$$

where v is the tangential velocity of the electron.

Then, using Eq. 2.3, the kinetic energy of the electron is

$$W_k = \tfrac{1}{2}mv^2 = \frac{q^2}{8\pi\epsilon_v r} \tag{2.4}$$

It is interesting to note by comparing Eqs. 2.4 and 2.2 that the kinetic energy of the electron in orbit is only half as great as the decrease in potential energy from the reference level. The law of conservation of energy then requires that half of the potential energy change be transferred to some other type of energy, since only half was transferred to kinetic energy. Observation of an ionized gas will reveal that electromagnetic radiation accounts for this energy transfer. This radiation is frequently in the visible spectrum and is the mechanism which produces the light in neon tubes or similar devices.

The total energy level of the electron is

$$W = W_p + W_k = -\frac{q^2}{4\pi\epsilon_v r} + \frac{q^2}{8\pi\epsilon_v r} = -\frac{q^2}{8\pi\epsilon_v r} \tag{2.5}$$

The period of the orbital motion is

$$T = \frac{2\pi r}{v} \qquad (2.6)$$

A frequency equal to $1/T$ is associated with the electron. There can be no electromagnetic radiation at this frequency as long as the radius remains constant because there can be no change in the total energy of the electron. Radiation or absorption of energy can only be associated with a change in radius and thus a change in energy level.

It has long been known that the atom can be stable only when the orbital electrons have certain discrete energy levels. The energy differences between these permissible levels indicate the amounts of energy or size of energy packets that can be either radiated or absorbed by the atom. In 1900, Max Planck showed that the relationship between the frequency f of the electromagnetic wave, either radiated or absorbed, and the discrete energy packet is

$$W = hf \qquad (2.7)$$

where $f =$ the frequency of the electromagnetic radiation

$h =$ Planck's constant 6.625×10^{-34} j sec

The lines on a spectrograph of a specific material could then be used to determine the size of the energy packets for a given material. When Planck made his discovery, the electron had not been discovered so it could not be known that the energy packets were the difference of permissible electron energy levels, or $W = W_1 - W_2$.

The development of wave mechanics provided an explanation for the discrete energy levels of the electron. If the electron in motion has the characteristics of a wave, the electron in a stable orbit must behave as a wave which has an integral number of wavelengths in one circumference of its orbital path. Otherwise, the electron waves would tend to cancel one another by interference, as illustrated in Fig. 2.2. The peaks and troughs of the wave are represented by the solid line. In 1924, DeBroglie postulated that the wavelength λ of the matter waves is

$$\lambda = \frac{h}{mv} \qquad (2.8)$$

where the wavelength λ is the distance between the peaks (or troughs) of a wave $(\lambda = v/f)$. Davisson, Germer, and Thompson later demonstrated the wave nature of electrons by obtaining interference patterns from crystal diffraction gratings placed in a stream of moving electrons. If we accept the postulate that there must be an integral number of wavelengths

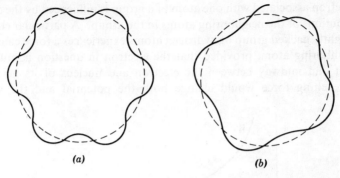

(a)   (b)

Fig. 2.2. Wave characteristics of an electron in (a) a stable orbit, (b) an unstable orbit.

in one circumference of the orbital path, it follows that

$$n\lambda = 2\pi r = \frac{nh}{mv} \tag{2.9}$$

where n is an integer.

Using Eq. 2.4 to solve for v in terms of r, we see that

$$v = \left(\frac{q^2}{4\pi\epsilon_v rm}\right)^{\frac{1}{2}} \tag{2.10}$$

Then

$$2\pi r = \frac{nh(4\pi\epsilon_v rm)^{\frac{1}{2}}}{mq} \tag{2.11}$$

Solving for the permissible values of $r = r_n$

$$r_n = \frac{n^2 h^2 \epsilon_v}{\pi m q^2} \tag{2.12}$$

The stable values of energy, from Eq. 2.5 are

$$W_n = -\frac{q^2}{8\pi\epsilon_v r_n} = \frac{-mq^4}{8\epsilon_v{}^2 h^2 n^2} \tag{2.13}$$

It should be remembered that the foregoing derivations are for the simplest configuration of a single hydrogen atom. The object was merely to illustrate the fact that the electrons associated with an atom may have only discrete values of energy in the stable state. This fact is illustrated in the energy diagram of Fig. 2.3. It should be evident that this basic principle applies to all atoms.

The precise energy levels of the electrons of an individual atom are modified by the presence of other atoms in near proximity. For example,

an electron associated with one atom of a group is influenced by the charge
distributions of the neighboring atoms in the group. A particular electron
in a tightly packed group of hydrogen atoms experiences a force caused by
a neighboring atom, provided that the electron in question is not equidistant and midway between the electron and nucleus of its neighbor.
The resulting force would change both the potential and the kinetic

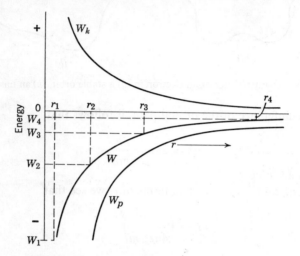

Fig. 2.3. Electron energy levels of a hydrogen atom.

energies of the electron. This effect applies to all electrons in the group.
Thus, when the atoms of a particular element are spread far apart, the
permissible energy levels of one atom are precisely the same as any other
atom; but, as the spacing between the atoms is decreased, the energy
levels of each electron are increasingly influenced by the charge distributions of the neighboring atoms. The magnitude of the influence depends
not only on the spacing but also on the location of the electron within
the group. Consequently, the discrete electron *energy levels* of the isolated
atoms change into *energy bands* when other atoms are in close proximity.

It is meaningful to talk about the spacing between individual atoms only
when they form a crystalline solid. Then the atoms have an orderly
arrangement with a rather precise spacing. This spacing between representative atoms in the crystal is known as the lattice constant. In general,
the semiconductor materials used in electronic devices are crystals, and
one of the manufacturing problems is to obtain a very pure, regular
crystal.

Figure 2.4 shows the energy bands as a function of lattice constant for
tetravalent crystals such as diamond (carbon), silicon, and germanium.

The energy bands between the permissible bands are known as *forbidden bands*. The actual valence electrons of one atom are indicated by a small circle with a negative sign inside. This condition is called a filled energy state. The small empty circles represent energy states which are available for but not occupied by electrons in a particular band. For example, there are eight energy states available in the valence shell of a carbon atom but

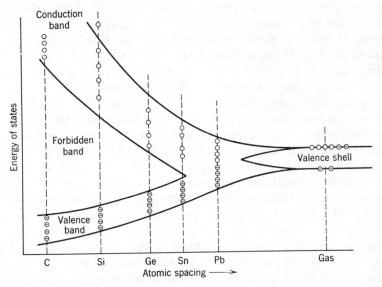

Fig. 2.4. Energy bands of a tetravalent crystal as a function of lattice spacing.

only four of them are actually occupied or filled. When the temperature is absolute zero, the electrons are in the lowest possible states. This condition is assumed in Fig. 2.4. The energy levels below the valence band are not shown because they are all filled and do not contribute to the electrical characteristics of the material.

Figure 2.4 shows that as the lattice spacing decreases from its initial large value, a single band is first formed. This band is a combination valence and conduction band. As the spacing is further reduced, the band divides into separate conduction and valence bands with a forbidden band between. In this case, at 0°K the valence band is completely filled and the conduction band is completely empty. It would be impossible to adjust the atomic spacing of a particular crystal arbitrarily. However, the lattice constant of crystals of different elements are different, so different elements having similar valence shells such as the tetravalent group could be used to provide variation of lattice constant in discrete steps. The spacing between nuclei would naturally increase with the complexity of the atom because of the larger atomic diameter. Typical energy-band configurations for carbon, silicon, germanium, tin, and lead are indicated in Fig. 2.4.

2.2 CONDUCTION IN A SEMICONDUCTOR

The conduction process depends on the availability of charge carriers which are able to move in the presence of an electric field. The acceleration of the carrier by an electric field increases the carrier's total energy. This increase of energy level can be accomplished only if an unfilled state is available at a slightly higher energy level. Referring again to Fig. 2.4, it is evident that lead is a good conductor because there are unfilled energy states in the same energy band as the valence electrons. On the other hand germanium, silicon, and diamond crystals are insulators at $0°K$ because their valence bands are completely filled and their conduction bands are completely empty. A comparatively large amount of energy would then be required to elevate a valence-band electron through the forbidden band to the conduction band. A very strong electric field could elevate an electron to the conduction band, but this would be a process known as the "voltage breakdown" rather than a normal conduction process. When the temperature is raised above absolute zero, the crystal atoms acquire vibrational kinetic energy. Some of the valence electrons may acquire sufficient energy to jump from the valence band to the conduction band. The crystal would then be a conductor of sorts because there would be carriers in the conduction band and also unoccupied states in the valence band. The conductivity would depend on the number of carriers in the conduction band. Thus, the higher the temperature, the better the conductivity. The crystal is called a *semiconductor* because near room temperature it has electrical conduction properties between those of a conductor and an insulator.

The conduction due to the electrons in the conduction band is a different process than the conduction due to the unfilled states left in the valence band. The latter is called conduction by "holes." In the intrinsic or pure semiconductor material, there are as many holes as there are free electrons, as the former is created by the latter. An analogy (which is attributed to Shockley) might be used to illustrate the conduction processes. A parking garage with two floors has the lower floor completely filled with automobiles and the upper floor completely empty. Under these conditions there can be no movement of automobiles on either floor. If one automobile is elevated from the lower to the upper floor, there can be motion of automobiles on each floor. The auto on the upper floor may move freely over comparatively large distances. In contrast, the motion on the lower floor is accomplished by moving one car at a time into the available space. Hence, an observer near the ceiling of the first floor would see the "hole" move rather than the automobiles. The hole would have less mobility than the auto on the upper floor. Nevertheless, both would contribute to the total motion.

A qualitative examination of the crystal structure may give additional insight into the behavior of the valence-band electrons. Under carefully

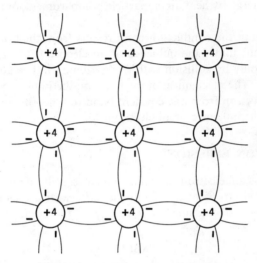

Fig. 2.5. Two-dimensional representation of covalent bonds in a tetravalent crystal.

controlled conditions, the molten material solidifies into an orderly arrangement of atoms. A *two-dimensional symbolic diagram* of this arrangement for a tetravalent material is shown in Fig. 2.5. Covalent bonds exist between each pair of atoms and hold the crystal together. In this manner, the atoms share their valence electrons, so each atom feels that it has realized its ambition to fill its valence shell. In fact, the total electron energy is less in the crystalline arrangement than it would be in a haphazard arrangement. Figure 2.4 show that the energy of the valence electrons is reduced as the crystal is formed. This reduction in energy accounts for the "latent heat of fusion" which occurs when a liquid freezes. In Fig. 2.5, each circle represents the nucleus and the closed shells of a tetravalent atom. Consequently, the net positive charge of this inert group is equal to the charge of the four valence electrons. Each minus sign represents a valence electron and the double lines represent the covalent forces or bonds which hold the atoms together. Thus, the diagram represents the condition of the entire intrinsic germanium crystal at 0°K. As the temperature is raised above 0°K, the energy of the crystal atoms is increased and they vibrate about their equilibrium positions. If an electron receives sufficient energy, it may escape from the valence position or break the covalent bond and drift through the crystal lattice. The electron has then received the energy required to jump from the valence band to the conduction band. This energy is about 0.78 *electron volt* for germanium and 1.2 *electron volts* for silicon at 0°K. The electron may receive this energy by heat, light, particle bombardment, or intense electric field.

Conduction in the conduction band results from the movement of the "free" electrons under the influence of an electric field; this movement is hampered only by collision with the stationary lattice atoms and local atomic fields. The mechanism of the hole conduction is merely the movement of an electron from one covalent bond to a nearby missing covalent bond under the influence of an electric field.

2.3 ELECTRON EMISSION

The process of electron emission which is utilized in electron tubes requires that electrons escape from the surface of a conductor into the surrounding gas or vacuum. The energy of the electron must then be

TABLE 2.1
Commonly Used Cathode Materials

Material	W_w (ev)	Melting Point (°K)
Cesium	1.81	299
Copper	4.10	1356
Nickel	4.60	1725
Thorium	3.40	2118
Tungsten	4.52	3643
Thorium on tungsten	2.60	. . .
Rare-earth oxides	1.00 (typical)	. . .

increased from the conduction-band level to essentially the zero-reference level at infinity, which is known as the vacuum level. The energy difference between the highest occupied state at 0°K and the vacuum level is known as the *work function* of the material. The electrons may receive sufficient energy for emission from heat, light, bombardment by particles, or intense electric fields. These types of emission are known as thermionic emission, photoemission, secondary emission, and high field emission, respectively. The emitted electrons are free charge carriers in the space surrounding the emitter. These electrons drift in the presence of an electric field and thus cause the space to be a conducting medium.

Some commonly used cathode materials are listed in Table 2.1. The work functions W_w and melting points are also given. An ideal thermionic emitter would have a low work function and a high melting point. The mechanical properties of the material also need to be considered. Commonly used thermionic emitters are the rare-earth oxides, tungsten, and thorium on tungsten. Cesium is sometimes used as a photo emitter.

2.4 CHARGE CARRIERS IN A SEMICONDUCTOR

The conductivity of a semiconductor depends on the charge-carrier density. Therefore, conductivity depends on the temperature, as previously discussed. In order to predict the conductivity characteristics of a material, a relationship between charge-carrier density and temperature must be developed. At temperatures above absolute zero, some valence electrons break their covalent bonds and become carriers. At the same time these electrons leave holes which act as positive carriers. In addition there is a continual recombination of electrons and holes. Therefore, the total number of carriers will reach a steady-state value at a particular temperature.

It would be impossible to predict the time of excitation or recombination of a particular electron. However, using the methods of statistics it is possible to accurately predict the number of electrons in the conduction band or the number of holes in the valence band at a particular temperature. This prediction is analogous to the accurate prediction of death rates of populations even though it may be impossible to predict the time of death of each individual.

Fermi and Dirac used statistical methods to determine the probability of occupancy of any particular energy state as a function of temperature. This is analogous to the probability that a person will die within a year as a function of age. The number of persons in a given age group who will die within a year may then be determined by multiplying the total number of persons in the group by the probability function. In a similar fashion, the number of occupied states at a given energy level and temperature can be determined by multiplying the total number of states by the probability that the states are occupied. The Fermi-Dirac probability function is

$$f(W) = \frac{1}{1 + e^{(W - W_F)/kT}} \tag{2.14}$$

where W = the energy level under consideration

k = the Boltzmann constant, 1.38×10^{-23} j/°K, which relates temperature to energy

T = the temperature in °K

W_F = a specific energy level known as the Fermi level

When the temperature is absolute zero, it may be seen from Eq. 2.14 that the probability is zero that an energy state of higher level than the Fermi

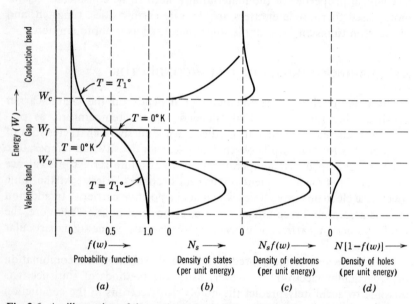

Fig. 2.6. An illustration of the method of calculating the densities of electrons per unit energy or holes per unit energy by taking the product of the probability function and the density of states per unit energy.

level is occupied and is unity that an energy state having lower energy than the Fermi level is occupied. Therefore, a rule concerning the Fermi level may be stated. *No electron can have energy higher than the Fermi level when the temperature is absolute zero.*

Again, Eq. 2.14 shows that *the probability of an energy state being occupied is one half when the state is at the Fermi level and the temperature is above* 0°K. This second rule is also useful in locating the Fermi level, as will be seen later. The Fermi-Dirac probability function is sketched for two different temperature values in Fig. 2.6a.

In order to determine the number of occupied states, and hence the number of charge carriers in a given volume of crystal, the density of available energy states which have energies within a narrow energy band

ΔW must be known as a function of energy. This, for example, is analogous to knowing the number of people in each age group as a function of age in the United States. The method of quantum mechanics provides the desired density of energy states having energies within the limits ΔW as a function of energy. First, Aldert van der Ziel has shown that the maximum possible density of electrons which can have velocities within the limits Δv is given by the relationship[1]

$$\Delta N_s = \frac{8\pi(m_e{}^*)^3 v^2}{h^3} \Delta v \qquad (2.15)$$

where ΔN_s is the number of available states per unit volume which can be filled by electrons having velocities within the limits Δv, $m_e{}^*$ is the *effective mass* of the electron,[2] and h is Planck's constant (6.625×10^{-34} j/sec.).

Writing Eq. 2.15 in differential form,

$$dN_s = \frac{8\pi(m_e{}^*)^3 v^2 \, dv}{h^3} \qquad (2.16)$$

The velocity v can be expressed in terms of the kinetic energy of the electron. Then substituting $W_k = mv^2/2$ and $dW_k = mv \, dv$ into Eq. 2.16 we have

$$dN_s = \frac{8(2)^{1/2}\pi(m_e{}^*)^{3/2} W_k{}^{1/2}}{h^3} \, dW_k \qquad (2.17)$$

When an electron receives sufficient energy to jump from the valence band to the conduction band, the potential energy of the electron is increased to the potential energy level of the conduction band, W_c. The electron usually receives more than enough energy to jump the gap and become free. The excess energy is retained by the electron in the form of kinetic energy, W_k. Therefore, the total energy of a conduction-band electron is $W = W_c + W_k$ and the kinetic energy is $W_k = W - W_c$. Note that $dW_k = dW$. Using these relationships, Eq. 2.17 becomes

$$dN_s = A_c(W - W_c)^{1/2} \, dW = A_c N_c(W) \, dW \qquad (2.18a)$$

where

$$A_c = 8(2)^{1/2}\pi(m_e{}^*)^{3/2}/h^3,$$

and the density of states is

$$N_c(W) = (W - W_c)^{1/2}.$$

---

[1] See *Solid State Physical Electronics*, by Aldert van der Ziel, Prentice-Hall, Englewood Cliffs, New Jersey, Section 3.3, p. 46.

[2] Classical mechanics can be used to determine the behavior of free carriers in a crystal provided that an effective mass $m_n{}^*$ (which accounts for the periodic crystal forces) is used instead of the electronic rest mass m. (See Table 2.2.)

It can be shown that the distribution of available states near the top of the valence band is the same as the distribution of states near the lower edge of the conduction band. In other words, Eq. 2.18a is applicable near the upper edge of the valence band when the term $(W - W_c)$ is replaced by $(W_v - W)$ and the effective mass of the hole $m_h{}^*$, which is different than the effective mass of the electron, is used in the constant A. Then

$$dN_s = A_v(W_v - W)^{\frac{1}{2}} \, dW = A_v \, dN_v(W) \, dW \qquad (2.18b)$$

A sketch of the available states N_s per unit energy as a function of energy W is given in Fig. 2.6b.

TABLE 2.2

**Some Physical Constants and Some Fundamental
Properties of Ge and Si**

Physical Constants

Electron charge q, coulomb	1.6×10^{-19}
Electron rest mass m, kg	9.11×10^{-31}
Proton rest mass, kg	1.67×10^{-27}
Planck's constant h, joule-sec	6.62×10^{-34}
Boltzmann constant k, joule/°K	1.38×10^{-23}
Avogadro's number, molecules/kg-mole	6.02×10^{26}
Permittivity of free space ϵ_v, farad/m	8.854×10^{-12}
Permeability of free space μ_v, henry/m	$4\pi \times 10^{-7}$
Speed of light, m/sec	3.00×10^8
Wavelength range of visible light, A	$4000 - 7200$

Specific Properties	Ge	Si
Atomic number	32	14
Atomic weight	72.60	28.06
Density (25°C) kg/m³	5.33×10^3	2.33×10^3
Melting point, °C	936	1420
Relative dielectric constant ϵ/ϵ_v	16	12
Effective mass ratio m*/m: Free electrons	0.55	1.1
holes	0.37	0.59
Intrinsic carrier density (300°K), n_i,	2.4×10^{13}	1.5×10^{10}
p_i, cm⁻³		
Gap energy W_g, electron volts: 0°K	0.782	1.2
300°K	0.67	1.1
Carrier mobility (300°K), m²/v-sec μ_n	0.39	0.12
μ_p	0.19	0.05
Diffusion constant (300°K) m²/sec D_n	98.8×10^{-4}	33.8×10^{-4}
D_p	46.8×10^{-4}	13×10^{-4}

Now, the number of electrons, or occupied states, per unit volume which have energies within the band dW may be obtained from the product of the number of states dN_s and the probability function $f(W)$.

$$dn = f(W)(dN_s) = A_c(W - W_c)^{1/2}f(W)\,dW \qquad (2.19)$$

where n is the number of electrons per unit volume.

The number of electrons per unit volume (n) as a function of energy is shown in Fig. 2.6c when the temperature $T = T_1$. Since a hole is an unoccupied state, the density of holes per unit energy may be determined by subtracting the density of occupied states n, per unit energy, from the total density of states N_s, per unit energy. Note that *the probability function is symmetrical about the Fermi level.* That is, the probability that states are filled at a given ΔW above the Fermi level is equal to the probability that states are empty $[1 - f(W)]$ at the same ΔW below the Fermi level. The Fermi level is shown in Fig. 2.6a near the center of the forbidden band or gap. This position will be verified later.

The total number of electrons per unit volume in the conduction band is obtained by integrating both sides of Eq. 2.19 over the entire conduction band.

$$n = \int_{W_c}^{\infty} A_c(W - W_c)^{1/2}f(W)\,dW \qquad (2.20)$$

An examination of the probability function $f(W)$, Eq. 2.14, suggests that a useful approximation may be made when $W - W_F$ is at least several times as large as kT. Then the exponential term is large in comparison with one and

$$f(W) \simeq e^{-(W-W_F)/kT} \qquad (2.21)$$

For the normal room temperature of 300°K, $kT = 4.14 \times 10^{-21}$ joule. The normal forbidden band or gap energy is of the order of *one electron volt* $= 1.6 \times 10^{-19}$ joule. The total gap energy is then about $40kT$. Since the Fermi level is near the center of the gap, or forbidden band, as indicated in Fig. 2.6, there are no states closer than about $20kT$ to the Fermi level. Equation 2.21, which is known as the classical approximation, is highly accurate under these conditions.

The number of occupied states, or electrons, per unit volume in the conduction band may now be determined. Using Eqs. 2.20 and 2.21

$$n = \int_{W_c}^{\infty} A_c(W - W_c)^{1/2}\,e^{-(W-W_F)/kT}\,dW \qquad (2.22)$$

If a change in variable from $(W - W_c)$ to x is made, this integral may be recognized as a standard form.[3] With the aid of the integral table,

$$n = \frac{A_c}{2}(kT)^{3/2}\pi^{1/2}\,e^{-(W_c-W_F)/kT} \qquad (2.23)$$

[3] See Eq. 508 in B. C. Pierce and R. M. Foster, *A Short Table of Integrals*, Fourth Edition, Ginn and Co., New York, 1956.

The previous technique may be used to determine the hole density in the valence band. The probability that states are not filled is

$$1 - F(W) = \frac{1}{1 + e^{(W_F - W)/kT}} \tag{2.24}$$

PROB. 2.1. Verify Eq. 2.24.

Since the energy level at the top of the valence band is several kT units below the Fermi level, $1 - F(W) \simeq e^{-(W_F - W)/kT}$. Using Eq. 2.18b

$$p = \int_{-\infty}^{W_v} A_v (W_v - W)^{1/2} \, e^{-(W_F - W)/kT} \, dW \tag{2.25}$$

Notice the similarity between Eqs. 2.22 and 2.25. A serious question, however, may be raised concerning the validity of Eq. 2.25, as the density of states function is only valid near the top of the valence band but the integration is to be performed over the entire energy range below W_v. This inconsistency will produce little error, however, because the probability function $1 - F(W)$ approaches zero at an exponential rate, and at normal temperatures the product $(1 - F(W))N_s$ is negligibly small for all energy levels for which $N_s = A_v (W_v - W)^{1/2}$ is not valid. The integral table may be used to integrate Eq. 2.25. Then

$$p = \frac{A_v}{2} (kT)^{3/2} \pi^{1/2} \, e^{-(W_F - W_v)/kT} \tag{2.26}$$

Calculation of either p from Eq. 2.26 or n from Eq. 2.23 requires a knowledge of the Fermi level W_F. W_F, however, vanishes from the product pn as shown in Eq. 2.27:

$$pn = \frac{A_v A_c}{4} (kT)^3 \pi \, e^{-(W_c - W_v)/kT} \tag{2.27}$$

where $W_c - W_v$ is the gap energy W_g which is known.

In the intrinsic material, the density of free electrons n_i must be equal to the density of holes p_i; therefore, $np = n_i p_i = n_i^2 = p_i^2$ and

$$n_i = p_i = \tfrac{1}{2}(A_c A_v \pi k^3)^{1/2} T^{3/2} \, e^{-(W_g/2kT)} = BT^{3/2} \, e^{-(W_g/2kT)} \tag{2.28}$$

The experimentally determined values of B (which give charge carriers per cubic meter) are:

$$B = 1.76 \times 10^{22} \text{ for germanium}$$

$$B = 3.88 \times 10^{22} \text{ for silicon}$$

PROB. 2.2. Calculate the theoretical values of B for both silicon and germanium and compare them with the experimentally determined values. Why are the values of B different for germanium and silicon?

A comparison between Eqs. 2.23 and 2.28 shows that the Fermi level would be at the center of the forbidden band or gap if A_c were equal to A_v. Actually, A_c differs from A_v because of the difference in the effective mass of the electron as compared with that of the hole in a crystal. Nevertheless, *the Fermi level is very near the center of the gap in the intrinsic crystal.*

The gap energy is a function of temperature because the atomic spacing increases with temperature owing to thermal expansion. The gap energy can be determined from the following relationships:

For silicon, $\quad W_g = 1.2 - (2.8 \times 10^{-4}T)$ electron volts

For germanium, $W_g = 0.782 - (3.9 \times 10^{-4}T)$ electron volts

At $300°K$ the gap energy is approximately 1.1 electron volts for silicon and 0.67 electron volts for germanium.

PROB. 2.3. Calculate the number of conduction electrons in 1 cc of intrinsic germanium at (*a*) $300°K$, (*b*) $200°K$, (*c*) $400°K$. One electron volt = 1.6×10^{-19} j. *Answer: (a) 2.56×10^{13} (b) 2.99×10^{10} (c) 6.35×10^{15}.*

PROB. 2.4. Calculate the number of conduction holes in 1 cc of intrinsic silicon at (*a*) $200°K$, (*b*) $300°K$, (*c*) $400°K$.

PROB. 2.5. Calculate the ratio of conduction electrons in germanium at room temperature ($300°K$) to the total number of atoms in the crystal. The density of Ge is 5.46 g/cm³. Its atomic weight is 72.6 grams, in which there are 6.024 × 10^{23} atoms (Avogadro's number).

2.5 RECOMBINATION

From the foregoing discussion, it is evident that free electrons and holes are being continually generated in a semiconductor crystal at normal temperatures. The number of charge carriers would increase indefinitely if the holes and electrons did not recombine. When the temperature of the crystal remains constant for a period of time, however, the rate of recombination is equal to the rate of generation and the carrier density remains essentially constant at the value predicted by statistical methods (Eq. 2.28). If the number of carriers were increased above the equilibrium value by some process, such as shining light on the crystal, the recombination rate would also increase because the opportunities for recombination are proportional to the number of carriers. This is analogous to the marriage rate being proportional to the population. After removing the light, the recombination rate exceeds the generation rate and the carrier density decreases exponentially toward the equilibrium value. This process is expressed by the following relationship; considering negative carriers:

$$n = n_c + \Delta n\, e^{-t/\tau} \tag{2.29}$$

where n_0 is the number of negative carriers at equilibrium, Δn is the increase in carriers due to the light, and τ is defined as the time required to reduce the excess carriers to $1/e$ times the number at the instant the light was removed at $t = 0$. τ is given the name "lifetime" and compares with the time constant of an electrical RC circuit. The rate of change of carrier density

$$\frac{dn}{dt} = -\frac{\Delta n}{\tau} e^{-t/\tau} \tag{2.30}$$

But from Eq. 2.29

$$\Delta n \, e^{-t/\tau} = n - n_0 \tag{2.31}$$

Then

$$\frac{dn}{dt} = \frac{n_0}{\tau} - \frac{n}{\tau} \tag{2.32}$$

The first term of Eq. 2.32 is the rate of generation and is a function of the temperature and the lifetime. The second term is the rate of recombination. It is proportional to the instantaneous carrier density and inversely proportional to the lifetime. When n is equal to n_0, the recombination rate is equal to the rate of generation and the density is in equilibrium.

According to Dewitt and Rossoff,[4] experimental measurements of the lifetime of various crystals reveal that the lifetime of similar crystals varies widely. The purer crystals have longer lifetimes. In addition, the shape of the crystal has a pronounced influence on the lifetime. The larger the ratio of volume to surface area, the longer is the lifetime. For example, a cubic crystal has a longer lifetime than a thin or long crystal. The measured lifetimes are always much shorter than predicted values based on the assumption that the recombination results purely from an electron coming in contact with a hole.

Investigators have postulated that the imperfections in the crystal act as a catalyst to speed up the recombination process. It is not known how these imperfections do this, but it is speculated that the imperfection somehow holds the carrier until an opposite type carrier comes along and recombination results. The probability of recombination would be increased by this mechanism. The imperfections are known as *deathnium centers* or traps. Actually the entire surface of the crystal is an extended imperfection. Therefore, a decrease in surface area for a given volume of crystal would reduce the number of traps and increase the lifetime of the carriers.

2.6 DRIFT AND CONDUCTIVITY

The motion of the charge carriers would be random in the absence of an electric field. According to the particle theory of matter, each free electron would travel in a straight path until it had a collision. If the collision were elastic, the electron would proceed in another direction. By this process the motion would be completely random but there would be an average length of path between collisions. This average path is known as the *mean free path*. Also there would be a *mean free time* and an *average particle velocity* associated with this time. The holes would also move from atom to atom in a random fashion. The hole mean free path would normally be shorter than that of the electron.

When an electric field is applied to the crystal, the carriers acquire a component of velocity in the direction of the field. Because of the increased kinetic energy of the carriers, they experience a greater energy loss at each collision. This energy loss accounts for the ohmic power loss in the conduction process. The carriers are deflected in random directions after each collision, but the component of velocity acquired in the direction of the field between collisions results in an average drift velocity v. The current density is equal to the product of the charge per unit volume and the drift velocity. Consequently, the current density due to electron drift is

$$J_n = nqv_n \tag{2.33}$$

where v_n is the average drift velocity of the electrons.

The hole drift would also contribute to the current density. Therefore,

$$J_p = pqv_p \tag{2.34}$$

where v_p is the average drift velocity of the holes.

The total current density

$$J = J_n + J_p = q(nv_n + pv_p) \tag{2.35}$$

Conductivity σ is defined as the ratio of current density to the electric field intensity.

$$\sigma = \frac{J}{\mathscr{E}} \tag{2.36}$$

Then, combining Eqs. 2.35 and 2.36

$$\sigma = \frac{q(nv_n + pv_p)}{\mathscr{E}} \tag{2.37}$$

It is convenient to use the concept of charge mobility μ which is defined as

$$\mu = \frac{v}{\mathscr{E}} \tag{2.38}$$

Then

$$\sigma = q(n\mu_n + p\mu_p) \tag{2.39}$$

where μ_n = the mobility of negative carriers

μ_p = the mobility of positive carriers

The carrier mobilities for a material may be determined experimentally by the use of the "Hall effect" which will be discussed later. The mobilities

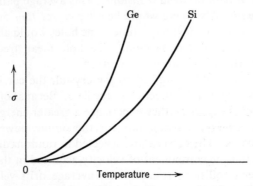

Fig. 2.7. Conductivity of germanium and silicon as a function of temperature.

of lightly doped germanium and silicon at 300°K as determined by M. B. Prince[5] are listed below.

	μ_n	μ_p
Germanium	0.39	0.19 m²/vsec
Silicon	0.12	0.05 m²/vsec

Carrier mobility decreases with increasing temperature because the increased vibrational energy increases the effective diameter of the atoms and thus reduces the mean free path of the carriers. The mobility temperature coefficient is often neglected for temperatures near 300°K because it is dwarfed by the exponential variation of thermal generation with temperature.

PROB. 2.6. Calculate the conductivity of pure germanium at room temperature (300°K). See Prob. 2.3. *Answer: 2.22 mhos/meter.*

PROB. 2.7. Calculate the conductivity of pure silicon at 300°K. See Prob. 2.4.

PROB. 2.8. What is the resistivity of (a) germanium and (b) silicon at 300°K? *Answer: (a) 0.45 ohm-meter. (b) 2400 ohm-meter.*

Figure 2.7 illustrates the variation of conductivity of intrinsic germanium and silicon as a function of temperature. This variable conductivity

[5] M. B. Prince, *Phys. Rev.*, Vol. 92, No. 3 (1953).

property is exploited in devices such as thermistors, which are used in applications such as thermal compensation of transistor circuits and automatic temperature control systems. In the thermistor, the nature of the variation of resistance over a given temperature range depends on the type of semiconductor material used, whereas the actual resistance at a given reference temperature depends on the size and shape of the device.

PROB. 2.9. A rectangular thermistor is made of pure germanium. Its dimensions are 0.1 cm × 0.2 cm × 1.0 cm. The electrodes are attached to the ends of the bar. Determine the resistance of the thermistor at 300°K and 350°K. Assume that the carrier mobilities at 350°K are approximately the same as they are at 300°K.

2.7 DOPED SEMICONDUCTORS

A semiconductor crystal which is impure or imperfect may be called an *extrinsic* semiconductor. As previously discussed, imperfections cause traps or deathnium centers. It would be expected that impurities would alter the energy levels and change the conductivity of the crystal. When impurity atoms are intentionally added, the semiconductor is said to be *doped.* Very small amounts of impurity may have a remarkable effect on the behavior of the crystal.

The conductivity of a semiconductor may be greatly increased if small amounts of certain impurities are introduced into the crystal. For example, if a few parts per million of elements such as *arsenic* or *antimony*, which have five valence electrons, are added to the semiconductor, the impurity atoms replace the germanium or silicon atoms in the crystal structure, as shown in Fig. 2.8. Four of the valence electrons will form covalent bonds with the neighboring atoms. The fifth electron will not fit into the lattice arrangement and, therefore, will be loosely bound to its nucleus. At 0°K the energy of this electron is only a few hundredths of an electron volt below the conduction band. Therefore, at normal temperatures the probability is very high that this electron will be a free electron in the conduction band. The electron is then said to be *activated.* Note that a negative carrier is produced *without* creating a hole or a positive carrier. A fixed positive charge remains in the lattice but no covalent bonds are broken.

A semiconductor to which a pentavalent atom has been added is called *n*-type because the majority of charge carriers are negative. The pentavalent impurity atoms are called donors because they provide the extra free electrons. If there is only one donor for each million intrinsic atoms, the number of free electrons and hence the conductivity may be increased many-fold. In *n*-type material, the holes produced by thermal generation

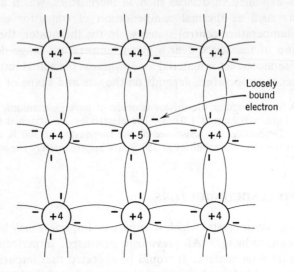

Fig. 2.8. Crystal lattice with a donor impurity.

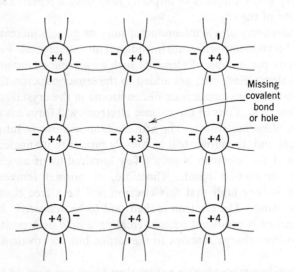

Fig. 2.9. Crystal lattice with an acceptor impurity.

readily recombine because of the abundance of free electrons. Therefore, conduction is due almost entirely to free electrons. In this case, the electrons are called *majority* carriers and the holes are called *minority* carriers. Consequently, the conductivity is

$$\sigma \simeq qn\mu_n \tag{2.40}$$

Each donor atom provides an allowed energy state in the forbidden band (of the intrinsic material) at an energy level of a few hundredths of an electron volt below the conduction band, as shown in Fig. 2.10a. This level is known as the *donor level*.

PROB. 2.10. Assuming that all the donor atoms provide a free electron, calculate the conductivity at 300°K of *n*-type germanium which has one donor atom per million germanium atoms. Compare the conductivity with that of pure germanium (Prob. 2.6).

If a small quantity of trivalent impurity is added to an intrinsic semiconductor, each impurity atom fits into the crystal structure but lacks one of the electrons needed to complete the covalent bonds. This situation is illustrated in Fig. 2.9. Each impurity atom is called an *acceptor* because it provides a hole or positive carrier. At normal temperatures these holes move freely through the material and become charge carriers because very little energy is required to move a valence electron from a neighboring atom into the hole provided by an acceptor atom.

Each acceptor atom provides an allowed energy state in the intrinsic forbidden band at an energy level a few hundredths of an electron volt above the valence band as shown in Fig. 2.10a. This level is known as the *acceptor level*.

A crystal which is doped with acceptor atoms such as *indium* or *gallium* is known as *p-type* because conduction is primarily by holes. In *p*-type material, the free electrons which are thermally generated in the intrinsic material quickly recombine because of the abundance of holes. Therefore, the conductivity of *p*-type material is

$$\sigma \simeq qp\mu_p \tag{2.41}$$

In the event that both donors and acceptors were added to an intrinsic semiconductor, it would be expected that the donor electrons would combine with the acceptor holes. The difference between the donor and acceptor concentrations should determine the effect of the doping. Equal concentrations should provide characteristics similar to the intrinsic material. Experimental evidence verifies that these assumptions are essentially correct.

The Fermi-Dirac distribution function is also applicable to the *extrinsic* or doped semiconductor. Determining the location of the Fermi level is usually the major problem in the application of this function. The Fermi level was found to be near the center of the forbidden band in the intrinsic semiconductor; the knowledge that the density of free electrons is equal

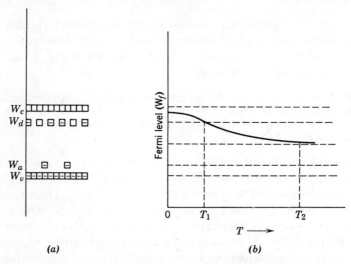

(a)   *(b)*

Fig. 2.10. Energy states of a "doped" semiconductor.

to the density of holes was used to make this determination. Similarly, the doping concentrations and the degree of activation of the impurity atoms must be known in the extrinsic semiconductor in order to locate the Fermi level. The degree of activation, and thus the Fermi level, is a function of temperature. Before we attempt to locate the Fermi level in a specific example, let us review the characteristics of the Fermi-Dirac distribution function.

1. The probability that states with energies above the Fermi level are filled is *always* less than one half.

2. The probability that states with energies below the Fermi level are filled is *always* more than one half.

3. At $0°K$ all states with energies above the Fermi level are empty and all states with energies below the Fermi level are filled.

Now let us consider a silicon crystal which has been doped with donor atoms. The foregoing rules clearly show that the Fermi level must be above the donor level at all temperatures below T_1, which is the temperature required to activate one half of the donors (see Fig. 2.10b). For temperatures above T_1, the Fermi level must drop below the donor level because less than half of the donor states are filled. T_1 is of the order of 50°K. At temperatures well above T_1, almost all the donors are activated and the negative carrier density is approximately equal to the donor density because the carriers generated from the intrinsic atoms are normally negligible. Whenever the carrier density is known, the Fermi level may be determined at a given temperature by the use of Eq. 2.23 because the Fermi level with reference to W_c is the only unknown in the equation.

PROB. 2.11. A silicon crystal is doped with 10^{21} donors per cubic meter. Find the Fermi level with respect to the bottom of the conduction band at 300°K. Assume the constant $A_c k^{3/2} \pi^{1/2}/2$ to be approximately equal to the constant B (Eq. 2.28). *Answer: 0.316 v below W_c.*

PROB. 2.12. Determine the probability that the donor states are filled in the doped crystal of Prob. 2.11 Assume that the donor level is 0.02 electron volts below the conduction band.

As the temperature is raised to such a high value that the carriers generated by broken covalent bonds in the intrinsic material have a density comparable with the donor density, the Fermi level must approach the center of the forbidden band because the hole density will then be comparable with the electron density and this situation can occur only when the Fermi level is near the center of the gap. The Fermi level is sketched as a function of temperature in Fig. 2.10b. A sketch of charge carriers as a function of temperature is shown in Fig. 2.11.

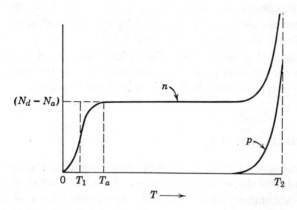

Fig. 2.11. A typical plot of charge carriers as a function of temperature for *n*-type crystal.

PROB. 2.13. Sketch the Fermi level as a function of temperature for a p-doped crystal.

It was previously shown by Eq. 2.27 that the product of positive and negative charge carriers pn is independent of the Fermi level, assuming a condition of thermal equilibrium. Therefore Eq. 2.27 is valid for doped as well as intrinsic crystals. In the intrinsic material, since $p_i = n_i$, we can write

$$pn = n_i^2 \qquad (2.42)$$

where n_i is the number of negative carriers in thermal equilibrium. In the doped crystal, the Fermi level is shifted away from the center of the gap and p is not equal to n. However, the product pn is a function of the gap energy and temperature only and is, therefore, the same as in the intrinsic crystal. Then

$$p = \frac{n_i^2}{n} \qquad (2.43)$$

Equation 2.43 is useful in determining the number of minority carriers per unit volume when the number of majority carriers and intrinsic carriers are either known or can be calculated easily. Inspection of Eq. 2.42 reveals that in the doped semiconductor the minority carriers are reduced from the number in the intrinsic material by the same ratio as the increase in majority carriers, which results from the doping. For example, consider an n-type crystal which has one hundred times as many negative carriers per unit volume as the intrinsic crystal would have at the same temperature. The p-type carriers would only be 0.01 as numerous as those in the intrinsic material. Physically, the reduction in holes results from the increased opportunities for recombination offered by the activated donor electrons. Mathematically, the increased probability that the holes are filled results from the elevated position of the Fermi level, compared with its central position in the intrinsic case. The end result is that the conductivity of either n- or p-type semiconductors is almost entirely due to the majority carriers.

2.8 THE HALL EFFECT

The phenomenon known as the Hall effect is significant in the discussion of semiconductor theory for two reasons. First, the Hall effect provides a method of determining the electron and hole mobilities for a given material. Second, the Hall effect demonstrates that conduction by holes is a different process than conduction by electrons. Frequently, the beginning student is reluctant to accept the concept of conduction by holes.

Figure 2.12 illustrates the Hall effect. A current is passed through a conductor or semiconductor as indicated. The current flows because of an axial, or x, component of electric field. A magnetic field is arranged so that the magnetic flux in the material is normal to the direction of current flow. Assume that the material is a p-type crystal and that the magnetic flux lines are coming out of the paper. The holes would then experience a downward force which would cause them to crowd together toward the bottom of the crystal as indicated by the closeness of the line spacing in the

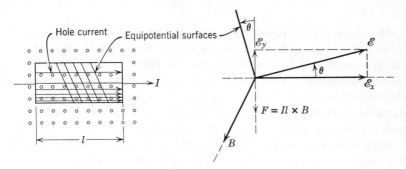

Fig. 2.12. The Hall effect.

figure. This uneven distribution of charge would produce a transverse, or y, component of electric field. Since there can be no appreciable transverse current flow in the crystal, the upward electrostatic force on each charge must be equal to the downward magnetic force. The resultant electric field in the crystal would be the vector sum of the axial and transverse components, as indicated by the vector diagram of Fig. 2.12. Then equating the transverse electric and magnetic forces,

$$F = BIl = pqAl\mathcal{E}_y \qquad (2.44)$$

where l = the length of the crystal

A = cross-sectional area

pq = charge density due to the holes

The axial component of electric field, using Eq. 2.36, is

$$\mathcal{E}_x = \frac{J}{\sigma} \qquad (2.45)$$

From Eq. 2.44

$$\mathcal{E}_y = \frac{BI}{pqA} = \frac{BJ}{pq} \qquad (2.46)$$

Then

$$\tan \theta = \frac{\mathcal{E}_y}{\mathcal{E}_x} = \frac{B\sigma}{pq} \qquad (2.47)$$

Using the relationship $\sigma = pq\mu_p$ (Eq. 2.41)

$$\tan \theta = B\mu_p \qquad (2.48)$$

The flux density B can be calculated or measured. The angle θ may be determined from careful measurements to find equipotential points on the face of the crystal. After a line is drawn through the equipotential points, the angle θ is measured between the equipotential line and the transverse line. The hole mobility for the type crystal used may then be calculated.

$$\mu_p = \frac{\tan \theta}{B} \qquad (2.49)$$

An n-type crystal could have been used for the preceding example instead of a p-type. The force exerted by the magnetic field on the moving charges would still be downward and the electrons would be crowded toward the bottom of the crystal. Therefore, the transverse component of electric field would also be downward and the equipotential surfaces would slope the opposite direction from the transverse surface, in comparison with the p-type crystal. Thus, the type of conductivity may be identified.

MKS units were used in the preceding development. If the magnetic flux density is given in webers/m², the mobility will be obtained in m²/v-sec.

PROB. 2.14. A Hall effect experiment is arranged as shown in Fig. 2.12. If the magnetic flux density B is 0.1 webers/m² and the angle which the equipotential surface makes with the horizontal x direction is 80°, determine the mobility and the type of majority carriers.

Actually the carrier mobility decreases as the temperature increases, because the carrier mean free path decreases. The mean free path decreases because the vibration amplitude of each atom about its equilibrium position increases. Therefore, the effective collision diameter of each atom increases with temperature. For this reason the resistance of a *conductor* increases with temperature.

PROB. 2.15. Let us assume that there exists an element for which the portion of filled electron states is not given by the Fermi-Dirac distribution but rather the function shown in Fig. 2.13. That is, $f = \dfrac{150}{T}\left(\dfrac{T}{300} - W - 7\right)$ $\dfrac{\text{filled states}}{\text{states}}$ where $W_1 > W > W_2$ and $f = 0$ for $W > W_1$ and $f = 1$ for $W < W_2$.

It has also been determined that

$$N(W) = A(W - W_c) \frac{\text{available states}}{\text{cm}^3 \, \text{ev}}$$

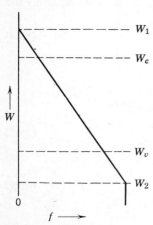

Fig. 2.13. Configuration for Prob. 2.15.

rather than $A_c(W - W_c)^{1/2}$, where $A = 10^{20}$ and W is in electron volts, for this particular element. (This expression is valid only in the lower part of the conduction band.)

Let $W_c = -6\,\text{ev}$, $\quad W_v = -8\,\text{ev}$, $\quad W_1 = -7 + \dfrac{T}{300}$, $\quad W_2 = -7 - \dfrac{T}{300}$.

(a) How many available states N are there with an energy of -5.5 ev in a cubic centimeter?

(b) How many available states are there with energies between -6 and -5.5 ev in a cm^3?

(c) What is the maximum temperature in degrees Kelvin for which there will be no electrons in the conduction band?

(d) Does any such temperature exist in the case of the Fermi-Dirac distribution? Why?

(e) What is the most probable number of electrons per cm^3 with an energy between -5.75 ev and -5.74 ev if $T = 450°\text{K}$?

(f) What is the maximum number of electrons per cm^3 which can be between the energy levels of -5.75 ev and -5.74 ev?

(g) If $T = 450°\text{K}$, how many electrons will there be in the conduction band for 1 cm^3 of the material?

PROB. 2.16. A large bar of germanium having the dimension shown in Fig. 2.14 is used for the following problems.

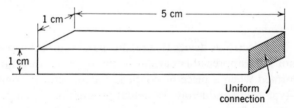

Fig. 2.14. Configuration for Prob. 2.16.

(a) What is the resistance of the bar at 400°K if there are no impurities in the germanium? Neglect edge effects and assume that the bar is enclosed in a light-proof box. Also assume that the mobility does not change with temperature.

(b) What changes will take place in the resistance if a bright light (which generates no heat) is suddenly turned on in such a way that all side surfaces are illuminated for one minute, then the light is turned off?

(c) Find the resistance at 400°K (no light) if arsenic atoms (pentavalent) are added in the ratio of 0.5 parts per million.

(d) Without calculating the new values of resistance, discuss the effects of reducing the temperature from 400°K to 300°K for the intrinsic germanium bar of part a and the doped bar of part c.

3

Diodes

A diode is an electronic device that readily passes current in one direction but does not pass appreciable current in the opposite direction. Such a device is formed when a piece of *n*-type semiconductor is connected to a piece of *p*-type semiconductor. In actual production, a single crystal of semiconductor is formed with half of the crystal doped with acceptor impurities and the other half of the crystal doped with donor impurities. Other types of diodes are constructed by placing an electron emitter (cathode) and an electron collector (plate) in a vacuum or in a controlled gaseous atmosphere. The properties of the various types of diodes are considered in this chapter.

3.1 THE *p-n* JUNCTION

Figure 3.1 illustrates the action of the *p-n* junction. Assume two pieces of semiconductor exist (Fig. 3.1*a*). The *p* material contains an extremely small percentage (in the order of $10^{-4}\%$) of atoms with a valence of $+3$. These acceptor atoms are represented in Fig. 3.1*a* as the circles with the negative signs. Associated with each acceptor atom is a hole, which is represented as a positive sign. An even smaller percentage of intrinsic atoms have lost electrons due to thermal agitation (or photo

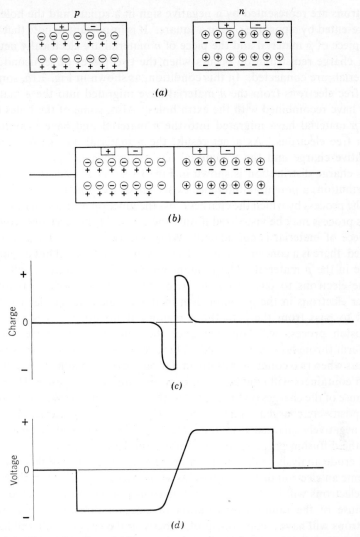

Fig. 3.1. The *p-n* junction. (*a*) Representation of *p*- and *n*-type material; (*b*) representation of *p-n* junction; (*c*) charge distribution of the *p-n* junction; (*d*) potential distribution of the *p-n* junction.

emission). These atoms are represented by the positive sign in the square. The free electrons released by this action are represented by the negative sign in the square. In the *n* material of Fig. 3.1*a*, the +5 valence atoms are represented by the circles with the positive sign. The free electrons due to these donor atoms are shown as negative signs. As in the *p* material, the intrinsic atoms form a few electron-hole pairs. Again, these electrons are represented by a negative sign in a square and the holes are represented by a positive sign in a square. It is important to note that both the piece of p material and the piece of n material are electrically neutral.

A charge redistribution occurs when the two pieces of semiconductor materials are connected. In this condition, as shown in Fig. 3.1b, some of the free electrons from the n material have migrated into the p material and have recombined with the extra holes. Also, some of the holes from the p material have migrated into the n material and have recombined witn free electrons. As a net result, the p material has assumed a net negative charge and the n material has assumed a net positive charge. This charge distribution is shown in Fig. 3.1c. As a result of the charge distribution, a potential difference exists across the junction (Fig. 3.1d).

The process by which the charges cross the junction is known as *diffusion*. This process may be visualized if only the action of the electrons from the n piece of material is considered. When the two pieces of material are joined, there is a concentration of electrons in the n material but essentially none in the p material. The random motion of the electrons will allow some electrons to pass from the n to the p region. Because there are fewer electrons in the p region than in the n region, fewer electrons will tend to pass from the p to the n region. If no other forces exist, the diffusion process will continue until the concentration of electrons is uniform throughout the material. This process is the same process which occurs when two containers of dissimilar pure gases are joined. Eventually both containers will contain a uniform mixture of both gases. However, because of the charges on the electrons, these electrons are attracted toward the positively charged n region. Similarly, the holes are attracted toward the negatively charged p region. Hence, an electric field is established (by the diffusion process), which inhibits the diffusion process.

A crude analysis of the diffusion process can be made. In this analysis, assume an electron distribution exists as shown in Fig. 3.2. The charge on the electrons will be ignored in this analysis but will be considered later. Because of the random distribution of electron directions, half of the electrons will have a component of velocity to the left and half will have a component of velocity to the right. Now, assume that all the electrons contained within the slice of crystal between x and $(x + \bar{l})$ are able to move a distance $\bar{l}$ in the x direction in the time $\bar{t}$. The term $\bar{l}$ is the mean free path of the electron in the x direction and $\bar{t}$ is the time required to travel this distance. Then, the total number of electrons crossing the line x of Fig. 3.2 from the right is one half the total electrons contained between x and $(x + \bar{l})$. But, the total number of electrons in a unit cross-sectional area is equal to the electron density per unit length multiplied by the total length. In this process, the total number of electrons per unit cross section is equal to the area under the curve of Fig. 3.2 between the points x and $(x + \bar{l})$. The total number of electrons per unit cross section is therefore approximately

$$N_{[x \text{ to } (x+l)]} = \bar{l}\left(n + \frac{1}{2}\frac{dn}{dx}\bar{l}\right) \tag{3.1}$$

The first term $\bar{l}n$ on the right of the equation is area 1 of Fig. 3.2; the

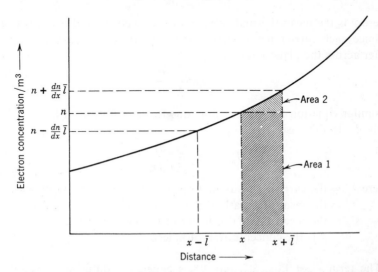

Fig. 3.2. A plot of electron distribution for use in deriving the diffusion equations.

second term is approximately equal to area 2 of the same figure. Area 2 is a triangle and hence has an area of $\frac{1}{2}\bar{l}\,\Delta n$ where Δn is given as $\dfrac{dn}{dx}\bar{l}$.

The total number of carriers per unit cross-sectional area which cross x from the right in time $\bar{t}$ is, therefore,

$$N_R = \frac{1}{2}\left(n\bar{l} + \frac{1}{2}\frac{dn}{dx}\bar{l}^2\right) \tag{3.2}$$

By similar reasoning, the total number of carriers per unit cross-sectional area which cross x from the left in time $\bar{t}$ is

$$N_L = \frac{1}{2}\left(n\bar{l} - \frac{1}{2}\frac{dn}{dx}\bar{l}^2\right) \tag{3.3}$$

The net flow of electrons per square meter across the surface at x in time $\bar{t}$ is

$$N_x = N_R - N_L = \frac{1}{2}\bar{l}^2\frac{dn}{dx} \tag{3.4}$$

The total flow per square meter per second is

$$N_t = \frac{1}{2} \frac{\bar{l}^2}{\bar{t}} \frac{nd}{ax} \tag{3.5}$$

or

$$N_t = \frac{\bar{l}\bar{v}_n}{2} \frac{dn}{dx} \tag{3.6}$$

where $\bar{v}$ is the mean thermal velocity of the electrons and is equal to $\bar{l}/\bar{t}$.

Since each carrier has a charge q, the total current flow per square meter across the plane x is equal to

$$J_n = q \frac{\bar{l}\bar{v}_n}{2} \frac{dn}{dx} \tag{3.7}$$

A similar equation for current flow due to the diffusion of holes can be derived. In this case,

$$J_p = -q \frac{\bar{l}_p \bar{v}_p}{2} \frac{dp}{dx} \tag{3.8}$$

where J_p = the current density in amps/m² (due to hole movement)
$\bar{l}_p$ = the mean free path of the holes in m
$\bar{v}_p$ = the mean thermal velocity of the holes in m/sec
p is the concentration of holes/m³

The term $\dfrac{\bar{l}\bar{v}}{2}$ of Eqs. 3.7 and 3.8 is called the diffusion constant D. Consequently,

$$J_n = qD_n \frac{dn}{dx} \tag{3.9}$$

and

$$J_p = -qD_p \frac{dp}{dx} \tag{3.10}$$

The diffusion constant is a function of the type of material and the temperature as well as the type of carrier. The values for lightly doped germanium and silicon at 300°K are given in Table 3.1.

TABLE 3.1

Values for Germanium and Silicon at 300°K

	Ge	Si
D_n	98.8×10^{-4}	$33.8 \times 10^{-4} \, m^2/sec$
D_p	46.8×10^{-4}	$13.0 \times 10^{-4} \, m^2/sec$

In the actual *n-p* junction, as stated previously, both types of semi-conductive materials are neutral before the junction is made. After the junction is made, the *n* material loses electrons due to diffusion and gains holes.

However, as the electrons enter the *p*-region, recombination with the numerous holes occurs. In fact, the hole population next to the junction is said to be "depleted," since practically all these holes are filled with electrons. The original electrically neutral nature of this region is replaced with negative ions wherever a +3 valence atom exists. Similarly, any holes which "travel" (or are *injected*) into the *n*-material are immediately removed by recombination with the free electrons near the junction. In the *n*-material, the free electrons are depleted and positive ions occur wherever a +5 valence atom exists. As a result of this action (the *p*-material becomes negative and the *n*-material becomes positive), an electric field is established at the junction. In the steady-state condition, this field is just strong enough to inhibit the diffusion action of the electrons from the *n*-material and the holes from the *p*-material.

The free electrons in the *n* material and the holes in the *p* material are known as *majority carriers*. But, because of thermal energy, photons, etc., some free electrons are produced in the *p* material and some holes are produced in the *n* material (as indicated by the signs in the squares in Fig. 3.1). Some of these carriers diffuse to the junction and are swept across the junction by the electric field. As mentioned in Chapter 2, these carriers are known as *minority carriers*. Since the potential hill at the junction is caused by the diffusion of the majority carriers, the minority carriers which are swept across the junction tend to reduce the height of the potential hill. As a result, an equilibrium condition is reached in which the flow of minority carriers is equal to the flow of majority carriers. The current resulting from the diffusion of the majority carriers is known as the *injection current* and the current resulting from the minority carriers is known as the *saturation current*.

As previously mentioned, the charge distribution of Fig. 3.1c causes a potential difference across the *p-n* junction (Fig. 3.1d). This potential difference is a few tenths of a volt at room temperature. It seems possible that a current would flow in an external circuit if a conductor were connected to the open ends of the *p-n* combination since they are at different potentials. This supposition is *not* true, because the contact difference of potential at the junctions of the crystal and the external conductor causes the total emf around the closed circuit to be zero, and no current will flow. For example, if a conductor is brought into contact with an *n* crystal, the net drift of electrons will be from the crystal to the conductor until the crystal becomes positive with respect to the conductor and equilibrium is reached.[1] Of course, the opposite is true if the conductor is connected to a p-type crystal.

The directions of the injection current I_I and the saturation current I_S are shown in Fig. 3.3b. In addition, the lengths of the current arrows indicate the relative magnitude of these currents. The net current flow in this case is zero, $I_I = I_S$. The majority carriers must have enough kinetic energy to "climb" the potential "hill" whereas all minority carriers just "slide down" this potential hill with no kinetic energy required. In fact, the minority carriers gain kinetic energy in traversing the junction.

If an external battery is connected with the positive terminal to the n-type material and the negative terminal to the p material, the potential difference across the junction will increase as shown in Fig. 3.3c. The height of the potential "hill" is increased by the amount of the external battery voltage. Then only those majority carriers which have a very large amount of kinetic energy can "climb" the potential "hill." As a consequence, the injection current I_I is greatly reduced as shown in Fig. 3.3c. Since the minority carriers still require no energy, the current I_S remains the same as in Fig. 3.3b. The external current flow is, therefore, mainly owing to the thermally generated minority carriers of the semiconductor. This current $I_S - I_I$ is known as the *reverse current* of the diode.

If the external battery is connected with the negative terminal to the n-type material and the positive terminal to the p material, the potential difference across the junction is decreased as shown in Fig. 3.3d. The potential "hill" is reduced by the magnitude of the external battery voltage, neglecting the IR drop in the crystals. As a result, a large number of the majority carriers are able to cross the junction. Therefore, the injection current I_I is greatly increased as shown in Fig. 3.3d. Since the minority carriers can still traverse the junction with no loss of energy (these carriers still gain kinetic energy but not as much as in Fig. 3.3b and Fig. 3.3c), the current I_S does not change. The *forward current* of the diode $I_I - I_S$ is, therefore, quite large. In fact, because of the large number of majority carriers as compared to the minority carriers, the forward current is usually thousands of times larger than the reverse current.

PROB. 3.1. A concentration of 10^{13} electrons/cm³ exists in germanium at point x and to the right of point x. The distribution decreases linearly to the left until 1 cm from x no electrons are present. (a) At the instant this condition exists, what is the rate at which diffusion electrons are passing a plane 0.01 cm to the left of point x? (Neglect the effects of charge on the electrons to find diffusion rate.) What current density does this electron flow represent? (b) Repeat part a for a plane $\frac{1}{2}$ cm to the left of point x. (c) Repeat part a for a plane 1.01 cm to the right of point x. Assume the mean free path of an electron is less than 0.01 cm.

[1] This establishment of a potential difference between a doped semiconductor and a conducting wire is used in the construction of point contact diodes.

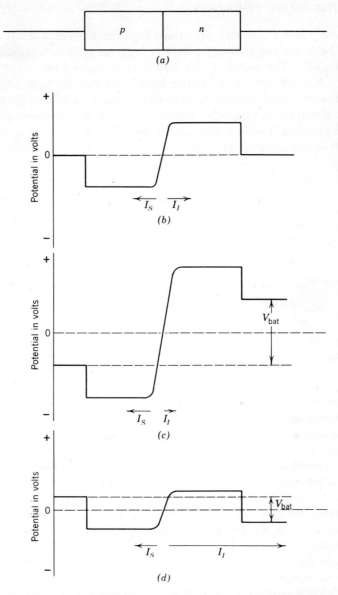

Fig. 3.3. The effect of an external voltage on the potential distribution of a *p-n* junction. (*a*) The *p-n* junction; (*b*) potential distribution with no external battery; (*c*) potential distribution with a reverse bias external battery; (*d*) potential distribution with a forward bias external battery.

3.2 THE DIODE EQUATION

When p and n materials are joined together, the Fermi levels of each must be at the same absolute level in order to provide thermodynamic equilibrium. The proof of this statement is beyond the scope of this book. Nevertheless, if the Fermi levels were not the same, a voltage could be measured between the open ends of the material, and the junction diode would act as a battery.[2] However, since no energy source is present in the material, it cannot generate an emf. Figure 3.4 is a diagrammatic sketch of the energy levels of the p-n combination. In the figure, W_{cp} is

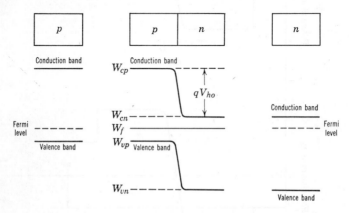

Fig. 3.4. Energy levels of a p-n junction.

the lowest conduction-band energy level in the p material and W_{cn} is the corresponding level in the n. In the n material, the Fermi level is near the donor level and, therefore, just below the conduction band as discussed in Chapter 2. In the p material, the Fermi level is near the acceptor level, just above the valence band. As the junction is formed, the diffusion of carriers occurs until the Fermi levels become aligned. The difference between the two conduction-level energies then becomes qV_{ho}, where V_{ho} is the potential difference between the conduction levels in volts. V_{ho} was called the potential hill in the previous section, but is also known as the *barrier potential*.

Since electron energies are shown in Fig. 3.4 and the potential energy of positive carriers or holes is shown in Fig. 3.1, the potential hill in Fig. 3.4 is inverted as compared with the one in Fig. 3.1.

Using the technique developed in Chapter 2, we may determine the

[2] A p-n junction can be forced to act as a generator if external energy is supplied in the form of heat or light, in which cases the Fermi level is displaced. These devices are known as thermoelectric and photovoltaic generators, respectively.

negative carrier density for each type of material. In the n material (see Eq. 2.23),

$$n_n = A'T^{3/2}e^{-(W_{cn}-W_f)/kT}.$$ (3.11)

All the constants of Eq. 2.23 have been absorbed by A' in Eq. 3.11. Similarly

$$n_p = A'T^{3/2}e^{-(W_{cp}-W_f)/kT}$$ (3.12)

where n_p is the negative carrier density in the p material. The ratio of Eqs. 3.11 and 3.12 is,

$$\frac{n_p}{n_n} = e^{-(W_{cp}-W_{cn})/kt}$$ (3.13)

But the energy difference, $W_{cp} - W_{cn} = qV_{ho}$. Then

$$n_p = n_n e^{-qV_{ho}/kT}$$ (3.14)

Equation 3.14 shows that the ratio of negative carriers in the two regions is dependent only on the barrier potential between these regions (for a given temperature). When an external voltage is applied to the diode, the barrier potential becomes V_h and

$$n_p = n_n e^{-qV_h/kT}$$ (3.15)

These electrons, n_p, are the ones which have sufficient energy to cross the potential barrier and, in so doing, become part of the injection-current density, J_I. The remaining part of the injection-current density results from the holes which have sufficient energy to cross in the opposite direction. From the discussion in Chapter 2 and the foregoing development, it is apparent that

$$p_n = p_p e^{-qV_h/kT}$$ (3.16)

The injection-current density is proportional to the number of majority carriers which pass through the potential barrier V_h. Then

$$J_I = B'(n_n + p_p)e^{-qV_h/kT}$$ (3.17)

But n_n and p_p are the majority-carrier densities in their respective materials and are essentially equal to the densities of donors and acceptors. Therefore, they may be included in a new constant B. Then

$$J_I = Be^{-qV_h/kT}$$ (3.18)

When there is no external connection, the injection-current density must be equal in magnitude but opposite in direction to the saturation-current density, as previously observed. Then

$$J_S = -Be^{-qV_{ho}/kT}$$ (3.19)

where V_{ho} is the height of the potential barrier when no external voltage is applied as previously indicated. Solving for B in terms of J_S,

$$B = -J_S e^{qV_{ho}/kT} \tag{3.20}$$

and, using Eq. 3.18,

$$J_I = -J_S e^{q(V_{ho}-V_h)/kT} \tag{3.21}$$

but the difference between V_{ho} and V_h must be due to an external voltage, V. Then

$$J_I = -J_S e^{qV/kT} \tag{3.22}$$

where V is part of the externally applied voltage. This voltage V differs from the externally applied voltage by the IR drop in the doped crystal.[3] The injection current is obtained by multiplying both sides of Eq. 3.22 by the cross-sectional area at the junction. Hence,

$$I_I = -I_S e^{qV/kT} \tag{3.23}$$

The algebraic sum of the injection and saturation currents must be the current in the external circuit.

$$I = -I_S e^{qV/kT} + I_S = -I_S(e^{qV/kT} - 1) \tag{3.24}$$

At room temperature (300°K) Eq. 3.24 reduces to

$$I = -I_S(e^{39V} - 1) \tag{3.25}$$

If V is about 0.1 volt or more negative, I is approximately equal to I_S. If V is 0.1 volt or more positive, the exponential term of Eq. 3.25 is large in comparison with unity, and I is approximately equal to the injection current.

The maximum rated current for a given diode is determined by the heat dissipation qualities of the mounting system and the cross-sectional area of the diode. In addition, the type of material used in the diode has a bearing on the maximum current rating.

PROB. 3.2. When 1 v reverse bias is applied to a junction diode, 1 μa of current flows. Calculate the approximate forward current when 0.256 v forward bias is applied to the *junction*. If the diode has 10 Ω internal resistance, what is the magnitude of external voltage required in order to obtain 0.1 v across the junction? *Answer v = 0.476 volts.*

PROB. 3.3. Plot a curve of I vs. V as given by Eq. 3.25 if I_S is 10^{-6} amp. Plot values from -5 v to $+0.3$ v.

[3] This is a point which should be stressed. Quite often an external battery is applied to the diode and the current through the diode is measured. Since these values do not agree with values obtained from Eq. 3.23 (with V_{bat} used for V) the reader may assume Eq. 3.23 is not valid. However, remember V is *not* equal to the battery voltage V_{bat} but will always be less.

3.3 SEMICONDUCTOR DIODE CHARACTERISTIC CURVES

A sketch of current vs. voltage as given by Eq. 3.24 is shown as the solid line in Fig. 3.5. The plot of current vs. voltage for an actual diode is similar to the expected curve, but considerable departure exists for large values of both negative and positive bias voltage. This departure is shown by the dashed line in Fig. 3.5. The departure in the reverse bias region from *a* to *b* is partially due to leakage along the surface of the junction. Other

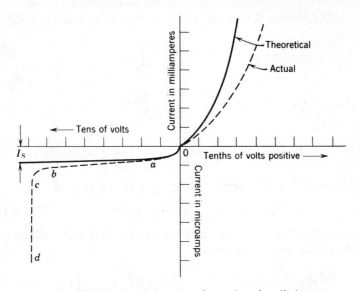

Fig. 3.5. Characteristic curve of a *p-n* junction diode.

leakage paths exist through the mounting material which protects the junction. As a result, this departure is known as the *leakage* component.

At point *c* of Fig. 3.5, a new effect known as the *breakdown* of the crystal is noted. In this "breakdown" region, high currents may be passed and they are limited only by the resistance in the external circuit. These high currents may generate enough heat to destroy the junction. Consequently, most diodes have a maximum reverse voltage rating. This maximum reverse voltage depends somewhat on the temperature of the diode. The "breakdown" region of the diode, as well as the region from *b* to *c*, is investigated in more detail in Section 3.6.

The departure from the theoretical curve in the forward bias region is caused by the *IR* drop in the doped crystal as previously mentioned.

3.4   TEMPERATURE AND SEMICONDUCTOR MATERIAL EFFECT ON THE CHARACTERISTIC CURVE

Equation 3.24 shows that the diode current is a function of temperature, which appears in the denominator of the exponent. However, the variation of the saturation current with temperature is much greater than the variation of the exponential term. The saturation current is proportional to the number of minority carriers which are swept across the p-n junction as previously discussed and the number of minority carriers swept across the junction is proportional to the minority-carrier density in the material under consideration. Using the relationship $pn = n_i{}^2$ (see Eq. 2.42),

$$p_n = \frac{n_i{}^2}{n_n} \simeq \frac{n_i{}^2}{N_a} \tag{3.26a}$$

and

$$n_p = \frac{n_i{}^2}{p_p} \simeq \frac{n_i{}^2}{N_d} \tag{3.26b}$$

Then

$$J_s \simeq C(p_n + n_p) = C\, n_i{}^2\left(\frac{1}{N_d} + \frac{1}{N_a}\right) = C'\, n_i{}^2 \tag{3.27}$$

where C and C' are constants. Using Eq. 2.28, we see that

$$pn = n_i{}^2 = B^2 T^3 e^{-(W_g/kT)} \tag{3.28}$$

The rate of change of J_s with temperature may be obtained by differentiating J_s with respect to temperature.

$$\frac{d(J_s)}{dT} = \frac{d(C'\, B^2 T^3 e^{-W_g/kT})}{dT} = C'\, B^2\left(\frac{3}{T} + \frac{W_g}{kT^2}\right) T^3 e^{-W_g/kT} \tag{3.29}$$

The fractional increase of J_s per °K can be determined at a given temperature T by dividing Eq. 3.29 by J_s. Then

$$\frac{1}{J_s}\left(\frac{dJ_s}{dT}\right) = \frac{3}{T} + \frac{W_g}{kT^2} \tag{3.30}$$

For germanium at 300°K, the fractional increase of J_s per °K is

$$\frac{1}{J_s}\left(\frac{dJ_s}{dT}\right)\Bigg|_{300°\mathrm{K}} = \frac{3}{300} + 39\left(\frac{0.68}{300}\right) \simeq 0.1 \tag{3.31}$$

For silicon at 300°K, the fractional increase per °K is

$$\frac{1}{J_s}\left(\frac{dJ_s}{dT}\right)\Bigg|_{300°\mathrm{K}} = \frac{3}{300} + 39\left(\frac{1.1}{300}\right) \simeq 0.16 \tag{3.32}$$

Therefore, the saturation current in germanium near 300°K increases approximately 10 per cent for each degree K and doubles for each 10°K increase in temperature, and the saturation current in silicon doubles for approximately each 6°K increase.

The foregoing derivation is valid for the semiconductor in the extrinsic range (or the range where the material behaves as n or p material). Germanium begins to be useless as a diode material at 100°C. However, silicon

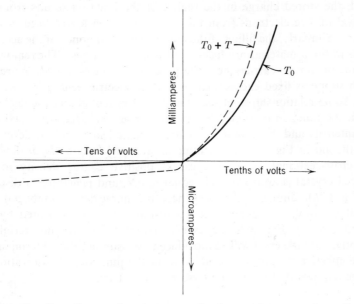

Fig. 3.6. The effect of increased temperature on the characteristic curve of a p-n junction diode.

does not generally begin to degrade too badly until 200°C or higher. Other materials such as silicon carbide[4] are usable to temperatures of 500°C or higher.

The effect of increased temperature on the characteristic curve of a p-n junction diode is shown in Fig. 3.6.

PROB. 3.4. (*a*) If a germanium diode has a saturation current I_0 of 10 μa at room temperature (300°K), what will the saturation current be at 400°K? (*b*) A silicon diode has a saturation current I_0 of 0.01 μa at room temperature. What will be the saturation current of this diode at 400°K? Assume the rate of increase to be constant at the 300°K value.

PROB. 3.5. The diodes of Prob. 3.4 have 0.2 v forward bias across the junction. (*a*) Find the current at room temperature if the diode is germanium.

---

[4] Westinghouse *R* and *D* Letter, Vol. 4, No. 5, February 1961.

(b) Find the current at 400°K if the diode is germanium. (c) Find the current at room temperature if the diode is silicon. (d) Find the current at 400°K if the diode is silicon. *Answer: (a) 24.4 mamp (b) 354 mamp (c) 24.4 µamp (d) 345 mamp.*

3.5 JUNCTION CAPACITANCE

A *p-n* junction and a charged capacitor are similar. As previously noted, the stored charge in the region of the junction results from the removal of free electrons from the *n* region, which leaves fixed positive donors. Similarly, the filling of the missing covalent bonds of the acceptor atoms in the *p* material produces fixed negative charges. The removal of the free or mobile carriers near the junction produces a *depletion* region which supports fixed excess charges and an electric field (Figs. 3.1 and 3.7). Some relationships between the barrier potential and the depletion width, the junction capacitance and the barrier potential, the maximum field intensity and the doping concentrations, and so on will be developed with the aid of Fig. 3.7, representing an abrupt junction *planar* diode of unit cross-sectional area. The excess positive charge density in the *n*-doped crystal is approximately equal to qN_d and penetrates a distance L_n (Fig. 3.7b). Similarly, the excess negative charge density in the *p*-doped crystal is $-qN_a$ and it penetrates a distance L_p. As indicated by the dashed lines in Fig. 3.7, the excess-charge regions do not terminate abruptly, but little error will be introduced by assuming abrupt termination at the effective distances L_n and L_p from the junction. Conservation of charge requires that the total charge be zero. Then

$$qN_dL_n = qN_aL_p \tag{3.33}$$

The electric field intensity (Fig. 3.7c) may be determined from Gauss' law, which states that the total electric flux DA passing through a given closed surface is equal to the coulomb charge enclosed by the surface. Imagine that a ZY plane is located through the depletion region to the left of the junction. The total charge to the left (and to the right) of the plane is $-qN_a(L_p + x)$. All the electric flux lines originate on positive charges to the right of the plane and terminate on the negative charges to the left of the plane. Then, since the cross-sectional area is unity,

$$\mathcal{E} = \frac{\mathbf{D}}{\epsilon} = -\frac{qN_a(L_p + x)}{\epsilon} \tag{3.34}$$

Since the imaginary plane is to the left of the junction, x is negative and the electric field reduces to zero at $x = -L_p$. The maximum field

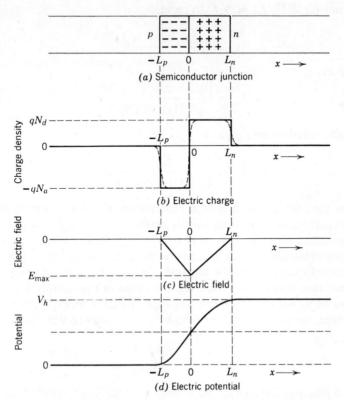

Fig. 3.7. The electric charge, field, and potential relationships in the depletion region associated with a *p-n* junction.

exists at $x = 0$ and is given by

$$\mathscr{E}_{max} = -\frac{qN_aL_p}{\epsilon} = -\frac{qN_dL_n}{\epsilon} \qquad (3.35)$$

The electric potential, using the p material to the left of L_p as the reference, is

$$V_h = -\int_{-L_p}^{L_n} \mathscr{E}\, dx \qquad (3.36)$$

Since the potential difference V_h across the barrier is equal to the negative of the area under the $\mathscr{E}$ curve, inspection of Fig. 3.7c shows that

$$V_h = \frac{\mathscr{E}_{max}(L_p + L_n)}{2} = \frac{qN_aL_p(L_p + L_n)}{2\epsilon} \qquad (3.37)$$

But from Eq. 3.33, $L_n = N_a L_p / N_d$ and

$$V_h = \frac{q N_a L_p^2 (1 + N_a/N_d)}{2\epsilon} \tag{3.38}$$

Therefore,

$$L_p = \left[\frac{2\epsilon V_h}{q N_a (1 + N_a/N_d)} \right]^{1/2} \tag{3.39}$$

A similar solution for L_n yields

$$L_n = \left[\frac{2\epsilon V_h}{q N_d (1 + N_d/N_a)} \right]^{1/2} \tag{3.40}$$

Note that the depth of charge penetration, L_p or L_n, is proportional to the square root of the total barrier potential V_h and is roughly inversely proportional to the square root of the doping concentrations.

A concentration of charge exists at the junction and also a potential difference appears across the junction. Whenever these conditions exist, a capacitance also exists. The usual definition of capacitance C is charge Q, divided by voltage V. When a change of charge results from a change of voltage, the dynamic value of capacitance C may be defined as

$$C = \frac{dQ}{dV} \tag{3.41}$$

For the junction, the charge and voltage are both functions of the distance L_p or L_n. Therefore, Eq. 3.41 may be written as

$$C = \frac{dQ/dL_p}{dV_h/dL_p} \tag{3.42}$$

A voltage increase dV_h will cause an increased depth of penetration dL_p to the left of L_p and an increased depth of penetration dL_n to the right of L_n. But, dQ for the increase to the left of L_p is

$$dQ = q N_a \, dL_p \tag{3.43}$$

or

$$\frac{dQ}{dL_p} = q N_a \tag{3.44}$$

We can take the derivative of Eq. 3.38 to obtain

$$\frac{dV_h}{dL_p} = \frac{2 q L_p N_a}{2\epsilon} \left[1 + \frac{N_a}{N_d} \right] \tag{3.45}$$

The value of L_p from Eq. 3.39 is substituted into Eq. 3.45 to yield

$$\frac{dV_h}{dL_p} = \left[\frac{2qN_a\left(1 + \dfrac{N_a}{N_d}\right)V_h}{\epsilon}\right]^{\frac{1}{2}} \tag{3.46}$$

Now, substitution of Eqs. 3.44 and 3.46 into Eq. 3.42 yields

$$C = \frac{qN_a}{\left[\dfrac{2qN_a(1 + N_a/N_d)V_h}{\epsilon}\right]^{\frac{1}{2}}} = \left[\frac{qN_a\epsilon}{2(1 + N_a/N_d)V_h}\right]^{\frac{1}{2}} \text{farad/m}^2 \tag{3.47}$$

Equation 3.47 can be written as

$$C \simeq KV_h^{-\frac{1}{2}} \tag{3.48}$$

where K is a constant.

PROB. 3.6. A given silicon diode has $N_d = 10^{16}$ atoms/cm^3 and $N_a = 10^{17}$ atoms/cm^3. Determine the effective length of the depletion region on each side of the planar junction in a silicon diode with 20 volts reverse bias applied. Assume the zero bias barrier voltage $V_{ho} \simeq 0.65$ v at this doping concentration. $\epsilon = 1.06 \times 10^{-10}$ f/m for silicon. *Answer: $L_p = 1.58 \times 10^{-5}$ cm, $L_n = 1.58 \times 10^{-4}$ cm.*

PROB. 3.7. What is the junction capacitance of the diode of Prob. 3.6 if the cross-sectional area of the junction is 10^{-6} m^2?

3.6 JUNCTION BREAKDOWN

The breakdown effect shown at point c in Fig. 3.5 will now be considered. One theory attributes the rather abrupt current increase to the high potential gradient (or electric field) which exists at the junction. According to this theory, the high electric field is able to disrupt the covalent bonds and therefore greatly increase the minority carriers. This effect which was proposed by Zener is known as *Zener* breakdown. Another accepted theory for the voltage breakdown is the *avalanche* breakdown. This theory was founded by Townsend while he was studying the behavior of gases subject to electron bombardment. Accordingly, this theory was originally applied to gaseous conduction but applies just as well to the semiconductor.

According to the avalanche theory, a few carriers are generated in the intrinsic semiconductor material owing to thermal action, as previously discussed. These carriers are accelerated by the high electric field near the junction until high velocities are acquired. A carrier with sufficient energy can produce an electron-hole pair when this carrier collides with a neutral atom. The new carriers so produced are free to be accelerated and in turn to produce additional carriers. The origin of the term *avalanche* can be seen by the foregoing explanation.

Since the electrons are much more mobile than the holes, most of the carriers are produced by electron collisions. The electrons have many random collisions as they travel through the semiconductor. In order for the avalanche effect to manifest itself, the electrons must obtain sufficient energy in traveling one mean free path to produce ionization of the atoms in the semiconductor. Hence, the electrons must have a kinetic energy equal to or greater than the gap energy of the semiconductor for an avalanche to be produced.

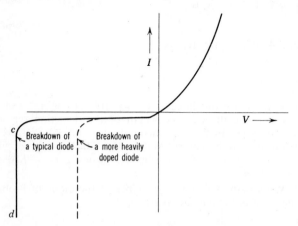

Fig. 3.8. The effect of impurities on the breakdown potential of a *p-n* junction.

The breakdown potential is a function of the impurity concentrations of the semiconductor. As can be noted by Eqs. 3.39 and 3.40, the depletion width varies inversely with the impurity concentration. Hence, as the impurity concentration increases, the depletion region becomes thinner. As the depletion region becomes thinner, the electric field intensity becomes higher for a given junction voltage. Higher electric field potentials produce higher electron energies per mean free path. Therefore, a heavily doped *p-n* junction will have a lower breakdown potential than a relatively lightly doped *p-n* junction. This effect is illustrated in Fig. 3.8.

Many diodes are designed and constructed for operation on the avalanche portion of the characteristic curve. These diodes are known as *zener diodes* or *reference diodes*. These diodes operate in a region (from *c* to *d* on the curve of Fig. 3.8) where the current is essentially independent of voltage. The uses of these diodes are discussed in Section 3.15.

Reference diodes are available with breakdown voltages ranging from about 3 v to well over 100 v. The avalanche appears to be the primary breakdown mechanism in diodes with reference voltages above about 7 v because the breakdown voltages of these diodes increase with temperature.

The reduced mean free path at elevated temperatures would account for this positive temperature coefficient. In contrast, diodes with breakdown voltages less than about 6 v have a negative temperature coefficient, which indicates that the zener breakdown mechanism is predominant in this range. The increased kinetic energy of the valence electrons would aid the high field in producing carriers and thus cause a negative temperature coefficient. Diodes which break down at about 6 to 7 v have essentially zero-temperature coefficient.

PROB. 3.8. Zener breakdown will occur in a silicon diode if the electric field intensity exceeds about 10^8 v/m. A given silicon diode has $N_a = N_d = 10^{18}$ atoms/cm^3. Will zener breakdown occur with 5.0 reverse bias applied to this diode? $V_{ho} \simeq 0.9$ v, $\epsilon = 1.06 \times 10^{-10}$ f/m. At what voltage will a zener breakdown occur?

3.7 THE DIODE SYMBOL

The symbol of a p-n junction diode is shown in Fig. 3.9b. The polarity signs are shown for forward bias. Notice the arrowhead points in the direction of conventional current (as opposed to electron flow) when the diode is forward biased.

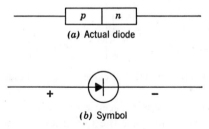

(a) Actual diode

(b) Symbol

Fig. 3.9. The p-n diode symbol.

3.8 THE TUNNEL DIODE

The tunnel diode is a junction diode which is very heavily doped with impurities. In fact, a good tunnel diode must contain impurity concentrations greater than 5×10^{19}/cm^3 for silicon and greater than 2×10^{19}/cm^3 for germanium.[5] This heavy concentration of impurities affects the electrical characteristics of the junction. As noted in Section 3.6, heavy doping reduces the thickness of the depletion region. Actually, the depletion width[6] will be in the order of 100 A (1 A = 10^{-8} cm) when the doping

[5] I. A. Lesk, N. Holonyak, and U. S. Davidsohn, "The Tunnel Diode-Circuits and Applications," *Electronics*, November 27, 1959, Vol. 32, No. 48, pp. 60–64.

[6] Bernard Sklar, "The Tunnel Diode—Its Action and Properties," *Electronics*, November 6, 1959, Vol. 32, No. 45, pp. 54–57.

concentration is in the order of 10^{20} atoms/cm³. To enhance this thin depletion region, the transition from n to p material must be as abrupt as possible.

As was previously mentioned, the heavy doping reduces the junction breakdown voltage. When the concentration of impurities reaches the values listed previously, the semiconductor begins to resemble an alloy

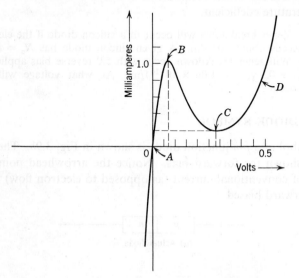

Fig. 3.10. The characteristic curve of a typical tunnel diode.

and the breakdown voltage is reduced essentially to zero.

An additional effect is to place the Fermi level of the n material in the conduction band. In addition, the Fermi level of the p material is in or is very near the valence band.

As a result of the foregoing effects, the voltage-current characteristics of the tunnel diode are as shown in Fig. 3.10. The reason for this unusual shape will now be considered.

As noted before, the Fermi levels in the n and p material must coincide in a diode with no external voltage. Accordingly, the energy diagram for no external voltage would be as shown in Fig. 3.11a. According to the "classical" concepts, the only electrons able to cross the junction are the few electrons with sufficient energy to climb the potential barrier. (This potential barrier is higher in heavily doped tunnel diodes than in conventional p-n junctions because of the location of the Fermi level.) However, according to quantum mechanics there is a *probability* that certain electrons which do not have enough energy to climb the potential hill can pass from the p to the n material (and also from the n to the p material). These electrons pass between the valence band of the p material and the conduction band of the n material. The electrons are said to *tunnel* through the potential barrier and hence the name *tunnel diode*. The quantum mechanics, therefore, predicts that current flow can occur in Fig. 3.11a. However, the probability that electrons will cross from the p to the n region is the same as the probability that electrons will cross from the n to the p region. Consequently, the two currents cancel in Fig. 3.11a. This condition corresponds to the origin (point A) of the curve of Fig. 3.10.

When a small forward bias is applied across the diode, the energy relation is given by Fig. 3.11b. Here there is a greater probability that the electrons will pass from the n to the p region than from the p to the n region. Consequently, a net flow of current occurs across the junction. This condition is shown as point B on the curve in Fig. 3.10. (This current is known as Esaki current after the Japanese inventor of the tunnel diode.)[7]

If the forward bias is increased beyond the level just considered, some of the electrons in the conduction band of the n material have the same energy as the forbidden band in the p material. These electrons cannot exist in the forbidden band and, therefore, must stay in the n material. Consequently, the number of electrons available for transfer across the junction is reduced. This action accounts for the region B to C in the characteristic curve of Fig. 3.10. In this region, an increase of bias causes fewer electrons to be available for transfer across the junction. Consequently, *more* forward bias results in *less* current across the junction. Finally, the condition is reached where most of the conduction-band electrons in the n material have the same energy as the forbidden band in the p material. This condition is shown in Fig. 3.11c, and the corresponding current is indicated by point C in Fig. 3.10.

As the bias is increased beyond point C (Fig. 3.10), more of the electrons in the n material are able to "climb" the potential barrier so the action is the same as in conventional diodes. This condition is shown in Fig. 3.11d and as point D on the current curve of Fig. 3.10.

Actually, the most useful section of the characteristic curve is the region from B to C, where an *increase* of voltage causes a *decrease* of current and the device behaves as if it were a *negative* resistance. The usefulness of this negative resistance characteristic is indicated in Probs. 3.11 and 3.12.

---

[7] The actual theory is much more involved than this description indicates. For example, the momentum of a tunneling electron must be the same on each side of the forbidden band. Momentum differences cause the diode material to vibrate mechanically.

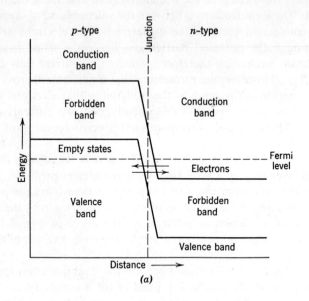

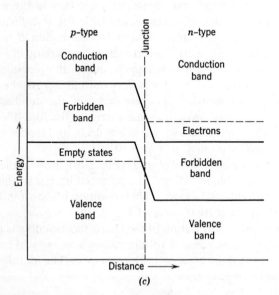

Fig. 3.11. Energy relationships in a tunnel diode. (*a*) No external voltage; (*b*) maximum Esaki current; (*c*) zero Esaki current; (*d*) regular junction current.

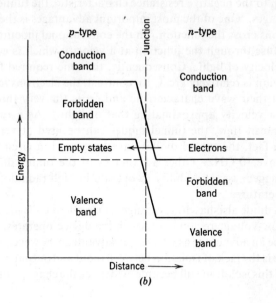

(b)

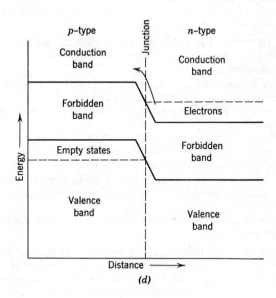

(d)

In addition to the negative resistance characteristic, the tunnel diode has other advantages. One of the most important advantages is the speed with which electrons cross the junction. In the conventional junction diode the electrons diffuse through the junction at a velocity which is considerably below the velocity of light. Consequently, the time required to cross the depletion region is relatively great. In contrast, the electrons in the tunnel diode exhibit their wave characteristic and cross the very thin depletion region with a velocity approximating that of light.[8] As a result of this very short transit time, the tunnel diodes can be used at very high frequencies. In fact, the tunnel diodes have been used in circuits with frequencies[9] above 10 GHz. Other advantages of the tunnel diode include small size, ruggedness, and ability to operate in high radiation fields and at high temperatures.

The tunnel diode also has disadvantages. One obvious disadvantage (Fig. 3.10) is the low-voltage region over which the device operates. (This low voltage can be an advantage as well as a disadvantage, however.) The main disadvantage is the lack of isolation between input and output circuits. The advantage of this isolation will become evident as the chapters on amplifiers are studied.

PROB. 3.9. What is the conductivity of n germanium at room temperature if 2×10^{19} impurity atoms are present in each cubic centimeter? Compare with Prob. 2.6. *Answer: 1.25 × 10⁶ mhos/m.*

PROB. 3.10. Determine the width of the depletion region in a silicon diode which has both n and p regions doped to a concentration of 5×10^{20} impurity atoms per cc. Assume $V_{ho} = 1.14$ v.

PROB. 3.11. A battery with a voltage V_B is connected in series with a 5-Ω resistor, a 5-mh inductance, and 0.05-μf capacitance.

(a) Determine the voltage across the inductance as a function of time if the circuit is connected together at time $t = 0$.

(b) Add a negative resistance of 5 Ω in series with the circuit in part a and then find the voltage across the inductance as a function of time.

(c) What use does this problem suggest for a tunnel diode?

PROB. 3.12. An a-c voltage generator has an RMS open terminal voltage of 0.01 v and an internal resistance of 10 Ω. The generator is connected to a resistive load of 100 Ω.

(a) Find the voltage across the load, the current through the load, and the power delivered to the load.

[8] This statement may seem to be in conflict with the principles stated in Chapter 1. However, an electromagnetic wave is able to move along a conductor at approximately the speed of light even though the electrons in the conductor move at a relatively slow speed. The *effect* is transferred down the conductor from carrier to carrier much faster than the carriers actually move. The same principle applies to the tunneling effect.

[9] The abbreviation GHz means gigahertz where giga (abbreviated G) is 10^9 and Hertz (abbreviated Hz) is cycles per second. This is standard IEEE notation and will be used in the remainder of the book.

(b) Add a negative resistance of 105 Ω in series with the circuit in part a. Find the voltage across the load, the current through the load, and the power delivered to the load under these conditions.

(c) What use does this problem suggest for a tunnel diode?

3.9 HIGH-VACUUM DIODES

The high-vacuum diode is constructed as shown in Fig. 3.12. The important components of this vacuum diode are: a heater wire, an electron-emitter surface, and an element known as a plate. This entire structure is placed in a glass or metal envelope. Most of the air in the envelope is removed so the active elements are surrounded by an effective vacuum. It is impossible to remove all of the air in the envelope, but the pressure inside the envelope is reduced to the vicinity of 10^{-6} mm Hg (Atmospheric pressure is 760 mm Hg.)

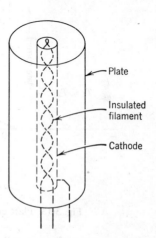

The heater wire is a piece of resistance wire and is heated by an electric current which flows through the wire. In some vacuum tubes, the heater wire and the electron-emitter surface are combined. In this case, the hot heater wire or *filament* emits the electrons. This type of emitter is known as a *filament-type emitter*. Other tubes use the heater wire or filament to heat a metal sleeve (Fig. 3.12). The metal sleeve, which is usually

Fig. 3.12. The high-vacuum diode.

coated with a good thermal electron emitter such as the rare-earth oxides is known as a cathode. The cathode is usually electrically insulated from the heater.

The heated cathode emits electrons into the vacuum. If the plate is more positive than the cathode, these electrons are attracted to the plate. As a consequence, current flows through the tube. If the plate is more negative than the cathode, the electrons are repelled back to the cathode and no current flows through the tube. The action is similar to the *p-n* junction action except the only carriers are electrons. A second difference exists because the plate cannot emit electrons at normal temperatures so no reverse current flows in the vacuum tube. In fact, since the electrons in actual tubes are emitted from the cathode with a finite velocity, some current flows in the forward direction for zero and even slightly negative plate voltages.

3.10 VACUUM DIODE CHARACTERISTIC CURVES

A plot of plate current as a function of plate voltage for a high-vacuum diode is given in Fig. 3.13. When the plate voltage is more than one or two volts negative, the current is zero. As the plate is made more positive, the current increases exponentially until point A is reached. At point A, saturation of the plate current occurs. This saturation exists because the

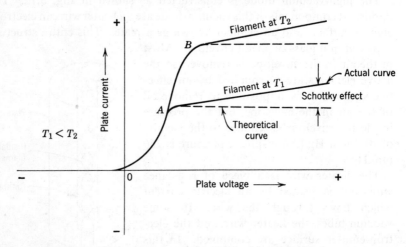

Fig. 3.13. Plate current vs plate voltage of a vacuum diode.

plate is collecting all the electrons the cathode is able to emit. If the temperature of the cathode is increased, the plate current increases to a higher value before saturation occurs. This behavior is shown by the T_2 curve of Fig. 3.13, where saturation exists at point B on the curve.

The value of saturation current for a given temperature can be found from a relationship known as Richardson's equation.

$$J = A_0 T^2 e^{-W_w/kT} \tag{3.49}$$

where J = the temperature-limited current density of the cathode

A_0 = an experimentally determined constant (different for each metal)

T = the temperature of the cathode in °K

k = Boltzmann's Constant

W_w = the work function of the cathode surface. (This W_w is the amount of energy an electron must have in order to escape from the cathode.)

This equation is very similar to the equation which gives the number of conduction-band electrons in a semiconductor material (Eq. 2.28). Since Eq. 2.28 gives the number of electrons in a material with sufficient energy to become carriers at a given temperature, and since Eq. 3.49 determines the number of electrons in a cathode with sufficient energy to escape from the surface of the cathode at a given temperature, the equations *should* be similar.

The constants for a few common materials are given in Table 3.2.

TABLE 3.2
Constants for a Few Common Materials

Material	A_0 [amp/m²-(°K)²]	W_w [ev]	Melting Temperature [°K]
Cesium	16.2×10^4	1.81	299
Copper	65×10^4	4.10	1356
Nickel	30×10^4	4.6	1725
Thorium	60×10^4	3.40	2118
Tungsten	60×10^4	4.52	3643
Thorium on tungsten	3.0×10^4	2.60	. . .
Oxide coated	0.1×10^4	1.00	. . .

PROB. 3.13. Calculate the saturation current for an oxide-coated cathode with an area of 2 cm² and a temperature of 300°K (room temperature). Repeat for a temperature of 1100°K.

PROB. 3.14. Calculate the saturation current for a 2 cm² tungsten emitter at 2500°K. *Answer: 0.571 amp.*

The actual plate current vs plate voltage curve (Fig. 3.13) does *not* exhibit true saturation. This actual curve digresses from the theoretical curve as a result of the *Schottky* effect. This Schottky effect is produced by the potential gradient at the cathode. This potential gradient becomes positive at the cathode when saturation is reached and increases as the plate potential increases. This positive gradient at the cathode helps some electrons, which have kinetic energies less than the work function of the cathode, to overcome the surface barrier of the cathode. Hence, as the plate becomes more positive, more electrons are "helped" out of the cathode and emission increases.

Commercial tubes are designed so that the saturation current is much higher than the maximum recommended plate current. Hence, if commercial tubes are operated at the manufacturers' suggested filament voltage, the tube will not be operated in the saturation region.

As Fig. 3.13 indicates, the current below saturation does not increase linearly with voltage but follows an exponential curve. The mutual repulsion of the electrons in the space between the cathode and plate is responsible for the exponential shape of the current vs voltage curve. A simple derivation will illustrate this behavior.

Assume that two infinite parallel plates exist. One plate represents the cathode, and the other plate represents the plate. A section of this

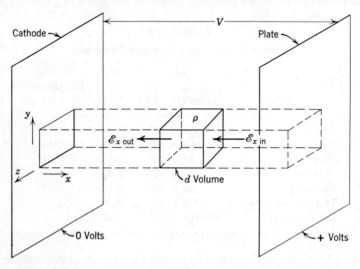

Fig. 3.14. Field distribution of a diode with a charge between the plates.

configuration is shown in Fig. 3.14. Also shown in Fig. 3.14 is a small volume of space between the plates which contains a charge density ρ. From Appendix I,

$$\frac{\partial \mathscr{E}_x}{\partial x} + \frac{\partial \mathscr{E}_y}{\partial y} + \frac{\partial \mathscr{E}_z}{\partial z} = \frac{\rho}{\epsilon} \tag{I.8}$$

For the field configuration shown in Fig. 3.14, $\dfrac{\partial \mathscr{E}_z}{\partial z} = \dfrac{\partial \mathscr{E}_y}{\partial y} = 0$. Therefore, Eq. I.8 becomes

$$\frac{d\mathscr{E}_x}{dx} = \frac{-d^2V}{dx^2} = \frac{\rho}{\epsilon_v} \tag{3.50}$$

The electric field $\mathscr{E}$ is equal to $-dV/dx$ and the value of ϵ for a vacuum is ϵ_v.

The second equation required is given in Chapter 1 as Eq. 1.12

$$\tfrac{1}{2}mv^2 = Vq \tag{1.12}$$

where V is the voltage through which the electron has been accelerated.

In this case, the charge on an electron q has been inserted in place of the general charge Q of the general Eq. 1.12.

The third relationship is

$$\frac{J}{v} = -\rho \tag{3.51}$$

where J = the current density in amp/m²

v = the velocity of the electrons which constitute the current in m/sec

$-\rho$ = the electronic charge density in coulombs/m³

When the value of v as given by Eq. 1.12 is substituted into Eq. 3.51,

$$-\rho = \frac{J(m)^{\frac{1}{2}}}{(2Vq)^{\frac{1}{2}}} \tag{3.52}$$

The quantity ρ is negative for the space current of electrons. The value of ρ as given by Eq. 3.52 can be substituted back into Eq. 3.50 to yield

$$\frac{d^2V}{dx^2} = \frac{J}{\epsilon_v}\left(\frac{m}{2q}\right)^{\frac{1}{2}} V^{-\frac{1}{2}} \tag{3.53}$$

This equation is difficult to integrate. However,

$$\frac{d\left(\frac{dV}{dx}\right)^2}{dx} = 2\frac{dV}{dx}\frac{d^2V}{dx^2} \tag{3.54}$$

Now, if both sides of Eq. 3.53 are multiplied by $2(dV/dx)$, Eq. 3.53 becomes

$$2\frac{dV}{dx}\frac{d^2V}{dx^2} = \frac{2J}{\epsilon_v}\left(\frac{m}{2q}\right)^{\frac{1}{2}} V^{-\frac{1}{2}}\frac{dV}{dx} \tag{3.55}$$

Both sides of this equation can now be integrated to give

$$\left(\frac{dV}{dx}\right)^2 = \frac{4J}{\epsilon_v}\left(\frac{m}{2q}\right)^{\frac{1}{2}} V^{\frac{1}{2}} + K_1 \tag{3.56}$$

At the cathode, V is zero and $\mathscr{E}$ is assumed to be zero due to the space charge.[10] Since $\mathscr{E}$ is equal to $-dV/dx$, K_1 must be equal to zero. Taking the square root of both sides of Eq. 3.56, we find that

$$\frac{dV}{dx} = \left[\frac{4J}{\epsilon_v}\left(\frac{m}{2q}\right)^{\frac{1}{2}}\right]^{\frac{1}{2}} V^{\frac{1}{4}} \tag{3.57}$$

---

[10] This development assumes that the electrons leave the cathode with zero velocity. Actually, the electrons leave the cathode with a wide distribution of velocities. Hence, $\mathscr{E}$ is not zero but actually a small negative value. The effect of ignoring the initial velocity of the electrons can be seen by referring to Fig. 3.15.

or

$$V^{-\frac{1}{4}}\,dV = \left[\frac{4J}{\epsilon_v}\left(\frac{m}{2q}\right)^{\frac{1}{2}}\right]^{\frac{1}{2}}dx \qquad (3.58)$$

Integration of both sides of Eq. 3.58 yields

$$\tfrac{4}{3}V^{\frac{3}{4}} = \left[\frac{4J}{\epsilon_v}\left(\frac{m}{2q}\right)^{\frac{1}{2}}\right]^{\frac{1}{2}}x + K_2 \qquad (3.59)$$

But, from Fig. 3.14, x is zero at the cathode. Since the voltage at the cathode is also zero, K_2 must be zero.

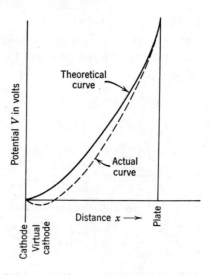

Fig. 3.15. A plot of V vs x as given by Eq. 3.62 and as exists in an actual diode.

A plot of V as a function of x (as given by Eq. 3.59) is shown as the theoretical curve in Fig. 3.15. This plot is seen to be different from the curve in an actual diode. The discrepancy between the two curves is due to the initial velocities of the electrons from the cathode. These electrons form a "cloud" of electrons, which is known as a *space charge*, a short distance from the actual cathode. The actual current in the tube is drawn from this electron cloud. Hence, a "virtual cathode" appears to exist a short distance from the actual cathode. This virtual cathode is at a more negative potential than the actual cathode. However, the curve from the virtual cathode to the plate does have the form given by Eq. 3.59 if the potential of the virtual cathode is used as the reference ($V = 0$) point.

Substituting zero for K_2 in Eq. 3.59 and solving for J, we find that the current density is

$$J = \frac{4\epsilon_v}{9(m/2q)^{1/2}} \frac{V^{3/2}}{x^2} \text{ amp/m}^2 \tag{3.60}$$

When the values of ϵ_v, m, and q are substituted into Eq. 3.60, the current density becomes

$$J = \frac{2.335 \times 10^{-6} V^{3/2}}{x^2} \text{ amp/m}^2 \tag{3.61}$$

where x is the distance from the cathode to the point in question in meters and V is the potential in volts x meters from the cathode. For a diode with a distance d meters between the cathode and the plate, the current density at the plate is

$$J = \frac{2.335 \times 10^{-6} V_p^{3/2}}{d^2} \tag{3.62}$$

where V_p is the potential difference between the plate and the cathode in volts.

This relationship is known as Child's Law. Equation 3.60 states that the current density is proportional to the voltage to the $\frac{3}{2}$ power at any given distance from the cathode. The fact that the amount of current leaving the cathode must be equal to the amount of current reaching the plate for steady-state conditions indicates that the current does not vary with x. Therefore, the potential is seen to vary as the $\frac{4}{3}$ power of x. (If Eq. 3.61 is solved for V, x appears to the $\frac{4}{3}$ power.) This derivation was for a plane electrode configuration, and a similar derivation for cylindrical electrodes leads to a similar but more complicated relationship.[11] Even in the cylindrical configuration, however, the current is theoretically proportional to voltage to the $\frac{3}{2}$ power. Hence, the exponential shape of the current vs voltage curve (Fig. 3.13) is due to the charge on the electrons which are in transit from the cathode to the plate.

PROB. 3.15. Justify Eq. 3.51.

PROB. 3.16. A plane electrode diode has the plate 5 cm from the cathode. A voltage of +100 v is applied between the plate and the cathode. (a) What is the current density at the plate? (b) If the tube is 1.5 cm by 5 cm, what is the total current of this tube? (c) If the plate voltage is raised to 200 v, what will be the plate current? *Answer:* (a) 0.93 amp/m² (b) 0.7 mamp (c) 1.98 mamp.

PROB. 3.17. A plane electrode diode has 1 cm distance between the plate and the cathode. The plate and cathode are each 1 cm by 5 cm. Plot the curve of plate current vs plate voltage for this diode from 0 to 200 plate v. (Use steps of 50 v.)

[11] K. R. Spangenberg, *Vacuum Tubes*, McGraw-Hill, New York, 1948, pp. 173–175.

PROB. 3.18. Plot the theoretical curve of voltage vs distance from the cathode for Prob. 3.17 if the plate is +100 v and the cathode is 0 v.

3.11 SYMBOLS FOR VACUUM DIODES

The symbols for the two types of vacuum diodes shown in Fig. 3.16 represent the actual element arrangements inside the tubes. Tube manuals, which can be purchased at most radio supply stores, list socket connections, characteristic curves, voltage and current ratings, and so forth, for most commercial tubes including diodes.

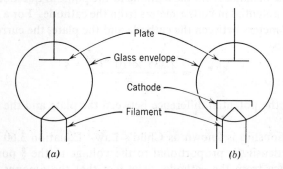

(a)   *(b)*

Fig. 3.16. Symbols for vacuum diodes (*a*) filament-type emitter (*b*) cathode-type emitter.

3.12 GAS DIODES

A gas diode may be constructed in the same manner as a vacuum diode. However, instead of maintaining a vacuum inside the envelope, the gas diodes have a carefully controlled amount of a pure gas present.

The exact behavior of a gaseous medium as an electrical conductor is very complicated.[12] In fact, the conductivity of the gaseous medium is a function of the gas pressure, the gas temperature, the material from which the electrodes are made, the magnitude of the applied voltage, and even the nature of the voltage source. As a result of this complication, the following discussion of the gaseous conduction process is somewhat superficial and oversimplified.

When the plate is more than a volt or two negative with respect to the cathode, no current flows in the gas diode. The electrons are then repelled back to the cathode as in the high-vacuum tube. When the plate voltage is made positive, electrons from the cathode are attracted

[12] A comprehensive treatment of gaseous conduction is given in *Gaseous Conductors* by James D. Cobine, Dover Publications, New York, 1958.

to the plate. These electrons must pass through the gas molecules on the way to the plate. Although the concentration of gas atoms is not nearly so great as is the concentration of atoms in a semiconductor, the action is somewhat the same.

If electrons are emitted from a heated cathode, these electrons diffuse through the gas molecules. This diffusion process tends to create a uniform electron distribution throughout the volume. If a plate of zero

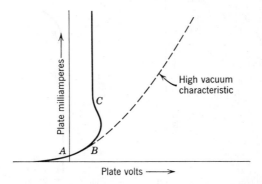

Fig. 3.17. A plot of current vs voltage for a hot cathode gas diode tube.

potential is inserted in this gas, each electron that strikes the plate will be captured. Consequently, a very weak current will flow to a plate of zero potential from a heated cathode. This condition is shown as point *A* of Fig. 3.17.

As the plate is made more positive, electrons drift through the gas molecules to the plate. These electrons will have many collisions with the gas molecules. However, as long as the energy of the electrons is small, each of these collisions will be elastic. (In an elastic collision, the electron has essentially the same kinetic energy after the collision as before the collision.) The current increases exponentially with voltage as shown from *A* to *B* in Fig. 3.17.

At point *B* of Fig. 3.17, the current digresses from the simple exponential curve of *A* to *B*. At this point, some of the electrons have enough energy to ionize the gas molecules on collision. The gas molecule receives enough energy from the free electron to allow a valence electron (in some cases more than one valence electron) to escape. As a result, the gas molecule becomes a positive ion. The electrons continue on to the plate and the positive ion travels toward the cathode. Because of its comparatively large mass, the positive ion travels much more slowly than the electron does. Therefore, the ionized gas acquires a positive charge which assists in the acceleration of the electron away from the cathode.

As the current density is increased, the voltage rises slightly at first, but then as additional current is drawn more ionizing collisions occur and the voltage across the diode decreases until the voltage is essentially equal to the ionization potential (usually about 12 v) of the gas. This condition is indicated as point C in Fig. 3.17. An increase of current beyond point C causes essentially no increase of voltage across the tube. (Actually the

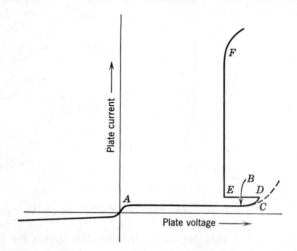

Fig. 3.18. The characteristic curve of a cold cathode gas tube.

voltage will increase if the current is raised to a high enough value, but this high value of current is beyond the maximum current rating of the diode.)

A second type of gas diode, also in wide usage, contains a plate and a cathode surface, but the cathode is *not* heated. Consequently, the tube is referred to as a *cold cathode diode* or (because of its principal usage) as a *voltage regulator diode.* The voltage-current characteristics of this type of tube are shown in Fig. 3.18.

In order to produce ions in the cold cathode tubes, a small amount of radioactive material is included inside the tube.[13] The radiation from this material produces positive and negative ions in the tube. Consequently, a small voltage across the tube attracts positive ions to the negative cathode and negative ions (or electrons) to the positive plate. When all of the ions produced in the tube are collected, the current through the tube reaches a saturation condition as indicated at point A in Fig. 3.18. At point B in Fig. 3.18, the current starts to increase with increasing potential.

[13] Glenn Cassidy, "Radioactive Krypton in Cold-Cathode Gas Tubes," *The Western Electric Engineer*, Vol. IV, No. 1, January 1960.

At this point, some of the electrons have enough energy to ionize the gas molecules on collision. The gas molecule is broken down to an electron (in some cases more than one electron) and a positive ion. The electrons continue on to the plate and the positive ion travels back to the cathode. As a result of this ionizing process, the current increases exponentially. This ionizing (voltage) region was first investigated by J. S. Townsend and accordingly is known as the Townsend I Region. The Townsend I region is shown in Fig. 3.18 as the region between *B* and *C*.

In gaseous conduction, the negative carriers are free electrons as in the semiconductor. In contrast, the positive carriers are the positive ions instead of the holes. However, because of the much greater mass of the positive ions (as previously mentioned), the positive carriers move at a much slower velocity than the electrons do.

Another phenomena occurs at point *C* of Fig. 3.18. At this point, the actual current again digresses from the expected curve. In this region the positive ions have enough energy when they strike the cathode to cause secondary electrons to be emitted.[14] As a result, the current increases above the value expected for pure gaseous conduction. This region is known as the Townsend II region and is shown in Fig. 3.18 as the region between *C* and *D*.

The phenomenon from the origin to *D* of Fig. 3.18 is known as a *dark discharge*; that is, there is no visible light emission from the tube. If the radiation is removed, the current drops back to zero. However, at point *D* a new phenomenon occurs. The ions produce a visible glow in the gas and the discharge becomes *self-sustaining*. In this case the number of secondary electrons from the cathode is sufficient to keep the current flowing. Hence, current is maintained even if the radiation is removed.

The self-sustaining condition is known as a *glow discharge*. The total voltage actually decreases across the tube as shown in the curve (part *D* to *E*) of Fig. 3.18. From point *E* to *F* of Fig. 3.18, the voltage remains almost constant whereas the current changes over quite a wide range. The change of current from *E* to *F* is much, much greater than the change of current from the origin to *D*. The current at point *E* flows through a restricted volume of the gas. As the current increases, the active volume of gas increases until point *F* is reached. When the tube is operating at point *F*, the entire volume between the cathode and the plate is active. When the current is increased beyond point *F*, the voltage across the tube increases again. However, if the voltage is increased very much beyond point *F*, an *arc discharge* occurs (much as in electric arc welding) and the tube is quickly destroyed because of excessive heat.

[14] Positive ions usually do not achieve sufficient speed to cause significant ionization in this voltage range.

Most cold cathode gas diodes are designed to be operated in the E to F region (Fig. 3.18) of the characteristic curve. In this region, the current is almost independent of voltage. Typical tubes have operating potentials from 75 v for some tubes to 150 v for other tubes. The type of gas in the tube and the pressure of the gas determines the operating potential. The potential at point D of Fig. 3.18 is known as the *striking potential*. The voltage across the tube must rise to this striking potential before the tube can drop back to the operating potential.

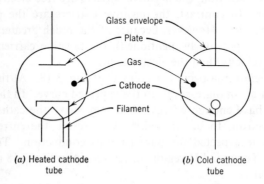

(a) Heated cathode tube   (b) Cold cathode tube

Fig. 3.19. Schematic representation of a gas diode.

The symbolic representations for gas diode tubes are shown in Fig. 3.19. The symbol for the heated cathode type is the same as the symbol for a high-vacuum diode except a small black dot is included in the envelope to represent the gas.

3.13 GRAPHICAL SOLUTION OF DIODE CIRCUITS

In order to use diodes intelligently, methods of analysis and design must be understood. In general, two basic approaches will be described. One approach (described in Section 3.14 and Section 3.15) uses an *equivalent circuit* for the diode. However, in this section the diodes and associated circuit elements will be analyzed by *graphical methods*.

In the graphical method of solution, the current vs voltage characteristics of the diode are expressed in graphical form. Frequently the tube manuals and manufacturers' data sheets present the characteristics of the diodes in graphical form. These plots of current vs voltage are known as *characteristic curves*. The characteristic curves furnished by the manufacturer represent *average* diodes of a given type. Hence, if very accurate curves are required, the characteristic curve for the particular diode in question must be plotted from measured voltages and currents.

With the diode's characteristics presented in graphical form, the current vs voltage characteristics of the circuit external to the diode must be presented in graphical form. Intersections of the various curves represent solutions of the circuit currents and voltages. An example will illustrate this procedure.

Example 3.1. A circuit is connected as shown in Fig. 3.20. Find the output voltage v_O if v_I has the form shown. The characteristics of a 5U4 tube are given in Fig. 3.21.

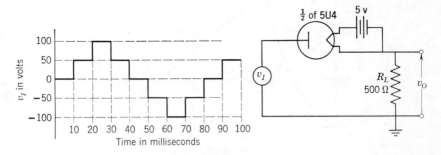

Fig. 3.20. A typical diode circuit.

When v_I is 0 v, essentially no current flows through the circuit. Hence, v_O is 0 if v_I is 0. However, when v_I is +50 v, some current will flow through the circuit. From Fig. 3.20, the voltage equation around the plate circuit loop is

$$v_P = v_I - i_P R_L \tag{3.63}$$

where v_I = the instantaneous input voltage

v_P = the instantaneous voltage across the diode (plate voltage)

i_P = the instantaneous current through the loop (plate current)

This equation contains two unknowns i_P and v_P. However, a second relationship between i_P and v_P is given by the diode characteristic curve (Fig. 3.21). Hence, enough information is available to solve for both i_P and v_P.

Since the characteristic curve is a graphical representation of the relationship between i_P and v_P, it would be desirable to find a graphical representation of Eq. 3.63. Fortunately, if v_P and i_P are the variable quantities of Eq. 3.63, this equation represents (graphically) a straight line. This line will have a slope of $-1/R_L$ and an intercept on the v_P axis (point A) of v_I. Accordingly, if v_I is 50 v, the line ABC represents Eq. 3.63. In this case, the intercept with the v_P axis (point A) is 50 v. A second point on this line is found by noting that if $v_P = 0$,

$$i_P = \frac{v_I}{R_L} \tag{3.64}$$

Here, with v_I of 50 v and R_L of 500 Ω, i_P is 100 ma and is indicated as point C in Fig. 3.21.

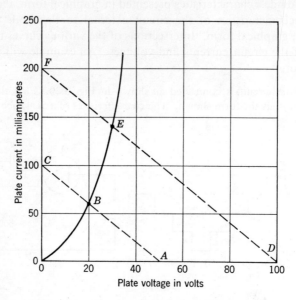

Fig. 3.21.   The characteristic curve of a 5U4 tube.

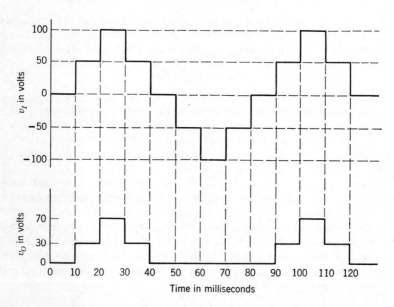

Fig. 3.22.   The voltages v_I and v_O for the circuit of Fig. 3.20.

There is only one point (point *B*) common to both the characteristic curve and line *AC*. Hence, point *B* is the only solution for Eq. 3.63 that also satisfies the voltage-current requirements of the diode. Thus, i_P is 60 ma and v_P is 20 v when v_I is +50 v. In this case, v_O is equal to i_P times R_L or v_O = 30 v.

Similarly, line *DEF* represents Eq. 3.63 when v_I is 100 v. Point *E* is the required operating point with i_P = 140 ma and v_O of 500 × 0.14 or 70 v.

Whenever the plate of the diode is more negative than the cathode, essentially no electrons will pass through the tube. Hence, v_O = 0 for all negative values of plate voltage. Accordingly, the relation between v_I and v_O is as shown in Fig. 3.22.

The foregoing circuit is known as a *clipper circuit*, since the negative portion of the input voltage waveform was clipped off. If the plate and cathode of the diode are interchanged in the circuit of Fig. 3.20, the positive portion of the input wave will be clipped.

PROB. 3.19. A circuit is connected as shown in Fig. 3.20. If R_L is changed to 1000 Ω, plot v_O. Repeat if R_L is increased to 10,000 Ω.

PROB. 3.20. A circuit is connected as shown in Fig. 3.20. What value must R_L have if v_O is 80 v when v_I is 100 v?

3.14 DIODE EQUIVALENT CIRCUITS

As mentioned in Section 3.13, an equivalent circuit can be used for analysis and design of diode circuits. The diode is replaced by linear circuit elements (resistors, capacitors, batteries, etc.) and switches the combination of which has *approximately* the same current vs voltage characteristics as the diode. With the equivalent circuit used in place of the diode, standard circuit analysis can be used to determine the circuit performance.

To illustrate the process of obtaining a suitable electrical network, consider the characteristic curve of the 6AL5 vacuum diode shown in Fig. 3.23. This characteristic curve is approximated (for the range 0 to about 7 v) quite closely by the dashed line of Fig. 3.20. This dashed line represents a linear relationship between voltage and current. Since a resistor has the same linear relationship, the diode can be approximated (at least in the voltage range of 0 to 7 v) by a resistor. In Fig. 3.23, 30 milliamperes of current flow when 6 v is applied. Hence, the dashed line represents 6/0.03 = 200 Ω. This dashed line resistance is known as the *static plate resistance* of the diode (at 30 ma.) and is given the symbol r_P.

If small voltage fluctuations (in the order of 1 v or so for Fig. 3.23) are encountered, a second type of equivalent resistance can be found. The *change* of diode voltage with diode current is the important relationship. Thus, if i_P is the instantaneous value of plate current and v_P is the instantaneous value of plate voltage,

$$r_p = \frac{\Delta v_P}{\Delta i_P} \tag{3.65}$$

or in the limit,

$$r_p = \frac{dv_P}{di_P} \qquad (3.66)$$

where r_p is known as the *dynamic* or *small signal* plate resistance. For example, if the plate of a 6AL5 tube is maintained near +6 v the dynamic plate resistance would have the slope given by the dotted line of Fig. 3.23.

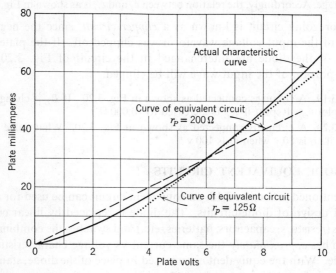

Fig. 3.23. A method of finding the impedance to be used in an equivalent circuit for a 6AL5 diode.

Hence, a change of 1 v causes a change of 8 ma or $r_p = \dfrac{1}{0.008} = 125\ \Omega$. The circuit in which the diode is used will determine which type of equivalent plate resistance to use. However, most diode circuits will require the use of the static rather than the dynamic plate resistance. In contrast, the concept of dynamic plate resistance will be very useful in analyzing the devices to be considered in Chapter 4.

Thus far, only part of the equivalent circuit for a diode has been found. The static plate resistance is only valid for the range 0 to 7 v (the dynamic plate resistance is very accurate for plate voltages from 5 to 8 v). In the 0 to 7 v range the equivalent circuit for the diode is as shown in Fig. 3.24a. If negative voltage is applied to the plate, essentially no current flows in the circuit, and the equivalent circuit for the tube becomes an open circuit as shown in Fig. 3.24b. The total equivalent circuit for the diode is as shown in Fig. 3.24c. The switch S_1 of this figure is in position 1 if a positive

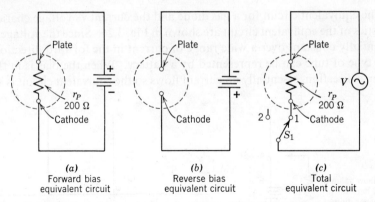

(a)
Forward bias
equivalent circuit

(b)
Reverse bias
equivalent circuit

(c)
Total
equivalent circuit

Fig. 3.24. Derivation of the equivalent circuit for a 6AL5 diode. The switch S_1 of part *c* is at position 1 for + voltage on plate and in position 2 for − voltage on plate.

voltage is applied to the plate, and in position 2 if a negative voltage is applied to the plate.[15]

The semiconductor diode can be represented by an equivalent circuit as shown in Fig. 3.25. Again, the switch operates as explained previously. In this diode, the resistance in the forward direction r_f is quite low (ohms or so) whereas the resistance in the reverse direction r_b is quite high (megohm or so). The current vs voltage characteristics of the equivalent circuit are also shown in Fig. 3.25. The equivalent circuit shown applies only to diodes operating in the voltage region before breakdown occurs. Manufacturers usually list the values of r_f and r_b for semiconductor diodes. In many cases diodes can be considered as simple switches which are ON in the forward direction ($r_f \simeq 0$) and OFF in the reverse direction ($r_b \simeq \infty$). A diode with this type of characteristics is known as an *ideal diode*.

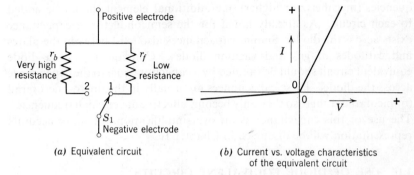

(a) Equivalent circuit

(b) Current vs. voltage characteristics
of the equivalent circuit

Fig. 3.25. Equivalent circuit of a semiconductor diode.

[15] The system of linear approximation given in Chapter 16 can be used with diodes to produce more accurate equivalent circuits.

The equivalent circuit for a gas diode and the current vs voltage characteristics of the equivalent circuit are shown in Fig. 3.26. Since the voltage is essentially constant over a wide range of current in the forward direction, this type of tube can be represented by a battery. When the bias is in the reverse direction, essentially no current flows so the equivalent circuit is an

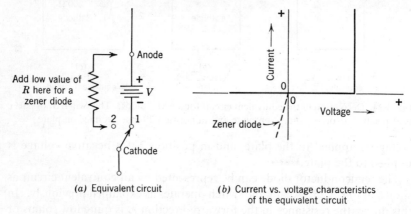

(a) Equivalent circuit   (b) Current vs. voltage characteristics
                                             of the equivalent circuit

Fig. 3.26. Equivalent circuit for a gas diode or for a zener diode.

open circuit. Again, the switch S_1 operates as outlined previously. Figure 3.26 can also be used to represent the zener diode in the constant voltage region of operation. Of course, the zener diode would *not* have *high* resistance if the bias voltage were reversed.

In all the foregoing equivalent circuits, the impedances of the elements in the equivalent circuits are not affected by frequency. For low frequencies, the circuits are quite accurate. However, for very high frequencies (megahertz or higher) one additional element should be added to each circuit. As already noted for the semiconductor, a capacitance exists across the diode. Similar capacitances also exist between the plates and cathodes of gas and vacuum diodes. Consequently, each diode equivalent circuit should be shunted by a capacitor equal to the capacitance across the diode. These capacitances are usually in the micro-microfarad (or picofarad) range, so they only become effective at very high frequencies. The use of this capacitance is an oversimplification. A more accurate representation will be discussed in Chapter 16.

3.15 USE OF DIODE EQUIVALENT CIRCUITS

Some simple examples may help illustrate the usefulness of the equivalent circuits just devised.

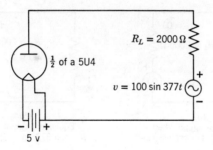

Fig. 3.27. Circuit for a half-wave rectifier.

Example 3.2. One section of a 5U4 diode is to be connected as shown in Fig. 3.27. If the characteristic curve of the 5U4 diode is as shown in Fig. 3.28, find an expression for the current through the load, R_L.

To find an accurate value for r_P, the peak voltage across the diode must be known. This peak value can be found by the graphical method of Section 3.13. In this example, the peak voltage applied to the circuit is 100 v and R_L is 2000 Ω. Therefore, the line AC (Fig. 3.28) represents the peak voltage conditions and point B indicates the maximum voltage across the diode. Since this maximum value of plate voltage is about 16 v, a resistance line is drawn which approximates the characteristic curve between 0 and 16 v. This line (when extended) indicates 100 ma flows when 40 v are applied. Hence r_P is equal to 40/0.1 or 400 Ω for the circuit given in Fig. 3.27.

The two equivalent circuits shown in Fig. 3.29 approximate the action of the

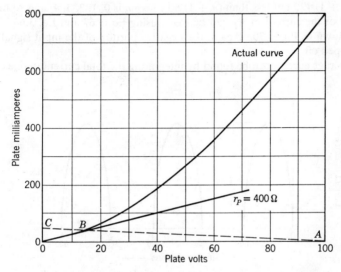

Fig. 3.28. Characteristic curve of a 5U4 diode (one section).

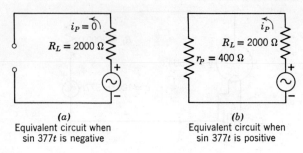

(a)
Equivalent circuit when
sin 377t is negative

(b)
Equivalent circuit when
sin 377t is positive

Fig. 3.29. Equivalent circuit for Fig. 3.27.

diode. Since $\sin 377t$ is positive for t from 0 to $\frac{1}{120}$ sec, the current i_P can be found by the relationship

$$i_P = \frac{100}{r_P + R_L} \sin 377t \tag{3.67}$$

$(\frac{1}{120} > t > 0)$

For this example, $100/(r_P + R_L)$ is equal to 0.042 amp. Also, since the $\sin 377t$ is negative for t between $\frac{1}{120}$ sec and $\frac{1}{60}$ sec

$$i_P = 0 \tag{3.68}$$

$(\frac{1}{120} < t < \frac{1}{60})$

Now, since the $\sin 377t$ is positive for t greater than $\frac{1}{60}$ sec but less than $\frac{3}{120}$ sec, Eq. 3.67 will also apply for this time interval. In fact, Eq. 3.67 applies for $t > n/60$ but less than $(2n + 1)/120$. By similar reasoning, Eq. 3.68 is valid for t greater than $(2n + 1)/120$ but less than $(n + 1)/60$ where n is 0, 1, 2, 3, 4, and so forth.

A plot of the current in R_L can be made using Eq. 3.67 and Eq. 3.68. This plot is shown in Fig. 3.30. Again, the negative portion of the input signal has been clipped off.

The average current can be found by integrating the total current in one cycle

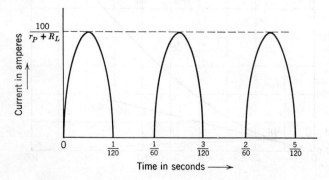

Fig. 3.30. The current output of the circuit in Fig. 3.27.

and dividing by the time for one cycle. Therefore,

$$I_{\text{ave}} = \frac{\int_0^{1/120} [100/(r_P + R_L)] \sin 377t \, dt}{1/60} \qquad (3.69)$$

or

$$I_{\text{ave}} = \frac{100}{(r_P + R_L)\pi} \qquad (3.70)$$

The example just considered is known as a *half-wave rectifier*. The rectifier circuits are used in power supplies which convert a-c to d-c power. If R_L is much larger than r_P in Eq. 3.67, r_P can often be ignored. When r_P is ignored, the diode is assumed to be an "ideal diode."

PROB. 3.21. A circuit is connected as shown in Fig. 3.27. Change R_L to 250 Ω and plot i_P.

PROB. 3.22. One section of a 6AL5 (see Fig. 3.23) diode is to be connected as shown in Fig. 3.27. If R_L is 20,000 Ω, plot i_P vs time.

Many times the manufacturers list only forward resistance r_f and reverse resistance r_b for the junction diodes. Following is an example which illustrates how this information may be used.

Example 3.3. A diode is connected in a circuit as shown in Fig. 3.31. The diode has a forward resistance of 100 Ω and a reverse resistance of 100,000 Ω. If a voltage with the waveform shown in Fig. 3.31 is applied to the input, plot the output voltage v_O.

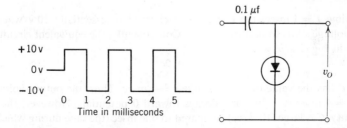

Fig. 3.31. A diode clamper circuit.

The capacitor in the circuit is assumed to be completely uncharged at the time $t = 0$. Then, at time $t = 0+$, the circuit would be as shown in Fig. 3.32a. This circuit is a simple series RC circuit whose loop equation can be written as

$$10 = r_f i + \frac{1}{C} \int i \, dt \qquad (3.71)$$

Solving this equation for i,

$$i = \frac{10}{r_f} e^{-t/r_f C} \qquad (3.72)$$

The term r_fC is known as the time constant of the circuit and is usually given the symbol τ.

Since v_O is equal to i times r_f,

$$v_O = 10e^{-t/\tau} \tag{3.73}$$

Thus at time $t = 0$, the output voltage is 10 v, but this output voltage decays rapidly (with a time constant of 10 μsec) to essentially zero. This portion of the output voltage is plotted (for 1 msec $> t > 0$) in Fig. 3.33.

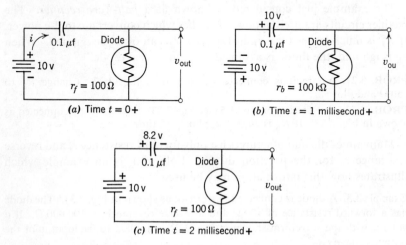

(a) Time $t = 0+$ (b) Time $t = 1$ millisecond+

(c) Time $t = 2$ millisecond+

Fig. 3.32. The equivalent circuits for Fig. 3.31.

At time $t = 1$ msec, the capacitor is charged to essentially 10 v when the input voltage shifts to become -10 v. Consequently, the equivalent circuit is as shown in Fig. 3.32b, where

$$v_O = -20e^{-t'/r_bC} \tag{3.74}$$

where t' has the value of 0 at the time $t = 1$ msec. Thus, the output voltage at time $t = 1$ msec is -20 v and decays toward 0 potential. However, the time constant r_bC is large (10^{-2} sec) compared to one msec (the time during which this circuit is valid), so the capacitor does not discharge appreciably before the input voltage reverses again. Actually,

$$v_O = -20e^{-0.1} = -18.2 \text{ v} \tag{3.75}$$

for the output voltage at the end of this portion of the cycle. This voltage variation is plotted in Fig. 3.33.

Since the capacitor discharged only 1.8 v during the period from the time $t = 1$ msec to $t = 2$ msec, a charge of 8.2 v remains on the capacitor. Hence, at time $t = 2$ msec the equivalent circuit is as shown in Fig. 3.32c. In this case,

$$v_O = 1.8e^{-t''/r_fC} \tag{3.76}$$

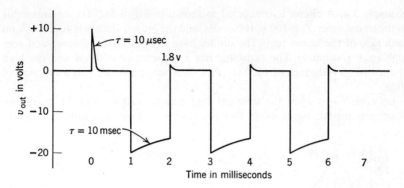

Fig. 3.33. A plot of v_{out} for Fig. 3.31.

where t'' has the value of zero at time $t = 2$ msec. As in the circuit in Fig. 3.32a, the capacitor quickly charges to 10 v again. From this point on, the action of the circuit is repetitious.

The foregoing circuit is known as a *clamper circuit*. In effect, this circuit has "clamped" the most positive portion of the input waveform to a value of 0 v. Many modifications of this circuit are used in various pulse circuit applications.

PROB. 3.23. Repeat Example 3.3 if a diode with a forward resistance of 100 Ω and a reverse resistance of 1 megohm is used. Does this diode improve the clamping action?

PROB. 3.24. Plot the output voltage waveform if the diode in Fig. 3.31 is reversed in the circuit. Assume $r_f = 100 \ \Omega$ and $r_b = 100,000 \ \Omega$.

The circuit considered in Example 3.2 removed the negative portion of an a-c signal and was called a half-wave rectifier circuit. The circuit for a *full-wave rectifier* is given in Fig. 3.34.

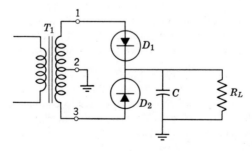

Fig. 3.34. A full-wave rectifier circuit.

Example 3.4. A circuit is connected as shown in Fig. 3.34. The voltage input to the transformer T_1 is 100 v, 100 cycles, and the output voltage is 400 v peak on each side of the center tap. The diodes have low forward resistance and very high back resistance. The capacitor has a capacitance of 10 μf and the load resistor has a resistance of 1000 Ω. Plot the voltage across R_L as a function of time.

Let time $t = 0$ when the terminal 1 of transformer T_1 is at the maximum positive potential, Since diode D_2 has a reverse voltage, very little current will

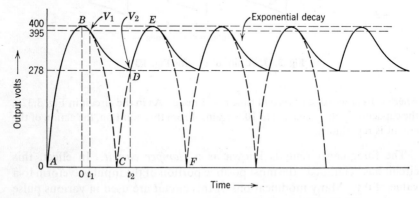

Fig. 3.35. Output voltage waveform of the circuit of Fig. 3.34.

flow through side 3 of the transformer. In fact, since the reverse current is so small, the reverse current can be ignored without introducing any appreciable error. Since side 1 is positive with respect to ground, a current will flow through diode D_1. This current will charge capacitor C as shown in Fig. 3.35 (curve A to B) and also cause current to flow through R_L. If the forward resistance of the diode and the resistance of the transformer are ignored, the capacitor will charge to the peak value of the voltage (400 v) across 1/2 of the transformer secondary. After the peak value of voltage is past, the voltage at point 1 will decrease as shown by the dashed line B to C of Fig. 3.35. As soon as the voltage at point 1 becomes less than the charge on the capacitor, the diode D_1 is biased in the reverse direction and the diode becomes an open circuit. The charge on the capacitor C starts to leak off through the resistor R_L as soon as D_1 is cut off.

The performance of this circuit can be analyzed mathematically. Thus, the voltage across the capacitor, v_C between time t_1 and t_2 is given by the equation

$$v_C = V_1 e^{-(t-t_1)/R_L C} \tag{3.77}$$

$(t_1 < t < t_2)$

where V_1 is the voltage at which diode D_1 ceases to conduct, and t_1 is the time when this cut-off of diode D_1 occurs. Also, the voltage on the transformer side of the diodes, v_T (curve $ABCDEF$, etc., in Fig. 3.35) is given by the equation

$$v_T = |V_m \cos \omega t| \tag{3.78}$$

where V_m is the peak value of transformer voltage and ω is the radian frequency of the power source.

Inspection of Fig. 3.35 indicates that V_1 occurs when the slope of v_C is equal to the slope of v_T.

$$\frac{dv_C}{dt} = -\frac{V_1}{R_L C} e^{-(t-t_1)/R_L C} \qquad (3.79)$$

and

$$\frac{dv_T}{dt} = -\omega V_m \sin \omega t \qquad (3.80)$$

Now, these two derivatives will be equal when $t = t_1$. Hence,

$$-\omega V_m \sin \omega t_1 = -\frac{V_1}{R_L C} \qquad (3.81)$$

The voltage, V_1, is equal to v_T at the time t_1. Therefore,

$$V_1 = V_m \cos \omega t_1 \qquad (3.82)$$

When Eq. 3.82 is substituted into Eq. 3.81,

$$\omega V_m \sin \omega t_1 = \frac{V_m \cos \omega t_1}{R_L C} \qquad (3.83)$$

or

$$\tan \omega t_1 = \frac{1}{\omega R_L C} \qquad (3.84)$$

This equation can be written as

$$\omega t_1 = \tan^{-1} \frac{1}{\omega R_L C} \qquad (3.85)$$

or

$$t_1 = \frac{1}{\omega} \tan^{-1} \frac{1}{\omega R_L C} \qquad (3.86)$$

If the value of t_1 from Eq. 3.86 is substituted into Eq. 3.82,

$$V_1 = V_m \cos \left(\tan^{-1} \frac{1}{\omega R_L C} \right) \qquad (3.87)$$

This equation can be simplified by referring to Fig. 3.36. If $\theta = \tan^{-1} 1/\omega R_L C$, θ has the value shown. Hence, the cos θ is $\omega R_L C/[1 + (\omega R_L C)^2]^{1/2}$ and Eq. 3.87 becomes

$$V_1 = \frac{V_m \omega R_L C}{[1 + (\omega R_L C)^2]^{1/2}} \qquad (3.88)$$

The value of V_2 (the voltage when diode D_2 begins to conduct) can be found by equating v_C and v_T at the time $t = t_2$. Accordingly, when the value of V_1 from Eq. 3.88 is substituted into Eq. 3.77 and

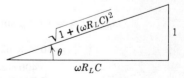

Fig. 3.36. A graphical representation of Eq. 3.91.

when Eq. 3.77 is equated to Eq. 3.78,

$$|V_m \cos \omega t_2| = \frac{V_m \omega R_L C}{[1 + (\omega R_L C)^2]^{1/2}} e^{-(t_2 - t_1)/R_L C} \tag{3.89}$$

or

$$|\cos \omega t_2| = \frac{\omega R_L C}{[1 + (\omega R_L C)^2]^{1/2}} e^{-(t_2 - t_1)/R_L C} \tag{3.90}$$

Since t_1 can be found from Eq. 3.86, and the values of ω, R_L, and C are known for a given circuit, the time t_2 is the only unknown in Eq. 3.90. Unfortunately, Eq. 3.90 cannot be solved directly and therefore must be solved either graphically or by trial and error.

For this example,

$$\omega R_L C = 628 \times 10^3 \times 10^{-5} = 6.28 \tag{3.91}$$

$$\tan^{-1} \frac{1}{6.28} = 9° = 0.157 \text{ radian} \tag{3.92}$$

$$t_1 = \frac{1}{628} \times 0.157 = 2.5 \times 10^{-4} \text{ sec} \tag{3.93}$$

$$V_1 = \frac{400 \times 6.28}{(1 + 39.4)^{1/2}} = 395 \text{ v} \tag{3.94}$$

$$t_2 \text{ by trial and error} \simeq 3.75 \times 10^{-3} \text{ sec}$$

$$V_2 = 278 \text{ v}$$

As mentioned previously, the current through each diode flows only during a short period of time each cycle. While the current flows, it has the value

$$i = C \frac{dv_T}{dt} + \frac{v_T}{R_L} \tag{3.95}$$

The term $C(dv_T/dt)$ represents the current used to charge the capacitor while the current v_T/R_L is the current delivered to the load. Usually the current required to charge the capacitor is many times greater than the current required by the load resistor. Neglecting the source resistance and inductance, the maximum current flow through the diode usually occurs at t_2 when dv_T/dt is greatest. Hence, a quick check allows the circuit designer to determine if the current through the diode exceeds the recommended maximum.

Substituting Eq. 3.80 and Eq. 3.78 into Eq. 3.95,

$$i_{\max} \text{ at } t_2 = C \omega V_m \sin \omega t_2 + \frac{V_m \cos \omega t_2}{R_L} \tag{3.96}$$

$$= 10^{-5} \times 628 \times 400 \sin (628 \times 3.75 \times 10^{-3})$$

$$+ \frac{400 \cos (628 \times 3.75 \times 10^{-3})}{1000}$$

$$= 1.77 + 0.283 = 2.053 \text{ amp}$$

Since actual circuits always contain some inductance and resistance, i_{max} occurs later than t_2 and is less than that given by Eq. 3.96.

A derivation similar to the foregoing can be made for the half-wave rectifier. In the half-wave rectifier, the time when conduction ceases (t_1) is the same as in the full-wave rectifier. However, the time when conduction begins (t_2) will be different. A plot is made in Fig. 3.37 to help determine the value of t_1 and t_2 for either the full-wave or half-wave rectifier.

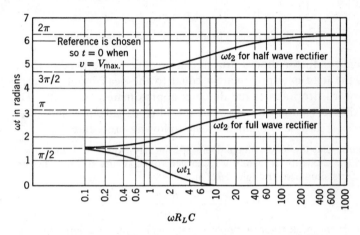

Fig. 3.37. A plot to help determine t_1 and t_2 in Fig. 3.35.

PROB. 3.25. Repeat Example 3.4 if C is changed to 100 μf. What is the peak current through the diode.

PROB. 3.26. The diode D_1 (in Example 3.4) has a failure and becomes an open circuit. Plot the output voltage waveform. What is the peak current through diode D_2?

The foregoing derivation of relationships in a rectifier-filter system is adequately rigorous, but disappointingly tedious from the standpoint of system design. Considerable simplification results when certain approximations, which will be discussed, are allowable. Whenever a capacitor is used in a rectifier system to improve the rectification efficiency and reduce the a-c component or *ripple* in the load, the capacitance value is usually chosen so that the ripple voltage is small in comparison with the d-c component of load voltage. Under this condition, the time constant of the load resistance and filter capacitance must be long compared with the period T of the input voltage (Fig. 3.38). Then the capacitor (and load) voltage decreases almost linearly at the initial discharge rate $V_{max}/R_L C$ (obtained from Eq. 3.79 by letting $t = t_1$ and assuming $v_1 = v_{max}$). This initial slope would reduce the load voltage to zero at $t = R_L C$ if it were allowed to continue.

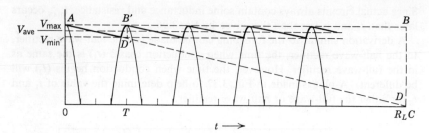

Fig. 3.38. Constructions used in the approximate solution.

If semiconductor diodes are used as rectifiers, the maximum voltage across the load is approximately equal to the peak input voltage, since the forward drop across the diode is approximately one volt. Then an approximate relationship between the filter capacitance and the ripple voltage can easily be obtained by the following procedure.

1. Assume that the load voltage decreases linearly from $t = 0$ until $t = T$, and then the capacitor is instantly recharged to V_{max} and so on. Then triangle $AB'D'$ is similar to triangle ABD and

$$\frac{T}{R_L C} = \frac{B'D'}{V_{max}} \tag{3.97}$$

2. $B'D'$ is the peak-to-peak ripple voltage which may be approximated from the specified rms ripple voltage. $B'D' \simeq 2\sqrt{2}\, v_{ripple}$.
3. The average or d-c load voltage is obtained by subtracting the peak ripple voltage $B'D'/2$ from V_{max}, or, more often, the maximum input voltage is obtained by adding the peak ripple voltage to the specified d-c load voltage.
4. The minimum value of load resistance. which is the worst case, may be obtained by dividing the d-c load voltage by the maximum specified load current.
5. The required value of capacitance can be obtained from the specifications for the power supply and with the aid of Eq. 3.97

$$C = \frac{T V_{max}}{2\sqrt{2}\, v_{ripple}\, R_L} \tag{3.98}$$

When a full-wave rectifier is used, the discharge period is approximately $T/2$ instead of T. Therefore, the required filter capacitance is reduced by a factor of two.

PROB. 3.27. Design a full-wave power supply with a capacitor filter which will provide 50 volts d-c at 1 ampere into a resistive load. The permissible rms ripple voltage is 2 per cent of the d-c load voltage. Use silicon rectifiers and determine the filter capacitance as well as the rms voltage of the transformer secondary. The primary power is 115 v 60 Hz.

A computer solution of the equations in Example 3.4 is presented in nomograph form in Fig 3.39. This nomograph is very useful when determining the ripple factor as a fraction of $\omega R_L C$.

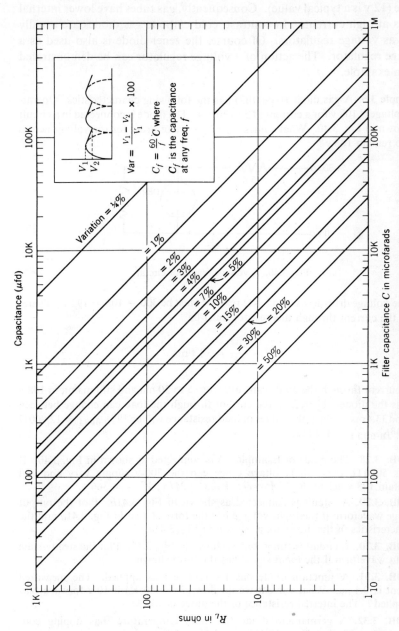

Fig. 3.39. A nomograph to help determine the size of filter capacitor in a full wave rectifier for 60 Hz.

Hot cathode gas diode tubes are frequently used as rectifiers. The voltage drop across these tubes is small in comparison with a vacuum diode (12 v is a typical value). Consequently, gas tubes have lower internal losses at high currents. In contrast, cold cathode gas diodes are usually used as voltage regulators. Of course, the zener diode is also used as a voltage regulator. The action of a voltage regulator can be demonstrated by an example.

Example 3.5. A gas diode (type 0B2) has the following characteristics. Operating voltage is 108 v for a current of 5 to 30 ma. The diode is connected in a circuit as shown in Fig. 3.40. What values may R_L have in order for the voltage across R_L to remain 108 v?

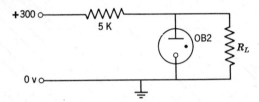

Fig. 3.40. A voltage regulator circuit.

The voltage drop across the 5 KΩ resistor must be $300 - 108 = 192$ v. Therefore, the current through this resistor must be

$$I = \frac{192}{5K} = 38.4 \text{ ma}$$

The current through the diode can vary from 5 to 30 ma and still maintain 108 v across the diode. Therefore, the current through the load can change between 8.4 and 33.4 ma. Hence, the values of load resistance will be $108/0.0084 = 12{,}900 \, \Omega$ to $108/0.0334 = 3240 \, \Omega$.

PROB. 3.28. The diode of Example 3.5 is connected as shown in Fig. 3.40. If R_L is 5000 Ω, over what voltage range can the 300-v supply vary and still maintain 108 v across R_L? *Answer:* $V_{\min} = 241$ v, $V_{\max} = 366$ v.

PROB. 3.29. A circuit is connected as shown in Fig. 3.41*b*. Plot the output voltage waveform if the input voltage has the form shown in Fig. 3.41*a* and the characteristics of the diode are as shown in Fig. 3.41*c*.

PROB. 3.30. A circuit is connected as shown in Fig. 3.42. Plot the steady-state output waveform if the input signal has the form shown.

PROB. 3.31. A junction diode has 1 v reverse bias applied. The measured current is 0.1 μa. What current would flow ($T = 300°$K) if 10 v forward bias is applied? The internal resistance of the diode is 0.25 Ω.

PROB. 3.32. A germanium diode (at room temperature) has doping concentrations such that $N_a = 10^{17}/\text{cm}^3$ and $N_d = 10^{15}/\text{cm}^3$.

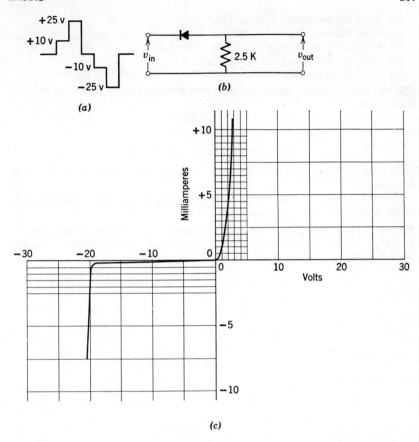

(a)

(b)

(c)

Fig. 3.41. Information required by Prob. 3.29. (a) Input voltage; (b) circuit configuration; (c) characteristic curves.

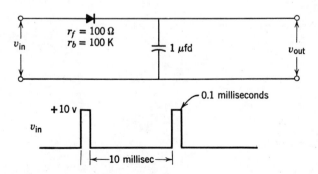

Fig. 3.42. Information for Prob. 3.30.

(a) What are the values of n_n and p_p?
(b) What are the values of n_p and p_n?
(c) What is the magnitude of the potential V_{ho}?
(d) What are the lengths of L_p and L_n?
(e) What is maximum electric field intensity in the depletion region?

PROB. 3.33. A silicon diode (at room temperature) has the following physical parameters:

$$N_a = 10^{17}/cm^3$$
$$N_d = 10^{15}/cm^3$$

Cross-sectional area = 0.01 cm²

(a) Determine the junction capacitance of this diode when no external voltage is applied.

(b) Make a plot of capacitance vs external voltage for this diode if the external voltage were to vary from −25 to 0 v.

PROB. 3.34. Write a computer program which will read-in values of ω, R_L, C, and V_m. The computer should solve the equations given in Example 3.4 and print (or punch) out the values of t_1, t_2, V_1, V_2, and V_{ave}.

4

Basic Amplifiers

The vast electronics industry is centered around the amplifier, a device capable of increasing the power level of an input signal. For example, the minute amounts of power collected by a radio-receiving antenna are entirely inadequate to operate a loudspeaker or provide a picture on a TV picture tube. Amplifiers and other electronic circuits are required in order to increase the power level of the received signals and make them suitable for operating the output devices. In addition to its major role in the communications area, the amplifier is a basic building block in automation and computer industries. Also, electronic instruments that employ amplifiers have become an essential part of the medical profession.

The amplifier is actually an energy converter. The input signal merely controls the current that flows from the power supply or battery. Thus, the energy from the power supply is converted by the amplifier to Signal energy. There are many types of amplifiers in current use, including hydraulic, pneumatic, magnetic, transistor, and vacuum tube amplifiers. Only part of the transistor and vacuum tube types will be included in this treatment. The basic principles of almost all types are similar, however, so a thorough understanding of one will give insight into all.

4.1 JUNCTION TRANSISTORS

When a semiconductor is arranged so that it has two *p-n* junctions as shown in Fig. 4.1*a*, it is known as a *p-n-p* junction transistor. The electrical potential in the transistor as a function of distance along the axis is sketched in Fig. 4.1*b*. If forward bias is applied to one junction and reverse bias is applied to the other junction, as shown in Fig. 4.1*c*, the potential diagram will be altered as indicated in Fig. 4.1*d*. The reduction in the height of the potential barrier of the forward biased junction will cause positive carriers from the left-hand region, which is known as the *emitter*, to be injected into the center section, which is known as the *base*. Some of the injected holes recombine with the negative carriers in the base region, but if the base region is made very thin, the majority of the injected

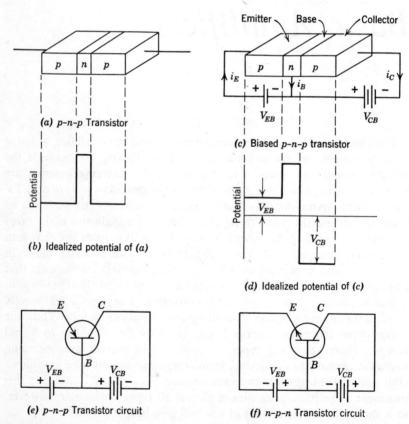

(a) *p-n-p* Transistor

(b) Idealized potential of (a)

(c) Biased *p-n-p* transistor

(d) Idealized potential of (c)

(e) *p-n-p* Transistor circuit

(f) *n-p-n* Transistor circuit

Fig. 4.1. The *p-n-p* junction transistor. (a) *p-n-p* transistor; (b) idealized potential of *a*; (c) biased *p-n-p* transistor; (d) idealized potential of *c*.

holes diffuse across the base and are accelerated through the reverse biased junction into the right-hand section, which is known as the *collector*. The holes drift across the collector region and cause current i_C to flow in the collector circuit. Also, a base current i_B flows as a result of recombinations in the base. A circuit diagram of the *p-n-p* transistor and bias batteries is given in Fig. 4.1e. The transistor could have been an *n-p-n* arrangement, in which all potentials and currents would be reversed. A circuit diagram including bias batteries and the transistor symbol for an *n-p-n* transistor is given in Fig. 4.1f.

From the preceding discussion, it would seem that either end of the transistor could be used as the emitter. This conclusion is generally not

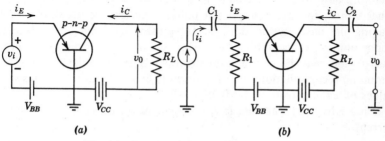

Fig. 4.2. Common-base transistor amplifiers.

true. The heat dissipation at the collector junction is much greater than the dissipation at the emitter junction because of the comparatively large potential difference across the collector junction. Therefore, the transistor is usually designed so that the heat can be most effectively conducted away from the collector junction. The power dissipation rating of the transistor depends on the thermal conductivity from the collector junction to the transistor case and thence to the ambient surroundings.

At this point, a few words should be said about conventional current and voltage directions. Actual current directions and potential polarities were shown in Fig. 4.1. However, IEEE standards require that currents which flow into the device be considered positive, and that currents which flow out of the device be considered negative (Fig. 4.2). Therefore, the collector and base currents which usually flow *out* of the *p-n-p* transistor are negative currents indicating that they flow in the opposite direction to the conventionial positive currents. Also, a potential is considered positive if it is positive with respect to common node. The arrow head points in the direction of positive potential, as shown in Fig. 4.2. In the *p-n-p* transistor, the collector is actually negative with respect to the base, which is the common node in the common base configuration. Therefore, the actual *p-n-p* collector voltage is negative.

When the voltage between the collector and the base is held constant, as in the preceding discussion, the fraction of the emitter current which reaches the collector terminal is called α. In addition to this current, the saturation current resulting from thermally generated carriers flows across the reverse biased collector-base junction, as discussed in Chapter 3. This saturation current was known as I_S in the diode but is known as I_{CO} or I_{CBO} in the transistor.[1] Since I_{CO} flows out of the collector in a *p-n-p* transistor, I_{CO} will be a *negative* current. Then the collector current is

$$-i_C = \alpha i_E - I_{CO} \tag{4.1}$$

Generally, the collector circuit can be thought of as the output circuit. It is therefore desirable to have as large a collector current as possible, or in other words, to have α approach unity. This can be accomplished by making the base section thin, as previously mentioned, to reduce the opportunities for recombination. Also, the doping concentration in the base region may be a minimum practical value in order to provide a minimum recombination rate. In currently available junction transistors, values of α range from about 0.95 to 0.998.

Using Kirchhoff's current law, it is evident from Fig. 4.1 that the base current is

$$-i_B = i_E + i_C \tag{4.2}$$

$$-i_B = i_E - (\alpha i_E - I_{CO}) = (1 - \alpha)i_E + I_{CO} \tag{4.3}$$

PROB. 4.1. A certain transistor has $\alpha = 0.98$. V_{BE} is adjusted so that $i_E = 10$ ma. Assuming that the collector junction is reverse biased and $I_{CO} = -10\ \mu a$, calculate i_C and i_B. *Answer: $i_B = 190\ \mu a$, $i_C = 9.82\ ma$.*

PROB. 4.2. At what magnitude of emitter current will the base current be equal to zero?

4.2 THE COMMON-BASE AMPLIFIER

If the emitter and base terminals are the input terminals and the collector and base terminals are the output terminals, the transistor is in the common base or grounded base configuration. A gain in signal power may be realized with this arrangement. The input resistance of this configuration is low because of the forward bias on the emitter-base junction. In contrast,

---

[1] The saturation current is frequently known as I_{CBO} in the literature. The three subscripts indicate this current flows from the collector (first subscript) to the base (second subscript) when the emitter circuit is open (the third subscript indicates the condition of the third terminal of the device). For example, when the emitter junction is reversed biased and the collector circuit is open the current which flows is known as I_{EBO}. Since the second subscript is always B when thermal currents are involved, this second subscript may be eliminated without loss of information.

the output resistance is high because of the reverse bias on the collector-base junction. Therefore, a load resistance which is high in comparison with the input resistance may be placed in the collector circuit. Since the output current may be almost equal to the input current, the ratio of power in the load resistance to the power input (known as power gain) may be almost equal to the ratio of load resistance to input resistance. If the input and load currents are almost equal, the voltage gain must be essentially equal to the power gain. When there is no means provided to separate the bias currents from the signal currents, the amplifier is said to be a d-c amplifier. A schematic diagram for a common base d-c amplifier is given in Fig. 4.2a.

Some practical problems may arise from the lack of common d-c potentials in the input and output circuits of this amplifier. These problems are avoided in the circuit of Fig. 4.2b. This circuit utilizes capacitors to isolate the bias currents from the signal currents. This amplifier is called an a-c amplifier. In this amplifier the bias supply voltage V_{BB} must be increased in order to compensate for the drop across R_1. The value of R_1 should be large in comparison with the input resistance of the transistor so the signal current in the emitter of the transistor is almost equal to the source current i_i. In either the d-c or the a-c circuit, a small variation in the input voltage causes a change in the height of the emitter-base junction potential barrier, which in turn causes a significant change in the injection current across this barrier. Most of the injected carriers drift across the narrow base region into the collector and thus cause collector-current variations which are almost equal to the emitter-current variations. The collector-current variations cause voltage variations across the load resistance R_L. These voltage variations may be much larger than the input voltage, v_i. The voltage variations across R_L constitute the output signal voltage, which may be isolated from the bias voltage by the capacitor C_2. Observe that the varying or signal components of current or voltage are the total values minus the bias values. Notice also that the bias potentials applied to the transistor, V_{EB} and V_{CB} are different from the bias battery potentials V_{BB} and V_{CC}.

When the load resistance is small in comparison with the transistor output resistance, i_c is approximately equal to αi_e. This statement will be verified later. Then, neglecting the shunting effect of R_1, we have

$$v_i = i_e R_{in} \tag{4.4}$$

$$v_o = -i_c R_L \simeq \alpha i_e R_L \tag{4.5}$$

The voltage gain is

$$G_v = \frac{v_o}{v_i} = \frac{\alpha i_e R_L}{i_e R_{in}} = \frac{\alpha R_L}{R_{in}} \tag{4.6}$$

The instantaneous power input is

$$p_i = i_e^2 R_{in} \tag{4.7}$$

The instantaneous power output is

$$p_o = i_c^2 R_L \simeq (\alpha i_e)^2 R_L \tag{4.8}$$

The power gain is

$$G_p = \frac{p_o}{p_i} = \frac{(\alpha i_e)^2 R_L}{i_e^2 R_{in}} = \frac{\alpha^2 R_L}{R_{in}} \tag{4.9}$$

The foregoing relationships are based on the following assumptions:

1. The input current is proportional to the input voltage, so that R_{in} may be defined.
2. The load resistance R_L is small in comparison with the output resistance of the transistor. It is evident that the output current i_c must approach zero as the load resistance approaches infinity.
3. The frequency of the signal components is such that all reactances in the circuit are negligible.

PROB. 4.3. A certain transistor has an input resistance of 50 Ω, an output resistance of 1 megohm, and an α of 0.98. Calculate the voltage and power gains in a common-base circuit which has a load resistance of 10 KΩ. Assume that the conditions listed are fulfilled. *Answer: $G_v = 196$, $G_p = 192$.*

4.3 GRAPHICAL ANALYSIS

In order to use a transistor intelligently, some basic relationships between its currents and voltages must be known. For example, the relationship between the emitter-base voltage and the emitter current might be very helpful. Also, the effects of emitter current and collector voltage on collector current would be very useful. These relationships could be calculated from theoretical considerations if sufficient information were supplied by the manufacturer. However, it is much easier and more accurate to determine these relationships experimentally. The diagram of a circuit which might be used to obtain the common-base characteristics is given in Fig. 4.3. The batteries and potentiometers which are used as variable bias sources in this circuit are customarily replaced by a-c operated power supplies with adjustable d-c output voltages. The emitter bias voltage would be low (a few tenths of a volt) and its adjustment would be rather critical if the resistor R were not included in the circuit. The voltmeters shown should be highly sensitive, preferably vacuum tube voltmeters, so that their operating currents do not make an appreciable contribution to i_C or i_E.

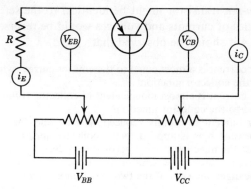

Fig. 4.3. A circuit for determining transistor characteristics.

There are four important variables in the circuit, as indicated by the meters. Some of these variables must be held constant while the relationships between others are found. For example, the emitter current must be held constant while the effect of the collector voltage on collector current is determined. When the collector current is plotted as a function of the collector-base voltage (with emitter current held constant), the resulting curve is known as a *collector-characteristic curve*. Each different value of emitter current will yield a different collector-characteristic curve. A set of several curves obtained from several representative values of emitter current is known as a *family* of collector-characteristic curves. A typical family or set of collector characteristics for a *p-n-p* transistor is shown in Fig. 4.4. The negative current indicates that the current is flowing out of the transistor, where the reference direction is into the transistor. A set of

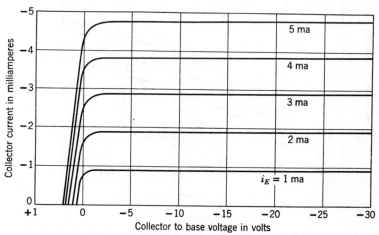

Fig. 4.4. A family of collector characteristic curves.

curves for an *n-p-n* transistor might be identical to the set shown except that the polarities of currents and voltages would be reversed.

From Fig. 4.4 it should be observed that:

1. The collector current is almost equal to the emitter current when reverse bias is applied to the collector junction.
2. The collector current is almost independent of collector voltage when reverse bias is applied to the collector junction.
3. The collector current is rapidly reduced to zero and then reversed when increasing forward bias is applied to the collector junction. This behavior occurs because the injection current across the collector junction opposes the injection current across the emitter junction. The collector current is essentially the algebraic sum of the two injection currents.

The emitter-base voltage does not appear in the set of collector characteristics. Therefore, a relationship is needed between emitter current and emitter-base voltage to determine the input resistance of the transistor. Experimentation reveals that the collector voltage has a slight influence on the emitter current. Therefore, a family of curves is needed to completely define the input characteristics of the transistor. Normally the emitter-base voltage is plotted as a function of the emitter current with the collector voltage held constant (Fig. 4.5). A curve is obtained for each different value of collector voltage.

The characteristic curves just described are known as *static-characteristic curves* because certain parameters were held constant while the relationships

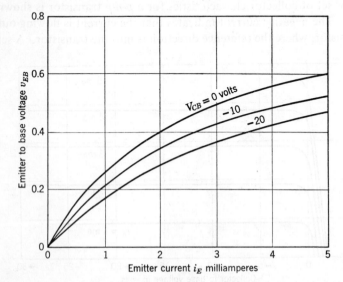

Fig. 4.5. Input characteristics of a typical transistor.

between other parameters were obtained. When a transistor is used as an amplifier, there must be a load impedance in the collector circuit to produce an output voltage. The variations in input or emitter current and the resulting variations in collector voltage represent the signal components in the circuit. The characteristics of an amplifier in which all terminal voltages and currents are allowed to vary simultaneously are known as *dynamic characteristics*. The dynamic characteristics could be obtained by placing a load resistance in the collector circuit and plotting a set of curves for each value of load resistance. However, this method would become very tedious if many values of load resistance were considered. A much easier method of determining the dynamic characteristics utilizes the static characteristic curves which are either furnished by the manufacturer or easily obtained in the laboratory. This method is developed as follows.

When a load resistance is placed in the collector circuit, as in Fig. 4.2, the collector-base voltage v_{CB} at any instant is the collector supply voltage V_{CC} minus the drop across the load resistor. Then, letting the voltages and currents carry their appropriate signs,

$$v_{CB} = V_{CC} - i_C R_L \qquad (4.10)$$

Solving for i_C

$$i_C = \frac{V_{CC} - v_{CB}}{R_L} \qquad (4.11)$$

or

$$i_C = -\frac{v_{CB}}{R_L} + \frac{V_{CC}}{R_L} \qquad (4.12)$$

Compare Eq. 4.12 with the familiar equation of a straight line

$$y = mx + b \qquad (4.13)$$

where $m =$ the slope of the line
   $b =$ the y axis intercept

It is evident that Eq. 4.12 is the equation of a straight line which has a slope of $-1/R_L$ and i_C axis intercept of V_{CC}/R_L. Equation 4.12 shows that when $i_C = 0$, $v_{CB} = V_{CC}$, or in other words, the v_{CB} axis intercept is V_{CC}. This line is known as the *load line*. When drawn on the static collector characteristics of a transistor, the load line gives the dynamic operating characteristics for any chosen value of load resistance. A typical family of collector characteristics is provided in Fig. 4.6a. The load line is drawn for a 5 KΩ load resistance with $V_{CC} = 25$ v. A bias point or *quiescent point* must be selected some place along the load line. If the expected input

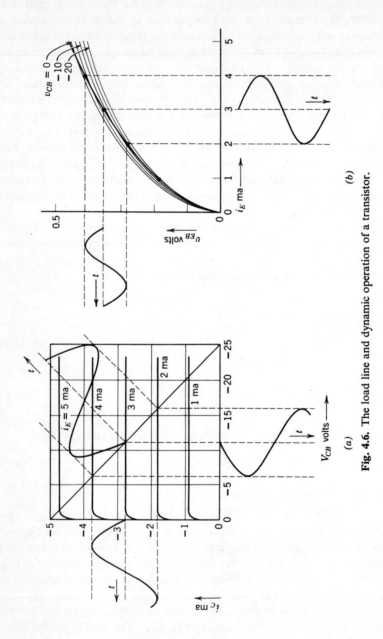

Fig. 4.6. The load line and dynamic operation of a transistor.

signals are symmetrical about the quiescent or bias value of i_C, it would be wise to select the quiescent or bias point at about the center of the load line. This would be the case for sinusoidal input signals. On the other hand, if a positive pulse were to be applied to the input, the quiescent point preferably might be located at the lower end of the load line.

The emitter-base voltage, for any combination of emitter current and collector voltage, may be found from the input characteristic curves, as previously discussed. Therefore, a dynamic operating line may be drawn on the input characteristics using the combinations of emitter current and collector voltage found along the load line on the collector characteristics. This dynamic input characteristic is illustrated in Fig. 4.6b.

The dynamic operation of the transistor amplifier can be visualized with the aid of the curves of Fig. 4.6. In this sketch, the emitter current is assumed to be varying sinusoidally about the chosen quiescent operating point with maximum amplitude $I_{e\,max} = 1$ ma as shown. Then, the amplitude and waveform of the collector-current variations are projected on the collector current axis as shown. Similarly, the collector-voltage variations are projected on the collector-voltage axis as indicated. Note that time axes have been drawn normal to the load line, current axis, and voltage axis, respectively. From the construction in Fig. 4.6a, it may be observed that the collector current and voltage have the same waveform as the emitter current, providing that the collector current is proportional to the emitter current, or in other words, if α is constant.

The magnitude and waveform of v_{EB} may be obtained from the input characteristics by projection of the assumed excursions of emitter current along the dynamic input characteristic to the v_{EB} axis as shown in Fig. 4.6b. Since the dynamic input characteristic is not straight, the waveform of v_{EB} is not the same as the waveform of i_E, or in other words, i_E is not proportional to v_{EB}. This behavior is to be expected from the preceding discussion of the properties of a p-n junction. The waveform of v_{EB} could be plotted quite accurately if we consider enough points at equally spaced time or degree intervals along the i_E curve and project them from the dynamic curve to produce the v_{EB} vs time plot. This detail is not warranted at this time, however. The change in waveform is known as *nonlinear distortion* and will be treated in detail in Chapter 10.

It may seem more reasonable to assume that the input voltage v_{EB} is sinusoidal and the input current i_E is distorted rather than vice-versa. This condition would be true if the signal source had an internal impedance small in comparison with the input resistance of the transistor. Then the transistor input voltage would be almost equal in magnitude and hence similar in waveform to the driving source emf. The emitter current and consequently the collector current and voltage would then have nonlinear distortion. However, if the driving source has an internal impedance which is large in comparison with the transistor input resistance, the variations in input resistance are very small in comparison with the total impedance in series with the driving emf (visualizing a Thevenin's equivalent circuit) and the input current has essentially the same waveform as the source emf. The transistor input voltage would then be distorted as in the example given in Fig. 4.6, but the output voltage would be essentially undistorted. It may be observed from Fig. 4.6b that the used segment of the dynamic input characteristic approaches a straight line as the emitter current variations are reduced in magnitude. Thus the distortion may be negligible under any conditions of operation if the signal amplitude is sufficiently small.

The voltage gain, current gain, and power gain of the amplifier may be obtained from the curves of Fig. 4.6 by a comparison of the relative magnitudes of the output excursions of current and voltage with those of the input. Comparison of peak-to-peak amplitudes yields the most accurate results because of the lack of symmetry of some of the waveforms. The power gain is the product of the voltage gain and the current gain, since the input impedance and load impedance are assumed to be resistive.

PROB. 4.4. Determine the voltage gain, current gain, and power gain of the transistor amplifier represented in Fig. 4.6. *Answer:* $G_v = 80$, $G_i = 0.98$, $G_p = 78.5$.

PROB. 4.5. Using the characteristic curves of Fig. 4.6, draw a load line for $R_L = 10$ KΩ and $V_{CC} = 20$ v. Assuming that the emitter signal current will be 0.5 sin ωt ma, select a suitable quiescent operating point and draw the dynamic input characteristic. Sketch the emitter-base voltage, collector voltage, and collector current and calculate the voltage gain, current gain, and power gain.

4.4 FACTORS WHICH AFFECT α

In the preceding discussion it has been implied that the current ratio α varies from one transistor to another but is constant for a particular transistor. This is not strictly true. The dimensions of the transistor as well as the doping concentrations, which are built into the transistor, do primarily determine α as previously mentioned, but the magnitude of applied voltages and currents also have some effect on α. The importance of this parameter α may not be appreciated at this point in the discussion of transistor amplifiers, but as the theme unfolds α will emerge as one of the chief characters. Therefore, an investigation will be made to determine what factors affect α.

Figure 4.7a is a sketch of the cross section of a typical alloyed junction transistor. The base section is a thin wafer a thousandth of an inch or so thick. The emitter and collector are small beads of doped material alloyed to the base. This sketch is much larger than an actual transistor. Other methods of manufacture, which produce physical structures quite different from this one, are in use. The physical construction for the various types of transistors is usually described in the transistor manuals.

The current flow through the base region is primarily by diffusion. The main objective is to have as few charge carriers as possible lost by recombination. Assuming the transistor to be a *p-n-p* type, the holes which are

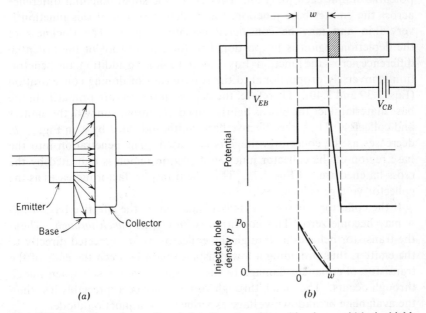

(a)   (b)

Fig. 4.7. Properties of an alloyed junction transistor (the base width is highly exaggerated).

injected into the base diffuse in a radial fashion as indicated in the figure. Those carriers which reach the collector junction are swept into the collector and contribute to the collector current. The carriers which strike the outside perimeter of the base will almost certainly recombine because of the deathnium centers or traps existing at the surface of the material. It is evident from the figure that the percentage of carriers which find their way to the perimeter is reduced as the base thickness is reduced. Also, the recombinations in the body of the base region may be made small by providing low doping concentrations and by making the base thin. The base thickness (or axial length) must be small in comparison with the diffusion length. The diffusion length is defined as the distance the carriers will travel before their number is reduced by recombination to p_0/e, where p_0 is the initial concentration and e is the base of the natural logarithm.

The ratio of the current which arrives at the collector junction to the initial current resulting from the carriers injected into the base is known as the *transport factor*, γ. This transport factor depends primarily on the thickness of the base and is always less than unity. The *effective base region* is that portion of the base in which there is essentially no electric field. This effective base width, therefore, excludes the depletion region or potential hill at each junction. Because of the small potential difference across the emitter-base junction, the depletion region of this junction is very thin and may be considered essentially zero. The thickness of the depletion region is proportional to the square root of the potential difference across the junction (Eqs. 3.39 and 3.40). In addition, the penetration is inversely proportional to the square root of doping concentration (Eqs. 3.39 and 3.40). Therefore, the depletion regions are primarily in the base material since the base is lightly doped in comparison with the emitter and collector. Thus, the effective base width, indicated by w in Fig. 4.7b, decreases as the collector voltage is increased. The penetration into the base region of the collector junction depletion region is indicated by the cross-hatched area of Fig. 4.7b. Thus the transport factor increases as the collector voltage is increased.

If the collector voltage is increased sufficiently, the effective base width w may become zero. This condition is known as *punch through*. Then, the transistor behaves as though the collector were connected directly to the emitter, thus providing a low resistance path between the ends of the transistor. Permanent damage to the transistor may result when punch through occurs. The punch through voltage may be appreciably less than the avalanche breakdown voltage experienced in a junction diode.

While holes are being injected across the emitter junction into the base (assuming a p-n-p transistor), electrons are being injected from the base into the emitter. The total injection current across the emitter junction is the sum of these injection currents. Only the injected holes are effective in causing carriers to flow into the collector, however. The ratio of injection current density from emitter to base to the total injection current density across the emitter junction is known as *emitter efficiency* η. Then

$$\eta = \frac{J_p}{J_p + J_n} \qquad (4.14)$$

where J_p is the current density resulting from injected holes and J_n is the current density resulting from injected electrons. In order to have η approach unity, J_p must be large in comparison with J_n.

The diffusion current density which flows as a result of a positive charge concentration (Eq. 3.10) is

$$J_p = -qD_p \frac{dp}{dx} \qquad (3.10)$$

The diffusion constant D_p has been evaluated for different types of material and the values for silicon and germanium at room temperature were listed in Chapter 3. Therefore, J_p can be calculated if the rate of change of charge concentration with axial distance, dp/dx, can be found. Referring to Fig. 4.7, the initial injected charge density in the base is assumed to be p_0. The density at the beginning of the depletion region near the collector junction is essentially zero because the carriers are swept into the collector region at that point. In reference to Eq. 3.10, dp/dx must be constant throughout the base if the diffusion current is constant through that region. Actually, this would be the condition if there were no recombinations. With no recombinations, then, there must be a linear decline of charge concentration from p_0 at the emitter junction to zero at the collector junction. This distribution is represented by the dashed line in Fig. 4.7b. The slope of this line is dp/dx. Then

$$\frac{dp}{dx} = -\frac{p_0}{w} \qquad (4.15)$$

and

$$J_p = \frac{qp_0 D_p}{w} \qquad (4.16)$$

The actual variation of p with x, including recombinations, is the solid line of Fig. 4.7b.

Let the injected electron density at the junction in the emitter region be n_0. If it is assumed that the emitter length is longer than the diffusion length L, the injected carrier density reduces to n_0/e at distance L from the junction.[2] The slope of the density vs the distance curve at the emitter junction is

$$\frac{dn}{dx} = \frac{n_0}{L} \qquad (4.17)$$

This situation is illustrated in Fig. 4.8. Then from Eq. 3.9

$$J_n = \frac{qn_0 D_n}{L} \qquad (4.18)$$

---

[2] As the negative carriers recombine in the emitter region, the diffusion current due to these negative carriers also decreases. However, the charge which tends to accumulate as a result of the recombinations causes a drift current to flow in the emitter region. The sum of the drift current and diffusion current produces a continuous current through the emitter.

The ratio of current densities is

$$\frac{J_n}{J_p} = \frac{n_0 D_n w}{p_0 D_p L} \tag{4.19}$$

In the interest of obtaining a high transport factor γ, the base width w must be small in comparison with L. In addition, the number of injected carriers is proportional to the carrier density in the material from whence the injected carriers came. Therefore, n_0 is small in comparison with p_0 because of the light doping of the base region. Thus, the factors which cause the transport factor to approach unity also cause the emitter efficiency to approach unity. Therefore, the emitter efficiency also increases as the collector voltage is increased.

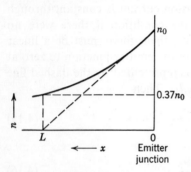

Another factor which may affect α is called collector efficiency, δ. This factor accounts for the carrier multiplication which may occur in the collector region. The collector efficiency is essentially unity except for rather high collector voltages which cause carrier multiplication by the process of ionization. This ionization results from high-velocity carriers as discussed in Chapter 3. The collector efficiency, δ, will then exceed unity. In fact, it may quickly increase to infinity as avalanche breakdown occurs. A

Fig. 4.8. Injected electron concentration as a function of x.

typical plot of δ as a function of collector voltage is given in Fig. 4.9a. The collector efficiency may be expressed by the formula

$$\delta = \frac{1}{1 - (V_C/V_A)^N} \tag{4.20}$$

where V_A is the avalanche breakdown voltage and N is an empirically determined exponent (usually about 3 for an alloyed junction transistor). The current ratio α is the product of the emitter efficiency, transport factor, and collector efficiency.

$$\alpha = \eta \gamma \delta \tag{4.21}$$

Alpha (α) is known as the *current amplification factor* of a transistor in the common-base configuration. The variation of α with collector voltage is sketched in Fig. 4.9. The reduced values of α at very low values of collector voltage occur because minority carriers accumulate at the collector junction. This accumulation occurs because the collector voltage is so low

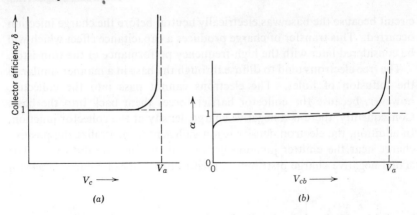

Fig. 4.9. (a) Collector efficiency as a function of collector voltage. (b) The variation of α with collector voltage.

that the iR drop in the collector region causes a slight forward bias across the collector-base junction and carriers are injected from the collector to the base region.

A scrutiny of this premise that the current flow through the base is due entirely to diffusion is in order. The charge density distribution (in the base of a typical transistor) which was given in Fig. 4.7b is enlarged and presented as curve p in Fig. 4.10. This injected charge tends to create a net positive charge and a resulting electric field in the base of a p-n-p transistor. This electric field causes free electrons in the base and connecting conductors to flow in a direction that neutralizes the charge. If the charge were completely neutralized, the excess electron density distribution would be indicated by the dashed curve n' in Fig. 4.10. There would then be no net field in the base and current flow would be entirely by diffusion as assumed. Note that the excess electrons must be furnished by the external

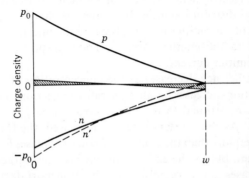

Fig. 4.10. Charge distribution in the base of a p-n-p transistor.

circuit because the base was electrically neutral before the charge injection occurred. This transfer of charge produces a capacitance effect which will be considered later with the high-frequency performance of the transistor.

The free electrons tend to diffuse through the base in a manner similar to the diffusion of holes. The electrons cannot pass into the collector, however, because the collector barrier forces them back into the base. Consequently, there is a negative charge density at the collector junction. In addition, the electron density is not sufficient to neutralize the positive charge near the emitter junction because of the electron diffusion. The actual negative charge distribution then follows the solid curve labeled n

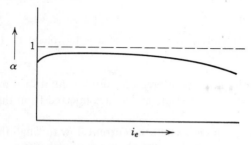

Fig. 4.11. Variation of α with emitter current.

in Fig. 4.10. The net charge distribution in the base is the difference between p and n as shown by the shaded area in Fig. 4.10. This unneutral-ized charge creates an electric field which opposes the electron diffusion. The field builds up to a magnitude which produces an electron drift current equal in magnitude and opposite in direction to the electron diffusion current.

The electric field in the base region is in a direction that accelerates the holes through the base. In other words, the hole diffusion is aided by drift due to the electric field. The transport factor is therefore increased by the net charge distribution in the base, and the charge distribution is in turn a function of the emitter current, because the injected charge density is proportional to the emitter current. The transport factor therefore increases with emitter current.

The emitter efficiency decreases as the concentration of electrons near the emitter junction increases because the rate of injection of electrons into the emitter is proportional to the free electron density on the base side of the junction. As the emitter current is increased, the transport factor increases more rapidly than the emitter efficiency decreases for small values of emitter current, but as the emitter current becomes larger, the emitter efficiency decreases more rapidly than the transport factor increases. Thus α is maximum at some specific value of emitter current in any given transistor. A sketch of α as a function of emitter current is provided in Fig. 4.11 in which the variation of α is exaggerated as compared with a typical transistor.

4.5 EQUIVALENT CIRCUITS .

As with the diodes, equivalent circuits approximating the behavior of amplifiers have been developed. The basic ideas for these equivalent circuits may be derived from Fig. 4.12. The amplifier usually contains two input terminals (or an input port) and two output terminals (or an output port). (One input terminal and one output terminal may be common.)

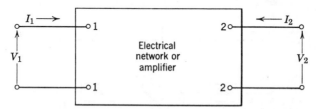

Fig. 4.12. A general four-terminal network or amplifier.

A circuit of this type is usually known as a two-terminal-pair network (or as a two-port network). Regardless of conditions inside the network, only four quantities can be measured in the external circuits. These quantities are input voltage and current (V_1 and I_1) and output voltage and current (V_2 and I_2).

If the currents I_1 and I_2 are assumed to be the independent variables, the voltage V_1 may be a function of both I_1 and I_2. Thus, if terminals 2-2 are open circuited ($I_2 = 0$) and a current I_1 is applied to the input terminals 1-1, a voltage V_1 (and also V_2) can be measured. The ratio V_1/I_1 can be expressed as an impedance Z_{11}. In a simple d-c situation, Z_{11} may be a single resistance. In contrast, if V_1 and I_1 are expressed in the Laplace transform form, the impedance Z_{11} may be a *function* of s. (For sinusoidal a-c signals, Z_{11} will be a function of $j\omega$.) Now, the input terminals 1-1 are open circuited and a current I_2 is applied to the output terminals 2-2. Again, the voltage V_1 (and also V_2) is measured. The ratio of V_1/I_2 is expressed as an impedance[3] Z_{12}. Thus, we may write

$$V_1 = Z_{11}I_1 \tag{4.22a}$$

and

$$V_1 = Z_{12}I_2 \tag{4.22b}$$

---

[3] Since Z_{11} involves the current and voltage at the same set of terminals, this impedance is called a *self impedance*. In contrast, Z_{12} involves the current at one set of terminals and the voltage at a second set of terminals and is known as a *transfer impedance*.

when both I_1 and I_2 are present and Z_{11} and Z_{12} are linear the law of superposition permits us to combine the foregoing equations and express V_1 as

$$V_1 = Z_{11}I_1 + Z_{12}I_2 \tag{4.23}$$

Similarly, the ratio of V_2/I_1 with the output open can also be found. This ratio is called Z_{21}. Also, the ratio of V_2/I_2 with the input open is

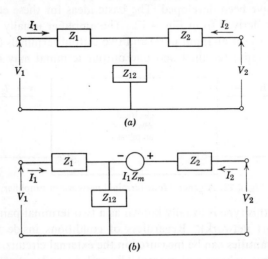

(a)

(b)

Fig. 4.13. (a) An equivalent T circuit for Fig. 4.12 where the network contains only R, L, and C components. (b) An equivalent T circuit for Fig. 4.12 where the network contains an amplifier.

found and is called Z_{22}. When these ratios are established, we can write

$$V_2 = Z_{21}I_1 \tag{4.24a}$$

and

$$V_2 = Z_{22}I_2 \tag{4.24b}$$

These equations, if linear, are combined (by the use of the law of super-position) to yield V_2.

$$V_2 = Z_{21}I_1 + Z_{22}I_2 \tag{4.25}$$

If the circuit contains only R, L, and C components, the circuit is known as a *passive* circuit and Z_{12} will be equal to Z_{21}. One equivalent circuit which represents Eq. 4.23 and Eq. 4.25 is given in Fig. 4.13a. The validity of this equivalent circuit may be checked by writing the loop equations.

$$V_1 = (Z_1 + Z_{12})I_1 + Z_{12}I_2 \tag{4.26}$$

$$V_2 = Z_{12}I_1 + (Z_{12} + Z_2)I_2 \tag{4.27}$$

These equations are the same as Eqs. 4.23 and 4.25 if

$$Z_{12} = Z_{21}, \quad (Z_1 + Z_{12}) = Z_{11} \quad \text{and} \quad (Z_{12} + Z_2) = Z_{22}$$

This configuration is known as the T configuration for obvious reasons.

In an amplifier circuit, Z_{12} is *not* equal to Z_{21}. This circuit is known as an *active* circuit. Either a voltage or current generating source can be added to the passive equivalent circuit to account for the difference between Z_{12} and Z_{21}. The circuit of Fig. 4.13a, must, therefore, be modified when the circuit is active. A modification is shown in Fig. 4.13b which correctly represents an amplifier. The loop equations for the circuit of Fig. 4.13b are

$$V_1 = (Z_1 + Z_{12})I_1 + Z_{12}I_2 \tag{4.28a}$$

$$V_2 = (Z_{12} + Z_m)I_1 + (Z_2 + Z_{12})I_2 \tag{4.28b}$$

The term Z_m has been added to Z_{12} to form Z_{21}. The term Z_m may be either positive or negative to fit a given situation. The voltage generator $I_1 Z_m$ also indicates how amplification may be accomplished.

As already noted, the values of the Z parameters can be found as follows:

Z_{11} = the input impedance when the output circuit is open.
Z_{12} = the ratio of the open circuit voltage at the input terminals to the current flowing in the output circuit.
Z_{22} = the output impedance when the input circuit is open.
Z_{21} = the ratio of the open circuit output voltage to the input current.

Some limitations on the accuracy of the equivalent circuits do exist. The impedances are assumed to be linear impedances and, as the reader has no doubt already observed, the characteristics of the tubes and transistors are not linear. However, for small-signal variations, the characteristics are essentially linear. In fact, the smaller the signal, the more nearly linear are the characteristics of the devices over the range of operation. Consequently, the equivalent circuits which have been developed and those yet to be developed in this chapter are *valid for small-signal amplifiers*. Larger signals can be handled if the characteristics of the device are approximately linear over the region of operation.

An equivalent T circuit for a transistor may now be drawn. Figure 4.14 shows the grounded base configuration and an equivalent circuit. The impedances which are essentially *pure resistances* at low frequencies are given subscripts corresponding to the terminals to which they connect.

Thus r_e is essentially the dynamic resistance of the forward biased emitter junction plus the small ohmic resistance of the fairly heavily doped emitter region. The dynamic junction resistance can be easily determined as a function of the bias value of the emitter current. The voltage-current relationship across the emitter-bias junction is expressed by the diode equation (Eq. 3.24)

$$i_E = -I_{EO}(e^{q(v_{EB}/kT} - 1)) \tag{4.29}$$

The dynamic conductance $g_e = 1/r_e = di_E/dv_{EB}$ evaluated at the bias

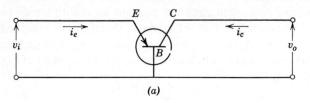

(a)

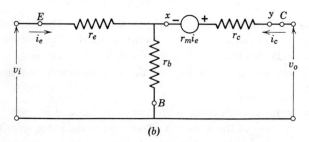

(b)

Fig. 4.14. An equivalent T circuit of a grounded base transistor.

value of emitter current I_E. Then, taking the derivative of Eq. 4.29 with respect to v_{EB},

$$g_e = -\frac{q}{kT} I_{EO} e^{qv_{EB}/kT} \tag{4.30}$$

But, using Eq. 4.29,

$$-I_{EO} e^{qv_{EB}/kT} = i_E - I_{EO} \tag{4.31}$$

When the emitter junction is forward biased 0.1 volt or higher, $i_E \gg I_{EO}$. Then

$$g_e \simeq \frac{q}{kT} i_E \simeq \frac{q}{kT} I_E \tag{4.32}$$

where I_E is the Q point, or bias value of i_E. Thus

$$r_e \simeq \frac{kT}{qI_E} \tag{4.33}$$

At 17°C, $q/kT = 40$, $g_e = 40I_E$ (amp) and $r_e = 25/I_E$ (ma).

The resistance r_b accounts for the effect of collector voltage variations on emitter current as well as the ohmic resistance of the lightly doped base. The collector voltage influences the emitter current because of the variation of effective base width with varying collector voltage. For this reason, r_b is frequently known as the base *spreading* resistance. Finally, the resistance r_c includes the effect which the varying collector voltage, and hence varying base width, has on the collector current, as well as the surface leakage resistance across the reverse biased diode. Also, r_c includes the effect of current multiplication due to avalanche effect in the collector-base depletion region. When high frequencies are considered, the equivalent circuit must also include capacitances. These will be treated in detail in Chapter 7. At low frequencies, the loop equations of the two loops of Fig. 4.14 are

$$v_i = (r_e + r_b)i_e + r_b i_c \tag{4.34a}$$

$$v_o = (r_m + r_b)i_e + (r_b + r_c)i_c \tag{4.34b}$$

When these equations are compared to Eqs. 4.23 and 4.25,

$$Z_{11} = r_e + r_b \tag{4.35a}$$

$$Z_{12} = r_b \tag{4.35b}$$

$$Z_{21} = r_b + r_m \tag{4.35c}$$

$$Z_{22} = r_c + r_b \tag{4.35d}$$

Combining Eqs. 4.35b and 4.35c,

$$r_m = Z_{21} - Z_{12} \tag{4.36}$$

A useful variation of the equivalent circuit shown in Fig. 4.14b is given in Fig. 4.15a. In this variation, the voltage generator between the points x and y (Fig. 4.14b) is replaced by an equivalent current generator. The parameters of this current generator are found by applying Norton's Theorem to the generator between points x and y of Fig. 4.14b. When the output circuit of Fig. 4.15a is shorted as shown in Fig. 4.15b, the direction of collector current will be as shown. Since the short circuit collector current will be α times as large as i_e, Kirchhoff's current law yields

$$\alpha' i_e + i_x = -i_c = \alpha i_e \tag{4.37}$$

Kirchhoff's voltage law applied to Fig. 4.15b gives

$$i_x r_c - i_b r_b = 0 \tag{4.38}$$

so

$$i_x = \frac{i_b r_b}{r_c} \tag{4.39}$$

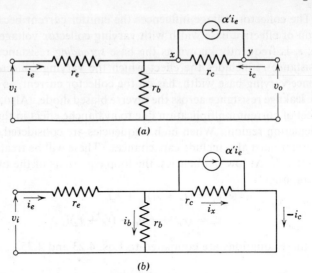

Fig. 4.15. A current source equivalent T circuit.

But, $i_b = (1 - \alpha)i_e$ since only small signal variations are being considered. Therefore,

$$i_x = \frac{(1 - \alpha)i_e r_b}{r_c} \tag{4.40}$$

When this value of i_x is substituted into Eq. 4.37,

$$\alpha' i_e + \frac{(1 - \alpha)i_e r_b}{r_c} = \alpha i_e \tag{4.41}$$

or

$$\alpha' = \alpha - (1 - \alpha)\frac{r_b}{r_c} \tag{4.42}$$

In the usual transistor, $r_b \ll r_c$ and $(1 - \alpha) \ll 1$. Therefore, α' is practically equal to α.

The relationship between the voltage generator of Fig. 4.14b and the current generator of Fig. 4.15a can now be found. If these two generators are equal, the open circuit voltages and the short circuit currents must be equal. Then,

$$r_m i_e = \alpha' i_e r_c \tag{4.43}$$

or

$$r_m = \alpha' r_c \simeq \alpha r_c \tag{4.44}$$

Table 4.1 lists a set of parameters for a typical low-power transistor.

TABLE 4.1

Parameters for a Typical Low-Power Transistor

$$\alpha = 0.984$$
$$r_e = 13 \ \Omega$$
$$r_b = 1000 \ \Omega$$
$$r_c = 1.8 \ \text{megohm}$$

PROB. 4.6. Find the value of α' for the transistor of Table 4.1. Is this value near the value of α? *Answer:* $\alpha' = 0.9839912$.

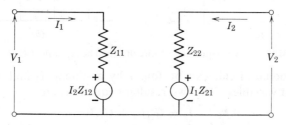

Fig. 4.16. An alternate z-parameter equivalent circuit.

Another equivalent circuit known as a z-parameter circuit which may be derived from Eqs. 4.23 and 4.25 is shown in Fig. 4.16. A check of the loop equations verifies that this is a valid equivalent circuit.

Actually, as the reader may have surmised, a large number of equivalent circuits can be devised. For example, if V_1 and V_2 of Fig. 4.12 are assumed to be the independent variables, a y-parameter circuit can be developed. Thus, if terminals 2-2 are shorted and a voltage V_1 is applied to terminals 1-1, the relationships $I_1/V_1 = Y_{11}$ and $I_2/V_1 = Y_{21}$ can be measured. Then, if terminals 1-1 are short circuited and a voltage V_2 is applied to terminals 2-2, the relationships $I_1/V_2 = Y_{12}$ and $I_2/V_2 = Y_{22}$ can be determined. Then, by the law of superposition we can write the two equations

$$I_1 = Y_{11}V_1 + Y_{12}V_2 \tag{4.45a}$$

$$I_2 = Y_{21}V_1 + Y_{22}V_2 \tag{4.45b}$$

One form of the y-parameter equivalent circuit is given in Fig. 4.17a. Nodal equations can be written to verify the validity of this equivalent circuit. Again, we may summarize the method of measuring the y-parameters.

Y_{11} = the input admittance with the output terminals shorted.

Y_{12} = the ratio of the short circuit current through the input terminals to a voltage which is applied to the output terminals.

Y_{21} = the ratio of the short circuit current through the output terminals to a voltage which is applied to the input terminals.

Y_{22} = the output admittance when the input circuit is short circuited.

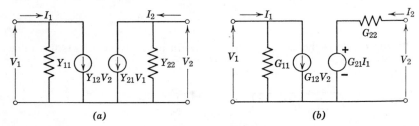

Fig. 4.17. (*a*) The equivalent Y circuit. (*b*) The equivalent G circuit.

An additional circuit can be found by assuming I_2 and V_1 are the independent variables. The two resultant equations are

$$I_1 = G_{11}V_1 + G_{12}I_2 \tag{4.46a}$$

$$V_2 = G_{21}V_1 + G_{22}I_2 \tag{4.46b}$$

One equivalent circuit which represents Eq. 4.46 is shown in Fig. 4.17*b*. The g-parameters are defined as follows:

G_{11} = the input admittance with the output terminals open.

G_{12} = the ratio of the short circuit input current to the current which is applied to the output terminals.

G_{21} = the ratio of the open circuit voltage at the output terminals to the voltage applied to the input terminals.

G_{22} = the output impedance when the input is short circuited.

The final equivalent circuit to be discussed here is known as the hybrid or h-parameter circuit. This circuit receives its name from the fact that it is a hybrid combination of the z- and y-parameter circuits. The h-parameters of transistors are most easily measured and therefore are given by most transistor manufacturers (y-parameters are given quite often for high-frequency applications).

In developing the h-parameter circuit, the independent variables are assumed to be I_1 and V_2. Then, the two characteristic equations have the form

$$V_1 = H_{11}I_1 + H_{12}V_2 \tag{4.47a}$$

$$I_2 = H_{21}I_1 + H_{22}V_2 \tag{4.47b}$$

where H_{11} = the input impedance when the output is shorted.

H_{12} = the ratio of voltage appearing at the open circuit input terminals to the applied voltage at the output terminals.

H_{21} = the ratio of current appearing at the short circuited output terminals to the input current.

H_{22} = the output admittance when the input is open.

Previous equations have used capitals to indicate voltages, currents, impedances, and admittances. This notation follows the IEEE recommendations for d-c or steady-state a-c signals (see pages xx and xxi of the

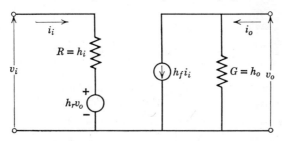

Fig. 4.18. An equivalent h-parameter circuit.

List of Symbols). When time-varying signals are considered, lower case letters are used. In addition, the h parameters as defined by the IEEE carry letter subscripts (capital subscripts for d-c values and lower case subscripts for time-varying signals). Thus, the preceding characteristic equations (Eqs. 4.47a and 4.47b) when applied to a small-signal variation about a fixed operating point in a transistor have the form:

$$v_i = h_i i_i + h_r v_o \tag{4.48a}$$

$$i_o = h_f i_i + h_o v_o \tag{4.48b}$$

where h_i = the input impedance when the output voltage v_O is held constant and thus $v_o = 0$.

h_o = the output admittance when the input current is constant.

h_r = the ratio of voltage induced in the input to the output voltage. It is called the open-circuit reverse voltage transfer ratio.

h_f = the ratio of short circuit output current to the input current. This is called the forward current amplification factor. When applied to the common-base transistor, this parameter is $-\alpha$.

An equivalent circuit represented by these equations is shown in Fig. 4.18.

One set of parameters may be obtained from another set of parameters by matrix manipulations. To aid the reader in making these manipulations, Table 4.2 is included.

TABLE 4.2

Formulas for Converting Parameters

Conversions from	Δ represents the term $(\Delta z = z_{11}z_{22} - z_{12}z_{21})$					
z's	$y_{11} = \dfrac{z_{22}}{\Delta z}$	$y_{12} = \dfrac{-z_{12}}{\Delta z}$	$h_{11} = \dfrac{\Delta z}{z_{22}}$	$h_{12} = \dfrac{z_{12}}{z_{22}}$	$g_{11} = \dfrac{1}{z_{11}}$	$g_{12} = \dfrac{-z_{12}}{z_{11}}$
	$y_{21} = \dfrac{-z_{21}}{\Delta z}$	$y_{22} = \dfrac{z_{11}}{\Delta z}$	$h_{21} = \dfrac{-z_{21}}{z_{22}}$	$h_{22} = \dfrac{1}{z_{22}}$	$g_{21} = \dfrac{z_{21}}{z_{11}}$	$g_{22} = \dfrac{\Delta z}{z_{11}}$
y's	$z_{11} = \dfrac{y_{22}}{\Delta y}$	$z_{12} = \dfrac{-y_{12}}{\Delta y}$	$g_{11} = \dfrac{\Delta y}{y_{22}}$	$g_{12} = \dfrac{y_{12}}{y_{22}}$	$h_{11} = \dfrac{1}{y_{11}}$	$h_{12} = \dfrac{-y_{12}}{y_{11}}$
	$z_{21} = \dfrac{-y_{21}}{\Delta y}$	$z_{22} = \dfrac{y_{11}}{\Delta y}$	$g_{21} = \dfrac{-y_{21}}{y_{22}}$	$g_{22} = \dfrac{1}{y_{22}}$	$h_{21} = \dfrac{y_{21}}{y_{11}}$	$h_{22} = \dfrac{\Delta y}{y_{11}}$
h's	$g_{11} = \dfrac{h_{22}}{\Delta h}$	$g_{12} = \dfrac{-h_{12}}{\Delta h}$	$z_{11} = \dfrac{\Delta h}{h_{22}}$	$z_{12} = \dfrac{h_{12}}{h_{22}}$	$y_{11} = \dfrac{1}{h_{11}}$	$y_{12} = \dfrac{-h_{12}}{h_{11}}$
	$g_{21} = \dfrac{-h_{21}}{\Delta h}$	$g_{22} = \dfrac{h_{11}}{\Delta h}$	$z_{21} = \dfrac{-h_{21}}{h_{22}}$	$z_{22} = \dfrac{1}{h_{22}}$	$y_{21} = \dfrac{h_{21}}{h_{11}}$	$y_{22} = \dfrac{\Delta h}{h_{11}}$
g's	$h_{11} = \dfrac{g_{22}}{\Delta g}$	$h_{12} = \dfrac{-g_{12}}{\Delta g}$	$y_{11} = \dfrac{\Delta g}{g_{22}}$	$y_{12} = \dfrac{g_{12}}{g_{22}}$	$z_{11} = \dfrac{1}{g_{11}}$	$z_{12} = \dfrac{-g_{12}}{g_{11}}$
	$h_{21} = \dfrac{-g_{21}}{\Delta g}$	$h_{22} = \dfrac{g_{11}}{\Delta g}$	$y_{21} = \dfrac{-g_{21}}{g_{22}}$	$y_{22} = \dfrac{1}{g_{22}}$	$z_{21} = \dfrac{g_{21}}{g_{11}}$	$z_{22} = \dfrac{\Delta g}{g_{11}}$

PROB. 4.7. The following measurements are taken on a two-port device:

Test 1

The output terminals are shorted and the following quantities are measured: $V_1 = 0.5$ v, $I_1 = 1$ ma, $I_2 = 50$ ma.

Test 2

The input terminals are short circuited and the following quantities are measured: $I_1 = 100\ \mu$ amp, $I_2 = 10\ \mu$ amp, $V_2 = 10$ v. Develop an equivalent circuit which could be used to represent this device. Determine the magnitude of the parameters in this equivalent circuit.

PROB. 4.8. The following tests are conducted on a two-port device:

Test 1

The input terminals (1-1) are open circuited, $V_2 = 10$ v, $V_1 = 0.01$ v and $I_2 = 10\ \mu$ amp.

Test 2

The output terminals (2-2) are open circuited, $V_1 = 0.1$ v, $I_1 = 1$ mamp, $V_2 = 10$ v.

(a) Draw an equivalent circuit for this device and indicate the magnitude of all parameters in the circuit. *Answer:* $Z_{11} = 100\ \Omega$, $Z_{12} = 1\ K\Omega$, $Z_{21} = 10\ K\Omega$, $Z_{22} = 1 M\Omega$.

(b) Convert this equivalent circuit to an *h*-parameter equivalent circuit. List the values of all parameters.

The *h* parameters for a transistor may be obtained from the characteristic curves of Fig. 4.19. (Remember that the equivalent circuits are valid for small-signal variations only.) The parameter h_o may be defined for the common base configuration[4] as

$$h_{ob} = \frac{di_C}{dv_C}\bigg|_{i_E=\text{constant}} \tag{4.49}$$

The value of h_{ob} at a given operating point is, therefore, equal to the slope of the characteristic curve at the given point on the set of collector characteristics. This slope is represented by the line *AB* of Fig. 4.19. The reader may question the value of 3 ma emitter current when the input circuit is supposed to be open. Remember, however, that the equivalent circuit is valid for the *small signal component* of current. Hence, if the time-varying component of emitter current is zero (emitter current is constant), the emitter circuit is effectively "open circuited" for the small signal component.

The parameter $h_f(\alpha)$ can be defined for the common base configuration as

$$h_{fb} = \frac{di_C}{di_E}\bigg|_{v_C=\text{constant}} \tag{4.50}$$

This equation represents the slope of a curve which could be drawn by plotting i_C as a function of i_E with the collector voltage held constant. The required currents and voltages are also given in the collector characteristics of the transistor. The line *CD* of Fig. 4.19 represents a constant collector voltage v_C. The ratio of the length of this line as measured by i_C to the

---

[4] Equation 4.49 defines the output admittance as the ratio of the change of collector current to the change of collector voltage with the emitter current maintained constant. This definition is obviously correct for small-signal variations.

A double subscript notation is used for transistor parameters. The first subscript indicates which parameter is involved and the second subscript indicates which element of the transistor is used as the common element to both input and output circuits. Hence h_{ob} indicates the output admittance, with the input current constant, for a common-base configuration.

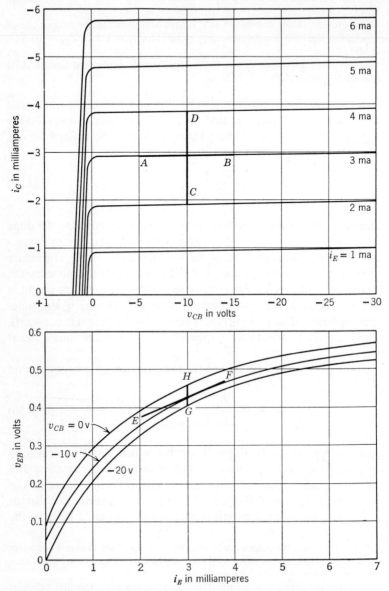

Fig. 4.19. Characteristic curves of a common-base transistor.

length of this line as measured by i_E gives approximately[5] the value of h_{fb} in this region.

Unfortunately, it is difficult to measure the currents accurately enough to determine an accurate value of h_{fb} (or h_{ob} for that matter) from these curves. A technique for determining h_{fb} (and h_{ob}) with greater accuracy will be given in Chapter 5. Note also that h_{fb} is *negative* because i_E is positive and i_C is negative.

The parameter h_i can be written for the common-base configuration as

$$h_{ib} = \frac{dv_E}{di_E}\bigg|_{v_C=\text{constant}} \tag{4.51}$$

Each curve of the input characteristics was plotted for a particular, constant collector voltage. Therefore, the slope of these curves represents h_{ib}. The line EF (Fig. 4.19) represents the value at the chosen operating point.

The parameter h_r can be written for the common-base configuration as

$$h_{rb} = \frac{dv_E}{dv_C}\bigg|_{i_E=\text{constant}} \tag{4.52}$$

This parameter is the slope of the curve obtained by plotting v_E as a function of v_C with the emitter current held constant. A vertical line on the input characteristic curves represents a constant emitter current. The line GH of Fig. 4.19 will yield an *approximate* value for h_{rb} at the indicated operating point. The length of this line in terms of emitter voltage divided by the length of this line in terms of collector voltage gives the approximate value of h_{rb}.

When Eqs. 4.49, 4.50, 4.51, and 4.52 are considered, two quantities affect v_E. These quantities are i_E (Eq. 4.45) and v_C (Eq. 4.52). Also, two quantities affect i_C. Again these quantities are i_E (Eq. 4.50) and v_C (Eq. 4.49). Then, by superposition the voltage and current relationships in the transistor may be expressed as

$$\Delta v_E = \frac{dv_E}{di_E}\bigg|_{v_C=k} \Delta i_E + \frac{dv_E}{dv_C}\bigg|_{i_E=k} \Delta v_C \tag{4.53}$$

$$\Delta i_C = \frac{di_C}{di_E}\bigg|_{v_C=k} \Delta i_E + \frac{di_C}{dv_C}\bigg|_{i_E=k} \Delta v_C \tag{4.54}$$

But, for small-signal variations, the small change of signal Δv_E can be equated to the time-varying component of voltage v_e. The input voltage v_i in Fig. 4.18 is equal to v_e in the common-base configuration. Similarly,

[5] In this approximation, the ratio $\dfrac{\Delta i_C}{\Delta i_E}\bigg|_{v_C=\text{constant}}$ is taken rather than $\dfrac{di_C}{di_E}\bigg|_{v_C=\text{constant}}$

we note that $\Delta i_E = i_i$, $\Delta v_C = v_o$, and $\Delta i_C = i_o$. When these values are substituted into Eq. 4.53 and Eq. 4.54 and the h parameters are substituted for the derivative terms, these equations become

$$v_i = h_{ib}i_i + h_{rb}v_o \tag{4.55}$$

$$i_o = h_{fb}i_i + h_{ob}v_o \tag{4.56}$$

These equations are the same as Eq. 4.48. Hence the hybrid equivalent circuit is valid for the transistor.

The foregoing treatment indicates that the hybrid equivalent circuit parameters can be found from the collector characteristic and input characteristic curves.

PROB. 4.9. Obtain the common-base h parameters for the transistor of Fig. 4.19 at the operating point indicated. Note the difficulty of obtaining accurate values for h_{ob} and h_{fb}. *Answer:* $h_{ob} \simeq 2 \times 10^{-6}$ *mho*, $h_{ib} \simeq 50\Omega$, $h_{rb} \simeq 3 \times 10^{-3}$, $h_{fb} \simeq -0.98$.

PROB. 4.10. Using the h parameters of Prob. 4.9, calculate the voltage and power gains of a common-base circuit which has a load resistance of 10 KΩ.

4.6 INPUT AND OUTPUT IMPEDANCE OF THE COMMON-BASE CONFIGURATION

The equivalent circuits will be used to illustrate the method of solution for transistor circuits. In order to calculate the *input impedance* of a transistor with the output shorted, the circuit of Fig. 4.20a is drawn. A voltage v_i is applied to the input and the input current i_e is calculated.

$$v_i = i_e r_e + (i_e + i_c)r_b \tag{4.57}$$

but with the output shorted,

$$i_c = -\alpha i_e$$

and

$$v_i = i_e r_e + (1 - \alpha)r_b i_e \tag{4.58}$$

Then, since h_{ib} is the input impedance with the output shorted,

$$h_{ib} = \frac{v_i}{i_e} = r_e + (1 - \alpha)r_b \tag{4.59}$$

Thus, h_{ib} is obtained in terms of the equivalent T parameters. From the equivalent circuit, it may be observed that the input impedance with the output open is $r_e + r_b = Z_{11}$. These values are the *minimum* and *maximum* values of input impedance for a given common-base transistor at the specified operating point. Intermediate values are obtained for *finite* values of load resistance.

The h parameters h_{ob} and h_{rb} may be obtained in terms of the r parameters with the aid of Fig. 4.20b. In this figure, the input is open and voltage v_c is applied to the collector. Since $i_e = 0$, the output resistance is $Z_{22} = r_c + r_b$ and

$$h_{ob} = \frac{1}{Z_{22}} = \frac{1}{r_c + r_b} \simeq \frac{1}{r_c} \tag{4.60}$$

The voltage v_c applied to the output terminals is $i_c(r_c + r_b)$ and the

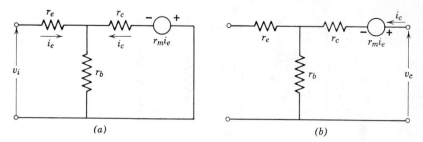

Fig. 4.20. Equivalent circuits for determining the relationship between r and h parameters.

voltage across the open circuit input terminals is $i_c r_b$. Therefore

$$h_{rb} = \frac{i_c r_b}{i_c(r_c + r_b)} = \frac{r_b}{r_c + r_b} = h_{ob} r_b \tag{4.61}$$

As previously mentioned, $h_{fb} = -\alpha$ and from Eq. 4.44, $\alpha \simeq r_m/r_c$.

The input resistance, output resistance, voltage gain (v_o/v_i), and current gain (i_c/i_e) of a transistor can be determined for any value of load resistance or source resistance by the solution of any valid equivalent circuit. The h-parameter circuit will be most commonly used in this text. For example, the input resistance can be determined from the equivalent circuit of Fig. 4.21a (or Eq. 4.48b) by noting that $-i_c = v_c/R_L$. Then,

$$-h_{fb}i_e = v_c\left(h_{ob} + \frac{1}{R_L}\right) \tag{4.62}$$

The loop equation for the input circuit is

$$v_i = i_e h_{ib} + h_{rb} v_c \tag{4.63}$$

When Eq. 4.62 is solved for v_c, and this value of v_c is substituted into Eq. 4.63, Eq. 4.63 becomes

$$v_i = i_e\left(h_{ib} - \frac{h_{rb}h_{fb}}{h_{ob} + \dfrac{1}{R_L}}\right) \tag{4.64}$$

Then,

$$Z_{in} = \frac{v_i}{i_e} = \left(h_{ib} - \frac{h_{rb}h_{fb}R_L}{1 + h_{ob}R_L} \right) \tag{4.65}$$

Although Eq. 4.65 is very useful, the reader should develop skill in solving the circuit equations rather than attempting to memorize the resulting equations.

By the same type of reasoning, the output impedance of a transistor amplifier can be found. In this case, the input signal voltage v_i is reduced

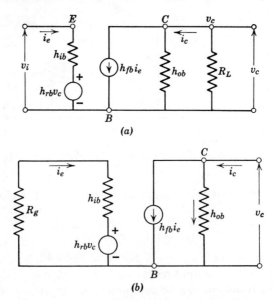

Fig. 4.21. Equivalent h circuit for determining input and output impedance.

to zero but the generator resistance R_g is still present across the input terminals. Then, an equivalent circuit is drawn as in Fig. 4.21b. In this circuit, the nodal equation for terminal C is

$$i_c = v_c h_{ob} + h_{fb}i_e \tag{4.66}$$

Also, the loop equation for the emitter loop is

$$h_{rb}v_e = -i_e(h_{ib} + R_g) \tag{4.67}$$

When Eq. 4.67 is solved for i_e and this value is substituted into Eq. 4.66,

$$Z_o = \frac{v_c}{i_c} = \frac{1}{\left(h_{ob} - \dfrac{h_{fb}h_{rb}}{h_{ib} + R_g} \right)} = \frac{h_{ib} + R_g}{h_{ob}h_{ib} + h_{ob}R_g - h_{fb}h_{rb}} \tag{4.68}$$

Note that both h_{fb} and i_e are negative. Also observe that the output impedance approaches $1/h_{ob}$ as R_g approaches an infinite value. However, as R_g approaches zero, the output impedance becomes much smaller than $1/h_{ob}$. In general, however, the input impedance is low and the output impedance is high for a common-base transistor. For emphasis, this low input impedance is due to the emitter-base junction being biased in the forward direction. Similarly, the high output impedance is due to the collector-base junction being biased in the reverse direction.

PROB. 4.11. From the equivalent T circuit, calculate the input impedance of the transistor of Table 4.1, when the load resistance is (a) $0\ \Omega$, (b) $10\ \mathrm{K}\Omega$. *Answer:* (a) 28 Ω, (b) 29 Ω.

PROB. 4.12. From the equivalent T circuit, calculate the output impedance of the transistor of Table 4.1, when the driving source resistance is (a) $100\ \Omega$ and (b) $100\ \mathrm{K}\Omega$.

PROB. 4.13. Derive an expression for the voltage gain of a common-base transistor amplifier as a function of load resistance using the h-parameter equivalent circuit. (*Hint:* Use Eqs. 4.62 and 4.63.) *Answer:* $G_v = -h_{fb}/(h_{ob}h_{ib} - h_{rb}h_{fb} + h_{ib}G_L)$.

PROB. 4.14. Derive an expression for the current gain of a common-base transistor amplifier as a function of load resistance using the h-parameter equivalent circuit (Fig. 4.21a).

4.7 THE TRIODE TUBE

The triode tube was invented in 1906 by Dr. Lee DeForest, who inserted a third element in the form of a wire mesh or screen between the cathode and plate of a high vacuum diode. The configuration which resulted is shown in Fig. 4.22. In this device, the electrostatic field between the control grid and the cathode is able to control the flow of electrons to the plate.

The action of the control grid can be visualized with the help of Fig. 4.23. Electrons are emitted by the hot cathode. Since the plate is maintained positive with respect to the cathode, an electrostatic field exists between the plate and cathode. The potential on the control grid "warps" this electrostatic field. If the control grid is positive, (Fig. 4.23a), most of the electrons near the cathode are attracted toward the plate. Since the control grid is a wire mesh, most of the electrons pass through the control grid to the plate. However, a few of the electrons are intercepted by the positive grid wires. The current through the tube then has the relationship

$$i_K = i_G + i_P \qquad (4.69)$$

where i_K is the cathode current, i_G is the grid current, and i_P is the plate current.

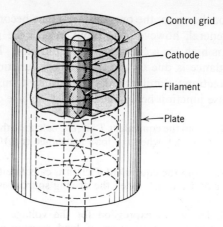

Fig. 4.22. A triode tube.

If the voltage on the control grid is at the same potential as the cathode (Fig. 4.23b), a fewer number of electrons near the cathode are attracted toward the plate. The reason for this reduced current (as compared to the positive grid case) is due to the reduced electric field intensity near the cathode. The electric field intensity is equal to $-dV/dx$ where x is distance. Therefore, the slope of the curves in Fig. 4.23 is a measure of the electric field intensity. A reduced electric field intensity results in a reduced flow of electrons, as discussed in Chapter 1. When the control grid is at the same potential as the cathode, the number of electrons collected by the grid is very small. Therefore, i_G of Eq. 4.69 is almost equal to zero for a grid potential of zero volts above the cathode.

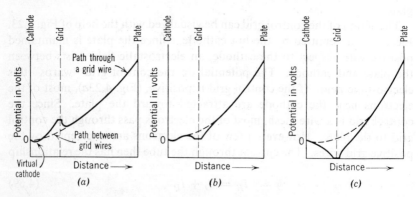

Fig. 4.23. A plot of the potential distribution inside a triode tube. (a) The control grid positive with respect to cathode; (b) the control grid at the same potential as the cathode; and (c) the control grid more negative than the cathode.

When the potential of the control grid is negative with respect to the cathode (Fig. 4.23c), the plate current is reduced even further. Also, since the control grid is negative, the electrons are repelled by the control grid and the grid current i_G is essentially equal to zero. However, plate current may still pass between the grid wires.

As indicated previously, the control grid is able to control the amount of current to the plate. In fact, the action is very similar to the action in a transistor. The electric field between the cathode and control grid region is analogous to the electric field in a transistor between the emitter and the base. Also, the electric field between the plate and control grid of a triode is analogous to the electric field between the base and collector of a transistor. Essentially no positive carriers exist in a high vacuum tube, so only electrons act as carriers. The triode *does* have an advantage over the transistor inasmuch as the control grid draws essentially no current if maintained more negative than the cathode.[6] In this condition, the parameter corresponding to α in the transistor is equal to unity. In addition, the control grid consumes essentially no power if it draws essentially no current. Consequently, the

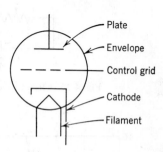

Fig. 4.24. Symbol for a triode tube.

triode tube is usually operated with a *negative* control grid. Cases where the control grid does draw current will be investigated in Chapter 10.

The symbol of a triode tube is given in Fig. 4.24. The similarity between this symbol and the actual tube is apparent.

If the control grid current is negligible, only three variable input and output quantities remain. These quantities are: voltage between the cathode and the control grid, plate (or cathode) current, and the voltage between the plate and the common electrode. The most commonly used triode circuit is the common cathode circuit to be investigated in Chapter 5. Consequently, practically all triode characteristic curves list the voltage between the plate and the cathode rather than the voltage between the plate and the control grid as a parameter.

The characteristic curves of a triode tube may be plotted by using the circuit in Fig. 4.25. In this circuit the three meters indicate the required three variables. A set of curves which corresponds with the set of collector curves of a transistor is plotted. The plate current is plotted as a function

---

[6] As will be discussed later, some current does flow in the control grid circuit due to capacitance between the control grid and other tube elements.

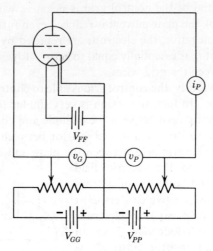

Fig. 4.25. Circuit used for plotting triode characteristic curves.

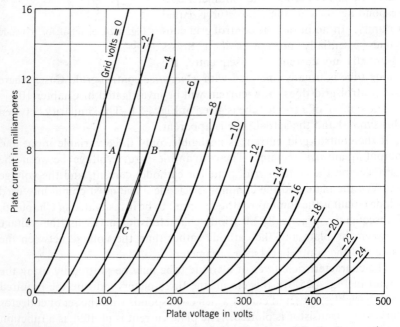

Fig. 4.26. Characteristic curves for a 6.15 triode. (Courtesy of Radio Corporation of America.)

of plate voltage. Since one curve is obtained for each different value of grid-to-cathode voltage, a family of these curves, which is known as a set of *plate characteristics* results. Figure 4.26 is a typical set of plate characteristics for a triode. The triode tube does not normally have a set of input characteristics since there are only three variables and *all* necessary information is obtainable from the collector or plate characteristics provided that v_G is negative.

4.8 THE TRIODE EQUIVALENT CIRCUIT

The vacuum triode circuit which corresponds to the common-base configuration of the transistor is shown in Fig. 4.27. In the vacuum tube, the circuit is known as a *grounded grid amplifier*. The equivalent circuit[7]

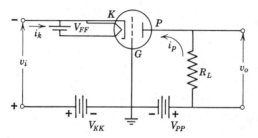

Fig. 4.27. The grounded grid amplifier.

for the triode is found by observing that the plate current i_P is dependent on the control grid-to-cathode potential v_{GK}, and also on the plate-to-cathode potential v_{PK}.

When the current is the dependent variable and two voltages are the independent variables, the situation is described by the y-parameter equations (Eq. 4.45). This form of equation can be used for i_P but the only independent equation we can write for i_K is $i_K = -i_P$. Thus, in

---

[7] A word on symbol nomenclature is in order at this point. In the early days of radio, batteries were used as the power sources. The *A* battery heated the filaments and the *B* battery supplied plate voltage. The *C* battery furnished negative control grid bias potential. Accordingly, most literature and, in fact, the old IRE standards use the symbols i_b and i_c for the instantaneous total currents in the plate and control grid circuits of a vacuum tube. The instantaneous time-varying components of current used are i_p and i_g. In this text, to avoid confusion between base and collector currents and to conform to recent IEEE standards, i_p and i_g will be used to indicate the total instantaneous currents. Similar subscripts will be used for voltages.

general form, the characteristic equations are

$$i_K = -i_P \tag{4.70a}$$

and

$$i_P = Y_{21}v_{GK} + Y_{22}v_{PK} \tag{4.70b}$$

In terms of time-varying components, these equations can be written as

$$i_k = -i_p \tag{4.71a}$$

$$i_p = g_m v_{gk} + \frac{1}{r_p} v_{pk} \tag{4.71b}$$

One form of equivalent circuit which represents Eq. 4.71 is shown in Fig. 4.28. Note that this circuit is similar to half the circuit in Fig. 4.17a,

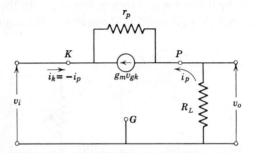

Fig. 4.28. An equivalent circuit for the tube of Fig. 4.27.

if the cathode is assumed to be the common element. Since both of the voltages in Eq. 4.71b use the cathode as reference, this result is not unexpected.

The parameter g_m (in Eq. 4.71b) is known as the *transconductance* of the vacuum tube and is defined as

$$g_m = \frac{di_P}{dv_{GK}}\bigg|_{v_{PK}=\text{constant}} \tag{4.72}$$

Also, the parameter r_p is known as the vacuum tube *plate resistance* and is defined as

$$r_p = \frac{dv_{PK}}{di_{PK}}\bigg|_{v_{GK}=\text{constant}} \tag{4.73}$$

The symbols and definitions of these parameters are standard in the vacuum tube industry.

A second equivalent circuit can be found by applying Thevenin's Theorem to the circuit of Fig. 4.28. In this circuit, the current generator between the cathode K and plate P is converted to a voltage generator. The internal impedance of this voltage generator will be r_p. (The value of internal impedance between terminals K and P when all current sources are open circuited and all voltages shorted.) In addition, the magnitude of the voltage source is equal to the open circuit voltage at the terminals K to P. For the generator of Fig. 4.28, this voltage is

$$v = g_m r_p v_{gk} \qquad (4.74)$$

Let a new parameter μ be defined as

$$\mu = -g_m r_p \qquad (4.75)$$

where μ is known as the voltage *amplification factor*. With these changes, the equivalent circuit of a grounded grid amplifier can be represented as

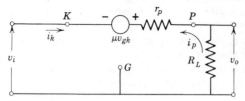

Fig. 4.29. A voltage source equivalent circuit for the tube of Fig. 4.27.

shown in Fig. 4.29. This circuit is known as a voltage source equivalent circuit for the triode. From this circuit it can be seen that if the plate current is held constant, the plate-to-cathode voltage will change μ times as much as the grid-to-cathode voltage. Accordingly, the parameter μ can be defined as

$$\mu = \frac{dv_{PK}}{dv_{GK}}\bigg|_{i_P=\text{constant}} \qquad (4.76)$$

Note that μ is negative since v_{GK} must increase in the negative direction as v_{PK} increases in the positive direction in order to maintain i_P constant.

As with the transistors, the value of the vacuum triode parameters can be found from the characteristic curves of the triode. For example, the value of r_p is shown in Fig. 4.26 as the reciprocal of the slope of the line BC. Here the control grid is maintained constant at -4 v and the relation between v_P and i_P is established. For example, a change of 40 v in v_P causes a change of 4.5 ma or

$$r_p = \frac{40}{4.5 \times 10^{-3}} \text{ ohms}$$

Hence, r_p is equal to 8900 Ω. In addition, the line AC represents a constant value of plate voltage (120 v). The relationship between v_G and i_P is established to obtain an *average* value for g_m. Δv_G is 2 v and Δi_P is 4.5 ma. Hence,

$$g_m = \frac{4.5 \times 10^{-3}}{2} = 2250 \text{ micromhos}.$$

Also, the line AB represents a constant value of plate current (8 ma). Therefore the amplification factor may be obtained from the relationship between v_P and v_G along this line AB. In this example, Δv_G is -2 v and Δv_P is 40 v. Therefore

$$\mu = \frac{40}{-2} = -20$$

PROB. 4.15. Find the values of μ, r_p, and g_m for the tube of Fig. 4.26 at the point where $v_P = 200$ v, and $v_G = -6$ v. *Answer:* $\mu = -19.6$, $r_p = 8.5\ K\Omega$, $g_m = 2{,}300\mu$ mhos.

PROB. 4.16. Is r_p the same for all points on the characteristic curves? What shape would the characteristic curves have if r_p were constant?

PROB. 4.17. Is μ the same for all points on the characteristic curves? What condition must the characteristic curves meet if μ is constant?

4.9   THE GROUNDED GRID AMPLIFIER

Just as the transistor can be used to provide power amplification, so is the triode tube capable of power amplification. As noted before, the circuit of the triode which conforms to the circuit of the common-base transistor is known as the grounded grid amplifier. The circuit of a typical grounded grid amplifier, together with the appropriate equivalent circuit, is shown in Fig. 4.30.

From the equivalent circuit of Fig. 4.30b, it is evident that $i_p = -i_k$ when reverse (normal) bias is applied between the cathode and the grid. Thus, the forward current gain is unity with reverse bias, but less than unity if forward bias is used (positive grid).

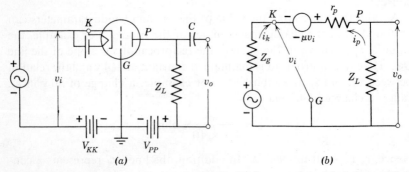

Fig. 4.30. The circuit diagram and equivalent circuit of a grounded grid triode amplifier.

Since v_i is v_{kg}, which is $-v_{gk}$, our loop equation is

$$v_i - \mu v_i = -i_p(r_p + Z_L) \tag{4.77}$$

$$-i_p = \frac{(-\mu + 1)v_i}{r_p + Z_L} \tag{4.78}$$

$$v_o = -i_p Z_L = \frac{(-\mu + 1)v_i Z_L}{r_p + Z_L} \tag{4.79}$$

The voltage gain,

$$G_v = \frac{v_o}{v_i} = \frac{(-\mu + 1)Z_L}{r_p + Z_L} \tag{4.80}$$

The input impedance, using Eq. 4.78,

$$Z_{in} = \frac{v_i}{i_k} = \frac{vi}{-i_p} = \frac{r_p + Z_L}{-\mu + 1} \tag{4.81}$$

The output impedance, from Fig. 4.3i,

$$Z_o = \frac{v_o}{i_p} \tag{4.82}$$

$$v_o = i_p(r_p + Z_g) + \mu v_{gk} \tag{4.83}$$

But $-v_{gk} = v_{kg} = i_p Z_g$

$$v_b = i_p(r_p + Z_g) - \mu i_p Z_g \tag{4.84}$$

$$Z_o = r_p + (-\mu + 1)Z_g \tag{4.85}$$

It should be observed that the common grid connection has high voltage gain, low input impedance, and high output impedance. The impedances

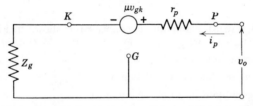

Fig. 4.31. Circuit for determining output impedance of the grounded grid amplifier.

are affected by the load and source impedances in a manner similar to the common-base transistor. In fact, the grounded grid amplifier acts as an impedance transformer having an impedance transformation ratio of $-\mu + 1$. The power gain for a resistive load is,

$$G_p = \frac{i_p{}^2 R_L}{i_p{}^2 R_{\text{in}}} = \frac{(-\mu + 1)R_L}{r_p + R_L} \tag{4.86}$$

For resistive loads,

$$G_p = G_v \tag{4.87}$$

Thus, it becomes evident that the characteristics of a common-base transistor amplifier are similar to a common-grid vacuum tube amplifier.

PROB. 4.18. Calculate the voltage gain, input impedance, and output impedance of an amplifier with $R_L = 50 \text{ K}\Omega$, $R_g = 10 \text{ K}\Omega$, $r_p = 8 \text{ K}\Omega$, and $\mu = -20$.

PROB. 4.19. A transistor is connected as shown in Fig. 4.32. The voltages and currents that were measured are shown on the diagram. Draw an equivalent circuit using h parameters for this transistor. Give values of each component in the equivalent circuit.

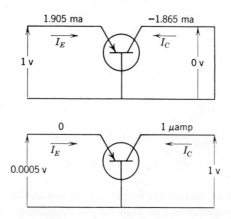

Fig. 4.32. The configuration for Prob. 4.19.

PROB. 4.20. A transistor amplifier is connected as shown in Fig. 4.33a. The transistor characteristics are given in Fig. 4.33b. If $v_g = 2 \sin \omega t$, find:

(a) The quiescent collector voltage and current.

(b) The current amplification of the amplifier.

(c) The voltage amplification of the amplifier.

(d) The power amplification of the amplifier.

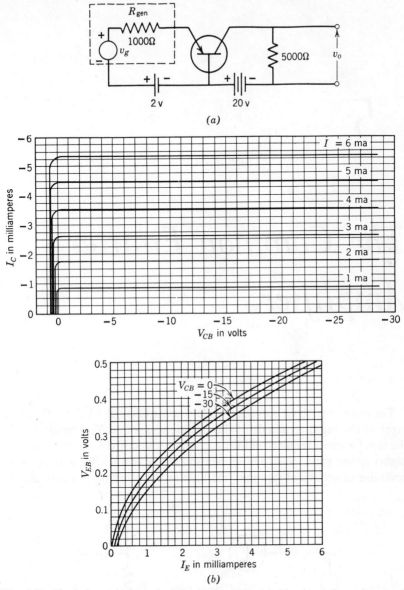

Fig. 4.33. The information required for Prob. 4.20. (a) Circuit configuration; and (b) characteristics of the transistor in part a.

5

The Common Emitter Amplifier

The reader may have surmised while reading Chapter 4 that a rearrangement of the input terminals of the common-base amplifier would reduce the input current requirement for a given output current and thus provide higher power gain. Such a configuration would employ the emitter as the common or grounded terminal, the base as the other input terminal, and

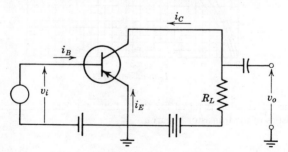

Fig. 5.1. A common emitter amplifier.

154

the collector as the other output terminal. This type of circuit is known as the common emitter configuration. Figure 5.1 is a simple circuit diagram of this arrangement for a *p-n-p* transistor. With the conventional current directions shown in this figure, i_B, i_C, and v_O are negative. Thus a polarity reversal occurs between the input and output signal voltages.

5.1 CURRENT GAIN OF THE COMMON EMITTER AMPLIFIER

In the common emitter configuration, the input current is the base current, i_B. But

$$i_B = -i_E - i_C \tag{5.1}$$

Since the collector current i_C is normally almost equal to the emitter current i_E, the base current i_B may be small in comparison with the collector current. Thus, current gain is achieved. Using Eq. 4.1 (reprinted below)

$$-i_C = \alpha i_E - I_{CO} \tag{4.1}$$

$$-i_E = \frac{i_C - I_{CO}}{\alpha} \tag{5.2}$$

Substituting this value of $-i_E$ into Eq. 5.1,

$$i_B = \frac{i_C - I_{CO}}{\alpha} - i_C \tag{5.3}$$

$$\alpha i_B = (1 - \alpha)i_C - I_{CO} \tag{5.4}$$

Solving for i_C explicitly,

$$i_C = \frac{\alpha}{1 - \alpha} i_B + \frac{I_{CO}}{1 - \alpha} \tag{5.5}$$

The term $\alpha/(1 - \alpha)$ is called the short circuit current gain or *current amplification factor* for the common emitter connection. This amplification factor is sometimes known as β (beta). Other symbols which are commonly used in the literature are α_{cb} and h_{FE}. Equation 5.5 may be rewritten:

$$i_C = \beta i_B + (1 + \beta)I_{CO} \tag{5.6}$$

PROB. 5.1. Prove that the coefficient of I_{CO} in Eq. 5.6 is correct.

PROB. 5.2. A transistor has $\alpha = 0.99$ and $I_{CO} = 1$ μa at a specified operating point. What value does β have? What will be the value of collector current when the base current is reduced to zero, assuming β to be constant? *Answer:* $\beta = 99$, $i_c = 0.1$ *ma.*

One way to visualize the control action of the base is to assume the forward bias between the base and emitter to be increased. This increased bias causes the height of the potential hill, or barrier field, to be reduced.

The injection current across the emitter-base junction is therefore increased. Most of the carriers which comprise this current, drift across the thin base region into the collector region. Thus, the increase in collector current may be much greater than the increase in base current. The collector current change is almost proportional to the base current change. Therefore, the base current is often assumed to be the control parameter. The reverse diode current I_{CO} is amplified because it is forced to flow across the base

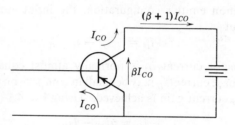

Fig. 5.2. An illustration of the process by which I_{co} is multiplied in the common emitter configuration when $I_B = 0$. Actual current directions are shown.

to emitter junction. As a result, a small forward bias is produced across that junction and the collector current is increased as though I_{CO} were added to the base current. The process by which I_{CO} is multiplied is shown in Fig. 5.2.

5.2 CHARACTERISTIC CURVES

A very useful set of curves is the family of collector characteristic, or i_C vs v_{CE} curves. A typical set of p-n-p collector characteristics is provided in Fig. 5.3. Comparison with the common base collector characteristics of Fig. 4.4 reveals that the following differences exist:

1. The base current i_B is a parameter in the common emitter set.
2. The curves of Fig. 5.3 are not evenly spaced, which indicates that i_C is not a linear function of i_B. This should be expected since α is a function of i_E as discussed in Section 4.4.
3. The collector current is approximately equal to zero when v_{CE} equals zero, regardless of the value of i_B. The reason for this behavior is that the collector-base junction has the same amount of forward bias voltage as the emitter-base junction when v_{CE} equals zero. This condition may be verified by observing from Fig. 5.1 that v_{BC} equals v_{CE} in polarity as well as magnitude when v_{CE} equals zero. The knee of each curve occurs when v_{CE} is increased sufficiently to reduce the collector-base junction bias to zero. Larger values of v_{CE} result in reverse bias.
4. The spacing between curves increases as v_{CE} increases because α and hence β increase with v_{CE}.

Because there are four independent transistor parameters, an additional set of curves is required. A set of input characteristics similar to the common base set of Fig. 4.5 is given in Fig. 5.4a. The curve obtained with v_{CE} equals zero is widely spaced from the others because the base current is increased as a result of the carriers injected across the collector-base junction. The transistor does not normally operate in this region of very small collector voltage, which is known as the *saturation region*. Notice in Fig. 5.4a that v_{BE} does not equal zero, generally, when i_B equals zero. This small forward bias when i_B equals zero results from I_{CO} flowing across the

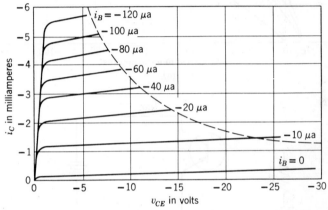

Fig. 5.3. Collector characteristics for the common emitter configuration.

emitter-base junction, as explained previously. The emitter-base junction voltage could be reduced to zero by the application of a small reversed base current as indicated in Fig. 5.4a. This reversed base current would be nearly equal to I_{CO} as shown in Fig. 5.4b and the collector current is reduced to nearly I_{CO}. The base and collector currents differ somewhat from I_{CO} because some of the carriers which comprise I_{CO} still (even with no bias) diffuse to the base-emitter junction where they are swept across this junction.

The curves provided for the common emitter connection contain the same information as those for the common base configuration, because $-i_E = i_C + i_B$. The common emitter curves are more useful, however, because i_E may be readily and accurately obtained by the addition of the other two currents, but it is difficult to accurately determine i_B from the common base curves because i_B is the difference of two currents which are nearly equal. Therefore, the common emitter curves are used for all transistor configurations.

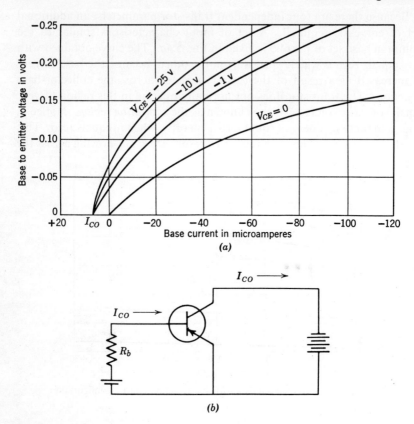

(a)

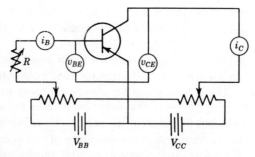

(b)

Fig. 5.4. An illustration of the reduction of the base-emitter junction voltage to zero and the reduction of the collector current to I_{co} by the application of a reverse base bias current equal to I_{co}. Actual current directions are shown. (a) Common emitter input characteristics. (b) The circuit diagram.

Fig. 5.5. Circuit for obtaining characteristic curve data.

Figure 5.5 is a circuit which may be used to obtain data for the common emitter curves. The batteries and potentiometers may be replaced by variable voltage power supplies. The variable resistor R should be very large compared with the base-to-emitter resistance of the transistor so the base current will remain essentially constant while the collector voltage is varied. This large value of R requires a rather high base supply voltage. In addition, an electronic-type voltmeter must be used to measure v_{BE}. The energizing current of a conventional meter may be larger than the base current and thus cause the reading of the meter which measures i_B to be completely erroneous. Also, a highly sensitive voltmeter, preferably an electronic type, should be used to measure v_{CE}.

5.3 TRANSISTOR RATINGS

The manufacturer specifies the maximum permissible collector voltage, collector current, and collector power dissipation of a transistor at a specified ambient temperature. This dissipation rating must be reduced as the ambient temperature increases. Under certain conditions, the dissipation rating may be exceeded for very short periods of time, but until these conditions are thoroughly understood, it is only safe to assume that the transistor will be permanently damaged if any rating is exceeded at any time. Transistor damage may be prevented if the area of safe operation for the transistor is clearly indicated. For example, if the absolute maximum ratings of the transistor whose collector characteristics are shown in Fig. 5.3 are;

$$i_C \max = -6 \text{ ma}$$

$$v_{CE} \max = -30 \text{ v}$$

$$\text{collector dissipation} = 35 \text{ mw at } 25°C$$

The dashed line on Fig. 5.3 marks the boundary of the area of safe operation. Before taking data for a characteristic curve plot, this area should be marked and kept vividly in mind so that no data points will be taken outside of the area of safe operation.

The maximum collector voltage rating for the common emitter connection may be considerably less than for the common base configuration. The reason for this reduced collector voltage rating may be seen from a study of Eq. 5.5 and Eq. 4.20. It should be observed that β approaches infinity as α approaches unity. Therefore, the collector current in the common emitter configuration will approach infinity, even with zero base current, as α approaches unity.

PROB. 5.3. A transistor has $\alpha = 0.99$ at low values of collector voltage. The avalanche voltage $V_A = 40$ v. The exponent $N = 3$. Calculate the collector voltage at which the collector current approaches infinity in the common emitter configuration. *Hint:* Using Eq. 4.20, assume that $\alpha = \eta\gamma$ at low values of collector voltage. Then, $\alpha = 1$ when $\delta = 1/\eta\gamma$. *Answer:* $v_C = 8.6\ v$.

The avalanche breakdown voltage, listed as V_A in Eq. 4.20, is commonly listed as V_{CBO} in manufacturer's ratings:

$V_{CBO} = $ *collector-to-emitter breakdown voltage with emitter circuit open*

The apparent breakdown voltage which occurs in the common emitter configuration when $\alpha = 1$ and $i_B = 0$ is known as V_{CEO}.

$V_{CEO} = $ *collector-to-emitter breakdown voltage with base circuit open*

when V_{CBO} and V_{CEO} are known for a given transistor, V_{CBO} is the highest and V_{CEO} is the lowest collector breakdown voltage of this transistor.

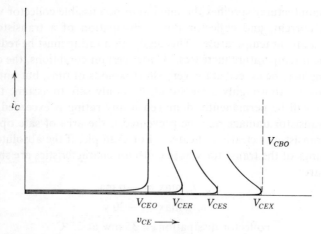

Fig. 5.6. Collector voltage breakdown characteristics and ratings for a typical transistor.

Intermediate values of breakdown voltage occur when finite resistance is placed between the base and the emitter in the common emitter configuration. This breakdown voltage is known as V_{CER} at a specified base circuit resistance.

$V_{CER} = $ *collector-to-emitter breakdown voltage with base resistance specified*

The highest V_{CER} occurs when the base is shorted to the emitter. This value of V_{CER} is known as V_{CES}.

$V_{CES} = $ *collector-to-emitter breakdown voltage with base shorted to emitter*

The common emitter breakdown voltage is increased slightly above V_{CES} and is essentially equal to V_{CBO} if reverse bias is applied between the base and emitter. This reverse-bias breakdown voltage is known as V_{CEX}.

V_{CEX} = *collector-to-emitter breakdown voltage with base reverse-biased*

The various breakdown voltages for a typical transistor are shown in Fig. 5.6.

5.4 THE GROUNDED CATHODE AMPLIFIER

The triode tube may be used in a configuration which corresponds to the common emitter configuration of the transistor. This circuit, known as a grounded cathode amplifier, is shown in Fig. 5.7. The resistor R_g provides

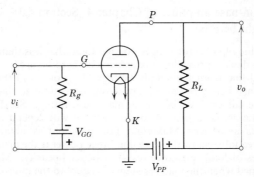

Fig. 5.7. The grounded cathode triode amplifier.

a conducting path between the grid and the bias supply. This grounded cathode circuit is by far the most widely used tube circuit. Consequently, the characteristic curves given by the manufacturers are for the grounded cathode circuit.

If the control grid potential is maintained negative with respect to the cathode, the grid current is essentially equal to zero. Consequently, the vacuum tube is a voltage actuated device, whereas the transistor may be considered a current actuated device. A family of collector characteristics for a typical triode is shown in Fig. 5.8*b*.

5.5 GRAPHICAL ANALYSIS

A common emitter (or common cathode) amplifier may be designed with the aid of the characteristic curves in the same manner as that indicated

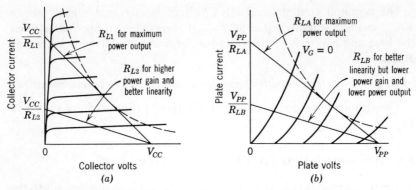

Fig. 5.8. Illustration of graphical analysis by the use of load lines. (*a*) Transistor amplifier; (*b*) triode amplifier.

for the common-base amplifier of Chapter 4 (Section 4.3). The following procedure might be used.

1. Choose a value of collector supply voltage somewhat less than the maximum rating of the device, providing a resistive load is to be used.
2. Draw a load line from the supply voltage (V_{CC} or V_{PP}) through the safe operating range below the maximum dissipation curve so that the load line intersects the current axis below its maximum rating. See Fig. 5.8 for an example. The actual choice of load resistance will depend on the requirements of the amplifier. Maximum power output is obtained when the maximum area falls below the load line, since power is the product of v and i. Larger values of load resistance result in better linearity. Maximum *power gain* is obtained when the load resistance is equal to the internal resistance of the amplifier. These statements will become more meaningful as the work progresses.
3. A quiescent operating point is selected in accordance with the requirements of the amplifier. If the input signals are symmetrical, an operating point near the center of the load line would provide maximum dynamic range. Such a point is selected for the examples of Fig. 5.9.

    The quiescent operating point of the transistor may be located on the input characteristic curves in the same manner as describe for the common base configuration. From these input characteristic curves the required forward bias voltage V_{BE} may be obtained. However, the required bias current is usually obtained, by using a supply voltage which is large compared with V_{BE}. The bias current is then controlled by a series-dropping resistor.

    The performance of the transistor amplifier can be determined by selecting a convenient collector voltage swing about the quiescent operating point. The collector current swing and base current variation required to produce this output may then be determined from the load line on the collector characteristics, and the input characteristics may be used to determine the required input voltage variation. Thus the current gain,

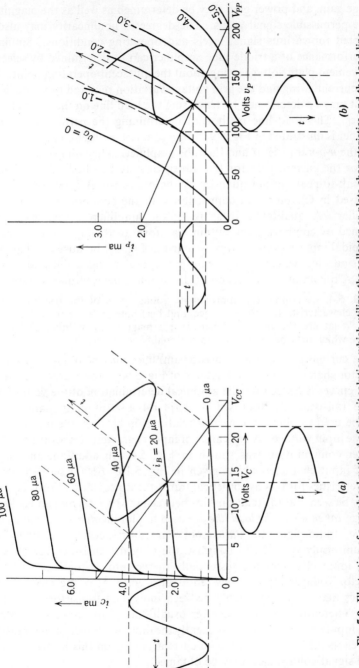

Fig. 5.9. Illustration of a graphical method of circuit solution which utilizes the collector or plate characteristics and the load line.

voltage gain, and power gain may be determined as well as the magnitude of the permissible signal levels. The degree of nonlinearity may also be predicted for various signal levels and operating conditions. Similarly, the performance of a triode tube amplifier can be determined by selecting a convenient plate voltage swing about the quiescent operating point. The plate current swing and the grid voltage variation required to produce this output may be determined by traversing the load line on the plate characteristics. This load line method of determining the performance of an amplifier is illustrated in Fig. 5.9 for the common emitter configurations of both the *n-p-n* transistor and the tube amplifier. The voltage gain for the tube or the current gain for the transistor may be obtained by dividing the peak-to-peak output quantity by the peak-to-peak input quantity, as discussed in Chapter 4 in connection with the common base transistor amplifier. A qualitative measure of the amplifier distortion may be obtained by comparing the output waveform to the input waveform. A sinusoidal input waveform was assumed in Fig. 5.9 because the departure from sinusoidal waveform in the output is easily recognizable and measurable. A quantitative discussion of distortion is delayed until Chapter 10.

PROB. 5.4. Determine the approximate voltage gain of the triode amplifier whose characteristics, load resistance, and bias potentials are provided in Fig. 5.9b. What are the maximum permissible magnitudes of input and output voltage which may be obtained with reasonably good linearity?

The current gain of the transistor amplifier may be obtained from the collector characteristics and load line of Fig. 5.9a. However, an additional set of curves is needed for the graphical determination of the voltage gain of the transistor. As discussed in Chapter 4, a set of input characteristics may be used to obtain the needed relationship between the input current and the input voltage. A typical set of input characteristics for the common emitter configuration was shown in Fig. 5.4. In addition, an unusual set of input characteristics is given in Fig. 5.10. Also a set of collector characteristics for this hypothetical transistor is provided. From Fig. 5.10 it may be seen that the relationships between the base current and collector voltage *taken along the load line* are used to plot the *dynamic input characteristic*. In this figure the *static* input characteristic curves are quite widely and uniformly spaced. In contrast, the typical transistor may have the static input characteristics essentially merge into a single curve for all collector voltages above a few tenths of a volt. Also, the input characteristics may vary appreciably between individual transistors of a given type. Therefore, the manufacturer usually does not provide a complete set of input characteristics. Frequently the input resistance of the transistor is given as a function of the base current, and from this information the small signal voltage gain may be obtained.

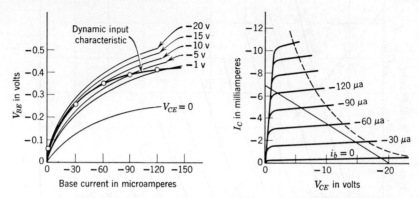

Fig. 5.10. Illustration of a method for determining the dynamic input characteristics of a common emitter transistor.

PROB. 5.5. A symmetrical input signal is applied to the transistor of Fig. 5.10. Determine the current gain and voltage gain of the amplifier with the load resistance indicated when the quiescent operating point is at $v_{CE} = -10$ v and the base current variation is from -30 μa to -90 μa. *Answer:* $G_i = 50, G_v = 65$.

A second graphical method of solution quite widely used is by a graphical plot which relates the input voltage (or current as the case may be) to the output current (or voltage). This graphical plot is known as the *dynamic transfer curve*. Example 5.1 illustrates the procedure for finding the dynamic transfer curve and also demonstrates how the dynamic transfer curve is used to find the output current (or voltage).

Example 5.1. A triode is connected as shown in Fig. 5.11. Find i_P if v_I has the form shown. The characteristic curves of the 6J5 are shown in Fig. 5.12. Assume R_L is 20,000 Ω.

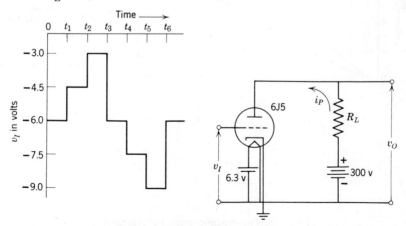

Fig. 5.11. Circuit for Example 5.1.

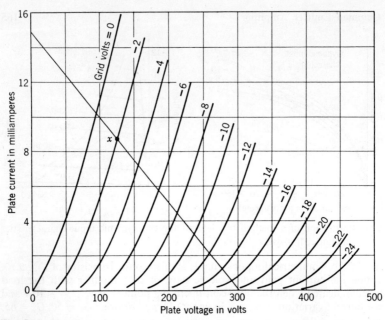

Fig. 5.12. The plate characteristic of a 6J5 tube. (Courtesy of Radio Corporation of America.)

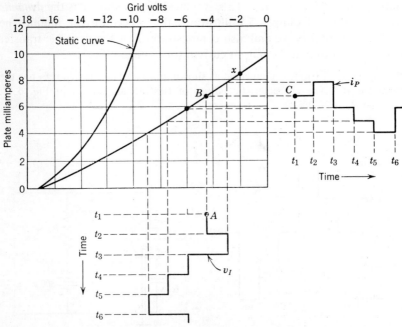

Fig. 5.13. The dynamic transfer characteristic.

166

As the first step, the load line is drawn on the plate characteristics of the tube (Fig. 5.12). Values of input voltage (grid voltage) are known and values of output current (plate current) are required. Thus a plot of i_P vs v_G is the required transfer curve. Since the tube will operate along the load line, the required values of i_P and v_G can be taken from the load line.

Hence, point x is chosen on the load line of Fig. 5.12. The value of grid voltage and the value of plate current corresponding to point x are noted. A point with the same value of grid voltage and plate current as point x is plotted on a new graph with v_G as one axis and i_P as the second axis. This new graph (with point x indicated) is shown in Fig. 5.13.

This procedure of transferring points from Fig. 5.12 to Fig. 5.13 is continued until enough points are plotted in Fig. 5.13 to draw the dynamic transfer characteristic curve. Note that as R_L approaches zero, the dynamic transfer curve approaches the *static* transfer curve.

After the dynamic transfer characteristic has been drawn, the input signal v_I is drawn as shown in Fig. 5.13. Values of voltage are then projected from the input signal (point A, Fig. 5.13) to the transfer curve (point B) and from the transfer curve to form the output signal (point C).

The same process can be used for finding the dynamic transfer characteristics of a transistor. If the transfer of base current i_B to collector current i_C (or collector voltage v_C) is wanted, the load line values of either collector current or collector voltage may be obtained as a function of base current from the collector characteristics. For example, the dynamic transfer characteristics of i_B vs i_C are given in Fig. 5.14b for a load resistance of 1250 Ω. However, if the transfer of base voltage v_B to collector current i_C is required, both the input and the output characteristics of the transistor are required. For example, in Fig. 5.14c a base potential of -0.49 v is shown as point x. (The dynamic input characteristics are required for this step.) Point x must then be transferred to the corresponding base current and collector voltage of the collector characteristics. (See point x in Fig. 5.14a.) From these curves the required collector current can be read and the corresponding point plotted on the v_B vs i_C characteristics. Figure 5.14d shows the total v_B vs i_C curve for the given load.

The dynamic transfer characteristic can be used to check the linearity of an amplifier. If the input signal is applied to a straight portion of the dynamic transfer characteristic, the output signal will have the same shape as the input signal. If, however, a curved portion of the dynamic transfer characteristic is used, the output signal will have a different shape than the input signal. This change of shape is known as *nonlinear distortion*.

Figure 5.14 shows that the relation between base current and collector current is more nearly linear than the relation between base voltage and

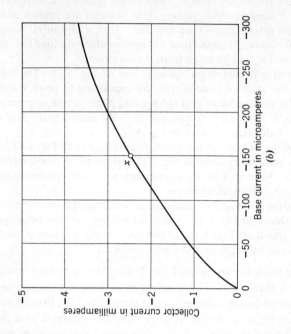

(a)

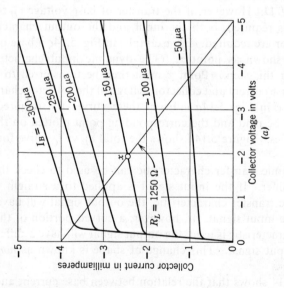

(b)

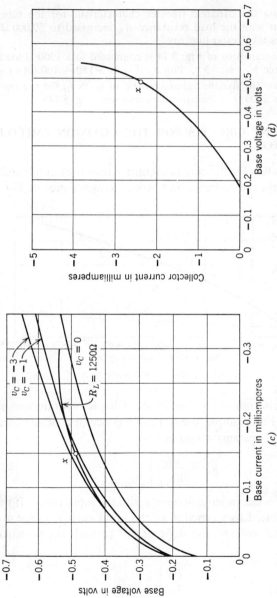

Fig. 5.14. The dynamic transfer characteristics for a transistor amplifier. (*a*) Output characteristics; (*b*) a plot of i_B vs i_C; (*c*) input characteristics; (*d*) a plot of v_B vs i_C.

collector current. Hence, the transistor is best used as a current-activated device.

PROB. 5.6. Draw the dynamic transfer characteristic for the tube used in Example 5.1, but with the load resistance R_L increased to 50,000 Ω. Which value of R_L gives the greater linearity?

PROB. 5.7. The transistor of Fig. 5.14 is connected to a 1000 Ω load resistor. The voltage source V_{CC} is −5 v. Plot v_C if i_B is $-150 + 100 \sin \omega t$ μa.

PROB. 5.8. Draw the dynamic characteristic of i_C vs i_B for the transistor of Fig. 5.14 if R_L is 2000 Ω. Compare this curve with Fig. 5.14b.

5.6 EQUIVALENT CIRCUITS FOR THE COMMON EMITTER TRANSISTOR

The h parameters for the common emitter transistor configuration may be obtained from the collector and input characteristics of Fig. 5.3 and

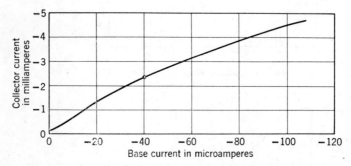

Fig. 5.15. Curve for obtaining h_{fe}.

Fig. 5.4 in the same manner as described in Chapter 4 for the common-base configuration. For example, the slope of a collector characteristic (v_{CE} vs i_C curve with i_B constant) would be

$$h_{oe} = \frac{di_C}{dv_{CE}}\bigg|_{i_B=\text{constant}} \tag{5.7}$$

This parameter is the *output admittance* with the input open. If the output current i_C is plotted as a function of the input current i_B for a constant value of collector voltage, the slope of this curve is the forward current transfer ratio

$$h_{fe} = \frac{di_C}{di_B}\bigg|_{v_{CE}=\text{constant}} \tag{5.8}$$

This parameter is the dynamic or *small signal* value of β, the *current amplification factor* of the common emitter configuration. The static or d-c value of β is frequently indicated by the symbol h_{FE}. Figure 5.15 is a plot of i_C as a function of i_B for the transistor of Fig. 5.3 at $v_{CE} = 10$ v. The slope of this curve at a given point is h_{fe} at that point. Note that in contrast to h_{fb} (which is negative) h_{fe} is *positive*.

The slope of the static input characteristic is the input impedance with the output shorted.

$$h_{ie} = \frac{dv_{BE}}{di_B}\bigg|_{v_{CE}=\text{constant}} \tag{5.9}$$

The input characteristics (Fig. 5.4) could be used to plot a family of v_{BE} vs v_{CE} curves with i_B as the constant parameter. This plot is made in

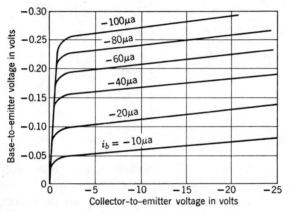

Fig. 5.16. Curves for obtaining h_{re}.

Fig. 5.16. The slope of any one of these curves at a particular point is the *reverse voltage transfer ratio* at that point.

$$h_{re} = \frac{dv_{BE}}{dv_{CE}}\bigg|_{i_B=\text{constant}} \tag{5.10}$$

The term h_{re} is also known as the *reverse voltage amplification* factor μ_{cb}.

As previously mentioned, h_{re} and h_{fe} may be determined by taking the ratio of incremental values of the pertinent variables about the operating point. Hence, it is not necessary to plot the curves of Figs. 5.15 and 5.16.

The differential equations which describe the operation of the transistor are,

$$\Delta v_{BE} = \frac{dv_{BE}}{di_B}\bigg|_{v_{CE}=k} \Delta i_B + \frac{dv_{BE}}{dv_{CE}}\bigg|_{i_B=k} \Delta v_{CE} \tag{5.11a}$$

$$\Delta i_C = \frac{di_C}{di_B}\bigg|_{v_{CE}=k} \Delta i_B + \frac{di_C}{dv_{CE}}\bigg|_{i_B=k} \Delta v_{CE} \tag{5.11b}$$

From the defining equations for the preceding h parameters (Eqs. 5.7 to 5.10) and the symbolism $\Delta v_{BE} = v_{be}$ etc., the common emitter h-parameter circuit equations for the time-varying components of voltage and current can be written.

$$v_{be} = h_{ie}i_b + h_{re}v_{ce}$$
$$i_c = h_{fe}i_b + h_{oe}v_{ce}$$

(5.12)

The common emitter h-parameter equivalent circuit is presented in Fig. 5.17. In solving this h-parameter circuit, it is important to remember that when a resistive load is connected to the output terminals, the voltage v_{ce} is negative.

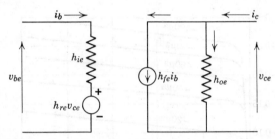

Fig. 5.17. Common emitter h-parameter equivalent circuit.

The solution of a common-emitter h-parameter circuit is easily carried out by assuming that the input current i_b is known. This method of solution is illustrated with the aid of Fig. 5.18, where the transistor load resistance is R_L. The output voltage

$$v_{ce} = \frac{-h_{fe}i_b}{h_{oe} + g_L}$$

(5.13)

where $g_L = 1/R_L$.

$$v_{be} = i_b h_{ie} + h_{re}v_{ce}$$

(5.14)

Substitution of Eq. 5.13 into Eq. 5.14 yields

$$v_{be} = i_b h_{ie} - \frac{h_{re}h_{fe}i_b}{h_{oe} + g_L}$$

(5.15)

The input resistance is

$$R_i = \frac{v_{be}}{i_b} = h_{ie} - \frac{h_{re}h_{fe}}{h_{oe} + g_L}$$

(5.16)

Note that except for the second subscripts, this equation (5.16) is the same as Eq. 4.64. In fact, all of the common emitter h-parameter equations have the same form as the corresponding common base h-parameter equations.

The voltage gain is (using Eqs. 5.13 and 5.15)

$$G_v = \frac{v_{ce}}{v_{be}} = \frac{-h_{fe}}{h_{ie}(h_{oe} + g_L) - h_{re}h_{fe}} \tag{5.17}$$

Note that G_v is a negative quantity which indicates a polarity reversal between output and input voltages. (The denominator will always be positive since $h_{ie} h_{oe}$ is greater than $h_{re} h_{fe}$.)

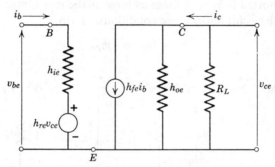

Fig. 5.18. An h-parameter circuit for a common emitter transistor with a load resistance R_L.

PROB. 5.9. Using the h-parameter circuit, solve for the current gain of the common emitter transistor in terms of the h-parameters and the load resistance.

PROB. 5.10. Solve for the output resistance of the common emitter amplifier in terms of the h-parameters and the driving source resistance R_s.

PROB. 5.11. Determine the common emitter h parameters for the transistor whose characteristics are shown in Fig. 5.14. Use the quiescent operating point indicated as x. *Answer:* $h_{ie} = 800\ \Omega$, $h_{re} = 1 \times 10^{-2}$, $h_{fe} = 15$, $h_{oe} = 2 \times 10^{-4}$ *mhos*.

PROB. 5.12. Using the h-parameters found in Prob. 5.11, calculate the current gain, voltage gain, and power gain of the transistor with a load resistance of 1.25 KΩ.

The two-generator h-parameter circuit is convenient for solving any common-emitter circuit problem. The one-generator equivalent T circuit will be developed, however, in order to provide a better understanding of the common-emitter configuration.

Figure 5.19a is the common emitter arrangement of the equivalent T circuit of Fig. 4.20. Inspection of the circuit will show that the input impedance with the output open (z_{11}) is $r_b + r_e$. Figure 5.19b illustrates the method of determining the input impedance when the output is shorted, (h_{ie}).

$$v_{be} = i_b r_b + (i_b + i_c)r_e \tag{5.18}$$

but $i_c = h_{fe}i_b$ when the output is shorted. Then

$$v_{be} = i_b r_b + (i_b + h_{fe}i_b)r_e \tag{5.19}$$

and (with the output shorted)

$$\frac{v_{be}}{i_b} = h_{ie} = r_b + (1 + h_{fe})r_e \tag{5.20}$$

Inspection of Eq. 5.20 and Eq. 4.59 reveals that the input impedance with the output shorted is $h_{fe} + 1$ times as large as the input impedance of the common-base circuit under these conditions. Then

$$h_{ie} = (h_{fe} + 1)h_{ib}. \tag{5.21}$$

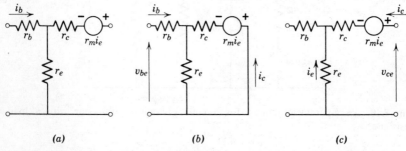

(a)   (b)   (c)

Fig. 5.19. An equivalent T circuit for the common emitter configuration.

PROB. 5.13. Prove Eq. 5.21 is valid and explain why the input impedance of the common emitter configuration is increased by this factor $(h_{fe} + 1)$.

Figure 5.19c illustrates the method of determining the output impedance when the input is open, $1/h_{oe}$.

$$v_{ce} = i_c r_c - i_e r_e + r_m i_e \tag{5.22}$$

but since $i_b = 0$, $-i_e = i_c$. Then

$$v_{ce} = i_c(r_c + r_e - r_m) \tag{5.23}$$

and the output impedance with the input open is

$$Z_{22} = r_c - r_m + r_e \tag{5.24}$$

From the relationship $r_m = \alpha' r_c$,

$$Z_{22} = (1 - \alpha')r_c + r_e \tag{5.25}$$

$$Z_{22} = \frac{1}{h_{oe}} = r_d + r_e \tag{5.26}$$

Where $r_d = (1 - \alpha')r_c$ by definition. Then $r_d = r_c/(h_{fe} + 1)$.

Since $r_d \gg r_e$ and $r_c \gg r_b$

$$h_{oe} = \frac{1}{Z_{22}} \simeq \frac{1}{r_d} = \frac{h_{fe} + 1}{r_c} \simeq (h_{fe} + 1)h_{ob} \qquad (5.27)$$

Thus it is seen that when the input is open, the output admittance of the common emitter configuration is $(h_{fe} + 1)$ times that of the common base.

An equivalent T circuit which would give a more obvious indication of the output impedance and also give the output current and voltage in terms of the input current would be a definite improvement over the

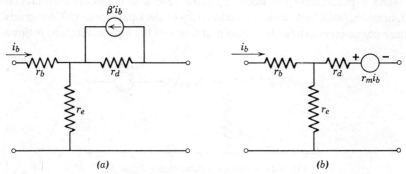

Fig. 5.20. Improved equivalent T circuits for the common emitter configuration.

equivalent T circuits of Fig. 5.19. Two circuits incorporating these advantages are given in Fig. 5.20. It is quite evident that the current generator of Fig. 5.20a would give the proper short-circuit collector current. From this circuit the open circuit generator voltage is

$$v_{\text{gen}} = \beta' i_b r_d \qquad (5.28)$$

$$v_{\text{gen}} = \frac{\alpha'}{1 - \alpha'} r_d i_b \qquad (5.29)$$

$$v_{\text{gen}} = \alpha' r_c i_b \qquad (5.30)$$

$$v_{\text{gen}} = r_m i_b \qquad (5.31)$$

This v_{gen} is the same as the open-circuit voltage of the generator of Fig. 5.20b. It is also the same open-circuit voltage as that provided by the generator of Fig. 5.19 because $i_c = 0$ and $i_b = i_e$ when the output is open.

PROB. 5.14. Prove that the short-circuit currents of the generators of Fig. 5.20a, Fig. 5.20b, and Fig. 5.19 are identical.

PROB. 5.15. Prove that $h_{fe} = -(h_{fe} + 1)h_{fb}$.

In the preceding development, all of the h parameters have been found in terms of the r parameters except $h_{re} = \mu_{cb}$. This parameter is the ratio of the voltage which appears at the open circuit input terminals to the voltage v_{ce} which produced this input terminal voltage. From Fig. 5.21,

$$v_{ce} = i_c(r_d + r_e) \tag{5.32}$$

$$v_{be} = i_c r_e$$

$$h_{re} = \frac{v_{be}}{v_{ce}} = \frac{i_c r_e}{i_c(r_d + r_e)} = \frac{r_e}{r_d + r_e} \tag{5.33}$$

The h parameters for both common base and common emitter configurations have been determined in terms of the r parameters. Conversely, the r parameters can be determined in terms of the h parameters as follows.

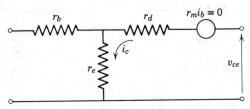

Fig. 5.21. Circuit for determining $h_{re} = \mu_{cb}$.

The value of $r_d + r_e$ in Eq. 5.26 is equal to $1/h_{oe}$. When this term is inserted into Eq. 5.33, we find that r_e is

$$r_e = \frac{h_{re}}{h_{oe}} \tag{5.34}$$

From Eqs. 5.20 and 5.34

$$r_b = h_{ie} - (1 + h_{fe})\frac{h_{re}}{h_{oe}} \tag{5.35}$$

From Eq. 5.26, $r_d + r_e = 1/h_{oe}$, and using Eq. 5.34

$$r_d = \frac{1 - h_{re}}{h_{oe}} \tag{5.36}$$

We note in Eq. 5.5 that β or h_{fe} is equal to $\alpha/(1 - \alpha)$. Thus

$$\alpha = \frac{h_{fe}}{h_{fe} + 1} \tag{5.37}$$

Also, all of the common emitter h parameters except h_{re} have been determined in terms of the common base h parameters. A summary of these relationships follow.

$$h_{ie} = (h_{fe} + 1)h_{ib} \qquad (5.21)$$

$$h_{oe} = (h_{fe} + 1)h_{ob} \qquad (5.27)$$

From Prob. 5.15, h_{fe} is

$$h_{fe} = -(h_{fe} + 1)h_{fb} \qquad (5.38)$$

Finally, from Eqs. 4.61, 5.35, and 5.27, h_{re} is

$$h_{re} = h_{ie}h_{ob} - h_{rb} \qquad (5.39)$$

PROB. 5.16. Find the common emitter h parameters for the transistor of Table 4.1.

PROB. 5.17. Verify Eq. 5.39.

The h parameters are most often given by the manufacturer. Since the h parameters as well as the r parameters vary with the terminal voltages and currents of the transistor, the parameters are normally specified or obtained at some specific operating point. In addition, a plot of the

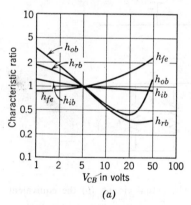
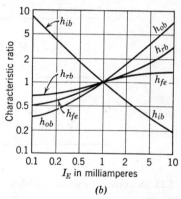

Fig. 5.22. A plot of the variation of the h parameters as a function of (a) collector to base volts; (b) emitter current.

parameters as a function of the terminal voltages and currents is sometimes given as shown in Fig. 5.22. This presentation makes it possible to obtain the parameters quickly at any other operating point. The parameter values are normalized to values listed by the manufacturer at the given operating point, that is, the point $i_E = 1$ ma and $v_{CB} = 5$ v in Fig. 5.22.

PROB. 5.18. A 2N527 transistor has $h_{fe} = 81$, $h_{ie} = 2.4$ K ohms, $h_{oe} = 30\,\mu$ mhos, and $h_{re} = 0.79 \times 10^{-4}$. Find the r parameters and also the common base h parameters for this transistor.

PROB. 5.19. Assume the h parameters given in Prob. 5.18 are valid for $v_{CB} = 5$ v and $i_E = 1$ ma. If the h parameters vary as given in Fig. 5.22, find the h parameters for $v_{CB} = 10$ v, and $i_E = 2$ ma. *Answer:* $h_{fe} = 128$, $h_{ib} = 18.1\ \Omega$, $h_{ob} = 0.43\ \mu\ mhos$, $h_{rb} = 6.5 \times 10^{-4}$.

5.7 THE EQUIVALENT CIRCUIT OF A COMMON CATHODE AMPLIFIER

A common cathode amplifier circuit is shown in Fig. 5.23a. The equivalent circuit for this configuration is given in Fig. 5.23b. This equivalent circuit can be obtained by merely rearranging the equivalent

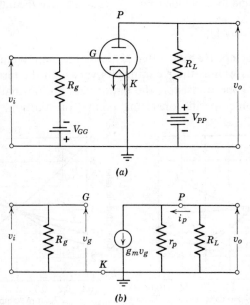

(a)

(b)

Fig. 5.23. A common cathode amplifier. (a) The actual circuit, (b) the equivalent circuit.

circuit for the grounded grid triode (Fig. 4.28). However, this circuit can also be found by the differential equation for plate current.

$$\Delta i_P = \left.\frac{di_P}{dv_G}\right|_{v_P=k} \Delta v_G + \left.\frac{di_P}{dv_P}\right|_{v_G=k} \Delta v_P \qquad (5.40)$$

where i_P is the plate current, v_G is the control grid voltage, and v_P is the plate voltage. In terms of small-signal components, this equation can be rewritten as

$$i_p = g_m v_g + \frac{1}{r_p} v_p \qquad (5.41)$$

where i_p, v_g, and v_p are the time-varying components of i_P, v_G, and v_P, respectively and r_p and g_m are as defined in Eqs. 4.73 and 4.72. Accordingly, an equivalent y-parameter circuit for the triode is shown in Fig. 5.23b.

If the control grid is maintained negative with respect to the cathode, essentially no current flows in the control grid circuit. Hence, the control grid is drawn in Fig. 5.23b as an open circuit. The foregoing equations and terms are exactly the same as those in Chapter 4 (Section 4). This similarity should have been expected since the derivation in Chapter 4 used the cathode as the reference electrode and the circuit just described also uses

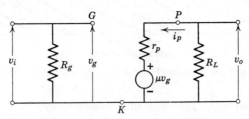

Fig. 5.24. An equivalent circuit containing a voltage generator.

the cathode as the reference electrode. This similarity can be carried one step further by replacing the current generator of Fig. 5.23b by a voltage generator. As in Chapter 4, Thevenin's theorem is used in this transition. The resulting circuit is shown in Fig. 5.24. The current generator has been replaced by a voltage generator with an open circuit potential μ times as great as the grid potential. As in Chapter 4, μ is negative and is given by Eq. 4.75

$$\mu = -g_m r_p \tag{4.75}$$

Of course, the values of r_p, μ, and g_m can be found from the characteristic curves as explained in Chapter 4.

The usual type of characteristic curves for a tube have the form shown in Chapter 4 (Fig. 4.26). However, other configurations may be used. For example, if the plate current is plotted as a function of grid voltage with the plate voltage held constant, the slope of the curve at any point is the transconductance at that point. This curve is known as a static transfer characteristic curve, as previously mentioned. A family of transfer characteristics is given in Fig. 5.25, where a curve is obtained for each different value of plate voltage.

Since the characteristic curves are not straight lines, the parameters of the tube (μ, g_m, and r_p) must not be constant. The typical variation of tube parameters with plate current is shown in Fig. 5.26. This figure indicates why the tube parameters must be found for the region in which a given

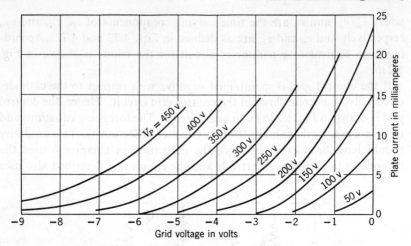

Fig. 5.25. Transfer characteristics for the 12AT7 triode.

tube will be operated. The same tube operating in a different region will have different parameters.

Equations can be derived[1] for the μ of a tube, and they indicate that μ is determined by the physical structure of the tube. The change of μ is due to variations in physical spacing of the elements and the edge effects of the elements. However, a similar equation for the g_m of the tube

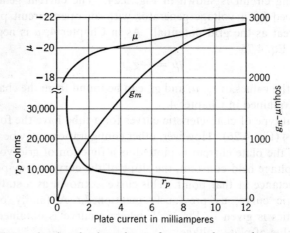

Fig. 5.26. Curves showing the dependence of μ, g_m, and r_p on the operating point of a 6J5 triode.

[1] For development of these equations, see Karl Spangenberg, *Vacuum Tubes*, McGraw-Hill, New York, 1958, pp. 125–128 and pp. 135–137.

indicates g_m is dependent not only on the physical structure of the tube but also on the current density in the tube. Hence, the great variation in g_m with plate current in Fig. 5.26 results. Since the plate resistance is equal to μ divided by g_m, r_p must behave as illustrated in Fig. 5.26.

PROB. 5.20. Find the values of μ, g_m, and r_p for the tube whose characteristic curves are given in Figs. 5.25 and 5.27. Use the operating (Q) point of $v_G = -1$ v and $v_P = 175$ v.

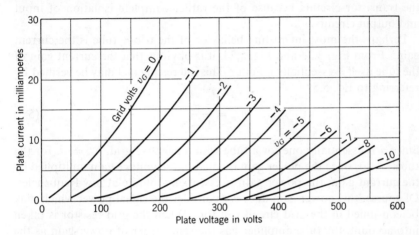

Fig. 5.27. Characteristic curves of a 12AT7 triode. (Courtesy of Radio Corporation of America.)

PROB. 5.21. Draw two equivalent circuits for the 12AT7 tube of Prob. 5.20.

The equivalent circuits of Fig. 5.23 or Fig. 5.24 may be used to determine the magnitude of the input and output impedances of the common cathode tube amplifier. Assuming the grid does not draw current, the input impedance of the tube itself is

$$Z_{in} = \infty \tag{5.42}$$

In a later section, it will be shown that an input capacitive term does exist. However, for low frequencies (less than hundreds of kilohertz) the input impedance of the tube may be considered as essentially infinite. There must be a d-c conducting path between the grid and the bias source, however, to maintain the desired bias on the grid. Therefore, the input impedance to the amplifier circuit is dependent on the resistance of this d-c conducting path and effective input capacitance of the tube and not on the load resistance. This behavior is in contrast with the transistor amplifier.

Because Z_{12} is zero, there is no reverse amplification factor for the triode tube. Therefore, in contrast with the transistor, the output impedance of a tube is not a function of the driving source impedance. It may be seen from the equivalent circuits that

$$Z_{\text{out}} = r_p \qquad (5.43)$$

Consequently, the triode tube amplifier circuits are easier to analyze than the transistor circuits because of the rather complete isolation of input and output circuits.

Perhaps the most interesting behavior of the triode tube is the current gain. From Fig. 5.23 and Fig. 5.24, it is obvious that the current gain of the tube itself is essentially infinite. This interesting fact may be verified by referring to Eq. 5.5.

$$h_{fe} = \frac{\alpha}{1 - \alpha} \qquad (5.5)$$

Since α is essentially one for a tube with a negative grid, $h_{fe} = \infty$ for the tube. Also, since the power gain is equal to the voltage gain multiplied by the current gain, the power gain is essentially infinite at low frequencies. Of course, this power gain does *not* consider the signal power which may be consumed in the grid circuit resistor. When the grid resistor is taken into account, the tube amplifier has the same order of power gain as the transistor amplifier.

We can find the voltage gain of a triode amplifier by using the equivalent circuit. For example, the circuit of an actual amplifier and an equivalent circuit of this amplifier are shown in Fig. 5.28. The capacitor C_c is very large and therefore blocks the d-c bias voltage due to V_{GG} but passes the time-varying signal v_i. Therefore, the signal component v_g of the total grid voltage v_G is equal to v_i. A loop equation can be written for the plate circuit.

$$-\mu v_i = i_p(r_p + R_L) \qquad (5.44)$$

or

$$i_p = \frac{-\mu v_i}{(r_p + R_L)} \qquad (5.45)$$

The output voltage is

$$v_o = -i_p R_L$$

for the direction of current and v_o shown. Thus,

$$v_o = \frac{\mu v_i R_L}{(r_p + R_L)} \qquad (5.46)$$

The total voltage gain is

$$G_v = \frac{v_o}{v_i} = \frac{\mu R_L}{(r_p + R_L)} \tag{5.47}$$

Since μ is negative the output voltage is *inverted* in relation to the input voltage. This *inversion* is characteristic of *all* grounded emitter circuits. Also, from Eq. 5.47, the voltage gain of the circuit increases as R_L increases. However, the maximum voltage gain of the circuit in Fig. 5.28 will never be greater than μ.

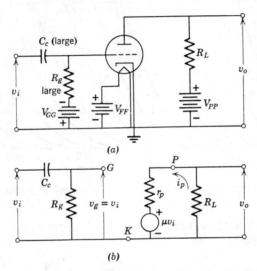

(a)

(b)

Fig. 5.28. A common cathode amplifier. (a) Actual circuit; (b) equivalent circuit.

PROB. 5.22. The plate characteristics of a 6J5 tube are shown in Fig. 5.29. If the 6J5 is connected as shown in Fig. 5.28, find the voltage gain. V_{PP} is 300 v and V_{GG} is −6 v. The value of R_L is 50,000 Ω. *Answer: $G_v \simeq -13$.*

PROB. 5.23. Repeat Prob. 5.22 if R_L is changed to 20,000 Ω. Compare the voltage gain and amplifier linearity for these two values of load resistance.

5.8 BIASING CIRCUITS FOR THE TRANSISTOR

The circuit diagrams used in the preceding discussion employ two bias batteries. In the common emitter transistor configuration the batteries have the same polarity with respect to the common electrode. Therefore, a single battery or d-c power source may be used as illustrated in Fig. 5.30 to provide the biases. The potential difference between the base and the emitter is normally very small in comparison with the collector supply

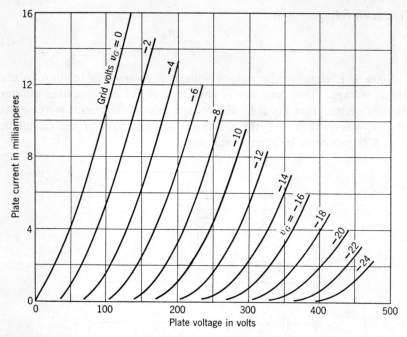

voltage V_{CC}. Therefore, nearly all of V_{CC} is dropped across R_f and the base bias current is

$$I_B \simeq \frac{V_{CC}}{R_f} \tag{5.48}$$

The value of R_f may be calculated after proper values of V_{CC} and I_B have been determined. This type of bias is known as *fixed bias* because the base bias current does not vary with the transistor parameters.

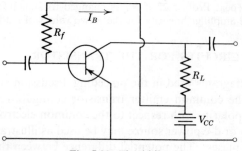

Fig. 5.30. Fixed bias.

Fixed bias is satisfactory providing the transistor parameters are accurately known and the temperature remains fairly constant. If the parameters change because of temperature change or substitution of transistors, the operating point will move along the load line as shown in Fig. 5.31. The initial design placed the quiescent operating point in the

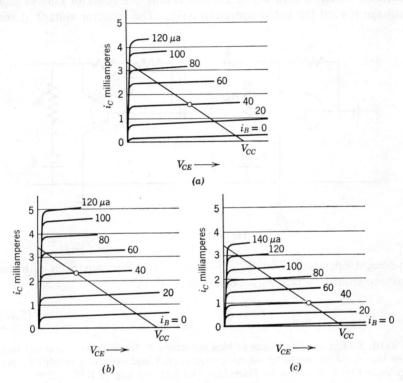

Fig. 5.31. Shift in quiescent operating point when fixed bias is used.

center of the load line, as indicated in Fig. 5.31a. An increased temperature causes the saturation current to increase and the characteristic curves to shift upward as shown in Fig. 5.31b. This moves the quiescent operating point upward on the load line. If a transistor with a lower current amplification factor were substituted, the characteristic curves would be compressed, as shown in Fig. 5.31c. The quiescent operating point would then move downward along the load line. Conversely, an increased h_{fe} would cause the operating point to move upward.

Several methods are used to stabilize the operating point. In the simplest method known as *self bias*, the base bias current I_B is derived from the collector potential v_{CE} rather than from the collector supply potential V_{CC}. This method of bias is illustrated in Fig. 5.32. Any change in parameters which would cause an increase in collector current would decrease the collector potential because of the IR drop across the load resistor. This decrease of collector potential would decrease the bias current, which in turn would tend to restore the collector current and voltage toward the initial operating point. The collector voltage at the

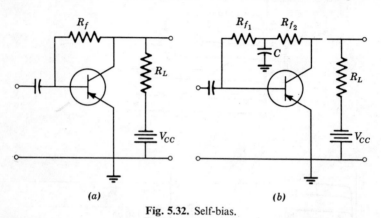

(a) (b)

Fig. 5.32. Self-bias.

quiescent operating point, V_{CE}, is usually large in comparison with the base-to-emitter voltage V_{BE}. Therefore,

$$R_f \simeq \frac{V_{CE}}{I_B} \tag{5.49}$$

PROB. 5.24. Calculate values of bias resistance R_f for both fixed and self bias for the transistor amplifier whose characteristics and operating conditions are given in Fig. 5.14. *Answer: Fixed bias 33.3 KΩ, self bias 13 KΩ.*

The degree of stabilization realized with self bias depends on the magnitude of the ohmic resistance of the load. In some cases a transformer is used to couple the signal components in the collector circuit to the load. In this case the ohmic resistance in the collector circuit is small, the collector voltage is almost equal to the supply voltage, and self bias would not provide much better stability than fixed bias. Another problem arising from self bias is that the signal (time-varying) components of collector voltage cause signal currents to flow through the bias resistor R_f. These currents are of opposite polarity to the input currents and tend to cancel them. This effect decreases the gain of the amplifier and is called *degeneration* or *negative feedback*. This degeneration can be eliminated by dividing the bias resistance R_f into two parts as shown in Fig. 5.32b and using the part which is attached to the collector in conjunction with a capacitor C to filter out the signal components. This method is not an ideal arrangement, however, because R_{f1} loads the input and R_{f2} loads the output of the transistor.

Another factor which needs to be considered in the stability problem is the variation of base-to-emitter voltage with temperature, for a given value of emitter current. The diode equation developed in Chapter 3, when applied to the emitter base junction becomes

$$i_E = I_{EO}(e^{qv_{BE}/kT} - 1) \tag{5.50}$$

where I_{EO} is the saturation current of the emitter-base junction. But I_{EO} varies widely with temperature as discussed in Section 3.4 and illustrated

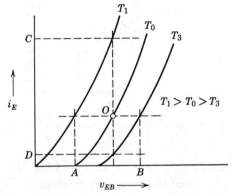

Fig. 5.33. Variation of v_{EB} or i_E with temperature.

in Fig. 3.6. Typical i_E vs v_{EB} curves are given in Fig. 5.33 for three different temperatures. Assume that T_0 is the ambient temperature and that the bias point is O. If the emitter current is held constant, the emitter-to-base voltage will decrease to A of Fig. 5.33 as the temperature is raised to T_1 or increase to B as the temperature is lowered to T_3. On the other hand, if the base bias voltage were to be held constant, the emitter current would vary from C to D as the temperature varied from T_1 to T_3. This would be the condition if battery bias were used with no series resistance. This situation could be approximated when transformer coupling is used. In case the bias source is a large voltage in comparison with v_{BE} and a resistance is used to control the bias current, as was done in the fixed and self bias circuits, the emitter-base junction voltage may vary with temperature and the emitter current is not affected appreciably by the variation of v_{EB} with temperature.

Differentiation of the diode equation will show that the voltage across a junction decreases approximately 2.2 mv per °C temperature increase if the current across the junction remains constant. This variation of junction voltage with temperature holds for silicon as well as for germanium transistors.

The effects of emitter and base circuit resistances on collector current thermal stability is shown in Fig. 5.34. In Fig. 5.34a, the emitter resistance is infinite and, therefore, all of I_{CO} flows through the base circuit resistor R_B and none across the emitter-base junction. Therefore, the thermal

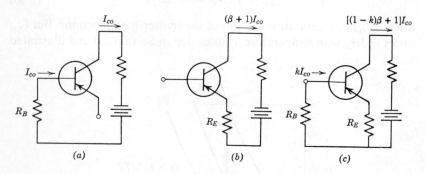

$$(a) \qquad\qquad (b) \qquad\qquad (c)$$

Fig. 5.34. The effects of base and emitter circuit resistances on the collector current thermal stability.

component of collector current is I_{CO}. In Fig. 5.34b, the base circuit is open and all of I_{CO} is forced to flow across the emitter-base junction and is amplified as shown in Fig. 5.2 and by Eq. 5.6. Therefore, the thermal component of collector current is $(\beta + 1)I_{CO}$. In Fig. 5.34c, both R_B and R_E are finite, so a fraction k of I_{CO} flows through R_B and the remainder $(1 - k)I_{CO}$ flows across the base-emitter junction and is amplified by β as shown. The fraction k depends on the ratio of R_E to R_B.

A commonly used collector current stability factor S_I (actually an instability factor) is defined as the ratio of the change in collector current (ΔI_C) to the change in $I_{CO}(\Delta I_{CO})$ or, considering incremental changes,

$$S_I = \frac{dI_C}{dI_{CO}}\bigg|_{\text{all bias values held constant}} \qquad (5.51)$$

The circuits of Fig. 5.34 provide stability factors (a) 1, (b) $\beta + 1$, and (c) $(1 - k)\beta + 1$, respectively, as may be observed. Note that (a) and (b) are the limiting values of the general case (c).

A practical transistor bias circuit must provide forward bias to establish the desired quiescent operating point in addition to providing suitable thermal stability to maintain the Q point within a desired or specified range. A circuit that will accomplish these purposes is shown in Fig. 5.35. This circuit is known as a *stabilized bias* circuit. In order to determine the current stability factor a Thévenin's equivalent circuit is drawn

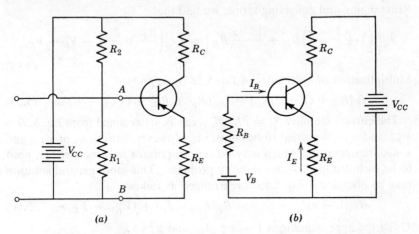

(a)   (b)

Fig. 5.35. (a) A stabilized bias circuit. (b) Thévenin's equivalent circuit for (a).

for the stabilized bias circuit as shown to the left of the points A and B in Fig. 5.35a. It may be seen by inspection of Fig. 5.35a that

$$R_B = \frac{R_1 R_2}{R_1 + R_2} \tag{5.52}$$

and

$$V_B = \frac{R_1 V_{CC}}{R_1 + R_2} \tag{5.53}$$

Kirchhoff's voltage equation may be written for the bias circuit of Fig. 5.35b.

$$I_E R_E + V_{EB} - I_B R_B - V_B = 0 \tag{5.54}$$

But the current stability factor involves I_C and I_{CO}, not I_E and I_B. Therefore, the following relationships must be used:

$$-I_E = I_C + I_B \tag{5.55}$$

$$I_C = \frac{\alpha}{1 - \alpha} I_B + \frac{I_{CO}}{1 - \alpha} \tag{5.5}$$

Then, from Eq. 5.5,

$$I_B = \left(I_C - \frac{I_{CO}}{1 - \alpha}\right)\frac{1 - \alpha}{\alpha} = \frac{1 - \alpha}{\alpha} I_C - \frac{I_{CO}}{\alpha} \tag{5.56}$$

Substitution of Eq. 5.56 and Eq. 5.55 into Eq. 5.54 yields

$$-\left(I_C + \frac{1-\alpha}{\alpha}I_C - \frac{I_{CO}}{\alpha}\right)R_E + V_{EB} - \left(\frac{1-\alpha}{\alpha}I_C - \frac{I_{CO}}{\alpha}\right)R_B - V_B = 0$$

$$(5.57)$$

Rearranging and collecting terms, we find that

$$I_C\left[\left(1 + \frac{1-\alpha}{\alpha}\right)R_E + \frac{1-\alpha}{\alpha}R_B\right] = I_{CO}\left(\frac{R_E}{\alpha} + \frac{R_B}{\alpha}\right) - V_B + V_{EB}$$

$$(5.58)$$

Multiplication of both sides of Eq. 5.58 by α, gives

$$I_C[R_E + (1-\alpha)R_B] = I_{CO}(R_E + R_B) + (V_{EB} - V_B)\alpha \quad (5.59)$$

The current stability $S_I = \partial I_C/\partial I_{CO}$ can be determined from Eq. 5.59 if V_{EB} and α are assumed to be constant. However, variations of V_{EB} and α with temperature, which may be very important in some circuits, need to be included in the total stability problem. This more general solution may be obtained if Eq. 5.59 is rearranged as follows.

$$R_B[(1-\alpha)I_C - I_{CO}] = R_E(I_{CO} - I_C) + (V_{EB} - V_B)\alpha \quad (5.60)$$

Using the approximations $1 - \alpha \simeq 1/\beta$ and $\alpha \simeq 1$,

$$R_B\left(\frac{I_C}{\beta} - I_{CO}\right) \simeq R_E(I_{CO} - I_C) + V_{EB} - V_B \quad (5.61)$$

The objective of the stabilized bias circuit is to confine the Q-point excursion to a predetermined range on the d-c load line for a specified range of ambient temperature, as shown in Fig. 5.36.

In order to illustrate the increase of β with temperature which occurs in some transistors, particularly the silicon type, collector characteristics are given for the maximum and minimum transistor temperatures. The high temperature curves are not required if a curve of h_{FE} (or β) is given as a function of temperature. I_{C1} and I_{C2} are the lower and upper limits of the Q-point collector current as set by the design engineer. These permissible current extremes are set so that clipping does not occur in the output in any prescribed condition of operation.

Assuming that the values of I_{C1} and I_{C2} are known, that I_{CO1} and I_{CO2} are the corresponding values of thermal current at T_1 and T_2, and that β_1 and β_2 are the corresponding values of β at these temperatures, Eq. 5.61 can be written twice—once with values substituted for temperature T_1 and again for values substituted for temperature T_2. The first of these equations can then be subtracted from the second with the following result.

$$R_B\left(\frac{I_{C2}}{\beta_2} - \frac{I_{C1}}{\beta_1} - \Delta I_{CO}\right) = R_E(\Delta I_{CO} - \Delta I_C) + \Delta V_{EB} \quad (5.62)$$

where $\Delta I_{CO} = I_{CO2} - I_{CO1}, \Delta I_C = I_{C2} - I_{C1}$ and $\Delta V_{EB} = V_{EB2} - V_{EB1}$.
Then,

$$R_B = \frac{R_E(\Delta I_{CO} - \Delta I_C) + \Delta V_{EB}}{\dfrac{I_{C2}}{\beta_2} - \dfrac{I_{C1}}{\beta_1} - \Delta I_{CO}} \qquad (5.63)$$

Observe that R_B may be determined as a function of R_E, or vice versa. Therefore, an appropriate value must be chosen for either R_E or R_B and

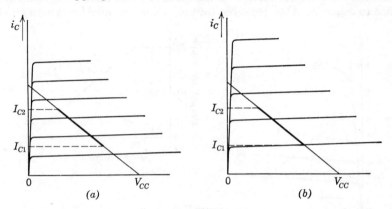

Fig. 5.36. Curves used to illustrate the determination of a stabilized bias circuit. (a) Collector characteristics at temperature T_1; (b) Collector characteristics at temperature T_2.

then the value of the other resistance may be determined from Eq. 5.63. A suitable value for R_E would be a value such that the voltage drop across it, $I_E R_E$, is large compared with ΔV_{BE} but small compared with V_{CC}. Values of $I_E R_E$ between one and three volts are typical. An example will be given to illustrate a method of determining the bias circuit components for a stabilized bias circuit.

Example 5.2. A germanium transistor is to be used in an R-C coupled audio frequency amplifier circuit which must furnish 1.0 ma peak signal current to a 3.3 KΩ load. The amplifier must operate properly over an ambient temperature range of 25°C to 50°C. The collector supply voltage $V_{CC} = -20$ volts.

We will first draw a 3.3 K load line on the collector characteristics as shown in Fig. 5.37a by the dashed line. But the total d-c load resistance includes the emitter circuit resistance R_E, which must, therefore, be chosen before an accurate d-c load line can be drawn. If the low temperature Q point is tentatively chosen at $v_{CE} = -12$ v and $I_C = -2.4$ ma, I_E would also be approximately 2.4 ma. Now let us select $I_E R_E \simeq 2.0$ v, and the desired value of $R_E = 820 \ \Omega$. An accurate d-c load line, the solid one, can now be drawn (Fig. 5.37a) and the low temperature Q points Q_1 set at $V_{CE} = -12$ v, $I_{C1} = -1.94$ ma. This collector current is high enough to permit the required 1 ma peak signal current without clipping. The maximum temperature Q point can now be determined. First, note from Fig. 5.37a that the collector current cannot exceed 4.5 ma for this load line. Therefore in order to avoid clipping of the one ma signal at the maximum temperature this Q point collector current I_{C2} must not exceed 3.5 ma. Thus, $\Delta I_C = I_{C2} - I_{C1} = -1.56$ ma.

In Chapter 3, Eq. 3.31, the thermal current of a germanium diode at 300°K was found to double for each 10°C increment of temperature. This rule will be used to determine ΔI_{CO}. However, the junction temperature limits must first be

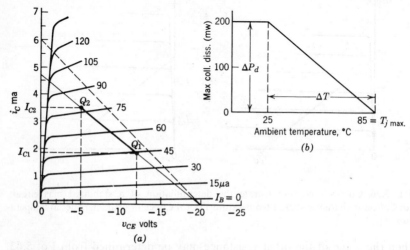

Fig. 5.37. (a) Collector characteristics used to illustrate the Q-point excursion. (b) Derating curve used to determine thermal resistance.

determined. The junction temperature is hotter than the ambient temperature because a *thermal resistance* θ_T exists between the junction and the ambient surroundings. The difference in junction and ambient temperature is equal to the power dissipated at the junction times the thermal resistance.

The derating factor (equal to $1/\theta_T$) is usually given by the transistor manufacturer for air-cooled transistors, but sometimes a derating curve, as shown in Fig. 5.36b, is given instead. Either the derating factor or the thermal resistance θ_T may be determined easily from the derating curve. The derating factor is the slope of the derating curve $\Delta P_d/\Delta T$ in watts (or milliwatts) per °C and the thermal resistance is the reciprocal of this slope, or $\Delta T/\Delta P_d$ in °C per watt (or milliwatt). The slope of the derating curve is the maximum dissipation rating P_d of the transistor, usually given at 25°C, divided by the temperature difference ΔT between this rating temperature and the maximum permissible junction temperature. In the example under consideration, the derating factor is 200 mw/60°C = 3.33 mw/°C and the thermal resistance $\theta_T = 1/3.33 = 0.3$°C per milliwatt.

The junction temperature limits can now be determined. The minimum junction temperature is

$$T_A + P_d\theta_T = T_A + (v_{CQ1}i_{CQ1})\theta_T = 25°C + (23.3)(0.3) \simeq 32°C$$

at the lowest Q-point limit. The maximum junction temperature is

$$50°C + (3.5 \times 5.58)(0.3) \simeq 56°C$$

Now, I_{CO} must be determined at these temperature limits.

The manufacturer usually gives maximum and typical values of I_{CO} at 25°C. The value of I_{CO} for a particular transistor can, of course, be readily measured. The maximum I_{CO} at 25°C for the given transistor is listed as -12 μa, which is a safe design value for any transistor of this type. The following relationship will determine I_{CO} at any junction temperature when a reference I_{CO} is given.

$$I_{CO}(T) = I_{CO}(T_o)2^{\frac{T_j - T_o}{T_d}} \tag{5.64}$$

where T_o is the reference temperature, T_j is the junction temperature, and T_d is the temperature difference over which I_{CO} doubles. Thus, in this example

$$I_{CO}\text{ min} = (-12\ \mu a)2^{7/10} = -19.5\ \mu a$$

and

$$I_{CO}\text{ max} = (-12\ \mu a)2^{31/10} = -103\ \mu a$$

Then,

$$\Delta I_{CO} = -83.5\ \mu a \text{ and } S_I \simeq \Delta I_C/\Delta I_{CO} = -1.56/0.0835 = 18.7.$$

As previously stated, the emitter-base voltage V_{EB} decreases approximately 2.2 millivolts per °C temperature increase. Since $\Delta T = 56°C - 32°C = 24°C$ in this example, $\Delta V_{EB} = 24(-2.2 \times 10^{-3}) = -0.053$. However, this decrease is partially offset by the increased emitter current at the higher temperature. In this example, the partial compensation due to emitter current change will be neglected.

The β of a germanium transistor varies mildly with temperature and therefore will be considered constant at a value of 90 over this small temperature range.

The value of R_B can now be calculated by using Eq. 5.63.

$$R_B = \frac{820[-83.5 \times 10^{-6} - (-1.56 \times 10^{-3})] - 0.053}{-\dfrac{1.56 \times 10^{-3}}{90} - (-83.5 \times 10^{-6})}$$

$$R_B = \frac{820(1.47 \times 10^{-3}) - 0.053}{-1.73 \times 10^{-5} + 83.5 \times 10^{-6}} = \frac{1.205 - 0.053}{66 \times 10^{-6}} = 17.4K\Omega \tag{5.65}$$

The resistors R_1 and R_2 (Fig. 5.35) must be determined in a manner that will provide the desired Q-point values. This may be accomplished by the simultaneous solution of Eqs. 5.52 and 5.53, repeated here for convenience.

$$R_B = \frac{R_1 R_2}{R_1 + R_2} \tag{5.52}$$

$$V_B = \frac{R_1 V_{CC}}{R_1 + R_2} \tag{5.53}$$

Solving Eq. 5.53 for R_2 yields the relationship

$$R_2 = \frac{R_1(V_{CC} - V_B)}{V_B} \tag{5.66}$$

Substituting this value of R_2 into Eq. 5.52 and solving for R_1, we have

$$R_1 = \frac{V_{CC} R_B}{V_{CC} - V_B} \tag{5.67}$$

and finally

$$R_2 = \frac{V_{CC} R_B}{V_B} \tag{5.68}$$

The voltage V_B must now be determined. Equation 5.54 can be rearranged to yield

$$V_B = I_E R_E + V_{EB} - I_B R_B \tag{5.69}$$

If the input characteristics for the transistor are available, V_{EB} can be accurately determined at the Q point. If these characteristics are not available, an adequately accurate estimation may be made. For example, V_{EB} may be estimated at 0.2 v for germanium and 0.5 v for silicon in small signal amplifiers. Using this estimate in our example,

$$V_B = 2 + 0.2 + (45 \times 10^{-6})(17.4 \times 10^3) = 2.98 \text{ v}$$

the Q-point base current I_{BQ} (which is equal to I_B in Eq. 5.69) can be determined as $-45 \ \mu a$ either from the collector characteristics in Fig. 5.36a or from I_{CQ}/h_{FE}, providing that h_{FE} at the Q point is known. The values of R_1 and R_2 can now be determined for our example:

$$R_1 = 17.4K(20)/(20 - 2.98) = 20.2 \text{ K}\Omega$$
$$R_2 = 17.4K(20)/2.98 = 117 \text{ K}\Omega$$

This completes the design of the bias circuit.

PROB. 5.25. Verify Eqs. 5.66, 5.67, and 5.68.

In this example, the emitter circuit resistor R_E was chosen so that $I_E R_E$ was large in comparison with ΔV_{EB}. Consequently, the ΔV_{EB} term in Eq. 5.63 can be dropped with little error, as illustrated by Eq. 5.65. Also, as assumed here, β is almost independent of temperature (over moderate ranges) in a germanium transistor. With these constraints, Eq. 5.63 can be simplified as follows.

$$R_B = \frac{R_E(\Delta I_{CO} - \Delta I_C)}{\dfrac{\Delta I_C}{\beta} - \Delta I_{CO}} \tag{5.70}$$

Multiplying both numerator and denominator by β, dividing both numerator and denominator by ΔI_{CO}, and using $\Delta I_C/\Delta I_{CO} = S_I$, Eq. 5.70 becomes

$$R_B \simeq \frac{\beta \, R_E(1 - S_I)}{S_I - \beta} = \frac{\beta R_E(S_I - 1)}{\beta - S_I} \tag{5.71}$$

and whenever $1 \ll S_I \ll \beta$, a further simplification can be made. Then

$$R_B \simeq S_I R_E \tag{5.72}$$

PROB. 5.26. A given transistor which has $h_{fe} = 100$ is used in a stabilized bias circuit which has $R_E = 1 \, \text{K}\Omega$. The required stability factor S_I is 10. Determine the base circuit resistance R_B by both the method of Eq. 5.71 and the approximate method (Eq. 5.72) and compare the values. Repeat the calculations for $S_I = 5$ and $S_I = 20$.

The resistor R_E will seriously reduce the gain of the amplifier unless a *bypass* capacitor is connected in parallel with R_E as shown in Fig. 5.38a. The voltage gain of the amplifier *without* the bypass capacitor is approximately equal to the ratio of the collector circuit resistance R_C to the emitter circuit resistance R_E. Since the voltage $i_E R_E$ is large compared with V_{EB}, the input voltage is almost equal to $i_E R_E$ and the output voltage is equal to $i_C R_C$. Then, since $i_C \simeq i_E$, the voltage gain is $G_v \simeq R_C/R_E$.

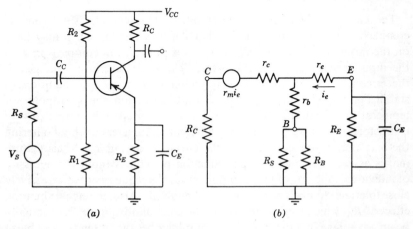

Fig. 5.38. (a) Stabilized bias including bypass capacitor. (b) Equivalent circuit as seen by C_E.

The stabilized amplifier essentially has full power gain over the range of frequencies for which the bypass capacitor is effective. The lowest frequency at which the bypass capacitance is considered effective is the frequency at which the magnitude of the capacitive reactance is equal to the resistance which is being bypassed. This frequency is called the low cutoff frequency f_1 (or ω_1 in radians per second). The capacitor C_E appears to be bypassing R_E, but actually R_E is in parallel with the transistor resistance as seen from the emitter terminal. In fact, this transistor resistance is usually so much smaller than R_E that R_E can be neglected.

The transistor resistance as seen from the emitter terminal can be determined with the aid of Fig. 5.38b. In practical circuits, R_C is very small in comparison with r_c and the desired resistance is the same as the input resistance of a common-base amplifier with output shorted (h_{ib}) except that the parallel combination of R_B and the driving source resistance R_S appear in series with r_b. Let this parallel combination be defined as R'_S, assuming that the reactance of the coupling capacitance C_C is negligible compared with R_S at the lowest frequency of interest. With these assumptions, the required bypass capacitance is determined to be

$$C_E \simeq \frac{h_{fe} + 1}{\omega_1(R'_S + h_{ie})} \tag{5.73}$$

Full power gain is achieved for the amplifier at frequencies $10\,\omega_1$ or higher. Thus, if frequencies down to ω_1 are to be *amplified with essentially no loss of gain*, a capacitor *ten times as large as that given* by Eq. 5.73 will be required.

PROB. 5.27. Derive Eq. 5.73.

The chief disadvantage of the stabilized bias circuit, aside from its complexity, is the shunting effect that the bias resistance R_B may have on the input signal in the event that R_B is not large in comparison with the input resistance of the transistor. There are several advantages of the circuit, however, that make this circuit attractive. In addition to stabilizing the Q point of a given transistor from the standpoint of temperature variation, the stabilized bias circuit permits interchanging transistors that have appreciably different parameters without altering the bias circuit (see Fig. 5.31 for the effect of varying h_{fe}). This feature makes assembly line amplifier production possible without the necessity of individual tailoring of bias components or the requirement of excessively close tolerance limits for the transistors involved. Also, the signal shunting effect of R_B, which was mentioned as the chief disadvantage, may actually be an advantage in a mass produced amplifier because it tends to stabilize the amplifier gain when transistors of varying h_{fe} are used. This feature results from the fact that transistors with high h_{fe} also have high input resistance ($h_{ie} = (h_{fe} + 1)h_{ib}$), and hence the shunting effect of R_B appreciably reduces the gain of only the higher gain transistors. Silicon transistors often have such small values of I_{CO} that thermal stabilization is not required; however, stabilized bias is usually used in order to gain the other benefits mentioned.

Measured values of I_{CO} (listed by manufacturers) include the surface leakage component. Therefore, the rate of I_{CO} increase with temperature is usually less than the values derived in Chapter 3. Although germanium transistors follow quite closely the rule of doubling I_{CO} every 10°C, silicon transistors, because of their relatively small ratio of thermal current to surface leakage current, usually have a much slower rate of increase than the theoretical doubling every 6 degrees. Manufacturers data should be consulted, especially in the case of silicon transistors.

PROB. 5.28. A 2N2712 *n-p-n* silicon transistor has the following characteristics: $h_{fe} = 200$, maximum collector dissipation = 200 mw at 25°C, maximum junction temperature = 100°C, $I_{CO} = 0.5 \mu a$ at 25°C. I_{CO} doubles for each 15°C temperature increase.

This transistor is used as a common emitter amplifier with $V_{CC} = 20$ v and $R_L = 10$ KΩ. The Q point (at 25°C) is at $V_{CE} = 10$ v and $I_C = 1$ ma. $V_{BE} = 0.5$ v at this Q point. Draw the diagram of a stabilized bias circuit and determine the value of all resistors which will permit a 1.0 v change in V_{CE} when the ambient temperature is raised from 25 to 85°C. Allow a 2.0 v drop across the emitter resistor. Use any *valid* approximations.

PROB. 5.29. Calculate the emitter bypass capacitance required for the amplifier of Prob. 5.28 if the desired lower half-power frequency is 15 Hz ($\omega_1 = 100$ rps) and the driving source resistance (*excluding* the bias circuit) is 5 KΩ. Verify the validity of the assumptions made in Prob. 5.27. Use $h_{ie} = 5$ KΩ.

5.9 CATHODE OR SELF BIAS FOR TUBES

The bias battery of a triode amplifier can be eliminated if cathode bias is used. The circuit which accomplishes this desirable simplification is shown in Fig. 5.39. The average d-c plate current, I_P, flowing through R_K produces a voltage drop with the polarity shown. Since the cathode is positive with respect to ground and the control grid is at ground potential, the grid is negative with respect to the cathode. This type of bias is also known as *self bias*.

The capacitor C_K is placed in the cathode circuit to bypass the time-varying signal to ground. If the resistor R_K is not bypassed, degeneration of the time-varying signal results. This degeneration can be visualized by observing that an increase in control grid potential causes an increase in cathode current. If C_K is not present, this increase of cathode current causes an increase of voltage across R_K. As a result, the total potential between grid and cathode is not as great as this potential would be if the voltage across R_K were constant. The capacitor C_K provides a low impedance path to ground for the time-varying signal. Therefore, the magnitude of the time-varying voltage across R_K is very small.

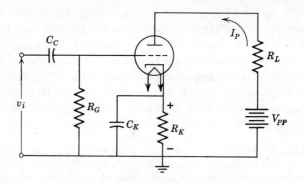

Fig. 5.39. A cathode-biased amplifier.

The desired value of R_K can be found by applying Ohm's law.

$$R_K = \frac{V_G}{I_P} \tag{5.74}$$

where V_G is the quiescent bias voltage desired and I_P is the quiescent plate current. Both of these values can be obtained from the load line on the characteristic curves.

The capacitor C_K must bypass R_K. However, as was indicated in the transistor configuration just considered, the input impedance of the tube (as viewed from the cathode) is also in parallel with R_K. As given in Eq. 4.81, the input impedance to the cathode is

$$Z_i = \frac{r_P + Z_L}{-\mu + 1} \tag{4.81}$$

Thus, if the reactance of the capacitance, C_K, at ω_1 is to be *negligible* (say $\frac{1}{10}$ or less) in comparison with R_K, the following relationship must hold.

$$C_K \geq \frac{10(R_K + Z_i)}{\omega_1 R_K Z_i} \tag{5.75}$$

If $Z_i \gg R_K$, this equation reduces to the simple form:

$$C_K \geq \frac{10}{\omega_1 R_K} \tag{5.76}$$

The bias circuit for the triode is much simpler than some of the stabilizing circuits required for a transistor. However, since the current through a tube is not affected by the temperature of the tube, the problem of stabilization does not enter. As an added advantage, the cathode bias circuit is self stabilizing. If plate current should tend to increase through the tube, the voltage drop across R_K would increase. This increased voltage drop causes the negative bias on the tube to increase, which tends to decrease the plate current.

PROB. 5.30. (a) Find the value of R_K which would be required in Example 5.1 if self bias is used instead of fixed bias. (b) Assume the amplifier must pass frequencies as low as 60 Hz, what size C_K should be used? (c) Draw the self bias circuit and give the proper values of components. Assume V_G (at the Q point) is -6 v. *Answer: (a) 1.05 $K\Omega$, (b) $C_K = 45$ μfd.*

PROB. 5.31. Design a 6J5 amplifier stage which will give a voltage gain of 15. Use a V_{PP} supply of $+300$ v and operate the tube at a quiescent control grid potential of -4 v. Use a cathode bias circuit. List the value of all resistors and capacitors if the lowest frequency to be amplified is 50 Hz.

PROB. 5.32. Using the curves of Fig. 5.3 and Fig. 5.4, select an operating point for $R_L = 10$ KΩ and determine the current, voltage, and power gain of the amplifier.

PROB. 5.33. A 6J5 tube is connected as shown in Fig. 5.11. (The characteristic curves are given in Fig. 5.12.) If the quiescent grid voltage is -6 v, and $R_L = 30$ KΩ determine the current gain, voltage gain, and power gain of the amplifier. (Use R_g of 500 KΩ)

PROB. 5.34. Draw the dynamic characteristics for v_C vs v_B for the transistor of Fig. 5.14. Assume R_L is 1500 Ω and V_{CC} is -5 v.

PROB. 5.35. Repeat Prob. 5.6 but use the dynamic transfer curve.

PROB. 5.36. Using an equivalent T circuit, derive an expression for the input impedance of a common emitter transistor which has a load resistance R_L in its output.

PROB. 5.37. A circuit is connected as shown in Fig. 5.11. If R_L is 30 KΩ and v_I is $(-4 + 0.002 \sin \omega t)$, what is the voltage output? Which method would be the most accurate in this problem, load line, transfer characteristic, or equivalent circuit?

PROB. 5.38. A given silicon transistor has $h_{fe} = 100$, maximum collector dissipation $= 200$ mw at 25°C, maximum junction temperature $= 175$°C, and $I_{CO} = 2.0$ μa at 75°C. This transistor is used in a circuit with $V_{CC} = 30$ v and a nominal Q point at $V_{CE} = 10$ v and $I_C = 2$ ma. The environment of the amplifier requires an ambient temperature variation between 50°C and 100°C. Design a stabilized bias network which will restrain the Q point range from $V_{CE} = 9$ v to $V_{CE} = 11$ v. Assume that I_{CO} follows the theoretical variation of I_{CO} with temperature.

PROB. 5.39. A given type transistor has a range of h_{fe} between 50 and 200. An amplifier manufacturer wishes to use these transistors in a circuit with $V_{CC} = 25$ v and a nominal Q point at $V_{CE} = 10$ v and $I_C = 3.0$ ma. Design a stabilized bias circuit that will confine the Q point between $V_{CE} = 9$ v and $V_{CE} = 11$ v, assuming that the junction temperature remains constant.

PROB. 5.40. Under certain conditions, it may be rather difficult to measure the voltage transfer ratio h_r and the current transfer ratio h_f. This statement is particularly true at high frequencies where not only a magnitude but also a phase angle must be included. Fortunately, it is possible to determine all four h parameters by making simple impedance or admittance measurements with a bridge. (An r-f bridge is required at high frequencies.) One set of circuit configurations which can be used is shown in Fig. 5.40 (the circuits are a-c). If the circuit represents a transistor, d-c bias would have to be supplied with appropriate blocking capacitors to isolate the a-c and d-c components.

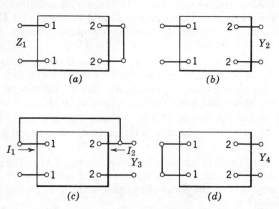

Fig. 5.40. Configurations which can be used to determine the h parameters by use of a bridge.

With a transistor connected as shown in Fig. 5.40, the following impedance and admittances are measured on an r-f bridge (Fig. 5.40):

$$Z_1 = 600^{\angle -300°} \text{ ohms} \qquad Y_2 = (5 \times 10^{-4})^{\angle 30°} \text{ mhos}$$

$$Y_3 = (6.8 \times 10^{-2}) \text{ mhos} \qquad Y_4 = (8.08 \times 10^{-4})^{\angle 18°} \text{ mhos}$$

Find the h parameters for this transistor. (*Hint:* Note that in (a) $V_2 = 0$, in (b) $I_1 = 0$, in (c) $V_1 = V_2$, in (d) $V_1 = 0$.)

PROB. 5.41. A radio set manufacturer has purchased a large quantity of *npn* silicon transistors for use in automobile radios. The variation of β of these transistors is from 50 to 200 and the maximum value of I_{CO} is 0.5 μa at 25°C. I_{CO} doubles, approximately, for each 10°C temperature increase.

The audio-frequency amplifier in the radio has $V_{CC} = 13$ volts, $R_C = 4.7$ KΩ. The maximum expected ambient temperature range is from -30°C to 75°C. Design a bias circuit which will confine the Q point within the limits $v_{CE} = 5$ volts and $v_{CE} = 8$ volts over this range with random selection of the transistors. Assume $v_{BE} = 0.5$ volt at 25°C. Select R_E and determine the base circuit resistors. (Common-emitter configuration.) θ_T 0.75°C per mw.

6

Multielectrode Tubes and Transistors

The triode tube was invented in 1906, but it was the early 1930's before anyone attempted to place more than one grid between the plate and cathode.[1] The first multigrid tube was the tetrode, which contains two grids in addition to the cathode and plate. The physical arrangement of a tetrode is shown in Fig. 6.1. This tube is a triode with an additional grid, placed between the control grid and the plate. This second grid is called a *screen grid* because it acts as an electrostatic shield for the plate.

6.1 TETRODE TUBES

The need for an additional grid became evident when amplification of radio frequencies was attempted with triode tubes. A certain amount of capacitance (usually in the order of several *pf*) exists between the plate and grid of a triode. Consequently, when the triode amplifier is designed

[1] Encyclopedia Britannica, Vol. 8, page 340H gives a short history of the development of the vacuum tube.

to produce high gain at high frequencies (frequencies above a fraction of a megahertz) this grid to plate capacitance is large enough to couple a significant amount of power from the plate circuit back into the grid circuit. As will be discussed later, this *feedback* of signal may cause the amplifier to oscillate and thus become useless as an amplifier. Consequently, elaborate circuits were designed to counteract the effects of the grid-plate capacitance. With the introduction of the screen grid, the interelectrode capacitance at lower radio frequencies ceased to be a

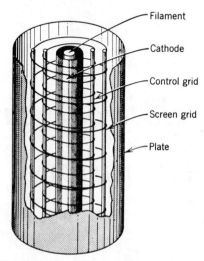

Filament

Cathode

Control grid

Screen grid

Plate

Fig. 6.1. The physical arrangement of a tetrode.

problem. The capacitance from the plate to grid of a conventional tetrode is of the order of a fraction of a *pf*.

The symbol for a tetrode is shown in Fig. 6.2. The general pattern of the symbol is evident.

The screen grid could be connected to ground or cathode and would serve as a good electrostatic shield between the plate and control grid. However, with the control grid negative and the screen grid at zero potential, the plate would be unable to attract an appreciable number of electrons. The plate current would, therefore, be very low. By maintaining the screen grid at a constant positive potential, the electrostatic shielding effect between the plate and control grid is maintained, but electrons from the cathode are attracted toward the positive screen grid. When the electrons arrive at the screen location some of these electrons are intercepted by the screen wires and become screen current. However, most of these electrons pass between the screen wires and continue on to the plate of the tube. For reasons to be explained later, the potential of the

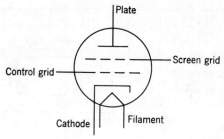

Fig. 6.2. The graphical symbol of a tetrode.

screen grid is usually lower than the potential of the plate. A typical circuit arrangement of a tetrode amplifier as well as typical values of supply voltages are shown in Fig. 6.3.

The characteristic curves for a type 24A tetrode are shown in Fig. 6.4. Notice that a change of plate voltage (above 90 v) causes very little change in the plate current. In effect, the electric field in the cathode-control grid region is shielded from the plate by the screen grid. Therefore, the value of r_p for a tetrode is very high. In fact, the plate resistance of the type 24A tube shown in Fig. 6.4 is about 0.5 megohm.

The unusual dips in the characteristic curves for plate voltages between 8 and 85 v require further explanation. When the curve of screen current vs plate voltage is displayed as well as the curve of plate current vs plate voltage, the reason for this unusual behavior becomes clear. Figure 6.5 illustrates the two curves as well as a curve showing the variation of total cathode current (plate current plus screen current) as a function of plate voltage. The total cathode current is seen to be almost independent of the plate voltage. However, as the plate voltage is increased above 8 v the plate current begins to decrease, because the kinetic energy required of a

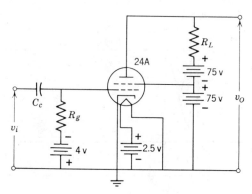

Fig. 6.3. Typical tetrode configuration.

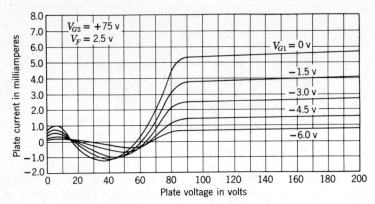

Fig. 6.4. Characteristic curves of a type 24A tetrode.

primary electron is about 8 to 10 ev (depending on the type of metal) in order to release a secondary electron from a metal sheet. Therefore, as the energy of the primary electrons reaches about 8 ev, some secondary electrons are emitted from the plate.

These secondary electrons are released in the region between the plate and the screen grid. Since the screen grid is more positive than the plate, the electrons are attracted to the screen grid. The net current to the plate is equal to the primary current minus the secondary current. Therefore, the total current to the plate decreases. At the same time, the current to the screen grid increases due to the additional secondary electrons. As the energy of the primary electrons increases, the number of secondary electrons also increases. In fact, as the curves of Fig. 6.4 indicate, when the plate voltage is between 15 and 60 v, the number of secondary electrons

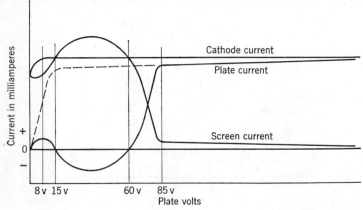

Fig. 6.5. Plate current and screen current characteristics for a tetrode.

may be greater than the number of primary electrons. The plate then acts as an *electron emitter*, and the plate current is *reversed*. As the plate potential becomes more positive than the screen potential, some of the secondary electrons are attracted back to the plate. When the plate voltage is 85 v or greater, essentially all of the secondary electrons are returned to the plate.[2] If the secondary electrons were not present, the characteristic curve would have the shape indicated by the dotted curve of Fig. 6.5.

The characteristic curve indicates that the tetrode has a *negative* plate resistance for low values of plate voltage. (An increase of plate voltage causes a decrease in plate current.) This negative resistance characteristic of the tetrode, like the tunnel diode, has been used to produce oscillations. Oscillators will be discussed in subsequent chapters. However, for most amplifier applications the dip in the characteristic curve is undesirable. This dip seriously reduces the useful operating range of the amplifier. Consequently, the regular tetrode has been largely replaced by the pentode or beam power tetrode which is discussed in Sections 6.2 and 6.4 of this chapter.

PROB. 6.1. Sketch v_O as a function of time if the tube of Fig. 6.4 is connected as shown in Fig. 6.3. $R_L = 30 \, \text{K}\Omega$ and $v_i = -4 \sin \omega t$. Would you recommend operation of this tube under these conditions? Why?

PROB. 6.2. Draw the dynamic transfer characteristic for the tube whose characteristic curves are given in Fig. 6.4 if (a) $R_L = 40 \, \text{K}\Omega$, (b) $R_L = 40 \, K\Omega$, (c) $R_L = 100 \, \text{K}\Omega$. Assume the tube is connected as shown in Fig. 6.3.

6.2 PENTODE TUBES

The undesirable secondary emission effects of the tetrode led to the development of the *pentode tube*. The pentode, which has three grids between the cathode and the plate is essentially a tetrode with a grid inserted between the screen grid and the plate. This third grid is called the *suppressor grid*. The physical arrangement and symbol for the pentode tube are shown in Fig. 6.6.

The suppressor grid is usually connected to the cathode. A basic pentode amplifier circuit is shown in Fig. 6.7. As in the tetrode, the field from the positive screen grid causes electrons to move from the cathode toward the screen grid. The screen grid intercepts some of these electrons but most of them continue on toward the plate. The suppressor grid

---

[2] About 90% of the secondary electrons are emitted with an energy of 10 ev or less. All of the electrons are emitted at different angles. As a result, the component of energy away from the plate is usually less than the net energy of the electron. Consequently, very few electrons have a net energy away from the plate greater than 10 ev.

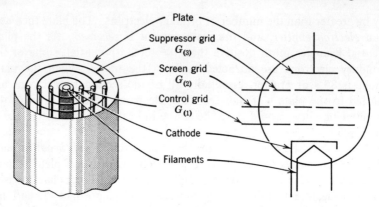

Fig. 6.6. The pentode construction and graphical symbol.

causes a field of low potential to exist between the screen grid and the plate. However, the electrons which were not captured by the screen grid have enough energy to pass through this low-potential field to the plate. A few electrons which travel straight toward the wire of the suppressor grid will either be returned to the screen grid or captured by the suppressor, depending on the energy they possess.

The electrons which arrive at the plate cause the emission of secondary electrons, as in the tetrode. However, the suppressor grid is negative in relation to the plate and returns the secondary electrons to the plate. The suppressor grid, therefore, does not suppress the *emission* of secondary electrons but does suppress the *effect* of the secondary emission.

The characteristic curves of a typical pentode are shown in Fig. 6.8. In this figure, the dip due to the secondary emission is absent. Except for this difference, the curves are very similar to the tetrode curves. The

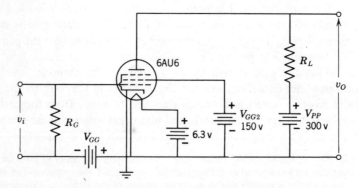

Fig. 6.7. A basic pentode amplifier circuit.

advantage of the pentode over the tetrode is obvious from the characteristic curve. The potential on the plate of the tetrode had to remain at least 10 v higher than the screen grid potential or the characteristic curves were nonlinear. In contrast, the plate of the pentode can be reduced far below the screen-grid potential and the operation is still on the linear

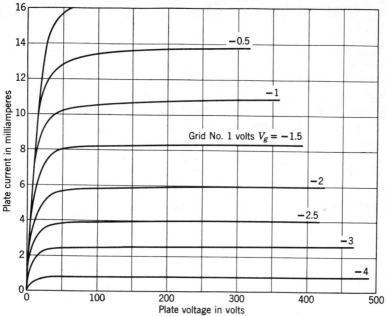

Fig. 6.8. Characteristic curves of a 6AU6 pentode ($V_{g2} = 150$ v). (Courtesy of Radio Corporation of America.)

portion of the characteristic curve. If the plate has a very low voltage, a cloud of electrons will accumulate near the suppressor grid. Consequently, a virtual cathode forms in this region, and the characteristic curves for very low plate voltages have the same form as the vacuum diode. As the voltage increases, all the electrons in the screen to plate area are attracted to the plate and a saturation condition exists in which the plate potential has a *very* small effect on plate current. Therefore, the plate resistance of a pentode is very high.

6.3 EQUIVALENT CIRCUITS FOR PENTODES

Equivalent circuits can be drawn to represent the tetrode or the pentode. Since the pentode contains one more grid than the tetrode, the equivalent circuit for the pentode will be found and modifications which will fit this development to the tetrode should be obvious.

The pentode contains three grids and a plate. Consequently, if the cathode is taken as reference, each of these electrodes should have an effect on the plate current. Then, for small signals, the law of super-position can be used to determine the characteristic equation for the pentode current.

$$\Delta i_P = g_m \Delta v_{G1} + g_{m2} \Delta v_{G2} + g_{m3} \Delta v_{G3} + \frac{1}{r_p} \Delta v_P \qquad (6.1)$$

where g_m indicates the effectiveness of v_{G1} in controlling the plate current. The parameter g_m can be measured by applying proper potentials to the various grids and plate. Then, note the change of i_P as v_{G1} is changed slightly. All other grid and plate potentials must be maintained constant while this change of plate current and grid 1 voltage occurs. Mathematically, this relationship may be written with the help of partial derivatives as

$$g_m = \frac{\partial i_P}{\partial v_{G1}} \qquad (6.2)$$

Similarly, the rest of the parameters in Eq. 6.1 can be written as follows:

$$g_{m2} = \frac{\partial i_P}{\partial v_{G2}} \qquad (6.3)$$

$$g_{m3} = \frac{\partial i_P}{\partial v_{G3}} \qquad (6.4)$$

$$r_p = \frac{\partial v_P}{\partial i_P} \qquad (6.5)$$

In a typical pentode amplifier circuit, the screen voltage v_{G2} and the suppressor voltage v_{G3} are maintained constant. Consequently, $\Delta v_{G2} = \Delta v_{G3} = 0$ and Eq. 6.1 can be written[3] as

$$\Delta i_P = g_m \Delta v_{G1} + \frac{1}{r_p} \Delta v_P \qquad (6.6)$$

This equation is identical to the characteristic equation of the triode. Consequently, the equivalent circuits for the pentode, for the tetrode, and for the triode are the same. For convenience, the two equivalent circuits for the pentode or tetrode are shown in Fig. 6.9. The foregoing derivation applies to the tetrode if g_{m3} is equated to zero or is omitted.

[3] By common usage, v_G in a pentode or tetrode tube is understood to be v_{G1}. Hence, the second subscript may be omitted when no confusion will result.

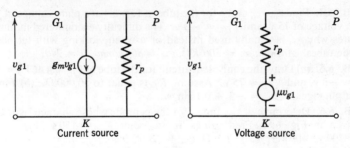

Fig. 6.9. Equivalent circuits for a pentode or tetrode.

PROB. 6.3. Draw the equivalent circuit of a pentode when the voltages of all the grids are permitted to vary.

Example 6.1. Find the small signal voltage gain of the circuit shown in Fig. 6.7. The equivalent circuit for the amplifier of Fig. 6.7 is shown in Fig. 6.10. The voltage v_o is found by writing the nodal equation for the plate circuit.

$$g_m v_{g1} = -v_0\left(\frac{1}{r_p} + \frac{1}{R_L}\right) \tag{6.7}$$

or

$$\frac{v_o}{v_{g1}} = K_v = -g_m \frac{r_p R_L}{r_p + R_L} \tag{6.8}$$

The gain of the pentode amplifier is, therefore, equal to g_m times the parallel resistance combination of r_p and R_L. If the pentode amplifier is coupled to another vacuum tube through a coupling capacitor C_c and a grid resistor R_g, the reference gain of the pentode amplifier is equal to g_m times the parallel resistance combination of R_L, r_p, and R_g. (This statement assumes that X_{cc} is much less than R_g.)

The usual value of r_p is very large. For instance, the plate resistance of the 6AU6 is approximately 1 megohm. If the load resistance is quite low in comparison to r_p, the parallel combination of r_p and R_L is approximately equal to R_L. Therefore,

$$K_v \simeq -g_m R_L \tag{6.9}$$

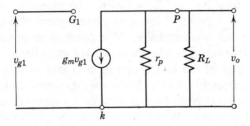

Fig. 6.10. The equivalent circuit of a pentode amplifier.

PROB. 6.4. Find r_p, g_m, and μ for the tube of Fig. 6.4 at a plate voltage of 120 v, screen voltage of 75 v, and $V_{G1} = -3$ v. The difficulty encountered in finding μ indicates why g_m is usually used instead of μ when working with tetrode and pentode tubes. *Answer:* $r_p = 300\ K\Omega, g_m = 800\ \mu mho, \mu = 240.$

PROB. 6.5. (*a*) Draw the equivalent circuit for the tube of Fig. 6.4 at $V_p = 120$ v, $V_{G1} = -3$ v, and $V_{G2} = 75$ v. Assume R_L is equal to 50,000 Ω. (*b*) Find the a-c output signal if $v_G = -3 + 0.1 \sin \omega t$.

PROB. 6.6. Determine μ, g_m, and r_p for the pentode whose characteristic curves are given in Fig. 6.8. Find values at the point $V_{G2} = 150$ v, $V_{G1} = -2$ v, $V_P = 200$ v. *Answer:* $r_p = 1\ M\Omega, g_m = 4200\ \mu mho, \mu = 4200.$

PROB. 6.7. If g_m of a 6AU6 (at a given operating point) is 5200 micromhos and r_p is 1 megohm, find the voltage amplification of a 6AU6 with a load resistance of 20,000 Ω. (*a*) Use Eq. 6.8. (*b*) Use Eq. 6.9. (*c*) Compare results. *Answer:* (*a*) $K_v = -102$ (*b*) $K_v = -104$ (*c*) 2 % *difference.*

PROB. 6.8. Repeat Prob. 6.7 if R_L is changed to 500,000 Ω. (*Note:* As indicated previously, g_m is a function of plate current. Hence, as R_L is increased, g_m tends to decrease. Ignore this change of g_m in this problem.)

6.4 GRAPHICAL SOLUTION OF PENTODE CIRCUITS

The graphical solution of a pentode circuit (or tetrode circuit) is very similar to the graphical solution of the triode circuit. However, some precautions must be observed when using pentode or tetrode tubes. The reason for the precautions can be seen most readily from the dynamic transfer characteristic. The dynamic transfer characteristics for load resistances of 20,000 Ω and 100,000 Ω are shown in Fig. 6.11. (A plate supply voltage of 300 v was assumed for both curves of Fig. 6.11.)

The dynamic transfer characteristic for $R_L = 20,000\ \Omega$ follows the static transfer characteristic very closely except when v_G approaches zero. However, as R_L is increased (to obtain greater voltage gain), the shape of the dynamic transfer characteristic changes quite radically. A very little change (0.3 ma) of plate current occurs as the grid voltage is reduced from 0 to -3 v. From -3 v to cutoff the dynamic transfer characteristic closely follows the static characteristic curve, as shown. The action of the pentode for large load resistors can be visualized by referring to the characteristic curves. For a load line of $R_L = 100$ K, the operation for $v_G = 0$ to $v_G = -2.5$ v is at a point of constant plate current and constant plate voltage on the plate characteristics. This point corresponds to the point known as collector saturation in the transistor amplifier.

The voltage gain of the 6AU6 of Fig. 6.11 can be found directly by plotting v_P vs v_G from Fig. 6.11*b*. The resulting curves, shown in Fig. 6.12, indicate that the total plate voltage change is essentially a constant for $R_L = 20,000\ \Omega$ or more. When R_L is large, the given change of plate voltage requires only a small change of grid voltage. This required grid

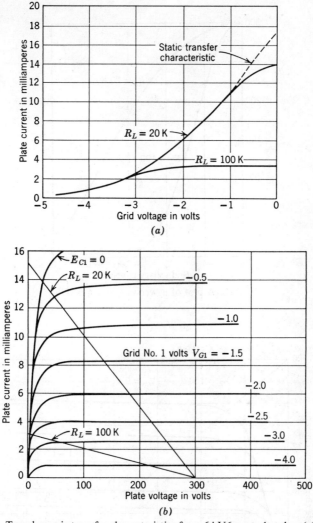

Fig. 6.11. Two dynamic transfer characteristics for a 6AU6 pentode tube. (*a*) Dynamic curve: (*b*) characteristic curve. (Courtesy of Radio Corporation of America.)

voltage change is approximately 1 v, peak-to-peak, and is centered approximately at $V_G = -4$ v. Therefore, this amplifier would operate very satisfactorily, providing the grid bias is held at about -4 v. However, it may be seen from Fig. 6.12 that a 0.6 v (15%) change in bias voltage will cause the quiescent operating point to move to either extremity of the useful operating range. Therefore, difficulty may be experienced in establishing and maintaining the quiescent operating point at the desired

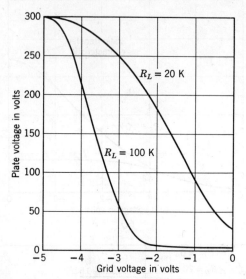

Fig. 6.12. A plot of v_P versus v_G for a 6AU6.

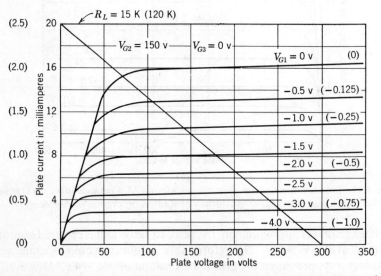

Fig. 6.13. The effect of reducing the screen grid potential on a 6AU6. Open values are for $v_{G2} = 150$ v and values in parentheses are for $v_{G2} = 37.5$ v.

location. In Fig. 6.12, the slope of the curves is the voltage amplification of the circuit.

In many applications it is desirable to operate a pentode with a large value of plate load resistance and still use the full grid swing, thus avoiding the critical biasing problem. Such operation is possible if the screen grid voltage is reduced. The effect of reducing the screen grid voltage is shown in Fig. 6.13.

Example 6.2. In Fig. 6.13, a 15 KΩ load line was drawn on a set of 6AU6 collector characteristics. The original screen grid voltage for this set of curves was 150 v and the load line was drawn through the knee of the $V_{G1} = 0$ curve. The plate current scale was then altered so that the load line previously drawn represents a 120 KΩ load instead of a 15 KΩ load. This required that the plate current values be reduced by a factor of 8. The reduced values are shown in parenthesis. This reduction in plate current can be obtained by a reduction in screen grid voltage. In order to determine the required value of screen grid voltage for the modified curves, it was assumed that the plate current is proportional to the $\frac{3}{2}$ power of the screen grid voltage. Then $150/(V_{G2}) = 8^{2/3} = 4$, and the new value of screen grid voltage ($V_{G2} = \frac{150}{4} = 37.5$ v. The values of control grid voltage also need to be revised because the grid voltage required for plate current cutoff is proportional to the screen grid voltage. Therefore, a reduction of screen-grid voltage by a factor of 4 also reduces the cutoff control grid voltage by a factor of 4. To meet this requirement, therefore, all values of control grid voltage must be reduced by a factor of 4 as shown in Fig. 6.13. The new values of V_{G1} are enclosed by parenthesis.

PROB. 6.9. Add the dynamic transfer characteristic of the 6AU6 with $V_{PP} = 300$ v, $V_{G2} = 37.5$ v, and $R_L = 100$ KΩ to those presented in Fig. 6.11a.

PROB. 6.10. Determine proper bias, maximum input signal and maximum output signal for linear operation of a 6AU6 if R_L is 15,000 Ω, $V_{PP} = 300$ v. $V_{G2} = 150$ v. *Answer:* $V_G = -2v$, $v_i \approx \pm 2v$, $v_O = 60$ to $285v$.

PROB. 6.11. Using the ideas developed in Example 6.2, find a new set of coordinates and determine the screen voltage and grid voltages if the 15 KΩ load line is to represent a 90 KΩ load line.

6.5 OPERATION OF A PENTODE FROM A SINGLE VOLTAGE SOURCE

The pentode amplifier circuit shown in Fig. 6.8 requires three batteries for proper operation. Through the use of resistors and capacitors, the number of batteries or power supplies required can be reduced to one. The circuit which accomplishes this saving of batteries is shown in Fig. 6.14.

The resistor R_K causes a voltage drop due to the flow of cathode current and provides self-bias in the manner discussed for the triode tube.

However, the cathode current for the pentode is

$$I_K = I_P + I_{G2} \tag{6.10}$$

where I_K is the quiescent cathode current, I_P is the quiescent plate current and I_{G2} is the quiescent screen grid current. Again,

$$R_K = \frac{V_{\text{bias}}}{I_K} \tag{6.11}$$

Also, C_K can be found as shown in Eq. 5.75. However, since $r_p \gg R_L$ for a pentode, $Z_i \simeq 1/g_m$. Thus,

$$C_K = \frac{10(g_m R_K + 1)}{w_1 R_K} \tag{6.12}$$

where w_1 is the lowest frequency the amplifier is designed to pass without loss of gain.

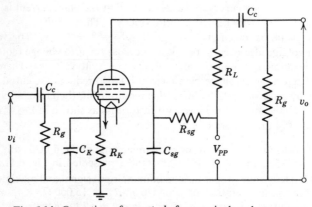

Fig. 6.14. Operation of a pentode from a single voltage source.

The screen grid voltage dropping resistor R_{sg} causes a voltage drop due to the screen grid current flowing through R_{sg}. The value of R_{sg} is found by the relationship

$$R_{sg} = \frac{V_{PP} - V_{G2}}{I_{G2}} \tag{6.13}$$

where V_{PP} is the value of the plate supply voltage and V_{G2} is the desired potential on the screen grid. Again, I_{G2} is the quiescent screen grid current.

In order for the screen grid to have a constant potential, the a-c impedance to ground in the screen circuit must be low. Otherwise, the a-c component of the screen current will produce an a-c component of voltage on the screen. Accordingly, the capacitor C_{sg} bypasses the screen grid to ground or cathode. However, to find the proper size for C_{sg}, the total resistance this capacitor must bypass needs to be determined.

Since the cathode, control grid, and screen grid have the same configuration in a pentode as the cathode, control grid, and plate have in a triode, an equivalent circuit can be derived for the screen grid circuit. This equivalent circuit is shown in Fig. 6.15, provided that v_P and v_{G3} are constant.

The parameter g_{m2} is given by the relation

$$g_{m2} = \frac{\partial i_{G2}}{\partial v_{G1}} \tag{6.14}$$

where i_{G2} is screen grid current and v_{G1} is control grid voltage. The parameter r_{g2} is known as the screen resistance and is given by the relation

$$r_{g2} = \frac{\partial v_{G2}}{\partial i_{G2}} \tag{6.15}$$

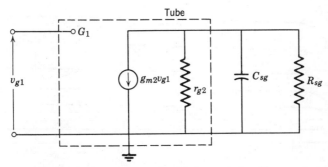

Fig. 6.15. Equivalent circuit for the screen grid of a pentode with v_P and v_{G3} constant.

where v_{G2} is the screen grid voltage. Figure 6.15 shows that the screen grid bypass capacitor C_{sg} is actually in parallel with both R_{sg} and r_{g2}. The rule of thumb, therefore, requires that

$$X_{csg} = \frac{R_{sg} r_{g2}}{10(R_{sg} + r_{g2})} \tag{6.16}$$

where X_{csg} is the reactance of the capacitor C_{sg} at the lowest frequency the amplifier is designed to pass.

The value of r_{g2} is seldom included in tube manuals. However, a quick experimental check will determine r_{g2}. In most cases, an estimation of r_{g2} is accurate enough for quick calculations. The similarity of the screen circuit to the plate of the triode has already been noted. It is not surprising, therefore, to find that r_{g2} has the same order of magnitude as the r_p of the triode tubes. However, since the screen only intercepts a portion of the total space current, the value of r_{g2} is higher than the value of r_p in a typical triode. Usual values of r_{g2} are in the order of 20,000 to 40,000 Ω. Of course, as the size of the capacitor C_{sg} is increased, the screen grid potential is held more constant. Therefore, Eq. 6.16 determines the *minimum* value C_{sg} should have whereas cost or size will dictate the maximum practical value in a given circuit.

The quiescent value of screen grid current is given in some tube manuals for typical voltages on the plate and various grids. In other manuals, sets of characteristic curves include the screen current characteristics with the plate characteristics. Such a set of curves is reproduced in Fig. 6.16.

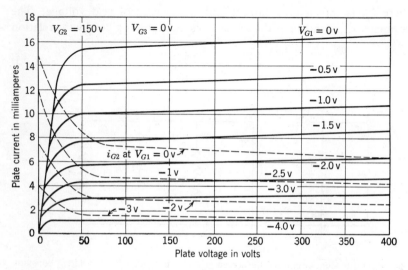

Fig. 6.16. Characteristic curves of a 6AU6 pentode including grid current characteristics.

The method outlined for operating a pentode from a single power supply can, of course, be used for operating a tetrode or any multigrid type of tube from a single power supply.

PROB. 6.12. Determine values for all the resistors and capacitors in the 6AU6 circuit of Fig. 6.14 if V_{PP} is 250 v and R_L is 25,000 Ω. (Bias the tube for maximum linearity.) Assume $r_{g2} = 30$ KΩ. Find the voltage gain and maximum power output. The lowest frequency to be amplified is 30 Hz. *Answer:* $R_K = 380\ \Omega$, $C_K = 140\ \mu f$, $R_{sg} = 45.5\ K\Omega$, $C_{sg} = 3\ \mu f$, $G_v = 63$.

6.6 BEAM POWER TUBES

Beam power tubes are large current tetrodes which are constructed so the screen grid wires have the same spacing as the control grid wires. The screen grid is then oriented so its wires are in the electrical "shadow" of the control grid wires. The negative potential of the control grid repels the electrons and forms an electron beam in the space between the control grid wires. Since the screen grid wires are directly behind the control grid wires, the screen grid intercepts a minimum number of electrons. The screen grid also tends to diffuse the electron beam somewhat. The relative locations of the grid wires and the general shape of the electron beams are

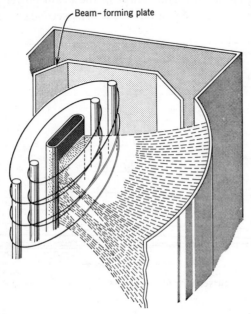

Beam-forming plate

Fig. 6.17. The action of the beam power tube.

shown in Fig. 6.17. To enhance the beam-forming qualities, beam-forming plates are also included as shown in Fig. 6.17.

If the plate potential of the beam power tube is quite low, the speed of the electrons decreases as the electrons approach the plate. The charge density, as noted in Chapter 3, is given by Eq. 3.51.

$$\frac{J}{v} = -\rho \tag{3.51}$$

Therefore, as the velocity of the electrons is decreased, the charge density is increased. Consequently, when the plate voltage is low, a negative charge is produced in the space between the plate and screen grid. If the screen grid is more positive than the plate, we might expect the electrons to reach their minimum velocity at the plate. However, electrons leaving the screen grid area experience a decelerating force due not only to the lower potential of the plate but also due to the negative charges on all the electrons between the screen grid and plate. Consequently, a minimum velocity is achieved *before* the electrons reach the plate. In fact, electrons are actually accelerated from this minimum value as they approach the more positive plate. Therefore, minimum potential in the screen-to-plate area occurs between the screen grid and the plate.

This *space charge* has the same effect in the beam power tube as the suppressor grid exerts in the pentode tube. The secondary electrons are

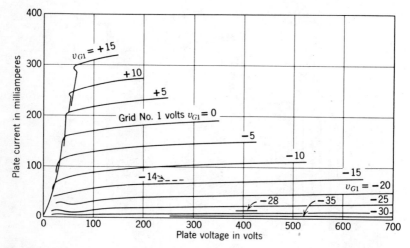

Fig. 6.18. Characteristic curves of a 6L6 beam power tube. (Courtesy of Radio Corporation of America.)

returned by the space charge to the more positive plate. As a result, the characteristic curves of a beam power tube are quite similar to the characteristic curves of a pentode tube. Characteristic curves of a beam power tube are shown in Fig. 6.18. Actually, the fairly linear portion of the plate characteristics of a beam power tube extend to lower plate voltages than the comparable pentode power tube. Therefore, greater power output and higher efficiency can be obtained from the beam power tube than can be obtained for a conventional pentode having similar ratings.

For proper suppression of secondary emission the beam power tube requires a large plate current compared to a pentode which might be used for voltage amplification; consequently, the word "power" in the title of the tube. Therefore, the pentode is usually used as a voltage amplifier whereas beam power tubes are usually used in output circuits which require a relatively large amount of power.

PROB. 6.13. Design a beam power stage similar to the pentode stage of Fig. 6.14 for a 6V6 tube if V_{PP} is 300 v and R_L is 3000 Ω, and $I_{G2} = 4.5$ ma. (a) Determine values of all resistors and capacitors used. (b) Determine the maximum output voltage signal. (c) Find voltage gain. (d) Find maximum signal power output. Assume $r_{g2} = 30$ KΩ. The lowest frequency to be amplified is 30 Hz.

6.7 TUBES WITH MORE THAN THREE GRIDS

Special purpose tubes are constructed with more than three grids. In fact, pentagrid converter tubes are made which have five grids in addition to the cathode and plate. These tubes are designed for use in the first detector stage of superheterodyne receivers. The primary use is to mix two or more electrical signals to produce new signals. Typical uses of these tubes will be covered in more detail in the later chapters in this book.

Many of the modern tubes contain several sections. For example, two triodes in a single envelope is very common. In fact, a 6SN7 is two 6J5 tubes in a single envelope. These two sections operate as two separate tubes as far as the electrical circuit is concerned. However, in terms of economy, one 6SN7 requires only one filament and one tube socket compared to two filaments and two tube sockets for the two 6J5 tubes. Also, the cost of two 6J5 tubes is higher than the cost of one 6SN7 tube. In addition, the space required for one 6SN7 is about one-half the space required for two 6J5 tubes. Therefore, multisection tubes are more economical and require less space than the several single-section tubes which they replace.

6.8 FIELD-EFFECT TRANSISTORS

The field-effect transistor (FET) is a voltage controlled semi-conductor which has a high input impedance, comparable to that of a vacuum tube. This transistor has only one p-n junction as shown in Fig. 6.19, and therefore, it is frequently known as a unipolar field-effect transistor (UNIFET).

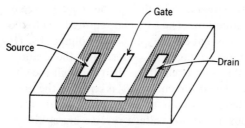

Fig. 6.19. Typical field-effect transistor structure.

The schematic representation in Fig. 6.20 will be used to explain the principles of operation of the field-effect transistor. Figure 6.20a shows that a narrow semiconductor channel provides a conducting path between the source and the drain. This channel may be either an n- or a p-type crystal. The n-type is used in this discussion. With no biases applied to the transistor, the channel conductance $G_c = \sigma(wt/l)$, where σ is the conductivity of the crystal and w, t, and l are the width, thickness, and length of the channel, respectively. If a reverse bias is applied between

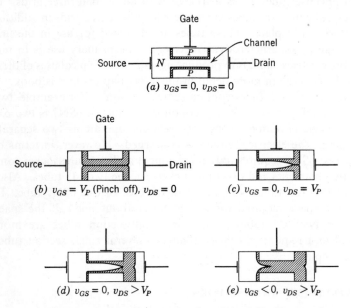

Fig. 6.20. Schematic representation of the field-effect transistor.

the gate and the source, the depletion region width is increased and the thickness of the channel is decreased. The reader will recall that the excess carriers (electrons for n-material) have been removed or "depleted" from the depletion region. Therefore the depleted region will not contribute to the conduction. The gate bias required just to reduce the channel thickness to zero is called the pinch-off voltage V_P (Fig. 6.20b).

If the gate-source voltage v_{GS} is zero and the drain is made positive with respect to the source, electrons drift through the channel because of the electric field. The drain current I_D is equal to the drain source voltage v_{DS} times the channel conductance G_c, providing that v_{GS} is very small. However, the positive drain voltage reverse biases the p-n junction near the drain end of the channel, and when the drain voltage is increased to the pinch-off voltage the channel thickness is reduced to zero at a point near the drain end of the channel. The drain current does not stop when the drain voltage reaches pinch-off because a voltage equal to V_P still exists between the pinch-off point and the source. Therefore, carriers are injected from the source into the depletion region. The resulting electric field continues to accelerate the carriers through the channel to the drain (Fig. 6.20c). As the drain voltage is increased beyond V_P, the depletion region thickness is increased between the gate and the drain, but is practically unchanged between the pinch-off point and the source (Fig. 6.20d). Therefore, the source current remains essentially constant as the drain voltage increases above V_P because the additional voltage appears across the depletion region and the electric field along the channel does not change. This saturated drain current is known as I_{DSS} (saturated short-circuit drain current), which is measured at $v_{DS} = V_P$, $v_{GS} = 0$, and $R_L = 0$.

The field-effect transistor normally operates with the drain voltage v_{DS} above V_P and reverse bias applied to the gate. The electric field (and thus the drain current in the channel) is then controlled by the gate-source voltage v_{GS} in a manner similar to the control of the plate current in a vacuum tube by the electric field between the grid and the cathode. The effect of the gate voltage v_{GS} on the channel conductivity is shown in Fig. 6.20e. The drain current is almost independent of drain voltage whenever the sum of the drain voltage and the reverse-bias gate voltage exceeds V_P.

The drain characteristics of a typical n-channel transistor are shown in Fig. 6.21a. Notice the similarity of these characteristics to the pentode characteristics. Like the pentode, the output resistance r_d is very high in the normal operating range of the transistor. Avalanche breakdown occurs at the junction whenever the drain-gate voltage exceeds a given value (about 35 v for the transistor of Fig. 6.21). The transfer characteristics are shown in Fig. 6.21b. Observe that, like the pentode tube, a single curve is adequate to describe the transfer characteristics for all drain voltages in the normal operating region. The slope of the transfer curve at any point is the trans-conductance g_m of the transistor at that point.

The input characteristics of the typical n-channel FET are shown in Fig. 6.21c. The gate current is the reverse-bias saturation current of the junction. This current is of the order of 10^{-8} amp in a small-signal silicon transistor. The input conductance is the slope of the input characteristics, which is very low in the normal operating range. The input resistance r_g is the order of 10^8 to 10^{10} ohms. Note that the input resistance remains high when forward bias not exceeding a few tenths of a volt is

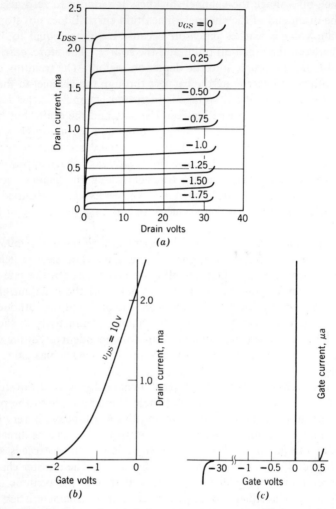

Fig. 6.21. Characteristics of a typical *n*-channel field-effect transistor. (*a*) Drain characteristics. (*b*) Transfer characteristics. (*c*) Input characteristics.

applied to the gate. Therefore, $v_{GS} = 0$ is a suitable Q point for a small-signal amplifier. Note that the input resistance drops abruptly when avalanche breakdown occurs. Avalanche breakdown occurs whenever the difference between the gate and drain potentials exceeds the avalanche breakdown voltage.

A d-c conducting path between the gate and the source must be provided in order to maintain the desired bias. The drain-gate saturation current

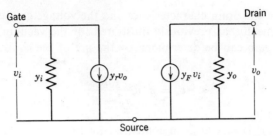

Fig. 6.22. *Y*-parameter equivalent circuit of an FET.

I_{DO} must flow through this path; therefore, the external gate-source resistance should not exceed a few megohms.

The equivalent circuit of Fig. 6.22 is a general *y*-parameter circuit which is applicable to the field effect transistor providing that the signal levels are small and, therefore, the *y*-parameters are linear. At low frequencies the depletion region capacitances may be neglected and the equivalent circuit is simplified (Fig. 6.23*a*). The high-frequency limitations of this transistor will be discussed in Chapter 7. Note the similarity of both the characteristic curves and the equivalent circuit of the field effect transistor as compared with the pentode tube. The output conductance g_d and the transconductance g_m can be determined from the curves given in Fig. 6.21 by the same techniques described for the vacuum tubes. The gate conductance g_g is so small over the normal range of operation that it cannot be determined from Fig. 6.21*c*.

A common source circuit is shown in Fig. 6.23*b*. In this circuit, the gate bias is zero, which is satisfactory for very small input signals because, as shown in Fig. 6.21*c*, the gate conductance g_g is negligible for forward bias voltages below about 0.2 v in a silicon transistor. A load line can

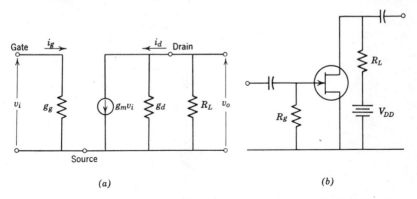

(a)   *(b)*

Fig. 6.23. *(a)* Equivalent circuit. *(b)* Actual circuit for a field-effect transistor.

be drawn on the drain characteristics and the voltage gain can be determined graphically, as previously illustrated for the vacuum tube. Also, the voltage gain can be determined by the use of the equivalent circuit, Fig. 6.23a.

$$v_o = g_m v_i \frac{r_d R_L}{r_d + R_L} \tag{6.17}$$

where $r_d = 1/g_d$.

Normally, r_d is very large in comparison with R_L; therefore,

$$G_v = \frac{v_o}{v_i} = \frac{g_m r_d R_L}{r_d + R_L} \simeq g_m R_L \tag{6.18}$$

Equation 6.18 holds only when the minimum drain voltage exceeds V_P. Otherwise, r_d is not large in comparison with R_L.

Figure 6.24a illustrates a technique for selecting a suitable transistor and a satisfactory operating point for a specified load resistance. A wide range of drain saturation current (I_{DSS}) values is available in the various

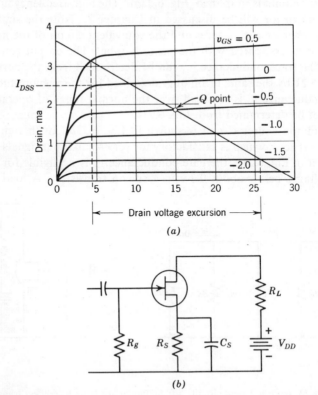

(a)

(b)

Fig. 6.24. (a) Load line on drain characteristics. (b) Typical circuit using source bias.

FET types. Therefore, a transistor which will permit the specified load line to pass near the knee of the $v_{GS} = 0$ curve ($v_{GS} = 0.5$ curve for silicon FET's) is usually available. After the load line is drawn, the Q point is selected so that the entire excursion of drain voltage will remain in the relatively flat portion of the drain characteristics (Fig. 6.24a).

Source bias (like cathode bias) may be utilized as shown in Fig. 6.24b. The bias resistance may be determined in the same manner as for a vacuum tube.

$$R_S = \frac{V_{GS}}{I_D} \tag{6.19}$$

The bypass capacitor must bypass the impedance looking into the transistor source terminal in parallel with R_S. This source impedance is $\Delta v_{GS}/\Delta i_S \simeq \Delta v_{GS}/\Delta i_D \simeq 1/g_m$. Therefore, the value of bypass capacitance C_S which will provide a low frequency cutoff ω_1 is

$$C = \frac{(g_m + G_S)\, 10}{\omega_1} \tag{6.20}$$

where $G_S = 1/R_S$.

The variation of drain current with temperature in a field effect transistor is determined by two factors. One factor is the temperature variation of depletion region width, which results from the temperature variation of barrier height ($V_{ho} - V$), discussed in Chapter 3, where V_{ho} is the zero-bias barrier height. As previously discussed, the temperature coefficient of this voltage is about -2.2 mv/°C, which results in an increased drain current with increased temperature. The other factor is the variation of majority carrier mobility with temperature. This mobility influences the transconductance g_m. As the temperature increases, the carrier mobility, and hence g_m, decrease and tend to compensate for the variation of V_{ho} with temperature. In fact, the proper choice of Q point will give essentially zero temperature coefficient of drain current from about -50 to 100°C. The temperature coefficient due to mobility change is about 0.7%/°C. Therefore, the condition for zero temperature coefficient is

$$0.007(-i_D)/°C = g_m(0.0022)/°C \tag{6.21}$$

$$\frac{i_D}{g_m} = -0.315 \text{ v} \tag{6.22}$$

The relationship of Eq. 6.22 can be expressed more conveniently in terms of the drain saturation current I_{DSS} and the transconductance g_{mo}. A typical relationship of i_D to I_{DSS} for a diffused gate transistor is

$$i_D = I_{DSS}\left(1 - \frac{v_{GS}}{V_P}\right)^2 \tag{6.23}$$

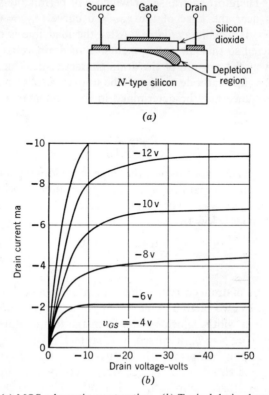

Fig. 6.25. (*a*) MOS schematic construction. (*b*) Typical drain characteristics.

where I_{DSS} is the value of i_D at $v_{GS} = 0$. Also, the transconductance g_m is related to v_{GS} by the following equation!

$$g_m = g_{mo}\left(1 - \frac{v_{GS}}{V_P}\right) \qquad (6.24)$$

where g_{mo} is the value of g_m at $v_{GS} = 0$. Then, substituting Eqs. 6.23 and 6.24 into Eq. 6.22,

$$\frac{I_{DSS}}{g_{mo}}\left(1 - \frac{v_{GS}}{V_P}\right) = 0.315 \text{ v} \qquad (6.25)$$

But, using Eq. 6.23,

$$g_{mo} = \frac{di_D}{dv_{GS}}\bigg|_{v_{GS}=0} = \frac{-2I_{DSS}}{V_P} \qquad (6.26)$$

Substituting this value of g_{mo} into Eq. 6.25,

$$V_P - v_{GS} = -0.63 \text{ v} \qquad (6.27)$$

or

$$v_{GS} = V_P + 0.63 \text{ v} \tag{6.28}$$

Equation 6.28 shows that zero thermal drift may be achieved if the FET is biased 0.63 v above the pinch-off voltage V_P. Note that V_P and v_{GS} are negative for an n-channel FET. All signs should be reversed for a p-channel FET.

A special type of field effect transistor is the metal-oxide-semiconductor (MOS) (Fig. 6.25). In this type, the depletion region is replaced by a thin layer of silicon oxide, which is a good insulator, and the semiconductor which formed the gate is replaced by a metal conductor. A schematic representation of a typical structure is shown in Fig. 6.25a. The principle of operation is similar to a conventional field effect transistor but is somewhat more complex. A detailed description of the principle of operation may be found in the literature.[4] The insulating layer permits large-signal operation with forward bias, provides extremely high input resistance, of the order of 10^{15} ohms, and reduces the input capacitance of the device. A typical set of drain characteristics for a MOS field-effect transistor is shown in Fig. 6.25b.

PROB. 6.14. The transistor of Fig. 6.21 is used as an amplifier with a resistive load and $V_{DD} = 35$ v. Design the amplifier for the Q point $v_{GS} = 0$. Draw a circuit diagram and determine the voltage and power gains. *Answer: $R_L = 6.8$ KΩ, $G_v = -12.3$.*

PROB. 6.15. The amplifier of Prob. 6.14 is to be biased for zero drift. Select the Q point, draw a circuit diagram, and determine the values of all components. Use source (like cathode) bias and bypass for frequencies down to 30 Hz. Determine the voltage and power gains.

6.9 THE UNIJUNCTION TRANSISTOR

The unijunction transistor is composed of a bar of n-type semi-conductor material with an electrical connection on each end. The leads to these two connections are called base leads—*base-one* B_1 and *base-two* B_2. A third connection is made at a position between the two end connections where a single p-n junction has been formed. The lead to this junction is called the *emitter* lead E. The construction of the unijunction transistor is reflected in the symbol which is given in Fig. 6.26a. The equivalent circuit for the transistor is given in Fig. 6.26b.

Under normal conditions, the base-one B_1 is connected as the common terminal. Then, if the emitter is opened, the transistor acts as a voltage

---

[4] *Electronics*, McGraw-Hill, November 1964.

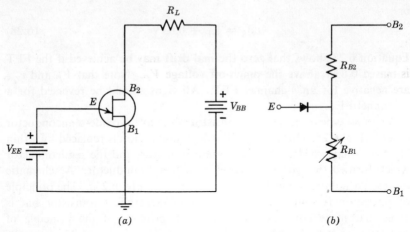

Fig. 6.26. (*a*) The symbol and biasing arrangement of a unijunction transistor. (*b*) An equivalent circuit for the unijunction transistor.

divider network and the emitter voltage is a given fraction of the base-two voltage.

$$V_{EO} = \eta V_{B2} \tag{6.29}$$

If the emitter is biased at a potential less than V_{EO}, the *p-n* junction is reverse biased and only the diode saturation current flows in the emitter circuit. If the voltage of the emitter is increased above V_{EO}, the junction becomes forward biased. Under these conditions, holes are injected from the *p*-material into the *n*-bar. These holes are repelled by the positive base-two end of the bar and they are attracted toward the base-one end

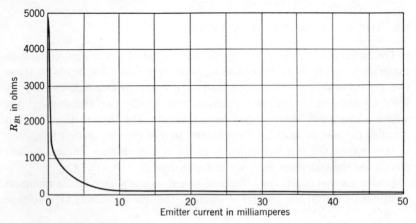

Fig. 6.27. A plot of R_{B1} vs emitter current for a 2N492.

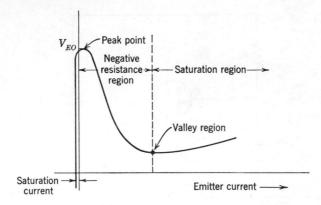

Fig. 6.28. The emitter current-voltage characteristics of a unijunction transistor.

of the bar. This accumulation of p-carriers in the emitter-to-base-one region results in a decrease of resistance for resistor R_{B1} (Fig. 6.27). The decrease of resistance R_{B1} results in a lower emitter voltage. Thus, a negative resistance results since more emitter current results in lower voltage. As more p-carriers are injected, a condition of saturation will eventually be reached. This action is shown in Fig. 6.27 and in the current-voltage characteristics in Fig. 6.28. The similarity of these characteristics to those of the tunnel diode is at once evident. The unijunction transistor, however, has three terminals. Therefore, in order to completely describe the characteristics, a family of curves (as given in Fig. 6.29) is required.

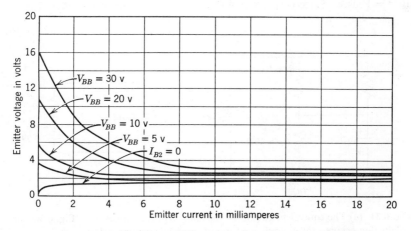

Fig. 6.29. Static characteristic curves of a unijunction transistor.

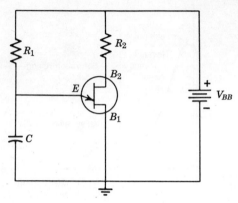

Fig. 6.30. A relaxation oscillator.

Unijunction transistors are used extensively in oscillator, pulse, and voltage sensing circuits. A typical application is illustrated by the relaxation oscillator of Fig. 6.30. This circuit will be used to illustrate a typical use for a unijunction transistor.

Example 6.3. A transistor is connected as shown in Fig. 6.30. If $V_{BB} = 12$ v, $R_1 = 100$ KΩ, $R_2 = 2.5$ KΩ, and $C = 0.01$ μfd, plot the output voltage across capacitor C. The transistor is a 2N492 with the following characteristics: $R_{B1} + R_{B2} = R_{BB} \approx 7.5$ KΩ, $\eta \approx 0.67$.

At time $t = 0$, the 12 v battery is applied. The capacitor is uncharged and a current of $12/(7.5$ KΩ $+ 2.5$ KΩ$) = 1.2$ ma flows through R_2. The base B_2 is at a potential of 9 v and V_{EO} (from Eq. 6.29) is $9 \times 0.67 = 6$ v. Thus, the emitter junction is reverse biased and can be considered as if it were an open circuit. The capacitor C charges through R_1 with a time constant of $R_1 C = 10^5 \times 10^{-8} = 10^{-3} = 1$ msec. Since C is charging toward 12 v, the equation for v_C is

$$v_C = 12(1 - e^{-(t/10^{-3})}) \tag{6.30}$$

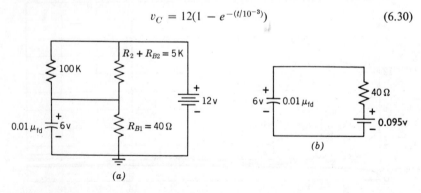

Fig. 6.31. (a) The equivalent circuit for the emitter of the transistor in Fig. 6.30 when conduction occurs. (b) A simplified form of this equivalent circuit.

The voltage on the capacitor will be 6 v in 692 μ seconds. At this time, t_1, the emitter becomes forward biased and current begins to flow into the emitter. The resistor R_{B1} decreases and more current flows into the emitter. This action is accumulative and occurs very rapidly driving the resistor R_{B1} into saturation.

From Fig. 6.27, the saturation resistance is about 40 ohms or so. Thus, the emitter circuit becomes approximately that shown in Fig. 6.31a. When a Thevenin's equivalent circuit is constructed for the network that connects to the capacitor, the circuit is simplified to the form shown in Fig. 6.31b. This circuit has a time constant of $4 \times 10 \times 10^{-8} = 0.4$ μ seconds. The capacitor is discharging toward *essentially* zero potential. Thus, in about 5 time constants, or 2 μ seconds, the capacitor C is essentially discharged. The excess holes are swept out of the emitter-to-base-one region and the resistance R_{B1} returns to its

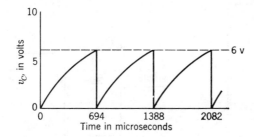

Fig. 6.32. The waveform of the circuit shown in Fig. 6.30.

normal condition. The circuit is now the same as at time $t = 0$, so the entire process is repeated. Thus, the voltage waveform across the capacitor has the form shown in Fig. 6.32.

The relaxation oscillator can be used in conjunction with other wave-shaping circuits to produce a variety of pulse circuits.[5] On a note of caution, the power ratings of the transistor should not be exceeded. Since R_{B1} may become very small, the voltage drop across and the current through R_{B2} may become large enough to damage the transistor.

PROB. 6.16. (*a*) Determine the power dissipated in the transistor of Example 6.3 when the emitter is cutoff. *Answer: 10.8 mw.*

(*b*) Determine the power dissipated when the emitter junction first becomes saturated. *Answer: 14.4 mw in R_{B2} and 900 mw in R_{B1}.*

(*c*) If the power in part *b* is assumed to be dissipated during the entire 2 μ second discharging time, what is the average power dissipated in this transistor? *Answer: 13.4 mw.*

PROB. 6.17. Repeat Example 6.3 if R_2 is changed to 7.5 KΩ, and R_1 is changed to 500 KΩ.

[5] For additional unijunction circuits see *G. E. Transistor Manual*, Seventh Edition, General Electric Co., Syracuse, New York, 1964, pp. 301–347.

6.10   THE SILICON CONTROLLED RECTIFIER

A semiconductor device known as a "Thyrode" or *Silicon controlled rectifier* (SCR) is constructed as shown in Fig. 6.33a. The action of this device can be explained by the equivalent circuit which is shown in Fig. 6.33b. This equivalent circuit is composed of an *n-p-n* transistor and *p-n-p* transistor connected as shown. In one condition, (gate negative) the bias to the gate (the base of the *n-p-n*) maintains the *n-p-n* transistor in the cutoff

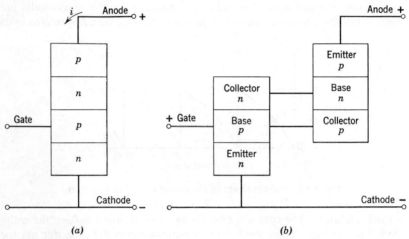

Fig. 6.33. The silicon-controlled rectifier. (*a*) Actual construction;   (*b*) equivalent electrical circuit.

condition. Since no collector current flows in the *n-p-n* transistor, the *p-n-p* transistor is also cutoff. Therefore, the impedance between anode and cathode is very high.

If the bias on the gate is changed so the *n-p-n* unit starts to conduct, a collector current will flow into the *n-p-n* collector from the base of the *p-n-p* unit. This flow of current from the *p-n-p* base causes collector current to flow in the *p-n-p* transistor. The collector current of the *p-n-p* transistor is fed to the base of the *n-p-n* transistor. The action is accumulative since an increase of current in one unit causes an increase of current in the other unit. As a result of this action, both transistors are driven to current saturation. Consequently, the impedance between anode and cathode becomes very low.

As soon as the self-regeneration commences, the gate (the reason for this name is now obvious) loses all control over the action. The collector current from the *p-n-p* unit is much larger than the external gate current.

As a result, the external gate circuit can turn the SCR ON but cannot turn the switch OFF. To turn the SCR OFF the gate bias must be in the reverse direction and the anode voltage reduced essentially to zero. In this condition, no current flows through the *p-n-p* unit and the gate regains control of the circuit.

If the gate is maintained at cutoff (negative potential) and the voltage on the anode is varied, the characteristics are as indicated in Fig. 6.34.

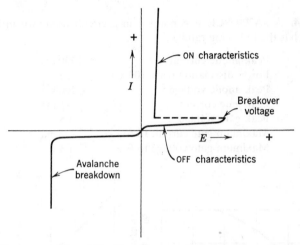

Fig. 6.34. The curve of *I* vs *V* for the silicon-controlled rectifier. (Courtesy of Solid State Products, Inc.)

At a positive anode potential, which corresponds somewhat with the avalanche breakdown potential in the reverse bias case, the SCR will turn itself ON. The potential required is known as the *"breakover voltage."* In effect, the current through the device does start to increase as in the regular avalanche breakdown. (Some junctions are forward biased and some are reverse biased.) However, this increasing current through the *p-n-p* section produces base current for the *n-p-n* section, and the regenerative action quickly takes over turning the SCR ON. The maximum voltage ratings of the device are chosen below the avalanche breakdown voltage and the breakover voltage.[6] Consequently, the SCR can only be turned ON with the gate as long as recommended maximum voltage ratings are not exceeded. An example will illustrate the usefulness of the silicon controlled rectifier.

[6] A *p-n-p-n* device with only two leads (corresponding to the anode and cathode) has also been developed. This device is known as a Shockley diode and uses the breakover voltage to switch the device ON. It is also possible to purchase a light-operated *p-n-p-n* device.

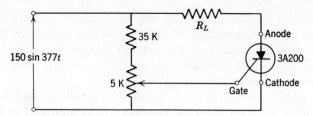

Fig. 6.35. A silicon-controlled rectifier connected to a load.

Example 6.4. A 3A200 SCR is connected in a circuit as shown in Fig. 6.35. The 3A200 has the following ratings:

Peak anode current	1000 ma
Power dissipation (case 100°C)	2.5 w
Peak anode voltage	±200 v
Peak gate current	25 ma
Peak gate voltage	±5 v
Maximum gate current to fire	+2 ma
Maximum gate voltage to fire	+3 v

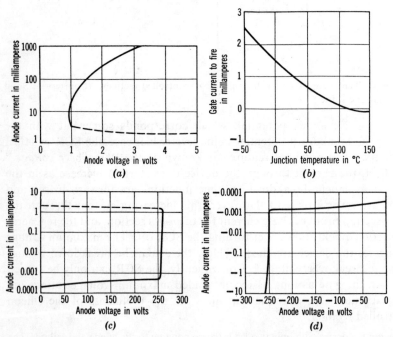

Fig. 6.36. Electrical characteristics of the 3A200 SCR. (*a*) Forward ON; (*b*) gate current to fire; (*c*) forward OFF; and (*d*) reverse. (Courtesy of Solid State Products, Inc.)

The electrical characteristics are as shown in Fig. 6.36. The load resistor R_L is 1000 Ω.

Assume the adjustable contact of the 5 KΩ resistor is adjusted so the gate is effectively connected to the junction of the 5 KΩ and 35 KΩ resistors.

The approximate gate input impedance can be found by dividing the maximum gate voltage to fire by the maximum gate current to fire. Hence,

$$r_{gate} = \frac{3}{2 \times 10^{-3}} = 1500 \ \Omega \tag{6.31}$$

The actual gate circuit can be drawn as shown in Fig. 6.37. The parallel resistance of the 5 K and 1.5 K resistors is 1.15 K. The voltage across the gate-cathode junction is

$$\frac{150}{35 \ K + 1.15 \ K} \ 1.15 \ K \sin 377t \tag{6.32}$$

or

$$4.77 \sin 377t \tag{6.33}$$

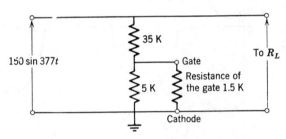

Fig. 6.37. Equivalent gate circuit for Fig. 6.35.

Now, from Fig. 6.36*b*, the gate current required to fire the SCR is 0.65 ma when the temperature is 50°C. (This 50°C is the assumed operating temperature.) If the gate resistance is constant,[7] the voltage across the gate-cathode junction will be

$$6.5 \times 10^{-4} \times 1.5 \times 10^3 = 0.975 \ v \tag{6.34}$$

This value of 0.975 v will be achieved when

$$0.975 = 4.77 \sin \theta \tag{6.35}$$

or

$$\theta = 11.8° = 0.206 \ radians \tag{6.36}$$

Therefore, the SCR will be turned ON when $377t = 0.206$ or $t = 0.000547$ sec. The SCR will remain ON until the anode potential is reduced essentially to zero.

[7] The gate resistance will, of course, change with the temperature and with the gate current magnitude. However, because operating temperatures are not precisely known, the solution is not precise. Hence, the error introduced by assuming $r_{gate} = 1.5$ KΩ can usually be ignored.

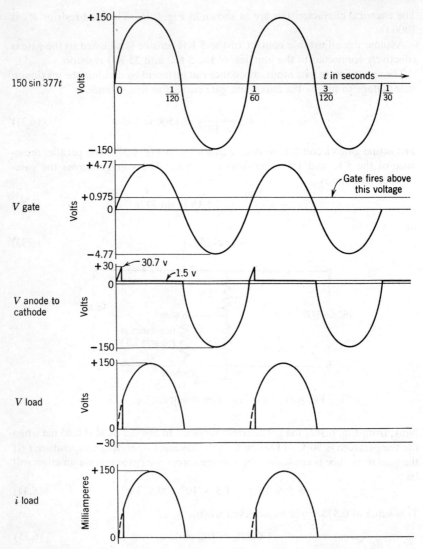

Fig. 6.38. The voltages and current in the circuit shown in Fig. 6.35.

(Actually, according to Fig. 6.36a the SCR will turn OFF when the anode potential is less than 0.8 v.)

When the SCR is turned ON, the voltage across the SCR is 0.8 v for a current of 3 ma and increases to 1.5 v at 150 ma anode current (Fig. 6.36a). At the instant the SCR is turned ON, the voltage across the load and SCR is

$$150 \sin 0.206 = 30.7 \text{ v} \qquad\qquad (6.37)$$

Approximately 1-v drop exists across the SCR and the remaining 29.7 v are across the load R_L. The current through the load is equal to $^{29.7}/_{1000}$ or 29.7 ma. At the instant peak voltage is applied, the voltage drop across the SCR is 1.5 v and the remaining 148.5 v is across the load. The peak current is, therefore, equal to 148.5 ma.

The voltages and current of the circuit are plotted in Fig. 6.38.

The 5 KΩ resistor in Fig. 6.35 can be adjusted so the SCR will not be turned ON until the voltage is almost at the peak value. The average current through the load can, therefore, be controlled over about a 2:1 range by the circuit just considered.

If the voltage to the gate is shifted in phase as well as amplitude, the current may be controlled from maximum to almost zero.

PROB. 6.18. The tap on the 5 KΩ resistor of Fig. 6.35 is set 1 KΩ above ground. Find the voltages and currents of the circuit under these conditions. Plot curves similar to those in Fig. 6.38 for these conditions.

PROB. 6.19. The voltage to the load and switch of Fig. 6.35 is 150 sin 377t. The voltage to the gate has been shifted

$$V_{\text{gate}} = 4.77 \sin (377t - 1 \text{ radian})$$

Find the voltages and currents of the circuit under these conditions. Plot curves of voltages and currents as functions of time.

6.11 THE GAS TRIODE OR THYRATRON

A gas-filled triode has characteristics quite similar to those of the SCR just discussed. As long as the control grid of the gas triode is maintained sufficiently negative, the tube is cut off and no plate current flows. If the plate has a positive potential and the control grid bias is reduced, a stream of electrons will start to flow between the cathode and plate. If the plate potential is well above the ionizing potential of the gas, these electrons will cause the gas to ionize and a self-sustaining glow discharge will result. The tube is said to "fire" when the glow discharge commences.

Once the gas in the tube has been ionized, positive ions will be attracted to the negative control grid. Since these positive ions travel slowly compared to the electrons, the space around the control grid will contain a net positive charge. As a consequence, the field of the control grid is neutralized by this positive space charge. Therefore, the control grid loses control as soon as the tube "fires." These positive ions also cause a current flow in the grid circuit. As a result, most thyratron circuits have a resistor inserted in series with the grid to limit this grid current to a safe value.

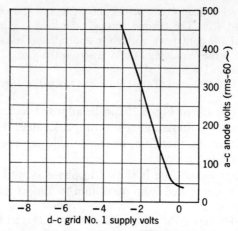

Fig. 6.39. Average firing characteristics of a 2D21 gas thyratron.

Once the tube has fired, the plate must be reduced below the ionizing potential of the gas before the control grid can regain control. The actual firing potential of the control grid is dependent on the potential on the plate. Typical firing conditions for a 2D21 are given in Fig. 6.39. The actual firing voltages are dependent on gas temperatures, gas pressures, condition on electrodes, etc.

PROB. 6.20. A gas triode is connected as shown in Fig. 6.40. Assume the tube has the same characteristics as the 2D21 of Fig. 6.39.

(a) Plot the applied voltage as a function of time.

(b) Plot the current through the 26,500-Ω resistor and the capacitor C as a function of time if C is (1) 1 μf, (2) 0.1 μf, (3) 0.01 μf. (Assume the grid draws no current for this part.)

(c) Plot the current through the 100-Ω load resistor for the three conditions of part b. When the tube fires, the plate to cathode potential is 10 v.

(d) Find the magnitude of the resistor R_S which will limit the maximum grid current to 2 ma. Neglect the internal resistance of the tube.

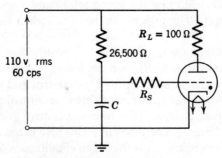

Fig. 6.40. The circuit for Prob. 6.20.

PROB. 6.21. Design a pentode amplifier stage which will give a voltage gain of 100. Use a 6AU6 tube and do not apply more than 300 v to the plate circuit. Indicate the size of all resistors and capacitors if 60 Hz is the lowest frequency to be used.

PROB. 6.22. The "typical operating conditions" of a 6J7 pentode are listed as

Plate voltage = 150 v   Plate current = 3.5 ma
Screen voltage = 100 v   Screen current = 0.5 ma
Grid voltage = −2 v

(*a*) Draw the circuit diagram for a pentode amplifier. (*b*) Use above voltages and currents to determine values of all resistors and capacitors in the circuit. A V_{PP} supply of 250 v is available and the lowest frequency to be amplified has an ω of 500. Assume $\Delta v_{G2}/\Delta i_{G2} = 40,000$.

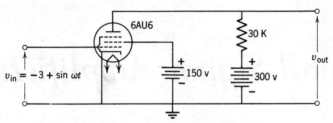

Fig. 6.41. The circuit configuration for Prob. 6.23.

PROB. 6.23. A 6AU6 tube is connected as shown in Fig. 6.41. Sketch the output signal listing maximum, minimum, and quiescent values.

7

Small-Signal Amplifiers

Electronic amplifiers are customarily used to amplify the signal from a transducer such as a microphone, phonograph pickup, radio antenna, or strain gage to a level which is adequate for the operation of another transducer such as a loudspeaker or recording device. For example, the amplifier in a public address system must raise the signal level of the few picowatts available from the microphone to the several watts of power required by the loudspeaker. The amplifier usually consists of several stages. A stage is composed of an amplifying device such as a vacuum tube or transistor along with its associated circuit components. The stages are usually connected in cascade; that is, the output of one stage is connected to the input of the following stage.

The final amplifier in the chain is required to furnish the necessary power to the transducer in the output. Therefore, this final amplifier is called a power amplifier. This power amplifier must operate at high signal levels to accomplish its purpose. If the power amplifier is a vacuum tube, it may require appreciable input voltage but very little signal power for its operation. Consequently, the amplifiers which precede the vacuum tube power amplifier are usually called voltage amplifiers. On the other hand, if the power amplifier is a transistor, it may require appreciable current but very little input power for its operation. The preceding amplifiers may then be referred to as current amplifiers.

Both current and voltage amplifiers may operate at very low power levels, so the efficiency of the amplifier is not usually of prime concern. Also, the signal levels are small compared with those of the power amplifier. These factors make it possible to design amplifiers which have negligibly small distortion. Under these conditions the equivalent circuits may be used with a high-degree of accuracy. This type of amplifier will be known as a small-signal amplifier in this treatment.

There is no intentional frequency selection in the untuned amplifier. In fact, an absence of frequency discrimination is desirable. This lack of discrimination is in contrast with the tuned amplifier which is usually designed to select a band of frequencies and reject those not lying within the desired band. Small-signal tuned amplifiers are discussed in Chapter 8.

The equivalent circuits will be used to predict the response of vacuum tube and transistor amplifiers for various types of excitation. The most direct approach would be to draw a complete equivalent circuit of the amplifier and its coupling device; then derive an equation for the transfer function which is the ratio of the output quantity, or response, to the input quantity, or excitation. This transfer function would be a function of the complex frequency s.[1] As a result, the complete response could be obtained for any specified excitation or driving function. The response as a function of time could be obtained for any given excitation by obtaining the inverse transform of the product of the transfer function and the s-domain excitation. The steady-state frequency response could be obtained by replacing s by $j\omega$ in the transfer function.

One major problem in the procedure just outlined is the complexity of the equivalent circuit which results when the stray capacitance of the circuit is included. This problem can be circumvented by resolving it into two parts. First, the transfer function may be obtained for the "low-frequency" equivalent circuit in which the small stray capacitance and inductance may be neglected. Next, the transfer function may be obtained for the "high-frequency" equivalent circuit, in which the large series capacitors become short circuits and large shunt inductors become open circuits. Then the transfer functions of these two simplified equivalent

---

[1] A complete treatment of the complex frequency concept is given in many circuit texts among them, *Network Analysis*, Second Edition by M. E. Van Valkenburg, Prentice-Hall, Englewood Cliffs, New Jersey, 1964. The reader who is unfamiliar with this concept can understand the material which follows, in a restricted sense, by substituting $j\omega$ for s in the equations and *sinusoidal steady state* in place of *s domain* in the written material. When nonsinusoidal waveforms are encountered, the response characteristics must be accepted without understandable proof unless the reader is familiar with the Laplace Transformation.

circuits may be combined to provide a complete transfer function of the amplifier stage. The transfer function of an amplifier which contains several stages is the product of the transfer functions of the individual stages, providing the amplifying devices (transistors, tubes, etc.) provide good isolation between the output and input of each stage.

7.1 THE *R-C* COUPLED AMPLIFIER

The resistance-capacitance coupled amplifier will be used to illustrate the foregoing procedure for determining the response of an amplifier. Typical *R-C* coupling circuits for both transistors and tubes are shown in

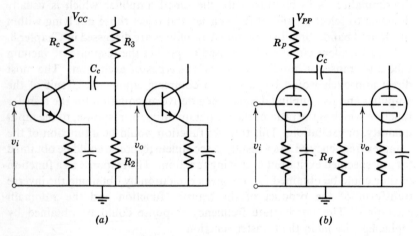

(a)   *(b)*

Fig. 7.1. Typical resistance-capacity coupled amplifiers. (*a*) Transistor amplifier; (*b*) tube amplifier.

Fig. 7.1. In the *R-C* coupled amplifier the signal components of voltage and current are transferred to the following amplifier or load while the bias components are blocked by the capacitor C_c. This *R-C* coupling, which is frequently known as resistance coupling, is a very commonly used method of coupling for amplifiers.

In the discussion which follows, the assumption is made that the emitter (or cathode) is perfectly bypassed over the useful frequency range of the amplifier. Then the frequency characteristics of the amplifier will depend on the coupling capacitor C_c and the stray circuit capacitance, but not on the emitter bypass capacitance. The validity of this assumption for a well-designed amplifier will be demonstrated in a following section.

Equivalent circuits for the amplifiers of Fig. 7.1 are drawn in Fig. 7.2. In the transistor amplifier equivalent circuit the bias resistors R_2 and R_3

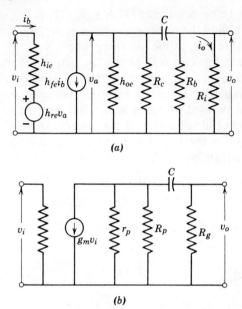

Fig. 7.2. Equivalent circuits for the amplifiers of Fig. 7.1. (*a*) Transistor; (*b*) tube.

of Fig. 7.1 were combined into their equivalent parallel resistance R_b. These equivalent circuits of Fig. 7.2 can be further simplified by combining the parallel resistances shown. Then, if the input circuits of the two equivalent circuits are omitted, the remaining simplified equivalent circuit can represent either the transistor amplifier or the tube amplifier. This simplified equivalent circuit is presented in Fig. 7.3. From Fig. 7.2, it may be seen that when the transistor circuit is being considered, the current source $i_1 = h_{fe}i_b$, Y_l is the sum of the load conductance $1/R_c$ and the transistor output admittance (approximately h_{oe}), and Y_r is the sum of the bias conductance $1/R_b$ and the input conductance ($1/R_i$) of the following transistor (approximately $1/h_{ie}$). Observation also reveals that when the

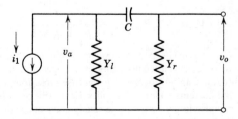

Fig. 7.3. The single equivalent circuit which results from the simplification of either circuit of Fig. 7.2.

vacuum tube is being considered, $i_1 = g_m v_{gk}$, Y_l is the sum of the load conductance $1/R_p$ and the plate conductance $g_p = 1/r_p$, and Y_r is the grid circuit conductance $1/R_g$ of the following tube.

The objective in this case is to obtain the output voltage v_o in terms of the forcing current i_1. In order to obtain a general solution without using differentials, the s-domain currents, voltages, admittances, and impedances will be used. Capital letters will be used to indicate these s-domain currents and voltages, and the complex frequency s will replace the frequency $j\omega$ in the impedance and admittance terms. Writing s-domain[2] nodal equations for the circuit of Fig. 7.3, we find that

$$(Y_l + sC)V_a - sCV_o = -I_1$$
$$-sCV_a + (Y_r + sC)V_o = 0$$

(7.1)

Solving for V_o (using determinants), we find that

$$V_o = \frac{-sCI_1}{(Y_l + sC)(Y_r + sC) - s^2C^2}$$

(7.2)

$$V_o = -I_1 \frac{sC}{Y_l Y_r + (Y_l + Y_r)sC}$$

(7.3)

$$V_o = \frac{-I_1}{Y_l + Y_r} \frac{s}{s + \dfrac{Y_l Y_r}{(Y_l + Y_r)C}}$$

(7.4)

but

$$\frac{Y_l + Y_r}{Y_l Y_r} = R_l + R_r$$

(7.5)

where

$$R_l = \frac{1}{Y_l} \quad \text{and} \quad R_r = \frac{1}{Y_r}$$

then

$$V_o = \frac{-I_1}{Y_t} \frac{s}{s + 1/(R_l + R_r)C}$$

(7.6)

where $Y_t = Y_l + Y_r$. Or in alternative form

$$V_o = -I_1 R_{sh} \frac{s}{s + 1/(R_l + R_r)C}$$

(7.7)

[2] As noted in the *List of Symbols* (p. xx), lower case letters with lower case subscripts are used to represent time-varying components of voltages and currents. Thus, v_o is understood to imply $v_o(t)$. Capital letters with lower case subscripts are used to represent s-domain voltages and currents. Thus, V_o implies $V_o(s)$. (Since $j\omega$ is a special case of $s(s = \sigma + j\omega)$, V_o may also imply $V_o(j\omega)$ if the steady-state sinusoidal problem is being considered.) The reader should be especially careful not to intermix s-domain and time-domain terms.

where

$$R_{sh} = 1/Y_t$$

let

$$\omega_1 = \frac{1}{(R_l + R_r)C} \tag{7.8}$$

ω_1 is then the angular frequency at which the reactance of the coupling capacitor has the same magnitude as the total resistance in series with it $(R_l + R_r)$ because from Eq. 7.8

$$R_l + R_r = \frac{1}{\omega_1 C} \tag{7.9}$$

Equation 7.7 may then be written

$$V_o = -I_1 R_{sh} \frac{s}{s + \omega_1} \tag{7.10}$$

In a vacuum tube amplifier where $I_1 = g_m V_{gk}$

$$V_o = -g_m V_{gk} R_{sh} \frac{s}{s + \omega_1} \tag{7.11}$$

The voltage transfer function, or voltage gain is

$$G_v = \frac{V_0}{V_{gk}} = -g_m R_{sh} \frac{s}{s + \omega_1} \tag{7.12}$$

When the complex frequency s becomes large in comparison with ω_1, the transfer function (Eq. 7.12) reduces to

$$G_v \simeq -g_m R_{sh} = -K_v \tag{7.13}$$

This K_v of Eq. 7.13 is commonly known as the *reference voltage gain* of the amplifier. Sometimes K_v is also known as the mid-frequency voltage gain.

As previously mentioned, when the transistor amplifier is considered, the current I_1 of Eq. 7.10 is $h_{fe}I_b$ and Eq. 7.10 becomes

$$V_o = -h_{fe}I_b R_{sh} \frac{s}{s + \omega_1} \tag{7.14}$$

In the transistor, the current transfer function or current gain is usually of greater interest than is the voltage gain. The current gain may be easily obtained after making the substitution

$$V_o = I_o R_i \tag{7.15}$$

where I_o is the current which flows through the input resistance R_i of the following transistor. Substituting Eq. 7.15 into Eq. 7.14, we have

$$I_o R_i = -h_{fe}I_b R_{sh} \frac{s}{s + \omega_1} \tag{7.16}$$

and

$$G_i = \frac{I_o}{I_b} = -\frac{h_{fe}R_{sh}}{R_i}\frac{s}{s + \omega_1} \tag{7.17}$$

As the frequency s becomes large in comparison with ω_1, Eq. 7.17 becomes

$$G_i \simeq -\frac{h_{fe}R_{sh}}{R_i} = -K_i \tag{7.18}$$

where K_i is the *reference current gain* of the transistor amplifier.

Equations 7.12, 7.13, 7.17, and 7.18 indicate that the transfer function of an *R-C* coupled amplifier (neglecting stray capacitance and inductance) may be written

$$G = -K\frac{s}{s + \omega_1} \tag{7.19}$$

where K is the reference (or mid-frequency) voltage or current gain of the amplifier under consideration. As noted before, the negative sign appears because of the polarity reversal experienced in the common-emitter amplifier. In other configurations, the negative sign would not appear.

PROB. 7.1. A typical small-signal transistor has $h_{ie} = 1\ \text{K}\Omega$, $h_{fe} = 100$, $h_{re} = 5 \times 10^{-4}$, and $h_{oe} = 5 \times 10^{-5}$ mhos, at a given operating point. Several of these transistors are used in cascade with d-c load resistors $R_c = 5\ \text{K}\Omega$. Neglecting the loading effect of the bias resistors and the reactance of the coupling capacitors, verify the assumptions that $R_o \simeq 1/h_{oe}$ and $R_i \simeq h_{ie}$. What are the percentage differences between R_i and h_{ie} and between the actual output admittance G_o and h_{oe}?

PROB. 7.2. Develop an expression for the reference voltage gain of a transistor amplifier. *Answer:* $G_v = h_f R_{sh}/(h_r h_f R_{sh} - 1)$.

7.2 SAG AND LOW-FREQUENCY RESPONSE

Since the transfer function is defined as the ratio of the s-domain response to the s-domain excitation, the s-domain voltage response is

$$V_o = V_i G \tag{7.20}$$

Then the s-domain response may be obtained for any specific excitation. For example, let us consider a negative step input (excitation) of magnitude M. Since the Laplace transform of a step function of magnitude M is M/s, the s-domain response of an $R-C$ coupled amplifier to this step function is

$$V_o = -\frac{M}{s}\left(-K\frac{s}{s + \omega_1}\right) = MK\frac{1}{s + \omega_1} \tag{7.21}$$

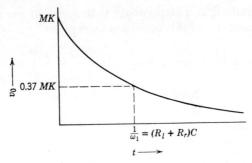

Fig. 7.4. Time response of an R-C coupled amplifier to a negative step input of magnitude M.

Taking the inverse transform of each side of Eq. 7.21, we find that

$$v_o = MKe^{-\omega_1 t} \tag{7.22}$$

A sketch of the output voltage v_o as a function of time is given in Fig. 7.4. The output approaches zero as time approaches infinity. This response is to be expected because a step voltage is merely a d-c voltage that is switched into the amplifier at the time of reference, $t = 0$. Since the coupling capacitor blocks d-c, the steady-state output must be zero. If the step input voltage had been of positive polarity, the polarity of the output voltage would, of course, be reversed.

Although the R-C coupled amplifier is not suitable for amplifying d-c signals, the information gained from the step function analysis is very useful in predicting the behavior of the amplifier when it is called on to amplify rectangular pulses. A series of rectangular pulses is shown in Fig. 7.5. These pulses have amplitude M, pulse duration d, and period (of repetition) T. In the case $d = T/2$, this signal is known as a square wave.

If we assume the excitation to be a series of voltage pulses as illustrated in Fig. 7.5, we may express the time-domain input voltage as the sum of a series of step voltages.

$$v_i = M[u(t) - u(t - d) + u(t - T) - u(t - (T + d)) + u(t - 2T) \cdots] \tag{7.23}$$

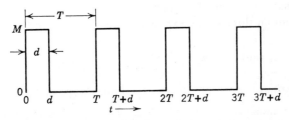

Fig. 7.5. A series of rectangular pulses.

The $u(t - a)$ symbolizes a step voltage that occurs at $t = a$ and so on. The Laplace transform of this excitation voltage is

$$V_i = M\left(\frac{1}{s} - \frac{e^{-ds}}{s} + \frac{e^{-Ts}}{s} - \frac{e^{-(T+d)s}}{s} + \frac{e^{-2Ts}}{s} \cdots\right) \quad (7.24)$$

The s-domain output voltage is

$$V_o = -MK\left(\frac{1}{s + \omega_1} - \frac{e^{-ds}}{s + \omega_1} + \frac{e^{-Ts}}{s + \omega_1} - \frac{e^{-(T+d)s}}{s + \omega_1} + \frac{e^{-2Ts}}{s + \omega_1} \cdots\right)$$

$$(7.25)$$

The time-domain response is obtained from the inverse transform[3]

$$v_o = -MK[e^{-\omega_1 t} - u(t - d)e^{-\omega_1(t-d)} + u(t - T)e^{-\omega_1(t-T)}$$
$$- u(t - T - d)e^{-\omega_1(t-T-d)} + u(t - 2T)e^{-\omega_1(t-2T)} \ldots] \quad (7.26)$$

The time response may be plotted by adding the exponential terms of Eq. 7.26, as illustrated in Fig. 7.6. Since the average steady-state current through the coupling capacitor must be zero, the cross-hatched area labeled A below the reference axis must approach the corresponding area labeled B above the axis after several periods T have elapsed.

Ideally, the output voltage should remain constant during the pulse. However, the output current and voltage decays exponentially as shown because of the charging of the coupling capacitor. The departure of the actual output from the ideal flat response at the termination of the pulse is called *sag*. From a consideration of the first pulse as shown in Fig. 7.6, the sag can be determined by solving Eq. 7.26 at $t = d$. Then

$$\text{Sag}_1 = KM(1 - e^{-\omega_1 d}) \quad (7.27)$$

The fractional sag, or ratio of sag to the output at the beginning of the pulse, is of greater significance than the amount of sag.

$$\text{Fractional sag} = \frac{\text{Sag}_1}{KM} = 1 - e^{-\omega_1 d} \quad (7.28)$$

If the pulse duration d is small in comparison with $1/\omega_1 = (R_l + R_r)C$, the fractional sag can be determined more easily than by the use of Eq. 7.28. The initial slope of the exponential decay is, using Eq. 7.26,

$$\text{Initial slope} = \frac{d(-KMe^{-\omega_1 t})}{dt}\bigg|_{t=0} = KM\omega_1 \quad (7.29)$$

The exponential sag closely follows the initial slope as long as the pulse

---

[3] This time transformation is treated in *Network Analysis*, Second Edition, by M. E. Van Valkenburg, Prentice-Hall, Englewood Cliffs, N.J., 1964.

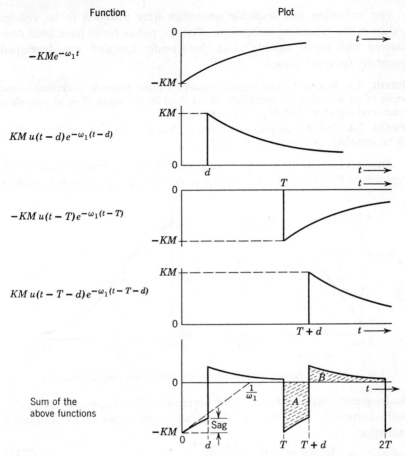

Function   Plot

$-KMe^{-\omega_1 t}$

$KM u(t - d)e^{-\omega_1(t - d)}$

$-KM u(t - T)e^{-\omega_1(t - T)}$

$KM u(t - T - d)e^{-\omega_1(t - T - d)}$

Sum of the
above functions

Fig. 7.6. The time response of an R-C coupled amplifier to a periodic rectangular pulse.

duration is small (0.1 or less) in comparison with the time constant $1/\omega_1$. Then the total sag is approximately equal to the pulse duration times the initial slope

$$\text{Sag} \simeq KM\omega_1 d \qquad (7.30)$$

and

$$\text{Fractional sag} \simeq \omega_1 d \qquad (7.31)$$

Equation 7.31 points up the desirability of a small value of ω_1 when rectangular pulses are to be amplified.

Figure 7.6 shows that the first pulse after $t = 0$ has greater sag than the succeeding pulses. The sag decreases somewhat as the transient dies out. However, the fractional sag remains constant if the pulse amplitude is measured from the base line.

The excitation and response quantities were assumed to be voltage pulses in the preceding discussion. Current pulses could have been considered with equal validity since the transfer function was developed generally for either case.

PROB. 7.3. A periodic rectangular pulse of 1 msec duration is applied to the input of an *R-C* coupled amplifier. What must be the value of ω_1 to provide a fractional sag of 0.05 or 5%? *Answer: $\omega_1 \simeq 50$.*

PROB. 7.4. The *R-C* amplifier of Prob. 7.3 has $R_l = 10\ \text{K}\Omega$ and $R_r = 2\ \text{K}\Omega$. What coupling capacitance is needed?

An expression of the gain as a function of frequency may be obtained by replacing s by $j\omega$ in Eq. 7.19. A plot of G as a function of ω is known as

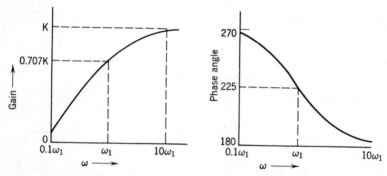

Fig. 7.7. Amplitude and phase response at low frequencies.

the frequency response curve of the amplifier. This frequency response is more accurately described as the steady-state response to sinusoidal excitation.

$$G(j\omega) = -K \frac{j\omega}{j\omega + \omega_1} \tag{7.32}$$

$$G(j\omega) = -K \frac{1}{1 - j(\omega_1/\omega)} = -K \frac{1}{1 - j(f_1/f)} \tag{7.33}$$

where $\omega_1 = 2\pi f_1$. Figure 7.7 is a plot of both phase and magnitude of $G(j\omega)$ as a function of ω. It is evident that Eq. 7.33 will yield the reference gain when ω is large compared with ω_1. The upper end of the low-frequency range is defined as $10\,\omega_1$. Above this frequency the gain does not differ from K by more than 1% and the phase shift through the amplifier is approximately 180°. The frequency and phase response plots are made on semilog-ruled paper.

PROB. 7.5. Write the gain (Eq. 7.33) in polar form for values of $\omega = 0.1\omega_1$, $\omega = \omega_1$, and $\omega = 10\,\omega_1$. Compare the results with the plots in Fig. 7.7. *Answer: At $\omega = 0.1\,\omega_1$, $G = (K/10)\underline{|-264°}$.*

PROB. 7.6. Determine the value of ω_1 for a vacuum tube amplifier which has $\mu = 20$, $r_p = 10$ KΩ, $R_p = 50$ KΩ, $R_g = 0.5$ megohm, and $C_C = 0.2$ μf. What would be the value of f_1?

In a pole-zero plot of Eq. 7.19 given in Fig. 7.8, the scale factor is $-K$. The frequency and phase response can be obtained directly from the pole-zero plot. For example, the distance from the origin to the specific value of ω is the magnitude of the numerator of Eq. 7.32. In addition, the angle between the positive real axis and the $j\omega$ axis is the angle of the numerator.

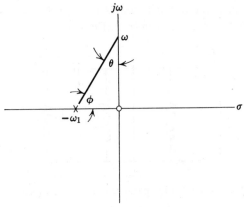

Fig. 7.8. A pole-zero plot for the R-C coupled amplifier. Stray capacitance has been neglected.

The distance between the pole and the specific ω is the magnitude of the denominator of Eq. 7.32. The angle of the denominator is the angle ϕ between the real axis and the line drawn between the pole at ω_1 and ω. Therefore, the phase angle of the fraction is the difference between these two angles which is θ in the figure. Note that when $s = j\omega_1$, $\theta = 45°$. The pole on the negative real axis indicates an exponentially decaying term in the transient response.

7.3 THE MID-FREQUENCY RANGE

The term "mid-frequencies" is used to designate the band of frequencies for which all the reactances in the circuit are negligible. In the mid-frequencies the reactances of the coupling capacitors and bypass capacitors are so small that these reactances are assumed to be zero. Consequently, the lower limit of the mid-frequency range is defined as the frequency which is ten times ω_1. Also, at mid-frequencies the reactance of the stray shunt capacitance, which is not shown in the circuit diagram, is so large that this reactance is assumed to be infinite.

The graphical analyses presented in the preceding chapters were based on the assumption that the resistor which is connected between the collector (or plate) and the power supply is the total load resistance on the amplifier. This resistor has been designated as R_L. However, it now becomes apparent that the load impedance of an R-C coupled amplifier decreases as the frequency increases toward the mid-frequency range. This a-c load impedance Z_L is represented in the equivalent circuit of Fig. 7.9 by the elements inside the rectangular enclosure. In the mid-frequency range the load impedance becomes essentially a pure resistance r_L. This a-c load resistance r_L is the parallel combination of the d-c resistance R_L and the resistance R_r, as may be seen from Fig. 7.9.

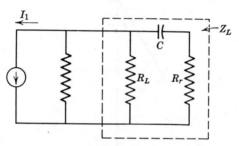

Fig. 7.9. The a-c load impedance of an R-C coupled amplifier.

The quiescent operating point of an amplifier must lie on the d-c load line which is determined by the d-c load resistance R_L and drawn in the manner described in the preceding chapters. However, in the mid-frequency range the time-varying current-voltage relationships of the collector circuit are determined by the a-c load resistance r_L. Therefore, an a-c load line can and should be drawn on the collector (or plate) characteristics to graphically display the dynamic operation of the amplifier. This a-c load line has the slope $-1/r_L$ and must pass through the quiescent operating point. The a-c load line may be readily drawn if a point in addition to the Q point is located. The x axis intercept may be located, as shown in Fig. 7.10, from the relationship

$$\Delta v_L = \Delta i_L r_L \qquad (7.34)$$

When the Q-point value (I_C or I_P) is chosen for Δi_L, then Δv_L will be the voltage difference between the Q-point voltage and the x-axis intercept of the a-c load line.

Since the a-c load impedance of an R-C coupled amplifier is less than the d-c load resistance, the a-c load line has a steeper slope than the d-c load line. In the transistor amplifier, the a-c load line is usually much steeper than the d-c load line because of the relatively low input resistance of the following transistor. This relatively steep slope of the transistor a-c load line is desirable because the objective in the transistor amplifier is to have maximum signal current transferred through the coupling capacitor to the following transistor or load. On the other hand, the vacuum tube is a voltage-operated device. Therefore, the ideal a-c load line would have the same slope as the d-c load line. Then the maximum voltage gain and maximum voltage swing would be achieved, as may be seen from Fig. 7.10*b*. However, the resistance between the control grid and the cathode would have to be infinite in order to make the a-c load line coincide with

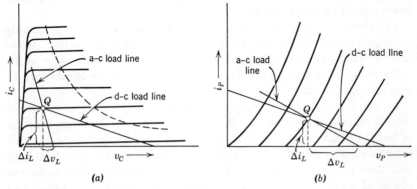

Fig. 7.10. Typical d-c and a-c load lines for *R-C* coupled (*a*) transistor and (*b*) triode tube circuits.

the d-c load line. Therefore, the grid resistor R_g is usually chosen in accordance with the maximum value recommended by the tube manufacturer.

The maximum permissible value of grid circuit resistance R_g depends on the characteristics of the tube and the completeness of the evacuation process. Since it is practically impossible to completely evacuate an enclosure, many molecules remain in a satisfactorily evacuated tube. Some ionization of these molecules occurs during normal operation of the tube. The positive ions are accelerated toward the grid because it is the most negative electrode. The grid may then become positive with respect to ground because the positive ions remove electrons from the grid and cause a small current flow in the grid circuit. If the grid circuit resistance is too high, the bias may be appreciably reduced by the IR drop in the grid circuit. This reduction of grid bias may cause serious consequences in a power amplifier which is normally biased at a point which fully utilizes the power dissipation capabilities of the tube. A significant reduction in bias from the design value then causes increased plate temperature and expulsion of gas from the electrodes. This additional gas causes increased ionization which results in increased grid current and a further reduction of bias. This cumulative chain of events will soon destroy the tube.

Electrons which leave the cathode may strike the grid even when the grid is a volt or so negative with respect to the cathode. The current which results is opposite in direction to that caused by ionization in the tube. In certain types of tubes such as high μ triodes, this contact-potential current is large compared with that due to ionization; first, because the operating bias is of the order of a volt and second, because the ionization in the tube is small compared with that of a power amplifier. This grid current reversal results from the smaller grid bias voltage and lower operating temperatures.

The electrons collected by the grid will not affect the bias appreciably if the grid circuit resistance is of the order of one megohm or less. However, if the grid circuit resistance is several megohms, a bias voltage of the order of one volt may be developed. This method is sometimes used to bias a high μ triode.

In the R-C coupled amplifier, the quiescent operating point is *not* usually located at the center of the d-c load line. The optimum location of the Q point is at least partially dependent on the value of the a-c load resistance. The design of an amplifier usually begins with the final load and then proceeds toward the input of the amplifier. The quiescent operating point of the amplifier is usually determined by the current and voltage requirements of the a-c load. The d-c load line can then be drawn through the Q point to the collector supply voltage. The a-c load can then be computed and the a-c load line drawn. This graphical construction provides visualization of the operation and linearity of the amplifier.

PROB. 7.7. A 2N192 transistor must furnish 4 ma peak-to-peak exciting current to a following transistor which has $h_{ie} = 200\ \Omega$ and shunting bias resistance $R_b = 500\ \Omega$. Choose a suitable Q point and calculate the d-c load resistance for $V_{CC} = -15$ v. Draw both the d-c and a-c load lines. Calculate the reference current, voltage, and power gains of the amplifier.

PROB. 7.8. The amplifier of Prob. 7.7 has V_{CC} raised to -25 v. Using the same Q point as Prob. 7.7, determine the d-c load resistance. Compare the current gain and temperature stability of the Q point for the two values of V_{CC}.

7.4 SHUNT CAPACITANCE IN AMPLIFIERS

Capacitance exists between the various parts of any circuit. Also, the conductors used to connect the parts have inductance. At low and middle frequencies the effect of this "stray" capacitance and inductance is negligible, but at high frequencies their effect must be taken into account. The high frequency range of an R-C coupled amplifier is the range in which the shunt capacitance affects the gain of the amplifier. Other factors which may limit the high frequency gain are discussed in a following section. The reactance of the connecting wires is usually negligible throughout the useful range of an *R-C* coupled amplifier.

The vacuum tube has capacitance between its various electrodes because these electrodes consist of conductors separated by vacuum or other insulating material. The magnitude of each interelectrode capacitance is listed in most tube manuals. These interelectrode capacitances are of the order of a few picofarads. Transistors also have capacitance between the base and each of the other two regions. This is the junction capacitance

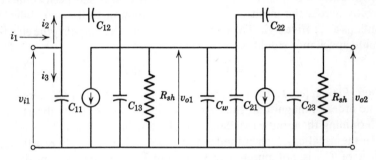

Fig. 7.11. Shunt capacitance in an *R-C* coupled amplifier.

discussed in Chapter 3. As noted, junction capacitance is dependent not only on the cross-sectional area of the junction but also on the electrode voltages of the transistor. Additional high-frequency limitations of transistor amplifiers will be discussed later in this chapter.

Figure 7.11 is a high-frequency equivalent circuit for a two-stage *R-C* coupled amplifier. The diagram includes lumped capacitances which represent the distributed circuit capacitances as well as the interelectrode capacitances of the amplifying device. In addition, the effective shunt resistance of each amplifier is shown as R_{sh}. The d-c blocking capacitors are not shown because their effects are usually negligible at the frequencies for which the shunt capacitances are effective.

Figure 7.11 will be used in determining the effective shunt capacitance at various points in the circuit. The input or driving point admittance of amplifier 1 will first be considered. This admittance may be determined if the input current i_1 can be expressed as a function of the input voltage v_{i1}. Referring to Fig. 7.11, and using s-domain variables, we find that

$$I_1 = I_3 + I_2 = sC_{11}V_{i1} + sC_{12}(V_{i1} - V_{o1}) \qquad (7.35)$$

where C_{11} is the effective capacitance between the input terminals and C_{12} is the effective capacitance between the input and output terminals of amplifier 1. But

$$V_{o1} = G_{v1}V_{i1} \tag{7.36}$$

where G_{v1} is the voltage gain of amplifier 1. Then

$$I_1 = s[C_{11} + C_{12}(1 - G_{v1})]V_{i1} \tag{7.37}$$

$$Y_i = \frac{I_1}{V_{i1}} = s[C_{11} + C_{12}(1 - G_{v1})] \tag{7.38}$$

The effective input capacitance of the circuit appears to be the bracketed term in Eq. 7.38. Notice that the mutual capacitance C_{12} has made a contribution which is $(1 - G_1)$ times as great as if it had been connected directly across the input terminals. In a common emitter amplifier, G_1 contains a negative sign. Then, for a common emitter amplifier the effective input capacitance would be

$$C_{\text{in}} = C_{11} + C_{12}(1 + |ReG_1|) \tag{7.39}$$

where ReG_1 refers to the real part of G_{v1}. In case C_{11} and C_{12} were of the same order of magnitude, the effect of C_{12} would completely dwarf C_{11} in determining the input capacitance of a high-gain amplifier.

In the usual case, when the load impedance is not purely resistive, the effect of C_{12} is not purely capacitive but includes either a positive or negative conductance term depending on the phase angle of the load. This fact may be verified in the following problems.

PROB. 7.9. If the input signal is $V \sin (5 \times 10^5)t$, calculate the input admittance of a common cathode triode amplifier which has $C_{gk} = 5$ pf, $C_{gp} = 4$ pf, and $G_v = 50\underline{|135°}$. Determine the effective input capacitance. *Answer:* $Y_i = (1.03 \times 10^{-4})\underline{|46.8°}$.

PROB. 7.10. What is the conductance and susceptance of the amplifier of Prob. 7.9 when $G_v = 50\underline{|225°}$?

It may be seen from Fig. 7.11 that the total effective capacitance in parallel with the effective shunt load resistance, R_{sh}, is the sum of the effective output capacitance of amplifier 1; the distributed wiring capacitance, C_w, and the effective input capacitance of amplifier 2. Again, the effective output capacitance of amplifier 1 may be determined by finding the sum of the currents which would flow through C_{12} and C_{13} as related to the output voltage v_{o1}. This sum, in the s domain, is

$$I_{o1} = sC_{13}V_{o1} + sC_{12}(V_{o1} - V_{i1}) \tag{7.40}$$

but, for an active amplifier, $V_{i1} = V_{o1}/G_{v1}$. Then

$$I_{o1} = s\left[C_{13} + C_{12}\left(1 - \frac{1}{G_{v1}}\right)\right]V_{o1} \tag{7.41}$$

Since G_{v1} is normally large in comparison with unity, the term $1/G_{v1}$ may be neglected. Consequently, the effective output capacitance is approximately $C_{13} + C_{12}$. The total shunt capacitance in parallel with R_{sh} is then

$$C_{sh} = C_{13} + C_{12} + C_w + C_{i2} \qquad (7.42)$$

where C_{i2} is the effective input capacitance of amplifier 2. From Fig. 7.11 and Eq. 7.38

$$C_{i2} = C_{21} + C_{22}(1 - |ReG_{v2}|) \qquad (7.43)$$

where ReG_{v2} is the real part of the transfer function $G_{v2}(j\omega)$.

As a result, the total effective capacitance in parallel with the load resistance of amplifier 1 is, within the useful range of the amplifier, approximately

$$C_{sh} = C_{13} + C_{12} + C_w + C_{21} + C_{22}(1 - |ReG_{v2}|) \qquad (7.44)$$

The reactance of capacitance C_{sh} is part of the load impedance of amplifier 1. The effect this reactance has on the response of the amplifier will be discussed in detail in the next section. However, some casual observations should be made at this point. First, the gain of an R-C coupled amplifier will decrease as the frequency increases because of the reduction in load impedance caused by the effective capacitance in parallel with the load resistance. Second, the effective input impedance of an amplifier becomes part of the load impedance of the preceding amplifier and therefore affects only the transfer function of the preceding amplifier. Similarly, the input impedance of the first amplifier stage becomes part of the load of the exciting source for that stage. Consequently, the input impedance of any stage does not affect the transfer function of that stage; but it does affect the character of its excitation.

At this point, the observing reader may be seized with a mild case of panic as he becomes aware that the transfer function of any amplifier is dependent on the input impedance and consequently the transfer function of the following amplifier. This condition, known as "interacting" stages, requires that a simultaneous solution be made of the entire amplifier rather than considering it one stage at a time. In addition, the negative conductance (or resistance) term which appears in the input admittance (or impedance) when the amplifier has an inductive load should cause concern over the stability of the amplifier because sustained oscillations frequently occur in devices which exhibit a negative resistance characteristic.

From the foregoing discussion and problems, it should be evident that capacitance between the input and output circuits of an amplifier may be very detrimental at high frequencies. As indicated in Chapter 6, the pentode tube is frequently an easy solution to the problem when the amplifier is called on to handle high frequencies. Also, transistors which have extremely small collector-base capacitance are available. The grounded grid or common base amplifier configurations may also be used to advantage under certain circumstances because the grid or base region tends to shield the input (emitter) circuit from the output (collector or plate) circuit. A technique known as neutralization is also used in some cases to eliminate the effects of the input-output capacitance. Essentially, neutralization is accomplished by providing a voltage 180° out of phase with the plate or collector voltage. An appropriate capacitance from this voltage point to the input circuit will cancel the effects of the initial input-output capacitance. This technique is discussed in detail in Chapter 8 in conjunction with tuned amplifiers.

7.5 AMPLIFICATION AT HIGH FREQUENCIES (SINGULARITIES FAR REMOVED FROM THE ORIGIN)

An equivalent circuit which is suitable for both high and mid-frequency amplification is given in Fig. 7.12. This circuit is based on the low-frequency equivalent circuit of Fig. 7.3. In the high-frequency circuit the

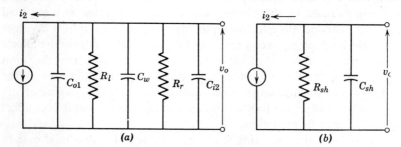

Fig. 7.12. High-frequency equivalent circuit for transistor or vacuum tube R-C coupled amplifier.

coupling capacitor has been removed because its reactance is negligible. In addition, the equivalent shunt capacitors have been added. The circuit of Fig. 7.12b has been further simplified by the combining of the parallel resistances into one equivalent resistance R_{sh} and the parallel capacitance into one equivalent capacitance C_{sh}. With this simplification, the output voltage is

$$V_o = \frac{-I_2}{Y} = \frac{-I_2}{sC_{sh} + 1/R_{sh}} \tag{7.45}$$

Finally

$$V_o = \frac{-I_2}{C_{sh}} \frac{1}{s + (1/R_{sh}C_{sh})} \tag{7.46}$$

Now, let ω_2 be the frequency at which $X_{C(sh)} = R_{sh}$. Then

$$\omega_2 = \frac{1}{R_{sh}C_{sh}} \tag{7.47}$$

and

$$V_o = \frac{-I_2}{C_{sh}} \frac{1}{s + \omega_2} \tag{7.48}$$

or

$$V_o = \frac{-I_2 R_{sh}}{R_{sh}C_{sh}} \frac{1}{s + \omega_2} = -I_2 R_{sh} \frac{\omega_2}{s + \omega_2} \tag{7.49}$$

For a vacuum tube amplifier $I_2 = g_m V_g$ and

$$G_v = \frac{V_o}{V_g} = -g_m R_{sh} \frac{\omega_2}{s + \omega_2} \tag{7.50}$$

or

$$G_v = -K \frac{\omega_2}{s + \omega_2} \tag{7.51}$$

Similarly, for a transistor amplifier $I_2 = h_{fe}I_{b1}$ and $I_{b2} = V_o/R_i$. Then,

$$G_i = \frac{I_{b2}}{I_{b1}} = -\frac{h_{fe}R_{sh}}{R_i} \frac{\omega_2}{s + \omega_2} = -K \frac{\omega_2}{s + \omega_2} \tag{7.52}$$

The time response may be obtained for any exciting function which may be specified in the s-domain. For example, to obtain the time response to a step voltage input, let $V_g = -V/s$. Then

$$V_o = \frac{VG_v}{s} = \frac{VK_v\omega_2}{s(s + \omega_2)} = \frac{A}{s} + \frac{B}{s + \omega_2} \tag{7.53}$$

where $A = VK_v$ and $B = -VK_v$. Then

$$v_o = VK_v(1 - e^{-\omega_2 t}) \tag{7.54}$$

A sketch of the output as a function of time is presented in Fig. 7.13. The output voltage rises exponentially toward the value VK_v. The "rise time" is, by definition, the time required for the voltage to rise from 10% of VK_v to 90% of VK_v. This rise time is about $2.2/\omega_2$ or $2.2R_{sh}C_{sh}$.

PROB. 7.11. An amplifier has $R_{sh} = 50 \text{ K}\Omega$ and $C_{sh} = 100$ pf. What will be the rise time of the response if a unit step function is applied to the input? *Answer: 11 usec.*

An expression for the steady-state frequency response may be obtained by letting $s = j\omega$. Then Eq. 7.52 becomes

$$G(j\omega) = -K \frac{\omega_2}{j\omega + \omega_2} = -K \frac{1}{1 + j(\omega/\omega_2)} \tag{7.55}$$

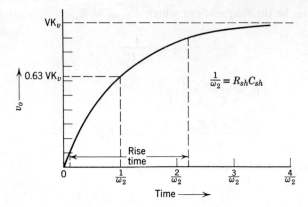

Fig. 7.13. The effect of shunt capacitance on the time response.

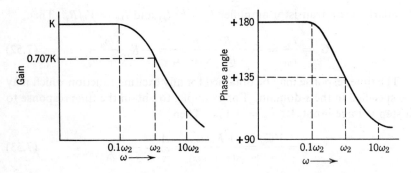

Fig. 7.14. Frequency and phase response at high frequencies.

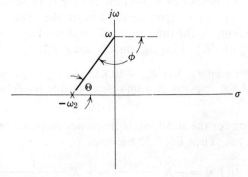

Fig. 7.15. Pole-zero plot for high-frequency case of an *R-C* coupled amplifier.

A sketch of gain and phase as a function of frequency is presented in Fig. 7.14. The high-frequency range is defined as these frequencies above $0.1\omega_2$.

A pole-zero plot of Eq. 7.52 (or 7.51) is given in Fig. 7.15. In this plot, there is a pole at $-\omega_2$, but there are no zeros except at infinity. The numerator in Eq. 7.52 is a constant (ω_2); therefore, the amplitude response at real frequencies is proportional to ω_2 divided by the distance from a specific value of s on the $j\omega$ axis to the pole at $-\omega_2$. In this case, the scale factor has a value of K.

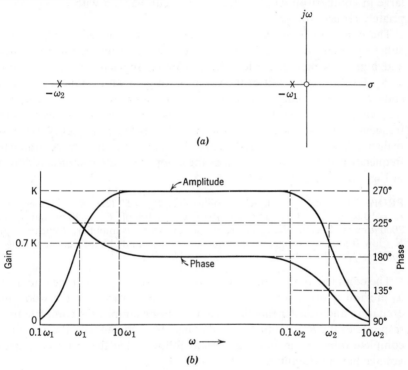

(a)

(b)

Fig. 7.16. Characteristics of an R-C coupled amplifier. (a) A pole-zero plot of the R-C coupled amplifier; (b) frequency response and phase shift of an R-C coupled amplifier.

The pole-zero plot for the high-frequency case (Fig. 7.15) and the pole-zero plot for the low-frequency case (Fig. 7.8) both represent the same R-C coupled amplifier. Therefore, a reasonable conclusion might be drawn that the poles and zeros of these two cases might be included in a single pole-zero plot, as shown in Fig. 7.16a. This is a pole-zero plot which represents the entire R-C coupled amplifier, including the stray shunt capacitance. From this pole-zero plot and inspection of the transfer functions for the low-frequency and high-frequency cases, the following transfer function may be written for the R-C coupled amplifier.

$$G = -K \frac{s\omega_2}{(s + \omega_1)(s + \omega_2)} \tag{7.56}$$

Notice that Eq. 7.56 reduces to the low-frequency equation 7.19 when s is small in comparison with ω_2. When s is large in comparison with ω_1, Eq. 7.56 reduces to the high-frequency equation 7.51. Also when s is large in comparison with ω_1 but small in comparison with ω_2, G appropriately reduces to $-K$.

The complete frequency response of the R-C coupled amplifier may either be obtained by piecing together the results from the low-frequency and high-frequency equivalent circuits or by replacing s by $j\omega$ in Eq. 7.56. To show the detail of the variation of gain with frequency at both ends of the frequency spectrum, it is necessary to use a logarithmic frequency scale. However, since the ear responds logarithmically to both frequency and amplitude variations, a logarithmic frequency scale is realistic. The gain scale may be either logarithmic or linear. A complete frequency response curve as well as the complete phase response is drawn in Fig. 7.16b.

PROB. 7.12. An R-C coupled amplifier has $R_p = 50$ KΩ, $R_g = 1$ megohm, $r_p = 10$ KΩ, $C_C = 0.05$ μf, $C_{o1} = 10$ pf, $C_{i2} = 100$ pf, $C_w = 20$ pf and $g_m = 2000$ μmhos. Sketch a frequency response curve for the amplifier. Indicate f_1, f_2, K, low-frequency range, mid-frequency range, and high-frequency range. Answer: $f_1 = 3.16$ Hz, $K_v = -16.5, f_2 = 148$ KHz.

The complete time response for any given input signal can be obtained, as previously discussed, by taking the inverse transform of the s-domain excitation and transfer function product. For example, the complete time response of the R-C coupled amplifier may be obtained with the aid of the complete transfer function Eq. 7.56 as follows. Let the input be a step-voltage having magnitude $-M$.

$$V_o = \frac{MK}{s} \frac{s\omega_2}{(s + \omega_1)(s + \omega_2)} = MK \frac{\omega_2}{(s + \omega_1)(s + \omega_2)} \tag{7.57}$$

Using partial fraction expansion, we find that

$$V_o = MK \frac{\omega_2}{(s + \omega_1)(s + \omega_2)} = \frac{A}{s + \omega_1} + \frac{B}{s + \omega_2} \tag{7.58}$$

From an evaluation of A and B,

$$A = \frac{MK\omega_2}{\omega_2 - \omega_1} ; \qquad B = -\frac{MK\omega_2}{\omega_2 - \omega_1}$$

Take the inverse transform of Eq. 7.58, noting that ω_2 is usually very large in comparison with ω_1; then

$$v_o \simeq MK(e^{-\omega_1 t} - e^{-\omega_2 t}) \qquad (7.59)$$

The plot of Eq. 7.59 is difficult to make for a well-designed amplifier because a time scale which is appropriate for showing the rise time will not illustrate the exponential decay caused by the coupling capacitor, and vice-versa. This problem is solved when the response is displayed on an oscilloscope by using a fast sweep to view the front edge response (rise time) and a slow sweep to view the exponential decay or sag. Figure 7.17 is a sketch of the response v_o as a function of time. In this sketch, the chosen ratio of ω_2 to ω_1 is small in comparison with a well-designed amplifier.

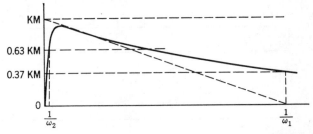

Fig. 7.17. The complete time response of an R-C coupled amplifier to a step function input.

As previously mentioned, the R-C coupled amplifier is commonly used to amplify periodic rectangular pulses. The time-response equation could be derived for a pulse input by the technique used to obtain Eq. 7.26. The derivation would be based on the complete transfer function Eq. 7.56. However, in making a plot of the time response for these pulses, it would be almost impossible to display the rise times. Hence the complete response would appear almost identical to Fig. 7.6, assuming the excitation to be the same in the two examples.

PROB. 7.13. Derive an expression for the time response of an R-C coupled amplifier to a periodic rectangular pulse of amplitude M, duration d, and period T.

7.6 DIFFUSION CAPACITANCE

The preceding discussion may have given the impression that the shunt capacitance of an amplifier is the only cause of deteriorated performance at high frequencies. This impression is approximately true for an R-C

coupled vacuum tube amplifier, but for a transistor, the junction capacitance is not strictly a shunt capacitance, as illustrated in the equivalent circuit of Fig. 7.18. In this figure the effective base resistance, r_b, prevents either C_1 or C_e from being a pure shunt capacitance. Actually, the base resistance is distributed throughout the thin wafer of base material, and a different resistance would exist between each point on either junction and the base electrode. Consequently, the equivalent circuit of Fig. 7.18 is a gross approximation, but it is a great improvement over the assumption that C_1 and C_2 are in shunt with the emitter-base and collector-base terminals, respectively. As far as the collector junction capacitance C_c is concerned, the resistance r_b produces the effect of a capacitor having loss.

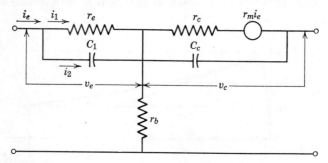

Fig. 7.18. An approximate high-frequency circuit for a transistor.

This resistive component will have little effect on the performance of an R-C coupled amplifier but will need to be included in the analysis of other types of amplifiers such as tuned amplifiers which will be considered in Chapter 8.

In reference to Fig. 7.18, the capacitance C_1 is actually composed of two different capacitances: one is the emitter-base junction capacitance C_e which has been discussed previously, and the other results from the carriers which are injected from the emitter into the base. The charge from these carriers is neutralized by oppositely charged carriers entering the base from the external circuit, as discussed in Section 4.4. For example, in a *p-n-p* transistor, the positive charge in the base which results from holes injected from the emitter is neutralized by negative carriers entering from the base electrode. This means that a positive charge will be transferred across the emitter junction whenever the emitter base voltage is increased, and this transfer will result in current flow in the base circuit to neutralize the charge. Conversely, a reduction in emitter-base voltage reduces the positive carriers in the base region. The extra negative carriers then flow back out the base lead. This transfer of charge into and out of the base region is analogous to the charge and discharge of a capacitor. This phenomenon is accounted for by a capacitance known as *diffusion capacitance*, C_D.

With the aid of Fig. 7.19, we may develop an expression for the diffusion capacitance. The figure shows the distribution of positive charge in the base region. The carrier density resulting from injected carriers is p_0 at the emitter junction ($x = 0$) when the emitter current is at the bias level. The carrier density at the collector junction depletion region ($x = w$) is essentially zero, as discussed in Section 4.4, and the carriers lost by recombination are neglected. Thus the charge density decreases linearly with

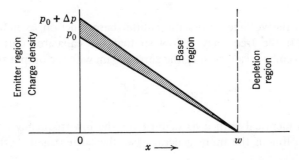

Fig. 7.19. Charge distribution in the base of a *p-n-p* transistor.

distance because dp/dx must be constant if the diffusion current is the same for all values of x. The density and distribution of negative carriers is approximately the same as that of the positive carriers, as discussed in Section 4.4. When the emitter junction voltage v_E is increased by Δv_E, the carrier density in the base at the emitter junction is increased by Δp. Then, the increase in positive charge in the base is

$$\Delta Q = \frac{q\,\Delta p w A}{2} \tag{7.60}$$

where A is the cross-sectional area of the active base region. The diffusion capacitance is

$$C_D = \frac{\Delta Q}{\Delta v_E} \tag{7.61}$$

But, in reference to Fig. 7.18,

$$\Delta v_E = \Delta i_1 r_e \tag{7.62}$$

And, using the diffusion equation (Eq. 4.16), we find that

$$\Delta i_1 = q D_p \frac{\Delta p}{w} A \tag{7.63}$$

Then, substituting Eqs. 7.60, 7.62, and 7.63 into Eq. 7.61 we have

$$C_D = \frac{w^2}{2D_p r_e} \qquad (7.64)$$

It may be seen from Fig. 7.18 that the signal current to the transistor is

$$i_e = i_1 + i_2 \qquad (7.65)$$

If, for example, a small input voltage is applied to the transistor

$$I_e = \frac{V_e}{r_e} + sC_1 V_e \qquad (7.66)$$

where V_e is the voltage across the emitter-base junction as indicated in Fig. 7.18. If the frequency is low so that the capacitor current I_2 is negligible in comparison with I_1, the current gain with the output shorted is

$$\alpha_0 = \frac{I_c}{I_1} = \frac{I_c r_e}{V_e} \qquad (7.67)$$

where α_0 is identical with α as defined for the low-frequency circuits of Chapter 4. But in the more general case, the current gain with output shorted is

$$\alpha = \frac{I_c}{I_e} = \frac{I_c r_e}{V_e + sC_1 V_e r_e} \qquad (7.68)$$

using the value of α_0 in Eq. 7.67, we have

$$\alpha = \frac{\alpha_0}{1 + sC_1 r_e} \qquad (7.69)$$

Let $\omega_\alpha = \dfrac{1}{C_1 r_e}$. Then

$$\alpha = \frac{\alpha_0}{1 + s/\omega_\alpha} \qquad (7.70)$$

or

$$\alpha = \alpha_0 \frac{\omega_\alpha}{s + \omega_\alpha} \qquad (7.71)$$

At the real frequency $s = j\omega_\alpha$, $|\alpha| = 0.707\alpha_0$. This frequency ω_α, or preferably $f_\alpha = \omega_\alpha/2\pi$, is known as the "alpha cutoff" frequency. Then

$$f_\alpha = \frac{1}{2\pi C_1 r_e} \qquad (7.72)$$

where C_1 is equal to $(C_D + C_e)$.

PROB. 7.14. A certain p-n-p germanium transistor has an effective base width $w = 2 \times 10^{-3}$ cm. Calculate C_D at $I_E = 0.5$ ma. If C_e is 10 pf, find the value of f_α. *Answer:* $C_D = 870\,pf, f_\alpha = 3.28\,MHz$.

Transistors which have uniform doping in the base usually have values of diffusion capacitance which are large in comparison with the junction capacitances C_e and C_c. However, manufacturing techniques which minimize this diffusion capacitance have made possible the production of high-frequency transistors with values of diffusion capacitance of the same order of magnitude as the junction capacitances. One common type of high-frequency transistor is the graded-base or drift-field transistor. In this type, the net base doping is almost zero at the collector junction but the doping increases rather rapidly with distance toward the emitter junction. This graded doping produces a nonuniform distribution of mobile carriers which tend to diffuse toward the collector junction and thus establish an electric field in the base which inhibits the diffusion of the majority carriers but assists the diffusion of carriers which have been injected from the emitter. This "built in" electric field adds to the field which results from the nonuniform distribution of neutralizing carriers which are present whenever carriers are injected into the base from the emitter.

The increased velocity of carriers in the graded base decreases the diffusion capacitance for a given collector current. Also, the collector-base junction capacitance is low because of the low doping concentration and wide depletion region at this junction. This wide depletion region also provides relatively high collector-base breakdown voltage. The relatively high doping concentration at the emitter junction requires that the emitter doping concentration must be unusually high for good emitter efficiency. These high doping concentrations result in low emitter-base breakdown voltage.

7.7 THE HYBRID-π EQUIVALENT CIRCUIT FOR A TRANSISTOR

All the h parameters become functions of frequency when the frequency is so high that the junction capacitances and diffusion capacitance can no longer be neglected. Also, these capacitances cannot be represented by simple lumped elements in the h-parameter circuit. Therefore, an equivalent circuit known as a *hybrid-π* has been developed and widely used to give insight into the high-frequency characteristics of a transistor amplifier. The hybrid-π, which is shown in Fig. 7.20, is a type of y-parameter circuit. The validity of this circuit will be investigated by comparing its parameters to those of the h parameters at low frequencies.

The input resistance of the hybrid-π with output shorted is very nearly $r_b + (h_{fe} + 1)r_e$ since r_c is very large compared with $(h_{fe} + 1)r_e$. This input resistance is essentially h_{ie}. The ratio of the open circuit input voltage to a voltage v_{ce} applied to the output terminals is $(h_{fe} + 1)r_e/r_c = r_d/r_e = h_{re}$. The short circuit output current is $g_m v'_{be}$. This current must be equal to $h_{fe}i_b$ at low frequencies if the circuit is valid. Then

$$g_m v'_{be} = h_{fe}i_b \tag{7.73}$$

But, from Fig. 7.20

$$v'_{be} = i_b(h_{fe} + 1)r_e \tag{7.74}$$

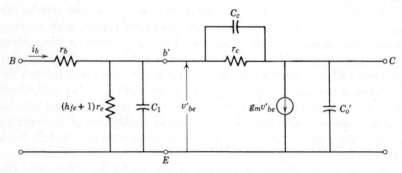

Fig. 7.20. The hybrid-π equivalent circuit.

Then

$$g_m i_b(h_{fe} + 1)r_e = h_{fe}i_b \tag{7.75}$$

and

$$g_m = \frac{h_{fe}}{(h_{fe} + 1)r_e} \tag{7.76}$$

But, as shown in Chapter 4, $1/r_e = g_e = \dfrac{q}{kT}|I_E|$. Also since $h_{fe}/(h_{fe} + 1) = \alpha$,

$$I_E = \frac{h_{fe}I_C}{h_{fe} + 1} \tag{7.77}$$

Then

$$g_m = \frac{q}{kT}|I_C| \tag{7.78}$$

where I_C is the Q-point value of collector current.

The capacitor C_1 was identified in the preceding section as the sum of the junction capacitance C_e plus the diffusion capacitance C_D. In Fig. 7.18 of that section, C_1 was shown as being in parallel with r_e, and in Fig. 7.20, C_1 is shown as being in parallel with $(h_{fe} + 1)r_e$. However, the circuit of Fig. 7.18 is a common-base circuit and the emitter current flows through r_e. In the common emitter circuit of Fig. 7.20, only the base current (approximately) flows through the fictitious resistance $(h_{fe} + 1)r_e$. The voltage developed across these two resistances is, therefore, the same in the two circuits.

The capacitor C_c represents the junction capacitance between the collector and the active portion of the base region. The capacitor C_o represents the capacitance which exists between the collector and emitter terminals exclusive of C_c. Thus C_o accounts primarily for header and lead capacitance plus the capacitance associated with the outer perimeter of the collector junction which does not involve r_b. Manufacturers frequently list a value of common-base output capacitance with input open C_{ob}. This value of C_{ob} is essentially equal to $C_o + C_c$.

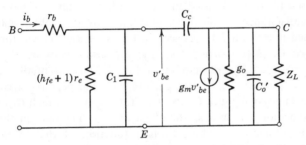

Fig. 7.21. A medium and high-frequency hybrid-π circuit.

At moderate and high frequencies, the reactance of C_c is small in comparison with r_c and the hybrid-π circuit can be simplified as shown in Fig. 7.21. In this circuit the admittance g_o has been added in the output to account for the effect which base width modulation (represented by r_c) has on the output admittance. This g_o is a function of driving source resistance and is equal to h_{oe} when the input is open (infinite source resistance).

A frequency known as the *beta cutoff frequency* is frequently associated with a transistor. This is the frequency at which the short circuit forward current gain is reduced to 0.707 of the low-frequency value. Since g_m is not a function of frequency, beta cutoff frequency occurs when v'_{be} is at 0.707 of its low-frequency value. But, assuming i_b is constant, Fig. 7.21 shows that v'_{be} will decrease to 0.707 of its low-frequency value when the reactance of $C_1 + C_c$ in parallel is equal to $(h_{fe} + 1)r_e$. Therefore,

$$\omega_\beta = \frac{1}{(h_{fe} + 1)r_e(C_1 + C_c)} \simeq \frac{\omega_\alpha}{h_{fe} + 1} \qquad (7.79)$$

PROB. 7.15. Verify both forms of Eq. 7.79 assuming $C_1 \gg C_c$.

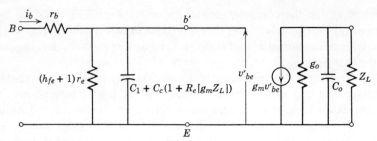

Fig. 7.22. Equivalent circuit showing the effect of Z_L on the effective shunt capacitance.

This ω_β is the radian frequency at which β (or h_{fe}) drops to 0.707 β_o where β_o is the low-frequency value of β.

When the transistor is used in an amplifier circuit, the base-collector junction capacitance is effectively multiplied by the voltage gain v_{ce}/v'_{be} as discussed in Section 7.4. As seen in Fig. 7.21, the current through the capacitance C_c is proportional to the difference between v'_{be} and v_{ce}. Since $v_{ce} = -g_m v'_{be} Z_L$, the circuit of Fig. 7.22 is essentially equivalent to the circuit of Fig. 7.21. The capacitance C'_o has been replaced by C_o in Fig. 7.22. This capacitance C_o accounts for the effect which C_c has on the output capacitance as well as the effect of C'_o. The current through C_c affects the voltage v'_{be}. Thus, C_o is a function of the driving source resistance as well as the frequency and is usually much larger than C_{ob}. For complete equivalence, a conductance $G = C_c$ (imag $g_m Z_L$) should be placed in parallel with C_1. This conductance is usually negligible in R-C coupled amplifiers, but becomes important in tuned amplifiers (Chapter 8).

In the preceding discussion, the transistor was assumed to be driven by a current source i_b. A comparison of Fig. 7.22 and Fig. 7.21 will show that the upper cutoff frequency of the amplifier will decrease from f_β when the real part of the load impedance increases from zero, assuming

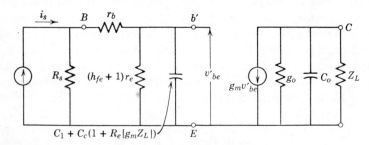

Fig. 7.23. Equivalent circuit showing the effect of source resistance R_s on the frequency response.

i_b to be constant. In contrast, the cutoff frequency of the amplifier may increase from f_β if the transistor is driven from a source which has finite resistance R_s, as illustrated in Fig. 7.23. The resistance $(h_{fe} + 1)r_e$ is in parallel with $r_b + R_s$, and thus the shunt resistance is reduced. The upper cutoff frequency in radians per second is

$$\omega_2 = \frac{1}{R_{sh}C_{sh}} = \frac{1}{[(h_{fe} + 1)r_e \parallel (r_b + R_s)][C_1 + C_c(1 + Re[g_mZ_L])]} \quad (7.80)$$

where the parallel bars $\parallel$ indicate the parallel combination of $(h_{fe} + 1)r_e$ and $(r_b + R_s)$. From Eq. 7.80, it can be seen that the maximum upper cutoff frequency is attained when both source and load resistances approach zero. Then

$$\max \omega_2 = \frac{1}{[(h_{fe} + 1)r_e \parallel r_b][C_1 + C_c]} \quad (7.81)$$

This maximum value of ω_2 is sometimes called the transverse cutoff frequency.

The value of ω_2 calculated from Eq. 7.80 will be higher than the actual cutoff frequency because the stray wiring capacitance and other shunt capacitances external to the transistor on the input side have not been included in the circuit. The resistance r_b prevents the inclusion of these capacitances directly in parallel with C_1. However, in a high frequency transistor, r_b is usually quite small and only a slight chance for error is introduced by lumping the input circuit capacitance with C_1. In lower frequency transistors, the stray circuit capacitance is usually negligible in comparison with the diffusion capacitance.

The junction capacitance of a field effect transistor can be included in the conventional y parameter circuit given in Chapter 6. However, the capacitance between the gate and the drain has an effectiveness

$$C_{gd}(1 + R_e |g_mZ_L|)$$

as previously discussed. Therefore, the high-frequency equivalent circuit for a field effect transistor is as shown in Fig. 7.24. The total shunt capacitance is

$$C_{sh} = C_w + C_{gs} + C_{gd}(1 + R_e |g_mZ_L|) \quad (7.82)$$

where

C_w is the stray circuit capacitance

C_{gs} is the gate-source capacitance

Then the upper cutoff frequency in radians per second is

$$\omega_2 = \frac{1}{R_{sh}C_{sh}} \quad (7.83)$$

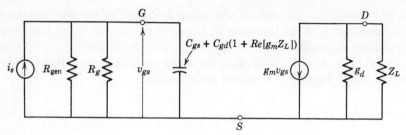

Fig. 7.24. High-frequency equivalent circuit for a field-effect transistor.

where R_{sh} is the parallel combination of R_g and the driving source resistance R_{gen}. Since the FET is especially attractive as an amplifier for signals which are provided by a high impedance source, some compromise of voltage gain may be necessary in applications which require a high value of ω_2. The term $C_{gd}(1 + Re\,|g_m Z_L|)$ is usually the predominant circuit capacitance.

PROB. 7.16. A given transistor has $h_{fe} = 100$, $h_{ie} = 1750\ \Omega$, $h_{oe} = 50\ \mu$mhos, $h_{re} = 6.25 \times 10^{-4}$, $C_{ob} = 10$ pf and $\omega_\beta = 4 \times 10^6$ radians per second at the quiescent operating point $I_C = 2.0$ ma and $V_{CE} = 5$ volts. Assuming the capacitance C_o to be 1 pf, determine the value of the elements of the hybrid π circuit shown in Fig. 7.20, including g_m, at the operating point given. Assume $T = 17°C$.

PROB. 7.17. A high-frequency transistor which is operated at $I_C = 10$ ma and $V_{CE} = 10$ volts has $h_{fe} = 100$, $r_b = 100\ \Omega$, $f_\beta = 3.0$ mc, and $C_c = 6$ pf. The a-c load resistance is $500\underline{/0°}\ \Omega$ and the driving source resistance is 1 KΩ.

  a. Determine the upper cutoff frequency of the amplifier.
  b. Determine the upper cutoff frequency if the driving source resistance is reduced to 100 ohms.

7.8 GAIN-BANDWIDTH PRODUCT

The product of gain and bandwidth is essentially constant for a specific tube. The bandwidth $B = \omega_2 - \omega_1$, but ω_1 is usually very small compared with ω_2. Therefore, $B \simeq \omega_2$. The gain is considered equal to the reference gain throughout the useful range of the amplifier. Therefore, the gain-bandwidth product for a tube amplifier is

$$GB = g_m R_{sh} \omega_2 \qquad (7.84)$$

But

$$\omega_2 = \frac{1}{R_{sh} C_{sh}} \qquad (7.85)$$

then

$$GB = \frac{g_m}{C_{sh}} \qquad (7.86)$$

When several cascaded amplifiers are required for a specific application, the tube should be selected at least partially on the basis of the ratio of transconductance to total tube capacitance. This ratio is defined as the *figure of merit* for a tube. The figure of merit of a stage could be defined as the ratio of the transconductance of the tube to the total capacitance of the stage C_{sh}.

Table 7.1 lists the figure of merit for several tubes. Triodes are not

TABLE 7.1

Figure of Merit for Some Typical Pentodes

Tube Type	C_i $\mu\mu f$	C_{gp} $\mu\mu f$	C_o $\mu\mu f$	g_m μmhos	g_m/C_{sh} 10^2 radians/sec
6CB6	6.5	0.010	3.0	6,200	653
6AK5	4.0	0.020	2.8	4,300	630
6AC7	11.0	0.015	5.0	9,000	562
6AU6	5.5	0.003	5.0	5,200	495
6SJ7	6.0	0.003	7.0	2,000	154

included because their effective capacitance is dependent on the gain of the amplifier.

The figure of merit of a transistor is usually considered to be the product of low-frequency common emitter current gain and the beta cutoff frequency. Thus

$$f_\tau = \beta_o f_\beta \tag{7.87}$$

where f_τ is the frequency at which the extrapolated value of common emitter current gain is unity. The alpha cutoff frequency is approximately equal to f_τ.

7.9 TRANSFORMER COUPLING

The transformer has some inherent advantages as a coupling device. For example, the ohmic resistance of the windings may be small in comparison with the a-c impedance. As a result, the efficiency may be much higher than in the *R-C* coupled amplifier. In addition, the turns ratio may be chosen so that impedance matching may be utilized to obtain maximum power gain, and hence, maximum voltage or current gain. For example, the input impedance of a vacuum tube may be higher than its output impedance; therefore, a step-up transformer could be used to increase the voltage amplification. The input impedance in a transistor is usually lower than the output impedance. Consequently, a step-down transformer could be used to increase the current gain of the amplifier. In each case the gain is approximately equal to the product of the gain of the amplifying device and the turns ratio of the transformer.

The circuit diagram of a typical transformer coupled transistor amplifier is shown in Fig. 7.25. Stabilized bias is used for this example. Observe, however, that signal currents do not flow through the bias resistors in the circuit shown. Therefore, a high degree of temperature stability may be realized without sacrificing signal power gain. In this circuit, the ohmic

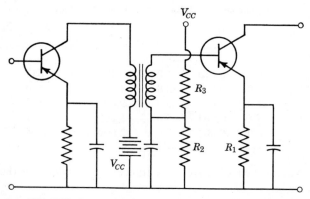

Fig. 7.25. A transformer coupled transistor amplifier.

resistance of the transformer secondary is part of the equivalent bias resistance R_B. The design of the amplifier may be carried out with the aid of the characteristic curves provided in Fig. 7.26. As a first step, the collector supply voltage V_{CC} is determined by the power output requirements of the amplifier. In this example, 9 v will be used for V_{CC}. The d-c load resistance is the ohmic resistance of the primary winding, which is normally quite small. Consequently, the d-c load line is almost vertical, as illustrated in Fig. 7.26. To obtain maximum power gain and hence maximum current gain, the a-c load line is drawn with a slope approximately equal to that of the collector characteristic at the operating point.[4] This small slope permits the quiescent point to be chosen at a low value of collector current. For convenience, the point selected in the illustration is the intersection of the d-c load line with the curve $i_B = -30 \ \mu a$. The relatively small collector current coupled with the small d-c voltage drop in the transformer primary yields a collector circuit efficiency which is high compared with that of an R-C coupled amplifier.

[4] Although the output admittance of the transistor may differ appreciably from h_o, the impedance match will be reasonably good if the output resistance is assumed to be $1/h_o$. A more precise matching procedure is presented in Chapter 9.

After the quiescent point has been selected, the bias circuit components may be determined in accordance with the temperature stability requirements as discussed in Chapter 5.

An equivalent circuit of the transformer coupled amplifier is given in Fig. 7.27. This equivalent circuit may represent either a transistor or a tube amplifier, depending on the specification of the current I. At this time, the transformer will be assumed ideal. That is, the coefficient of coupling

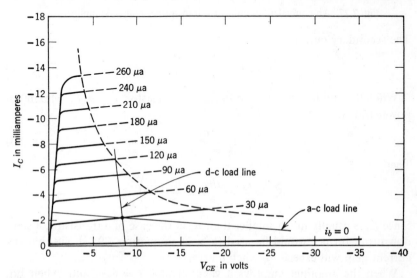

Fig. 7.26. Characteristic curves used for the design of a transformer coupled transistor amplifier.

will be considered unity, the magnetizing current negligible, and the ohmic resistance of each winding negligible. Then the voltage and current ratios of the transformer are proportional to the turns ratio. In Fig. 7.27 the ratio of primary turns to secondary turns is a. Then the source current

$$-I = \frac{av_o}{R_o} + \frac{i_o}{a} = \frac{av_o}{R_o} + \frac{v_o}{aR_i} \tag{7.88}$$

$$v_o\left(\frac{a}{R_o} + \frac{1}{aR_i}\right) = -I \tag{7.89}$$

$$v_o = -I\frac{aR_oR_i}{a^2R_i + R_o} \tag{7.90}$$

Maximum power will be transferred to the load when $R_o = a^2R_i$. In this case

$$v_o = -I\frac{a(a^2R_i{}^2)}{2a^2R_i} = \frac{-IaR_i}{2} \tag{7.91}$$

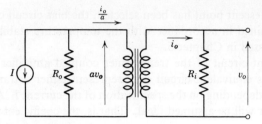

Fig. 7.27. An equivalent circuit for a transformer coupled amplifier.

The secondary current

$$i_o = \frac{v_o}{R_i} = \frac{aI}{2} \tag{7.92}$$

When the amplifier is a common emitter transistor, $I = h_{fe}i_b$. Maximum power transfer is attained when

$$i_o = \frac{ah_{fe}i_b}{2} \tag{7.93}$$

Then

$$K_i = \frac{i_o}{i_b} = \frac{ah_{fe}}{2} = \frac{h_{fe}}{2}\left(\frac{R_o}{R_i}\right)^{1/2} \tag{7.94}$$

Since R_i is usually much smaller than R_o in the case of a transistor, a step-down transformer would be used $(a > 1)$. Equation 7.94 shows that the current gain will exceed h_{fe} when a exceeds two.

When the amplifier employs a vacuum tube $I = g_m v_g$ and, when Eq. 7.91 for maximum power gain is used,

$$v_o = \frac{g_m v_g a R_i}{2} \tag{7.95}$$

And

$$K_v = \frac{v_o}{v_g} = \frac{g_m a R_i}{2} = \frac{g_m R_o}{2a} \tag{7.96}$$

since $R_o = a^2 R_i$.

For a triode tube, R_i is usually large in comparison with R_o which is r_p. Then a step-up transformer is used $(a < 1)$. When $1/a$ exceeds 2, the voltage gain exceeds $g_m r_p$ which is μ.

PROB. 7.18. Calculate the current gain of the transistor amplifier of Fig. 7.26 if $R_o \simeq 1/h_{oe} = 30$ KΩ, $R_i \simeq h_{ie} = 1.5$ KΩ, and $h_{fe} = 50$. Specify the turns ratio of the transformer. Compare this gain with that of an R-C coupled amplifier using the same transistors. Assume R_o and R_i to be the same in each case and neglect the signal currents through the biasing resistors. Also assume that the d-c load resistor R_c in the R-C coupled amplifier is large in comparison with R_i. *Answer: $a = 4.47$, $K_i = 111.7$, $K_i = 45.4$ for R-C amp.*

The approximation that $R_o = 1/h_{oe}$ and $R_i = h_{ie}$ will not be valid under all conditions. Accurate values of R_i may be obtained from the equivalent circuit of a particular transistor configuration if the load impedance is known. Therefore, the design of an amplifier normally proceeds from the load toward the input. Since the transistor does not provide complete isolation of its input circuit from its output circuit, a simultaneous solution of the entire amplifier circuit would be required in order to obtain ideal impedance matching for a specified set of conditions. However, this method of solution may be very complex and tedious. Fortunately, the order of accuracy required does not justify a simultaneous solution. The output impedance of the transistor may be obtained with sufficient accuracy when the input is furnished by a transformer if it is asssumed that the driving source impedance is h_{ie}.

7.10 FREQUENCY RESPONSE OF A TRANSFORMER COUPLED AMPLIFIER

The transformer may be represented by an equivalent Tee as illustrated in Fig. 7.28a.[5] R_1 and L_1 are the resistance and leakage inductance of the primary. Also, the resistance and leakage inductance of the secondary, R_2 and L_2, have been referred to the primary by the multiplication factor a^2, where a is the turns ratio of the primary to secondary. In addition, the mutual inductance M and load resistance R_i have been referred to the primary. The distributed winding capacitance and circuit wiring capacitance have been neglected.

Basic text books which treat inductively coupled circuits show that the

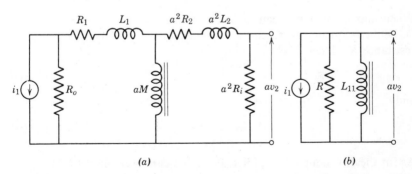

(a)   (b)

Fig. 7.28. (a) The equivalent T circuit is used to represent the transformer in a transformer coupled amplifier. (b) The low-frequency equivalent of (a) for a tightly coupled transformer.

[5] Hugh Hildredth Skilling, *Electrical Engineering Circuits*, Second Edition, Wiley, p. 341, New York, 1965.

mutual inductance is

$$M = k(L_{11}L_{22})^{1/2} \tag{7.97}$$

where k is the coupling coefficient, L_{11} is the self-inductance of the primary, and L_{22} is the self-inductance of the secondary. Then, since $L_{22} = L_{11}/a^2$,

$$aM = kL_{11} \tag{7.98}$$

Figure 7.28 shows that the total self-inductance of the primary is

$$L_{11} = L_1 + aM = L_1 + kL_{11}$$

Then

$$L_1 = (1 - k)L_{11} \tag{7.99}$$

The term $1 - k$ is the fraction of primary flux which does not couple the secondary winding. Then L_1 is the leakage inductance of the primary. A typical coupling transformer has a coefficient of coupling k of the order of 0.99 or higher. Therefore, at low and middle frequencies, the leakage inductances may be neglected because their reactances are small in comparison with the reactance of the primary and the associated amplifier resistances R_o and R_i. Also the resistance of the transformer windings, R_1 and R_2 are negligible in comparison with R_o and R_i. Consequently, a simplified low-frequency circuit may be drawn as shown in Fig. 7.28b, where R is the parallel combination of R_o and a^2R_i. The output voltage is

$$aV_2 = -I_1 \frac{RsL_{11}}{R + sL_{11}} \tag{7.100}$$

$$aV_2 = -I_1R \frac{s}{s + R/L_{11}} \tag{7.101}$$

When maximum power gain is achieved, $a^2R_i = R_o$ and $R = R_o/2$. Let ω_1 be the frequency at which the reactance of the primary is equal to the resistance R. Then

$$\omega_1 = \frac{R}{L_{11}} \tag{7.102}$$

and

$$aV_2 = -I_1R \frac{s}{s + \omega_1} \tag{7.103}$$

As for the R-C coupled amplifier, Eq. 7.103 can be reduced to

$$G = -K \frac{s}{s + \omega_1} \tag{7.104}$$

where K is the reference gain of the transformer coupled amplifier (Eq. 7.94 or Eq. 7.96). The negative sign may or may not precede K, depending on the method of connecting the transformer. The gain equation has the same form as the R-C coupled amplifier in the low-frequency range. The frequency, phase, and time response would be identical in the two types of amplifiers in this range, providing that ω_1 is the same in each case.

PROB. 7.19. A common emitter transistor amplifier has $R_o = 20$ KΩ. A coupling transformer provides an impedance match to the following transistor. What primary inductance will be required if $f_1 = 30$ Hz? *Answer: L = 53 h.*

PROB. 7.20. Approximately what primary inductance will be required for the transformer of Prob. 7.19 if a 10% sag is permitted for a rectangular pulse of 1 msec?

The chief disadvantage of the transformer as a coupling device may be the large inductance required for satisfactory amplification of long pulses or low frequencies. Under these conditions, the transformer would be

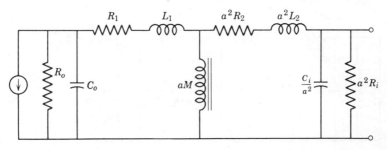

Fig. 7.29. High-frequency equivalent circuit for a transformer-coupled amplifier.

costly and bulky. As a result, the cost or weight may be a major concern and may outweigh the several advantages of a transformer. Miniature transformers are available for coupling transistor amplifiers. However, those designed for audio frequency amplification generally have poor low-frequency response. In contrast, rectangular pulses of rather short duration [a few microseconds] may be amplified with little distortion when a miniature transformer is employed.

The leakage inductance cannot be neglected at high frequencies or large values of s. The shunt capacitance of the circuit, as well as distributed capacitance of the transformer, also needs to be considered. An equivalent circuit which includes the circuit capacitance is given in Fig. 7.29. In this circuit, the capacitance C_o includes the distributed capacitance of the primary, and C_i includes the distributed capacitance of the secondary. As a word of caution, considerable inaccuracy results from representing distributed capacitance by a lumped capacitor. However, fairly good qualitative ideas may be gained concerning the transformer performance.

If a highly accurate equivalent circuit were devised, the circuit complexity would present a formidable solution. The reactance of the magnetizing inductance aM is so large at high frequencies that it can be removed from the equivalent circuit. Consequently, the leakage inductance a^2L_2 can be combined with L_1 to produce a total leakage inductance $2L_1$. This follows because

$$L_2 = (1 - k)L_{22} \qquad (7.105)$$

or

$$a^2L_2 = a^2(1 - k)L_{22} \qquad (7.106)$$

but since $a^2L_{22} = L_{11}$,

$$a^2L_2 = (1 - k)L_{11} = L_1 \qquad (7.107)$$

The simplified equivalent circuit is presented in Fig. 7.30a. A further simplification is shown in Fig. 7.30b. In this circuit the secondary resistance referred to the primary a^2R_2 has been lumped with the primary ohmic

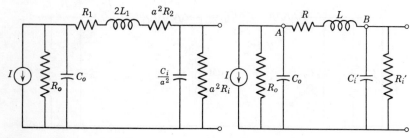

Fig. 7.30. Simplified high-frequency equivalent circuits of the transformer-coupled amplifier.

resistance to form R. To simplify the symbolism, symbol C_i/a^2 has been changed to C'_i and a^2R_i has been changed to R'_i. The nodal equations for the circuit of Fig. 7.30b are

$$\left.\begin{aligned}
\left(G_o + sC_o + \frac{1}{R + sL}\right)V_A - \frac{1}{R + sL}V_B &= -I \\[2mm]
-\frac{1}{R + sL}V_A + \left(G'_i + sC'_i + \frac{1}{R + sL}\right)V_B &= 0
\end{aligned}\right\} \qquad (7.108)$$

where

$$G_o = 1/R_o \text{ and } G'_i = 1/R'_i$$

Solving for V_B, we find that

$$V_B = \cfrac{-I/(R + sL)}{\left(G_o + sC_o + \cfrac{1}{R + sL}\right)\left(G'_i + sC'_i + \cfrac{1}{R + sL}\right) - \cfrac{1}{(R + sL)^2}}$$

$$(7.109)$$

Expanding the denominator, we have

$$V_B = \frac{-I/(R + sL)}{(G_o + sC_o)(G'_i + sC'_i) + \dfrac{G_o + sC_o + G'_i + sC'_i}{R + sL}} \tag{7.110}$$

The transfer function of the transformer is

$$G = \frac{V_B}{I} = -\frac{1}{(G_o + sC_o)(G'_i + sC'_i)(R + sL) + (C_o + C'_i)s + G_o + G'_i} \tag{7.111}$$

$$G = -\frac{\dfrac{1}{C_oC'_iL}}{\left(s + \dfrac{G_o}{C_o}\right)\left(s + \dfrac{G'_i}{C'_i}\right)\left(s + \dfrac{R}{L}\right) + \dfrac{C_o + C'_i}{C_oC'_iL}\left(s + \dfrac{G_o + G'_i}{C_o + C'_i}\right)} \tag{7.112}$$

Equation 7.112 is a third-order equation.

This third-order equation can be solved by conventional means if the coefficients are in numerical form. However, if a general solution is required, all possible numerical answers must be found. The root-locus technique allows us to make a plot of all possible roots in the denominator. This root-locus method is briefly presented in Appendix II.

Equation 7.112 may be arranged in proper form for root-locus solution as follows.

$$G = \frac{-\dfrac{1}{C_oC'_iL\left(s + \dfrac{G_o}{C_o}\right)\left(s + \dfrac{G'_i}{C'_i}\right)\left(s + \dfrac{R}{L}\right)}}{1 + \dfrac{C_o + C'_i}{C_oC'_iL}\left[\dfrac{s + (G_o + G'_i)/(C_o + C'_i)}{\left(s + \dfrac{G_o}{C_o}\right)\left(s + \dfrac{G'_i}{C'_i}\right)\left(s + \dfrac{R}{L}\right)}\right]} \tag{7.113}$$

Equation 7.113 is of the form

$$G = \frac{N}{1 + HF} \tag{7.114}$$

where N is the numerator, $H = (C_o + C'_i)/(C_oC'_iL)$ and F is the fraction in the denominator which involves s.

In applying the root-locus technique, the poles and zeros of F are first plotted on the s plane as shown in Fig. 7.31. Then the locus of all values of s which cause the angle of F to be $180°$ is drawn as indicated in Fig. 7.31. Again, the object is to factor the denominator of Eq. 7.112. The roots of the denominator occur at values of s which make $HF = 1/\underline{180°}$. Consequently, a value of s must be found for which $H = 1/|F|$ on each branch

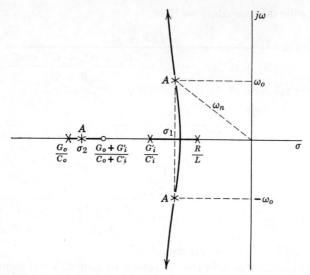

Fig. 7.31. The root-locus plot of the denominator of Eq. 7.113.

of the locus. The spirule, which is a device especially designed for the solution of root-locus problems, may be used to locate the point for which $H = (C_o + C'_i)/(C_o C'_i L)$ on each branch of the locus.

Each root-locus branch begins on a pole of F and terminates on a zero of F, either finite or at infinity. Thus, there are as many root-locus branches as there are poles of F. In this figure, there are three branches. Since the value of H must be zero at a pole of F and infinite at a zero of F, the values of s which are the roots of the denominator of Eq. 7.112 move away from the poles of F as H increases. Therefore, when H is small, all the roots lie on the negative real axis. The time response, then, which is obtained by taking the inverse transform of Eq. 7.112, would consist of exponential functions. These functions are of the same form as those obtained for the R-C coupled amplifier and result in the same general type of response as the R-C coupled amplifier. In order for H to be small, however, the leakage inductance L and the effective winding capacitances C_o and C'_i must be large. But C_o, C'_i, and L, in conjunction with their associated resistances (or conductances), determine the location of the poles of F. To have good high-frequency response or short rise times, the poles of the transfer function and hence the poles of F must occur at large values of s. Then C_o, C'_i, and L should each be small to provide good frequency and time response. This response criterion usually leads to values of H which place the poles of the transfer function (Eq. 7.113) off the real axis on the two branches which depart from the real axis and seek zeros at infinity. A typical location of the poles of the transfer function might be at the points labeled A in Fig. 7.31. The response here is said to be under-damped in contrast to the overdamped case in which all the poles are located on the real axis. Critical damping occurs when a double pole is located at the point where the root-locus branches depart from the real axis.

In the usual underdamped case, the transfer function of the transformer-coupled amplifier may be written as follows.

$$G = -K \frac{1/C_o C'_i L}{(s + \sigma_1 + j\omega_o)(s + \sigma_1 - j\omega_o)(s + \sigma_2)} \quad (7.115)$$

where σ_1, ω_o, and σ_2 are obtained from Fig. 7.31

$$G = -K \frac{1/C_o C'_i L}{(s + \sigma_2)(s^2 + 2\sigma_1 s + \sigma_1^2 + \omega_o^2)} \quad (7.116)$$

Equation 7.116 may be written in the form

$$G = -K \frac{1/C_o C'_i L}{(s + \sigma_2)(s^2 + 2\zeta\omega_n s + \omega_n^2)} \quad (7.117)$$

where ω_n is the natural resonant frequency $(\omega_o^2 + \sigma_1^2)^{1/2}$ and ζ is the damping ratio $= \sigma_1/\omega_n$.

The pole-zero plot of a typical transformer-coupled amplifier, including the low frequency pole and zero, is shown in Fig. 7.32. Since the damping ratio $\zeta = \sigma_1/\omega_n$, the cosine of the angle θ is also equal to ζ. The complete transfer function of the transformer-coupled amplifier can be written from

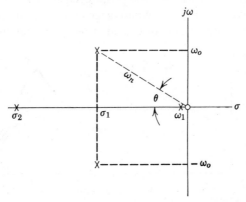

Fig. 7.32. The complete pole-zero plot of a typical transformer-coupled amplifier.

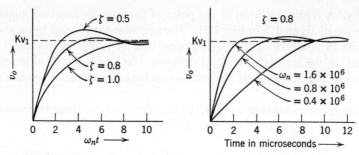

Fig. 7.33. Front edge response of a transformer-coupled amplifier.

inspection of Eqs. 7.104, 7.117, and Fig. 7.32.

$$G = -K \frac{s/C_oC'_iL}{(s + \omega_1)(s + \sigma_2)(s^2 + 2\zeta\omega_n s + \omega_n^2)} \qquad (7.118)$$

The factors ζ and ω_n primarily determine the high-frequency or rise time response characteristics of the transformer. The front edge or rise response to a step input voltage is plotted in Fig. 7.33a for various values of ζ, with ω_n held constant. The response is plotted for various values of ω_n in Fig. 7.33b with ζ held constant. The frequency response of the amplifier is presented in Fig. 7.34 for various values of ζ. It is evident from the figures that a high resonant frequency, ω_n, will provide a short rise time and good high-frequency response. The high value of ω_n can be accomplished by providing small values of C_o, C'_i, and L. For a specific value of coupling, the leakage inductance is proportional to the primary inductance which is set by the value of R_o and the desired ω_1, as previously discussed. For a specific value of primary inductance the leakage inductance can be reduced by increasing the coefficient of coupling k. High permeability cores and special winding techniques are frequently employed in high-quality transformers to provide very tight coupling.

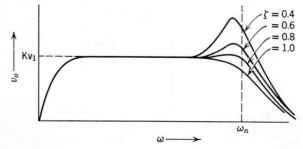

Fig. 7.34. Frequency response of a transformer-coupled amplifier.

The distributed capacitance of the windings increases with the number of turns. Consequently, a step-up transformer would have a comparatively large secondary capacitance which is divided by a^2 in referring it to the primary. Thus C'_i may become very large if a large step-up turns ratio is used. As previously discussed, ω_n decreases as C'_i increases. As a consequence, the step-up ratio of the transformer is restricted by the acceptable value of resonant frequency. Usually, a step-up ratio of 3 is about the maximum usable value for a good quality transformer. In contrast, C'_i may be very small when a step-down transformer is used. Reducing the reluctance of the magnetic path is helpful in reducing winding capacitance, because the number of turns would be reduced for a specific value of inductance. In addition, special winding techniques may also be used to minimize the distributed capacitance. The transformer connections recommended by the manufacturer must be used to realize minimum winding capacitance.

From Figs. 7.33 and 7.34 it is evident that a value of ζ much lower than 0.8 would cause an appreciable overshoot when the input is a step function. or an appreciable peak in the steady-state frequency response. Of course, small values of leakage inductance are helpful in producing large values of ζ. In addition, the resistance of the windings may be used as a control parameter. However, an increased winding resistance may result in a reduced efficiency.

7.11 THE COMMON COLLECTOR CONFIGURATION

In the preceding paragraphs, some of the shortcomings of the transformer have been discussed. From this discussion, it is evident that the bandwidth of the transformer is limited by its ratio of primary inductance to leakage inductance. As a consequence, a device which would perform the function of impedance transformation throughout a wider range of frequencies would be very useful. Fortunately, the common collector amplifier configuration meets these requirements in addition to increasing the power level of the signal. The vacuum tube version of this type of amplifier is commonly known as a cathode follower. Similarly, the transistor version is frequently known as an emitter follower.

Figure 7.35a is the circuit diagram of a typical common collector transistor amplifier. In this circuit, the load is placed between the emitter and the common ground terminal. Furthermore, the input signal is applied between the base and the common ground terminal. The collector is connected directly to the collector supply voltage V_{CC}. Since the collector supply must be adequately bypassed, the collector is maintained at the same signal or a-c potential as the common ground terminal. Thus the

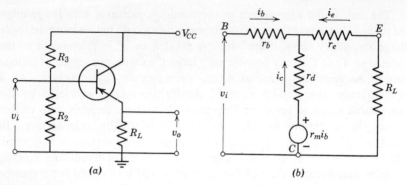

Fig. 7.35. The common collector transistor amplifier. (*a*) Circuit diagram; (*b*) equivalent circuit.

time-varying input signal actually appears between the base and the collector, whereas the output signal appears between the emitter and collector, hence the name common collector or grounded collector.

An equivalent Tee circuit of the common collector connection is shown in Fig. 7.35*b*. In this circuit, the short-circuit current gain may be determined by letting $R_L = 0$. Then

$$-i_e = i_b + i_c = i_b + h_{fe}i_b \tag{7.119}$$

$$h_{fc} = \frac{i_e}{i_b} = -(1 + h_{fe}) \tag{7.120}$$

Equation 7.120 shows that the forward current amplification factor of the common collector configuration is slightly greater in magnitude than that of the common emitter connection. The input voltage v_i is found from the equation

$$v_i = v_o + v_{be} \tag{7.121}$$

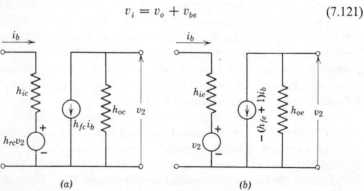

Fig. 7.36. The *h*-parameter equivalent circuit for the common collector configuration (*a*) using common collector *h* parameters and (*b*) using common emitter *h* parameters.

The base-to-emitter voltage v_{be} is normally small compared with v_o. Therefore, the voltage amplification is approximately unity, and the power gain is approximately equal to the current gain. Therefore, the power gain of the common collector is smaller than that of the common emitter configuration.

The input and output impedances of the common collector configuration may be determined in terms of the equivalent Tee parameters by writing Kirchhoff's equations for the circuit of Fig. 7.35b. However, it is more convenient to use an h-parameter equivalent circuit as shown in Fig. 7.36a. The forward current amplification factor h_{fc} has already been found in terms of the common emitter current amplification factor (Eq. 7.120). Thus

$$-h_{fc} = h_{fe} + 1 \simeq h_{fe} \qquad (7.122)$$

Figure 7.35b shows that with the output shorted, the common collector configuration is indistinguishable from the common emitter configuration. Therefore, the low-frequency input resistance with the output shorted is

$$h_{ic} = h_{ie} \qquad (7.123)$$

When the input is open, it can be seen from Fig. 7.35b that the output resistance is $r_e + r_d$ since i_b, and hence $r_m i_b$, is equal to zero. Then

$$h_{oc} = h_{oe} \qquad (7.124)$$

Figure 7.35b also shows that

$$h_{rc} = \frac{r_d}{r_d + r_e} \simeq 1 \qquad (7.125)$$

Thus it should be observed that the common collector h parameters are almost identical in magnitude with the common emitter h parameters, with the exception of h_{rc} which is practically unity. The common collector h-parameter equivalent circuit is redrawn in Fig. 7.36b, using the common emitter h parameters.

With a load resistance R_L placed in the emitter circuit the low-frequency input resistance may be calculated from the equivalent circuit of Fig. 7.37a. Observing that there is no polarity reversal in the emitter follower, we see that

$$v_i = h_{ie} i_b + v_2 \qquad (7.126)$$

but

$$v_2 = \frac{(h_{fe} + 1) i_b}{h_{oe} + G_L} \qquad (7.127)$$

where $G_L = 1/R_L$.

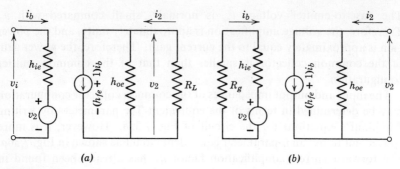

Fig. 7.37. Equivalent circuits for calculating (a) input resistance and (b) output resistance of the common collector circuit.

Substituting Eq. 7.127 into Eq. 7.126, we have

$$v_i = h_{ie}i_b + \frac{(h_{fe} + 1)i_b}{h_{oe} + G_L} \tag{7.128}$$

The input resistance

$$R_i = \frac{v_i}{i_b} = h_{ie} + \frac{h_{fe} + 1}{h_{oe} + G_L} \tag{7.129}$$

Usually G_L is large in comparison with h_{oe}. In this case,

$$R_i \simeq h_{ie} + (h_{fe} + 1)R_L \tag{7.130}$$

PROB. 7.21. Show that the input resistance of the emitter follower approaches r_c as the load resistance becomes very large.

The equivalent circuit of Fig. 7.37b may be used to obtain the mid-frequency output conductance when the driving source resistance is R_g.

$$i_2 = h_{oe}v_2 - (h_{fe} + 1)i_b \tag{7.131}$$

$$-i_b = \frac{v_2}{h_{ie} + R_g} \tag{7.132}$$

Then

$$i_2 = h_{oe}v_2 + \frac{(h_{fe} + 1)v_2}{h_{ie} + R_g} \tag{7.133}$$

$$Y_o = \frac{i_2}{v_2} = h_{oe} + \frac{h_{fe} + 1}{h_{ie} + R_g} \tag{7.134}$$

Observe from Eq. 7.134 and Eq. 7.129 that the emitter follower is an impedance transformer with an impedance ratio equal to $h_{fe} + 1$. The total resistance in the output circuit is multiplied by $h_{fe} + 1$ and added to

h_{ie} to produce a very high input resistance for normal values of load resistance. Similarly, the total output conductance is h_{oe} plus the input circuit conductance multiplied by $h_{fe} + 1$.

PROB. 7.22. A transistor has the following coefficients: $r_e = 25\ \Omega$, $r_b = 500\ \Omega$, $r_c = 1$ megohm, $\alpha = 0.99$. Calculate the input resistance of the common collector connection with (a) $R_L = 1$ KΩ. (b) $R_L = 20$ KΩ. *Answer:* (a) $R_i = 94\ K\Omega$.

PROB. 7.23. Calculate the output resistance of the common collector configuration of the transistor above with driving source resistance R_g (a) 1 KΩ, (b) 50 KΩ.

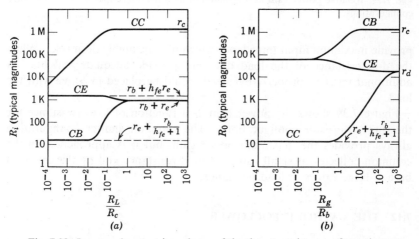

Fig. 7.38. Input and output impedance of the three transistor configurations.

The variation of input impedance as a function of load resistance for each transistor configuration is plotted in Fig. 7.38a. Similarly, the output impedance is plotted as a function of driving source impedance in Fig. 7.38b. These impedances will all be resistive at mid-frequencies but will be complex in the low and high frequency ranges. As the frequency approaches beta cutoff (f_β), the current gain of the common collector configuration decreases in the same manner as in the common emitter configuration. In addition, the input impedance decreases in the same fashion as the current gain.

The load lines and quiescent operating point of the common collector amplifier may be located on the collector characteristics in the same manner as for the common emitter configuration. The biasing circuits may also be similar to those of the common emitter. The d-c resistance of the load may be sufficient to provide good current stability with the stabilizing resistor (R_2) between the base and ground removed. The bias resistor (R_3) would then carry only the base bias current. This arrangement would

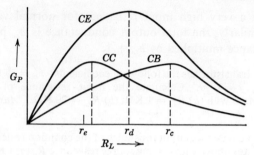

Fig. 7.39. Relative power gain as a function of load resistance for the three transistor configurations.

provide maximum input impedance which may be highly desirable. When the d-c resistance of the load does not provide adequate stability, an additional resistor, properly bypassed, could be placed in series with the load.

Figure 7.39 shows the power gain as a function of load resistance for the three transistor configurations. The common emitter configuration always provides the maximum power gain, but it is approached by the common collector at small values of load resistance and by the common base at large values of load resistance.

7.12 THE CATHODE FOLLOWER

The vacuum tube version of the common collector amplifier is called the cathode follower. In this circuit, the load is in the cathode side of the circuit and the plate is connected directly to the V_{PP} supply voltage as

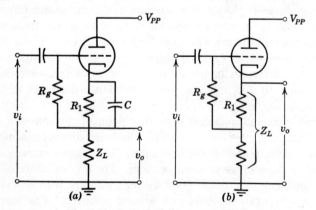

Fig. 7.40. Cathode-follower amplifiers.

illustrated in Fig. 7.40. Cathode or self-bias may be used in a fashion very similar to that of a common cathode amplifier as shown in Fig. 7.40a. The voltage drop across resistor R_1 is used to provide the desired d-c potential between cathode and grid. In this circuit the capacitor C is used to bypass the a-c components of the cathode current. On the other hand, the bias resistance R_1 may be part of the load resistance Z_L as shown in Fig. 7.40b. The capacitor C is then unnecessary. In some circuits where a large amount of bias or a small load resistance is desired, the resistance R_1 may be the entire d-c load resistance. The grid resistor R_g will then return to ground as in the common cathode amplifier.

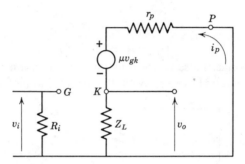

Fig. 7.41. An equivalent circuit for the cathode follower.

Inspection of the circuits of Fig. 7.40 will reveal that for mid-range signals,

$$v_i = v_{gk} + v_o \qquad (7.135)$$

A mid-frequency equivalent circuit of the cathode follower is provided in Fig. 7.41 (remember that μ is a negative term). Writing Kirchhoff's voltage equation around the loop, we have

$$-\mu v_{gk} = i_p(r_p + Z_L) \qquad (7.136)$$

$$i_p = \frac{-\mu v_{gk}}{r_p + Z_L} \qquad (7.137)$$

$$v_o = i_p Z_L = \frac{-\mu v_{gk} Z_L}{r_p + Z_L} \qquad (7.138)$$

Equation 7.138 would be more useful if the output voltage were obtained in terms of the input voltage v_i instead of the grid to cathode voltage v_{gk}. Using Eq. 7.135, we find that

$$v_{gk} = v_i - v_o \qquad (7.139)$$

Then

$$v_o = \frac{-\mu Z_L(v_i - v_o)}{r_p + Z_L} \tag{7.140}$$

$$v_o\left(1 - \frac{\mu Z_L}{r_p + Z_L}\right) = \frac{-\mu Z_L v_i}{r_p + Z_L} \tag{7.141}$$

$$v_o(r_p + Z_L - \mu Z_L) = -\mu Z_L v_i \tag{7.142}$$

The reference gain

$$G = \frac{v_o}{v_i} = \frac{-\mu Z_L}{r_p + (-\mu + 1)Z_L} \tag{7.143}$$

or

$$G = \frac{[-\mu/(-\mu + 1)]Z_L}{[r_p/(-\mu + 1)] + Z_L} \tag{7.144}$$

Equation 7.144 has the same form as the gain equation of the common cathode amplifier. However, both the amplification factor and plate

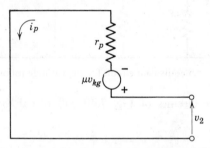

Fig. 7.42. Circuit for determining the output impedance of the cathode follower.

resistance have been reduced by the factor $(-\mu + 1)$. This reduction causes the gain to approach $-\mu/(-\mu + 1)$, as the load impedance becomes large in comparison with $r_p/(-\mu + 1)$. It is evident from this and from Eq. 7.135 that the voltage gain must be less than unity.

To check the validity of the assumption that the output impedance of the amplifier is $r_p/(-\mu + 1)$, a voltage v_2 is applied at the output terminals as shown in Fig. 7.42. Writing Kirchhoff's voltage equation around the loop, we have

$$v_2 - \mu v_{kg} = i_p r_p \tag{7.145}$$

In case the grid resistor returns to ground, the grid remains at ground potential and

$$v_2 = v_{kg} \tag{7.146}$$

Then

$$v_2(-\mu + 1) = i_p r_p \tag{7.147}$$

and

$$R_o = \frac{v_2}{i_p} = \frac{r_p}{-\mu + 1} \qquad (7.148)$$

Consequently, the equivalent circuits of Fig. 7.43 can be drawn for the cathode follower.

In case the grid resistor is returned to a tap on the cathode circuit as shown in Fig. 7.40a, the grid does not remain at ground potential when a voltage v_2 is applied to the output terminals; then, the output impedance rises. If the driving source impedance were infinite, the circuit of Fig. 7.40a would have an output impedance equal to r_p because $v_{gk} = 0$. In practical cases, however, the grid resistance R_g may be made large in comparison

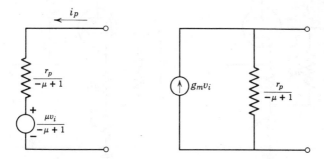

Fig. 7.43. *A*-c equivalent circuits for the cathode follower.

with the driving source resistance and the equivalent circuits of Fig. 7.43 are approximately correct.

PROB. 7.24. Determine the output impedance and maximum obtainable gain from a 12AT7 tube (one triode) when used as a cathode follower. Assume that none of the output voltage is fed back into the grid circuit. Also assume $\mu = -60$ and $r_p = 15$ KΩ. *Answer:* $Z_o = 246\ \Omega$.

PROB. 7.25. Develop an expression for the output impedance of a cathode follower when a fraction of the output voltage $k = r_g/(r_g + R_G)$ appears between grid and ground in the circuit of Fig. 7.40b. Let r_g be the impedance of the driving source.

PROB. 7.26. Calculate the voltage gain of a 12AT7 cathode follower when $R_L = 5$ KΩ. *Answer:* $G_v = 0.938$.

The input admittance of the amplifier may be determined by applying an input voltage v_i and solving for the resulting current. Referring to Fig. 7.44, we find that

$$I_g = sC_{gp}V_i + sC_{gk}(V_i - V_o) \qquad (7.149)$$

Using the relationship $V_o = GV_i$, we have

$$I_g = V_i[sC_{gp} + sC_{gk}(1 - G)] \tag{7.150}$$

$$Y_g = \frac{I_g}{V_i} = s[C_{gp} + (1 - G)C_{gk}] \tag{7.151}$$

and the effective input capacitance is

$$C_{\text{eff}} = C_{gp} + (1 - G)C_{gk} \tag{7.152}$$

Since the gain of the cathode follower approaches unity and has a positive sign, the effect of C_{gk} is negligibly small. If a pentode tube were used as

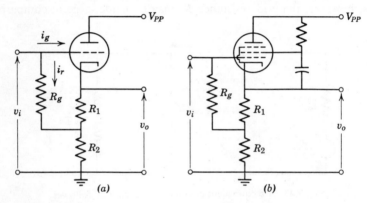

Fig. 7.44. Circuit for determining input impedance of a cathode follower.

illustrated in Fig. 7.44b, the grid-to-cathode capacitance would be essentially eliminated and the total effective input capacitance would be negligibly small.

Referring again to Fig. 7.44a, we see that if R_g is much greater than R_2 or R_1, then

$$i_r = \frac{v_i - Av_o}{R_g} \tag{7.153}$$

where

$$A = \frac{R_2}{R_1 + R_2} = \frac{R_2}{R_L} \tag{7.154}$$

$$i_r = v_i \frac{(1 - AG)}{R_g} \tag{7.155}$$

In case G is real,

$$R_i = \frac{v_i}{i_r} = \frac{R_g}{1 - AG} \tag{7.156}$$

When $R_2 = 0$, $A = 0$, $R_i = R_g$: but if R_2 approaches R_L, A approaches unity and

$$R_i \simeq \frac{R_g}{1 - G} \qquad (7.157)$$

Since the voltage gain of the cathode follower may be almost unity, the current gain and power gain may be almost equal to the ratio of the input resistance to the load impedance. This would be true when the $-\mu$ of the tube is 10 or higher and the load impedance is large in comparison with the output impedance.

PROB. 7.27. Calculate the effective input capacitance of a cathode follower which has $C_{gk} = 4$ pf, $C_{gp} = 4$ pf and $G = 0.90$. *Answer: $C_i = 4.4$ pf.*

PROB. 7.28. Calculate the effective input capacitance of a pentode cathode follower which has $C_i = 10$ pf, $G = 0.90$ and $C_{gp} = 0.003$ pf.

PROB. 7.29. Calculate the input resistance of a cathode follower which has $R_g = 0.5$ megohm, $R_1 = 1$ KΩ, $R_2 = 10$ KΩ, $\mu = -20$, and $r_p = 10$ KΩ. *Answer: $R_i = 2.94$ MΩ.*

The gain bandwidth product of a cathode follower circuit is approximately the same as a common cathode amplifier. However, the input signal level may be much higher than that of the common cathode connection, because

$$v_i = v_{gk} + v_o \qquad (7.158)$$

$$v_i = v_{gk} + Gv_i \qquad (7.159)$$

$$v_i(1 - G) = v_{gk} \qquad (7.160)$$

$$v_i = \frac{v_{gk}}{(1 - G)} \qquad (7.161)$$

As the gain approaches unity, the input voltage may be very large in comparison with the grid to cathode or bias voltage.

Figure 7.45 illustrates a method of graphical solution of the cathode follower. A 300-v V_{PP} supply voltage has been chosen and a load line drawn for $R_L = 20$ K. A bias of -2 v has been selected as suitable for symmetrical input signals. The required bias resistance R_1 is 400 Ω since $I_P = 5$ ma. The remainder of the d-c load resistor R_2 is then 19,600 Ω. The d-c drop across the tube is 195 v and the d-c drop across the load resistance is 105 v. The maximum peak-to-peak grid-to-cathode voltage swing is 6 v. This yields a peak-to-peak voltage swing across the load resistance of $300 - 110 = 190$ v. Consequently, the peak-to-peak input voltage is $190 + 6 = 196$ v, since the peak-to-peak grid voltage is 6 v. The voltage gain is $\frac{190}{196} = 0.974$. If the a-c load impedance is appreciably different than the d-c value, an a-c load line should be drawn through the quiescent point.

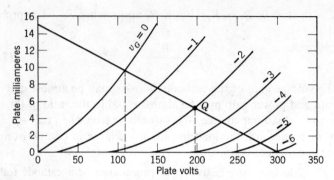

Fig. 7.45. Graphical solution of the cathode follower.

The distortion of the cathode or emitter follower is usually very low because the output voltage is so nearly equal to the input voltage at all times. If the input voltage were sinusoidal, the output current would be almost sinusoidal. This would require that the grid-cathode or base-emitter voltage be nonsinusoidal, as may be seen from Fig. 7.45 where the peak grid voltage is only 2 v on the positive half cycle but is 4 v on the negative half cycle. This grid-cathode voltage waveform is sketched in Fig. 7.46. If the operating point is assumed to remain at $V_G = -2$ v and the peak-to-peak amplitude of the input voltage is the maximum permissible value of 196 v, the output voltage would have a peak amplitude on the positive half cycle of $98 - 2 = 96$ v and a peak amplitude on the negative half cycle of $98 - 4 = 94$ v. This 2-v amplitude difference between the two half cycles of the output voltage is only about 1 % of the peak-to-peak amplitude of the output voltage, and therefore, represents a very small percentage of distortion.[6] Actually, the lack of symmetry of

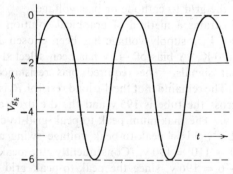

Fig. 7.46. A sketch of the grid-cathode voltage waveform of the cathode follower when the excitation is a sinusoid of maximum permissible amplitude.

[6] A quantitative discussion of distortion is given in Chapter 10.

the output signal slightly increases the average plate current, which in turn slightly increases the bias. This increased bias tends to improve the output waveform.

Frequently the input signal is a positive pulse instead of a symmetrical signal. Maximum signal-handling capability is then provided if the quiescent bias is near plate current cutoff. Under these conditions, the grid may be maintained at d-c ground potential and the entire d-c load resistance used as bias. In the foregoing example, the operating or Q point would be located at approximately $V_G = -6$ v, and $V_P = 300$ v. This would permit a peak pulse input voltage of 196 v and a pulse output voltage of 190 v.

PROB. 7.30. Given a tube with g_m of 5000 μmhos and an r_p of 1 megohm. (*a*) Design an *R-C* coupled amplifier with a pass band from 30 Hz to 2 MHz. Assume wiring and interelectrode capacitance is 50 pf. Also assume the grid resistor to the following stage has a value of 1 megohm. (*b*) What is the midband gain of this amplifier?

PROB. 7.31. Two pentode tubes are to be connected in cascade. The following parameters are listed for the tubes: $g_m = 2000\ \mu$mhos; $r_p = 1$ megohm. The maximum permissible grid leak resistor is 1 megohm. (*a*) Design an *R-C* coupled amplifier using the two tubes in cascade. The frequency response should be down 3 db at 60 Hz and at 200,000 Hz. (Note that the *gain of each stage* must *not* be down 3 db at the frequencies listed.) (*b*) What is the maximum voltage gain possible from this amplifier?

PROB. 7.32. A cathode follower is connected as shown in Fig. 7.47. Note that the total load resistance $R_L = R_1 + R_2$. This load resistance is to be set at 15,000 Ω. The input signal v_i is sinusoidal. The magnitude of the input signal, and the magnitude of the bias resistor R_1 are each of such a value that the grid-cathode voltage swings from zero volts at one extreme to -4.0 v at the other extreme. The internal impedance of the source that delivers v_i is 10 KΩ; the

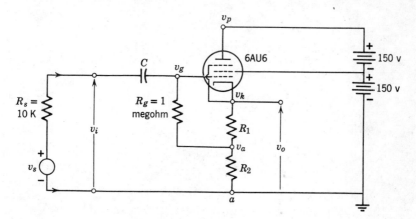

Fig. 7.47. The circuit configuration for Prob. 7.32.

reactance of the coupling capacitor is 1 KΩ; whereas, R_g has a resistance of 1 megohm. Find the value of R_1 in ohms. Find the maximum, average, and minimum values of voltages at the five different points indicated on the diagram. (v_i, v_g, v_a, v_k, and v_p). Express all voltages in respect to point a as a zero reference.

PROB. 7.33. A 2N2712 transistor is to be used as an amplifier to provide 25 milliwatts of power to a 500 Ω capacitively-coupled load. The driving-source resistance is 2.0 KΩ and is capacitively coupled. A thermal stability factor $S_I = 10$ is adequate for this application. Design the amplifier. Determine all component values assuming the low frequency cutoff to be approximately 30 Hz. Determine the upper cutoff frequency and the rise time of the amplifier. Neglect wiring capacitance.

8

Small Signal Tuned Amplifiers

The need frequently arises for an amplifier which will amplify only those frequencies which lie within a certain frequency range, or band. This type of amplifier is known as a tuned amplifier or band pass amplifier. Radio and television receivers, for example, use tuned amplifiers to select one radio signal from the many which are being broadcast. Several types of tuned amplifiers are discussed in this chapter. The gain and bandwidth of each type will be of interest. It will be assumed, in the discussion of tuned amplifiers, that the input signal is a modulated signal which has a basic frequency ω_o. In this case the amplifier should be tuned to ω_o, and the required bandwidth will depend on the nature of the modulation (or variation) of the signal. The bandwidth requirements of interrupted carrier modulation are considered in this chapter. However, the band-width requirements of other types of modulation are necessarily delayed until later chapters where these other types of modulation are considered.

8.1 SINGLE TUNED, CAPACITIVELY COUPLED AMPLIFIERS

The *R-C* coupled amplifier may be transformed into a band pass amplifier by replacement of the collector or plate circuit resistor with an inductor, as shown in Fig. 8.1. A current source equivalent circuit which

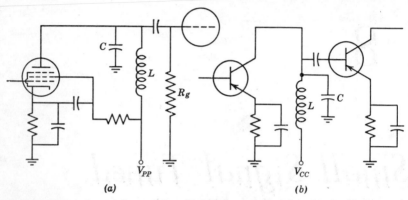

(a)   (b)

Fig. 8.1. (*a*) Tuned pentode amplifier with inductance in the plate circuit. (*b*) Common-emitter amplifier with an inductance in the collector circuit.

will represent either of the amplifiers of Fig. 8.1 is given in Fig. 8.2. In this circuit, C is the total shunt capacitance and R_{sh} is the total shunt resistance of the amplifier and R_s is the effective series resistance of the inductor. The bypass and coupling capacitors do not appear in the equivalent circuit because their reactances should be negligible at the operating frequency.

The equivalent circuit of Fig. 8.2 may be simplified if the series combination of L and R_s is transformed into an equivalent parallel combination, as follows. Considering the real frequency domain, we find that

$$Z_L = R_s + j\omega L \tag{8.1}$$

$$Y_L = \frac{1}{Z_L} = \frac{1}{R_s + j\omega L} \tag{8.2}$$

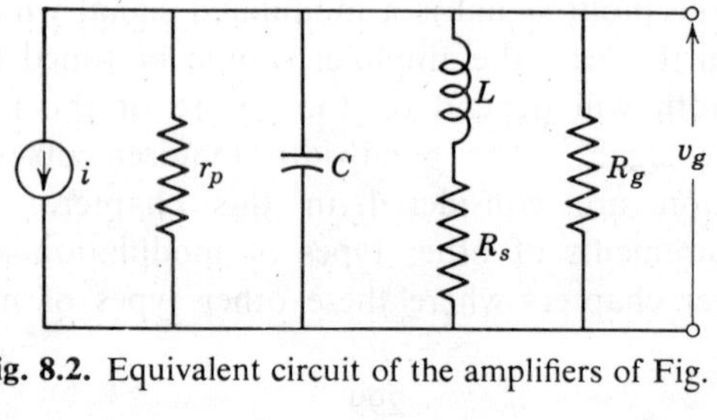

Fig. 8.2. Equivalent circuit of the amplifiers of Fig. 8.1.

Rationalizing, we have

$$Y_L = \frac{R_s - j\omega L}{R_s^2 + \omega^2 L^2} \tag{8.3}$$

or

$$Y_L = \frac{R_s}{R_s^2 + \omega^2 L^2} - j\frac{\omega L}{R_s^2 + \omega^2 L^2} \tag{8.4}$$

This is of the form $Y = G + jB$. ωL is usually large in comparison with R_s. When $\omega L \geq 10R_s$, which is known as the *high Q* case,

$$Y \simeq \frac{R_s}{\omega^2 L^2} - j\frac{1}{\omega L} \tag{8.5}$$

This admittance could be produced by a resistance in parallel with an

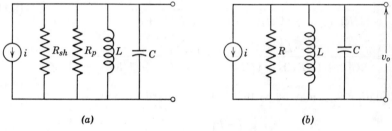

(a)   *(b)*

Fig. 8.3. Equivalent circuits for a tuned amplifier.

inductive admittance. The resistance

$$R_p = \frac{1}{G} \simeq \frac{\omega^2 L^2}{R_s} \tag{8.6}$$

But

$$Q_o = \frac{\omega L}{R_s} \tag{8.7}$$

where Q_o is the Q of the coil at the specified value of ω. Then

$$R_p \simeq Q_o \omega L \tag{8.8}$$

In the high Q case ($Q \geq 10$), the percentage variation of either Q or ω is negligible within the usable frequency range of the amplifier, as will be shown later. The effective parallel resistance R_p may then be considered to be constant.

It is evident from Eq. 8.5 that the inductance of the equivalent parallel circuit is approximately equal to that of the series combination because $\omega L_n \simeq 1/B = \omega L$. The equivalent parallel circuit is shown in Fig. 8.3a.

The equivalent parallel resistance R_p may be combined with R_{sh} to obtain the total shunt resistance R as illustrated in Fig. 8.3b. Using the relationship of Eq. 8.8, we may define the circuit Q, sometimes called the loaded Q, as

$$Q = \frac{R}{\omega_o L} = R\omega_o C \tag{8.9}$$

At the resonant frequency ω_o, the total impedance is R because the impedance of the lossless resonant circuit is infinite. Then the output voltage is

$$V_o = -IR \tag{8.10}$$

Referring to Fig. 8.3b, we may obtain the s-domain[1] output voltage V_o as a function of the s-domain current source I.

$$V_o = \frac{-I}{(1/R) + sC + (1/sL)} = \frac{-sL1}{s^2 LC + s(L/R) + 1} \tag{8.11}$$

$$V_o = \frac{-sLI}{LC[s^2 + (1/RC)s + (1/LC)]} = \left(\frac{-I}{C}\right)\frac{s}{s^2 + (1/RC)s + (1/LC)} \tag{8.12}$$

Equation 8.12 may be written in the standard form as

$$V_o = \left(\frac{-I}{C}\right)\frac{s}{s^2 + 2\zeta\omega_n s + \omega_n^2} \tag{8.13}$$

where ω_n is the undamped resonant frequency $(LC)^{-\frac{1}{2}}$ and the damping ratio $\zeta = 1/2R\omega_n C$. From Eq. 8.9 we can see that $\zeta = 1/2Q$ in the high Q case because $\omega_o \simeq \omega_n$.

In case the amplifier is a vacuum tube amplifier, the current $I = g_m V_g$ and

$$G = \frac{V_o}{V_g} = -\frac{g_m}{C}\frac{s}{s^2 + 2\zeta\omega_n s + \omega_n^2} \tag{8.14}$$

Now, from a consideration of the amplifier response to a negative step function of magnitude V, the output voltage is

$$V_o = -\frac{VG}{s} = \frac{g_m V}{C}\frac{1}{s^2 + 2\zeta\omega_n s + \omega_n^2} \tag{8.15}$$

---

[1] The capital I or V with lower case subscripts will be used to denote currents and voltages in the frequency domain. This should not cause confusion because if the current or voltage is in the complex (s) frequency domain, the equations will contain the parameter s. In the real $(j\omega)$ frequency domain the equations will contain the parameter ω.

The inverse transform of Eq. 8.15 can be most readily obtained by arranging this equation into the standard form

$$V_o = \frac{g_m V}{C} \frac{1}{(s + \zeta\omega_n)^2 + \omega_n^2(1 - \zeta^2)} \qquad (8.16)$$

$$V_o = \frac{g_m V}{\omega_o C} \frac{\omega_o}{(s + \zeta\omega_n)^2 + \omega_o^2} \qquad (8.17)$$

where $\omega_o = \omega_n(1 - \zeta^2)^{\frac{1}{2}}$

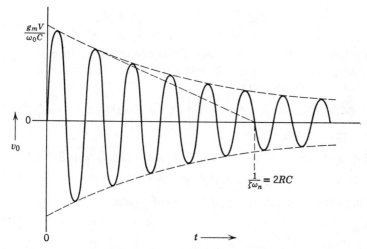

Fig. 8.4. The time response of a typical tuned amplifier to a negative step-voltage input of magnitude V.

Taking the inverse transform of Eq. 8.17, we have

$$v_o = \frac{g_m V}{\omega_o C} e^{-\zeta\omega_n t} \sin \omega_o t \qquad (8.18)$$

This time domain output voltage is sketched in Fig. 8.4. Although a step input voltage may be an unusual type of excitation for a tuned amplifier, the resulting response is interesting and informative. This exponentially decaying sinusoid is the transient response and is frequently known as *ringing*. The time constant of the decay is $2RC$ in contrast to the usual time constant RC obtained when a circuit contains resistance and capacitance only.

As previously discussed, the tuned amplifier is usually tuned to the desired excitation frequency. The excitation will then be assumed to be $v_g = V \sin \omega_o t$, and the s-domain excitation is $V\omega_o/(s^2 + \omega_o^2)$. Using

Eq. 8.14, we have

$$V_o = \frac{V\omega_o}{s^2 + \omega_o^2} G = -\frac{g_m V}{C} \frac{\omega_o}{s^2 + \omega_o^2} \frac{s}{s^2 + 2\zeta\omega_n s + \omega_n^2} \quad (8.19)$$

Rearrangement of Eq. 8.19 into the form of Eq. 8.17 gives

$$V_o = -\frac{g_m V}{C} \frac{\omega_o s}{(s^2 + \omega_o^2)[(s + \zeta\omega_n)^2 + \omega_o^2]} \quad (8.20)$$

Using partial fraction expansion, we find that

$$V_o = -\frac{g_m V}{C}\left[\frac{As + B}{s^2 + \omega_o^2} + \frac{Cs + D}{(s + \zeta\omega_n)^2 + \omega_o^2}\right] \quad (8.21)$$

The arbitrary constants A, B, C, and D may be evaluated by equating the numerators of Eqs. 8.21 and 8.20 (after the equations have been reduced to a common denominator).

$$(As + B)[(s + \zeta\omega_n)^2 + \omega_o^2] + (Cs + D)(s^2 + \omega_o^2) = \omega_o s \quad (8.22)$$

Expanding, we have

$$As^3 + 2A\zeta\omega_n s^2 + A\zeta^2\omega_n^2 s + A\omega_o^2 s + Bs^2 + 2B\zeta\omega_n s + B\zeta^2\omega_n^2$$
$$+ B\omega_o^2 + Cs^3 + C\omega_o^2 s + Ds^2 + D\omega_o^2 = \omega_o s \quad (8.23)$$

Equating the coefficients of equal powers of s gives

$$A + C = 0 \quad (8.24)$$

$$2A\zeta\omega_n + B + D = 0 \quad (8.25)$$

$$A\zeta^2\omega_n^2 + A\omega_o^2 + 2B\zeta\omega_n + C\omega_o^2 = \omega_o \quad (8.26)$$

$$B\zeta^2\omega_n^2 + B\omega_o^2 + D\omega_o^2 = 0 \quad (8.27)$$

Some simplifications can be made by recognizing that $\zeta^2\omega_n^2$ is very small in comparison with ω_o^2 when the circuit Q is 10 or higher as previously assumed. Then $\zeta \simeq 1/2Q$. In this case, from Eq. 8.27, $D \simeq -B$. Then from Eq. 8.25, $A \simeq 0$ and from Eq. 8.24, $C \simeq 0$. Substituting these values into Eq. 8.26, we have

$$2B\zeta\omega_n \simeq \omega_o \quad (8.28)$$

$$B \simeq \frac{\omega_o}{2\zeta\omega_n} \quad \text{and} \quad D \simeq -B \simeq -\frac{\omega_o}{2\zeta\omega_n} \quad (8.29)$$

Equation 8.21 then becomes

$$V_o = -\frac{g_m V}{2\zeta\omega_n C}\left(\frac{\omega_o}{s^2 + \omega_o^2} - \frac{\omega_o}{(s + \zeta\omega_n)^2 + \omega_o^2}\right) \quad (8.30)$$

Since $2\zeta\omega_n = 1/RC$ and $g_m R = K$, the reference gain, or gain at the resonant frequency,

$$V_o = -KV\left(\frac{\omega_o}{s^2 + \omega_o^2} - \frac{\omega_o}{(s + \zeta\omega_n)^2 + \omega_o^2}\right) \tag{8.31}$$

Taking the inverse transform, we find that

$$v_o = -KV(\sin \omega_o t - e^{-\zeta\omega_n t} \sin \omega_o t) \tag{8.32}$$

From the substitution of $2\zeta\omega_n = 1/RC$,

$$v_o = -KV(1 - e^{-t/2RC}) \sin \omega_o t \tag{8.33}$$

A sketch of the response which is expressed by Eq. 8.33 is given in Fig. 8.5a along with a sketch of the sinusoidal excitation. In addition, the response to an interrupted or pulse modulated carrier is given in Fig. 8.5b. In this case the exponential decay of the output following the cessation of the input was deduced from the known transient response of the RLC

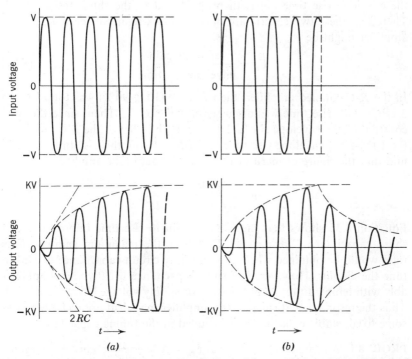

Fig. 8.5. A sketch of the response of a tuned amplifier to (a) sinusoidal excitation of frequency ω_0, switched on at time = 0; (b) interrupted or pulse-modulated carrier excitation of frequency ω_0.

circuit. The form of this transient response was obtained from the first example in this section in which the excitation was a step voltage (see Fig. 8.4).

The desirability of a tuned amplifier, like other amplifiers, is measured by both the amplification and the preservation of the waveform of the excitation. As shown in Fig. 8.5, the tuned amplifier cannot faithfully follow instantaneous changes in the excitation amplitude. In other words, the tuned amplifier has a rise and decay time which is very similar to the R-C coupled amplifier counterpart. Two essential differences exist between the tuned amplifier and the untuned or video amplifier. First, in the case of the tuned amplifier, it is the *envelope* of the output signal and not the individual cycle which rises and decays exponentially when the sinusoidal excitation is instantly started or stopped. Second, the time constant of the envelope rise or decay is $2RC$ in contrast to the time constant RC of the untuned or video amplifier.

Again, as in the untuned amplifier, the tuned amplifier would ideally have a very high gain and a very small rise time. But the reference gain and the envelope rise time are both proportional to the shunt resistance R. Therefore, these two criteria are in conflict. A figure of merit F_a for the amplifier might be

$$F_a = \frac{\text{reference gain}}{\text{envelope rise time}} \tag{8.34}$$

In the R-C coupled amplifier, the rise time (10%–90%) was found to be $2.2RC$. This rise time was discussed in Chapter 7. Then, since the time constant of the envelope rise is $2RC$, or double that of the R-C amplifier, the 10%–90% envelope rise time is $4.4RC$. Using this rise time, we can find that the figure of merit of the tuned vacuum tube amplifier is

$$F_a = \frac{g_m R}{4.4RC} = \frac{g_m}{4.4C} \tag{8.35}$$

Equation 8.35 shows that the ratio of gain to rise time improves as the shunt capacitance C decreases. Therefore, the maximum gain-rise time ratio would be obtained when only the stray circuit capacitance is used to tune the circuit. However, this stray capacitance usually varies appreciably with temperature, amplifier gain, or supply voltage (for a transistor). Thus the resonant frequency of the amplifier may drift appreciably unless some fixed, stable capacitance is included in the tuning capacitance.

PROB. 8.1. A pentode tube which has $g_m = 2000$ μmhos and $r_p = 1$ megohm is used as an r-f amplifier. The total shunt capacitance in the plate circuit is 25 pf. The grid resistor in the following amplifier is 1 megohm.

(a) Calculate the inductance required to tune the plate circuit to 2 MHz.

(b) Calculate the reference voltage gain of the circuit if the Q of the coil is 100.

(c) What is the circuit Q? *Answer: (a) 253 μhen, (b) 388, (c) 62.*

PROB. 8.2. An input signal $v_g = 2 \sin(4\pi \times 10^6 t)$ is suddenly applied to the amplifier of Prob. 8.1.

(a) Write the equation for the output voltage v_o.

(b) Sketch the envelope of the output signal v_o from $t = 0$ to $t = 100$ μsec.

(c) Determine the rise time of the envelope.

(d) Discuss the relationship between the envelope rise time and the circuit Q.

PROB. 8.3. Prove that the time response of the transistor amplifier of Fig. 8.1b is given by

$$i_o = -KI(1 - e^{-t/2RC}) \sin \omega_0 t$$

when the input current is $i_i = I \sin \omega_0 t$ beginning at $t = 0$.

The steady-state sinusoidal response of the amplifier may be determined from the transfer function, Eq. 8.14. Replacing s by $j\omega$, $2\zeta\omega_n$ by $1/RC$, and $\omega_n{}^2$ by $1/LC$, we have

$$G(j\omega) = -\frac{g_m}{C} \frac{j\omega}{-\omega^2 + \dfrac{j\omega}{RC} + \dfrac{1}{LC}} \tag{8.36}$$

Dividing both numerator and denominator of Eq. 8.36 by $j\omega$ and multiplying both numerator and denominator by RC, we find that

$$G(j\omega) = -g_m R \frac{1}{1 + j\omega RC + (R/j\omega L)} \tag{8.37}$$

But

$$R = Q\omega_o L = \frac{Q}{\omega_o C} \tag{8.38}$$

Then, recognizing that $g_m R = K$, the reference gain,

$$G(j\omega) = -K \frac{1}{1 + \dfrac{j\omega Q}{\omega_o} + \dfrac{Q\omega_o}{j\omega}} \tag{8.39}$$

$$G(j\omega) = -K \frac{1}{1 + jQ\left(\dfrac{\omega}{\omega_o} - \dfrac{\omega_o}{\omega}\right)} \tag{8.40}$$

Figure 8.6 is a sketch of the voltage gain as a function of ω. The half-power frequencies ω_H and ω_L occur when the magnitude of the denominator of Eq. 8.40 is equal to $(2)^{\frac{1}{2}}$. Therefore

$$\left| Q\left(\frac{\omega_H}{\omega_o} - \frac{\omega_o}{\omega_H}\right) \right| = \left| Q\left(\frac{\omega_L}{\omega_o} - \frac{\omega_o}{\omega_L}\right) \right| = 1 \tag{8.41}$$

Then

$$\frac{\omega_H}{\omega_o} - \frac{\omega_o}{\omega_H} = \frac{\omega_o}{\omega_L} - \frac{\omega_L}{\omega_o} \tag{8.42}$$

Rearranging terms, we have

$$\frac{\omega_H}{\omega_o} + \frac{\omega_L}{\omega_o} = \frac{\omega_o}{\omega_L} + \frac{\omega_o}{\omega_H} \tag{8.43}$$

$$\frac{\omega_H + \omega_L}{\omega_o} = \frac{\omega_o(\omega_H + \omega_L)}{\omega_H \omega_L} \tag{8.44}$$

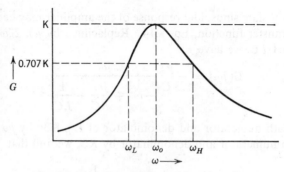

Fig. 8.6. Variation of gain as a function of ω.

Therefore,

$$\omega_H \omega_L = \omega_o^2 \tag{8.45}$$

$$\omega_o = (\omega_H \omega_L)^{1/2} \tag{8.46}$$

Rearranging the first term of Eq. 8.41, we find that

$$Q \frac{\omega_H^2 - \omega_o^2}{\omega_o \omega_H} = 1 \tag{8.47}$$

From a combination of Eq. 8.46 and 8.47,

$$Q \frac{\omega_H^2 - \omega_H \omega_L}{\omega_o \omega_H} = 1 \tag{8.48}$$

$$Q \frac{\omega_H - \omega_L}{\omega_o} = 1$$

Then

$$\omega_H - \omega_L = \frac{\omega_o}{Q} \tag{8.49}$$

The bandwidth B is defined as $\omega_H - \omega_L$. Then

$$B = \frac{\omega_o}{Q} \tag{8.50}$$

Note that the bandwidth is in radians per second when ω_o is in radians per second.

PROB. 8.4. Calculate the bandwidth of the amplifier of Prob. 8.1. Express this bandwidth in KHz. *Answer: 32.3 KHz.*

The gain bandwidth product of the single tuned vacuum tube amplifier may be of interest.

$$KB = g_m R \frac{\omega_o}{Q} \tag{8.51}$$

But

$$R = Q\omega_o L = \frac{Q}{\omega_o C} \tag{8.38}$$

Then

$$KB = \frac{g_m}{C} \tag{8.52}$$

This is the same gain bandwidth product as that of the *R-C* coupled amplifier (Section 7.5), providing that the shunt capacitance is the same in each case. It may seem peculiar that the tuned amplifier has the same gain-bandwidth product as its *R-C* amplifier counterpart, when the envelope rise time is twice as great as the comparable *R-C* amplifier. The reason for this behavior will be understood after the amplitude modulation process has been studied (Chapter 14).

8.2 TAPPED TUNED CIRCUITS

The single-tuned circuit discussed in the preceding paragraphs does not provide any means of impedance transformation. The output impedance of a pentode tube amplifier is fairly well matched to the input impedance of a following tube amplifier; therefore, when used to couple pentode tubes, the single-tuned circuit described would provide nearly maximum available power gain. The power gain of a triode tube or transistor amplifier circuit could be materially increased, however, if an impedance matching feature were included in the coupling device. A tap on the coil in the tuned circuit provides this feature. An illustration is provided in the transistor amplifier of Fig. 8.7. In the equivalent circuit, Fig. 8.7b, R_o is the output resistance of the driving transistor, R_1 is the series resistance of

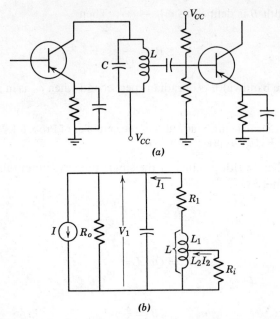

Fig. 8.7. A tuned coupling device which will provide impedance transformation.

the coil, and R_i is the input resistance of the following transistor stage. There are n_2 turns between the tap and the r-f ground terminal of the coil.

To obtain maximum power transfer, the impedance looking back into the tapped tuned circuit should be equal to R_i. If there were no power loss in the tuned circuit, maximum power transfer would be obtained also when the impedance looking into the collector side of the tuned circuit is R_o. Although there are actually no lossless tuned circuits available, the tuned circuit may be made mathematically lossless by transforming the coil resistance R_1 to its equivalent parallel value R_p by the process previously discussed and then adding this equivalent resistance in parallel with the output resistance R_o. This technique is illustrated in Fig. 8.8. The modified output resistance R'_o in the high Q case, using Eq. 8.8, is

$$R'_o = \frac{R_o Q_o \omega_o L}{R_o + Q_o \omega_o L} \tag{8.53}$$

where ω_o is the desired resonant frequency. The value of the inductance L is not known at the moment, but will be determined later. Then R'_o can be calculated.

The driving point impedance of the tapped coil and its load R_i will now be found. Writing loop equations for the tapped coil and its load, we have

$$-V_1 = j\omega L I_1 - j\omega(L_2 + M)I_2 \Big\rbrace$$
$$0 = -j\omega(L_2 + M)I_1 + (R_i + j\omega L_2)I_2 \Big\rbrace \quad (8.54)$$

where M is the mutual inductance between L_2 and L_1. Solving for I_1, we find that

$$I_1 = \frac{-(R_i + j\omega L_2)V_1}{j\omega L(R_i + j\omega L_2) + \omega^2(L_2 + M)^2} \quad (8.55)$$

The driving point impedance of the tapped coil is

$$Z_1 = \frac{-V_1}{I_1} = \frac{j\omega L(R_i + j\omega L_2) + \omega^2(L_2 + M)^2}{R_i + j\omega L_2} \quad (8.56)$$

$$Z_1 = j\omega L + \frac{\omega^2(L_2 + M)^2}{R_i + j\omega L_2} \quad (8.57)$$

The second term on the right side of Eq. 8.57 is the impedance coupled into the coil because of the load R_i. Since this term is complex, the effective reactance of the coil, and consequently the resonant frequency of the tuned circuit, will change with R_i. This effect is highly undesirable because R_i changes with bias, temperature, etc. It can be seen from Eq. 8.57 that the coupled impedance will be almost purely resistive if ωL_2 is small in comparison with R_i. Actually, R_i will always be large in comparison with ωL_2 in the high Q case, since the circuit Q is the ratio of the effective shunt resistance to the shunt inductive reactance. Then the driving point

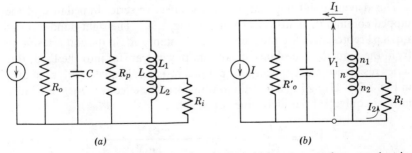

(a)   (b)

Fig. 8.8. (a) The equivalent parallel resistance R_p, which represents the power loss in coil L is combined with the transistor output resistance R_0 to produce the modified output resistance R'_0 in b.

impedance becomes,

$$Z_1 \simeq j\omega L + \frac{\omega^2(L_2 + M)^2}{R_i} \tag{8.58}$$

In the usual coil configuration, the length of the winding space is short in comparison with the diameter of the coil. Then, the coefficient of coupling approaches unity, and the inductance of a coil is proportional to the number of turns squared. Then

$$L_2 \simeq \left(\frac{n_2}{n}\right)^2 L \tag{8.59}$$

where n_2 is the number of turns in that part of the coil which is common to both input and output and n is the total number of turns in the coil. Also

$$L_1 \simeq \left(\frac{n_1}{n}\right)^2 L$$

The mutual inductance is

$$M = k\sqrt{L_1 L_2} = k\frac{L n_1 n_2}{n^2} \tag{8.60}$$

Since $n_1 = n - n_2$,

$$M = kL\left(\frac{n_2}{n} - \frac{n_2^2}{n^2}\right) \tag{8.61}$$

Eq. 8.58 then becomes

$$Z_1 \simeq j\omega L + \frac{\omega^2\left[\left(\frac{n_2}{n}\right)^2 L + kL\left(\frac{n_2}{n} - \frac{n_2^2}{n^2}\right)\right]^2}{R_i} \tag{8.62}$$

$$Z_1 = j\omega L + \frac{\omega^2 L^2\left[(1 - k)\left(\frac{n_2}{n}\right)^2 + k\frac{n_2}{n}\right]^2}{R_i} \tag{8.63}$$

This driving point impedance Z is the effective series impedance of the tapped coil and its load R_i as shown in Fig. 8.9a. The right-hand term of Eq. 8.63 represents the equivalent series resistance R'_s in the coil L resulting from the load R_i. To obtain maximum power transfer into the load, this series resistance must appear as a parallel resistance equal to R'_o as shown in Fig. 8.9b. Using Eq. 8.6 again to transform the effective series resistance into its equivalent parallel value, we see that

$$R'_o = \frac{(\omega L)^2}{R'_s} = \frac{(\omega L)^2}{\dfrac{\omega^2 L^2\left[(1 - k)\left(\dfrac{n_2}{n}\right)^2 + k\dfrac{n_2}{n}\right]^2}{R_i}} \tag{8.64}$$

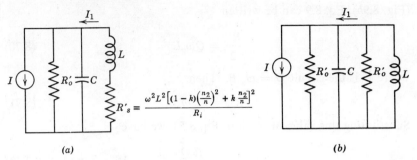

$$R'_s = \frac{\omega^2 L^2 \left[(1 - k)\left(\frac{n_2}{n}\right)^2 + k \frac{n_2}{n}\right]^2}{R_i}$$

(a)

(b)

Fig. 8.9. The equivalent series resistance of (a) is transformed into the equivalent parallel resistance R'_0 in (b).

or

$$\left[(1 - k)\left(\frac{n_2}{n}\right)^2 + k \frac{n_2}{n}\right]^2 = \frac{R_i}{R'_o} \tag{8.65}$$

$$(1 - k)\left(\frac{n_2}{n}\right)^2 + k \frac{n_2}{n} \mp \left(\frac{R_i}{R'_o}\right)^{1/2} = 0 \tag{8.66}$$

Solving for $\frac{n_2}{n}$, we see that

$$\frac{n_2}{n} = -\frac{k}{2(1 - k)} \mp \left[\frac{k^2}{4(1 - k)^2} \mp \frac{(R_i/R'_o)^{1/2}}{1 - k}\right]^{1/2} \tag{8.67}$$

The signs in Eq. 8.67 must be chosen so that n_2/n is real and positive. Then

$$\frac{n_2}{n} = \left[\frac{k^2}{4(1 - k)^2} + \frac{(R_i/R'_o)^{1/2}}{1 - k}\right]^{1/2} - \frac{k}{2(1 - k)} \tag{8.68}$$

Remember that Eq. 8.68 is valid only for coils with fairly good magnetic coupling.

A test coil could be wound on the desired coil form and the value of k determined for that particular configuration. For tightly coupled r-f coils, typical values of k range from about 0.8 to 0.9. It can be seen from Eq. 8.66 that when k approaches unity

$$\frac{n_2}{n} \simeq \left(\frac{R_i}{R'_o}\right)^{1/2} \tag{8.69}$$

As previously mentioned, the value of R'_o cannot be calculated until the coil inductance L is known, or vice versa. Two equations which involve both R'_o and L are Eq. 8.9 and Eq. 8.53. Since the effective shunt loading resistance on the tuned circuit is $R'_o/2$ in the maximum power transfer case

(Fig. 8.9b), Eq. 8.9 can be written

$$\frac{R'_o}{2} = Q\omega_o L \tag{8.70}$$

where Q is the circuit $Q = \omega_o/B$. Then

$$R'_o = 2Q\omega_o L \tag{8.71}$$

Substituting this value of R'_o into Eq. 8.53, we have

$$2Q\omega_o L = \frac{R_o Q_o \omega_o L}{R_o + Q_o \omega_o L} \tag{8.72}$$

$$2Q = \frac{R_o Q_o}{R_o + Q_o \omega_o L} \tag{8.73}$$

$$2QR_o + 2QQ_o\omega_o L = R_o Q_o \tag{8.74}$$

$$L = \frac{R_o(Q_o - 2Q)}{\omega_o 2 Q_o Q} = \frac{R_o}{\omega_o}\left(\frac{1}{2Q} - \frac{1}{Q_o}\right) \tag{8.75}$$

Observe that the inductance L determined by Eq. 8.75 will provide the desired bandwidth when maximum power transfer is achieved. Also notice that maximum power transfer cannot be achieved unless the coil Q_o is more than twice as great as the circuit Q. Since the circuit Q is usually determined by the bandwidth requirement, the minimum coil Q_o which will provide maximum power transfer can be quickly calculated once the resonant frequency and bandwidth are set. Of course, the coupling efficiency and hence the total stage gain increases as the coil Q_o is increased above this minimum value. In the development it has been assumed that the loss in the tuning capacitor is negligible and the circuit Q is high (ten or more).

The number of turns of wire for a cylindrical coil configuration can be determined from the empirical formula

$$L = \frac{n^2 r^2}{9r + 10l} \times 10^{-6} \tag{8.76}$$

where r is the mean radius of the coil in inches, l is the length of the coil in inches, and L is the inductance in henries. After the coil form with its radius r and winding space l has been selected, the total number of turns n can be calculated from Eq. 8.76. Then the number of turns to the tap n_2 can be calculated from Eq. 8.68.

PROB. 8.5. A transistor with $R_o = 10$ KΩ is to be coupled to a transistor with $R_i = 1$ KΩ. The resonant frequency is 5 MHz and the desired bandwidth is 200 KHz. Using a tapped tuned circuit to provide maximum power transfer, determine the total number of turns and the location of the tap. The coil is to have a $Q_o = 100$ and it is to be wound on a 0.2 inch diameter form and fill a 0.25 inch winding length. Assume $k = 0.8$. *Answer: $n = 32.8$, $n_2 = 16$.*

PROB. 8.6. Assuming that k approaches unity, calculate n and n_2 for the coil of Prob. 8.5. Compare this coil with the one designed for $k = 0.8$.

PROB. 8.7. A long, small diameter coil has a small value of k. Assuming k to be approximately zero so that $L_2 = (n_2/n)L$, derive an expression for n_2/n in terms of R_i and R'_o. Compare the results with the tightly coupled case.

The foregoing problems lead to the conclusion that sufficient accuracy may be obtained for most applications if Eq. 8.69, which was obtained for

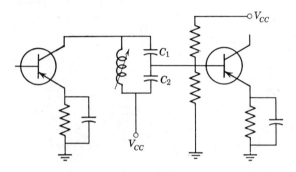

Fig. 8.10. An alternate impedance matching system.

the case $k \simeq 1$, is used for *all* degrees of coupling in the tapped coil. In this case, the tap location can be determined directly from a knowledge of the load resistance R_i and the modified output resistance R'_o.

The impedance transformation could have been accomplished by "tapping the capacitor" instead of the coil as shown in Fig. 8.10. The relationship between the capacitive reactances in this case would be the same as the relationship between the inductive reactances of the tapped coil where $k = 0$, (i.e., the reactance is proportional to the number of turns). Provision is always made to vary at least one of the tuning elements to tune the circuit. The nontapped element is the only single element which can be conveniently varied without changing the impedance ratio.

PROB. 8.8. The circuit of Fig. 8.10 is to be used to couple the transistors of Prob. 8.5. Calculate the value of each of the tuning capacitors. *Answer: $C_1 = 5.75\ pf$, $C_2 = 7.1\ pf$.*

8.3 INDUCTIVELY COUPLED SINGLE-TUNED CIRCUITS

Impedance transformation may also be accomplished by inductively coupling the tuned circuit to either the source or the load. This method

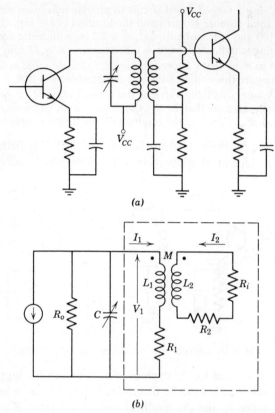

Fig. 8.11. (a) Transistor circuit and (b) equivalent circuit which accomplish impedance transformation by inductive coupling.

is illustrated in the transistor circuit of Fig. 8.11. In reference to the equivalent circuit, Fig. 8.11b, voltage equations can be written for the coupling circuit which is within the dashed enclosure. In this case, R_i will be included as part of Z_{22}.

$$\left.\begin{array}{l} V_1 = I_1 Z_{11} + I_2 Z_{12} \\ 0 = I_1 Z_{21} + I_2 Z_{22} \end{array}\right\} \tag{8.77}$$

where $Z_{11} = j\omega L_1 + R_1$
$Z_{22} = j\omega L_2 + R_2 + R_i$
$Z_{12} = Z_{21} = j\omega M$

Solving for I_1, we have

$$I_1 = \frac{V_1 Z_{22}}{Z_{11} Z_{22} - Z_{12}^2} \tag{8.78}$$

The driving point impedance of the primary is

$$Z_{\text{in}} = \frac{V_1}{I_1} = \frac{Z_{11}Z_{22} - Z_{12}{}^2}{Z_{22}} = Z_{11} - \frac{Z_{12}{}^2}{Z_{22}} \tag{8.79}$$

Substituting the values of Z_{11}, Z_{12}, and Z_{22} above,

$$Z_{\text{in}} = R_1 + j\omega L_1 + \frac{(\omega M)^2}{R_2 + R_i + j\omega L_2} \tag{8.80}$$

The last term in Eq. 8.80 represents the impedance coupled into the primary. To achieve good efficiency and minimize the reactance coupled into the primary, R_i should be large in comparison with both R_2 and ωL_2. Then

$$Z_{\text{in}} \simeq R_1 + j\omega L_1 + \frac{(\omega M)^2}{R_i} \tag{8.81}$$

To provide good coupling efficiency, the coupled resistance should be large in comparison with the ohmic resistance of the primary R_1. If R_1 is not negligibly small, its parallel equivalent can be lumped with R_o to provide R'_o as was done for the tapped tuned circuit. Then

$$Z_{\text{in}} \simeq j\omega L_1 + \frac{(\omega M)^2}{R_i} \tag{8.82}$$

The simplified equivalent circuit of Fig. 8.12 can then be drawn. The parallel resistance of the tuned circuit at resonance must be equal to R'_o to provide maximum power transfer. Using Eq. 8.6

$$R_p = R'_o \simeq \frac{(\omega L_1)^2}{[(\omega M)^2/R_i]} = \left(\frac{L_1}{M}\right)^2 R_i \tag{8.83}$$

Note the similarity between the transformation ratio of the tapped tuned circuit and the inductively coupled circuit. The latter has the advantage in most transistor circuits because the bias circuit may be isolated from the signal circuit, as illustrated in Fig. 8.11a. Higher current gain may therefore be achieved because the bias resistors do not absorb signal power.

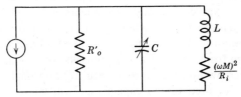

Fig. 8.12. A simplified equivalent circuit.

The value of $M = k(L_1L_2)^{1/2}$ may be substituted into Eq. 8.83. Then

$$R'_o = \frac{L_1}{k^2L_2} R_i \tag{8.84}$$

Practical values for L_2 may be determined from the requirement that ωL_2 be small in comparison with R_i (for example, one tenth) as previously mentioned. Also the value of L_1 will be determined by the bandwidth requirement of the amplifier. As for the tapped tuned circuit, the total shunt resistive load on the tuned circuit at the resonant frequency is $R'_o/2$.

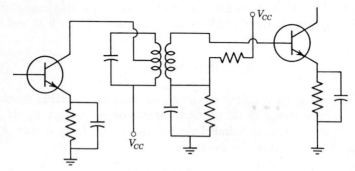

Fig. 8.13. An inductively coupled tapped circuit.

Then

$$Q = \frac{R'_o}{2\omega_oL_1} = \frac{\omega_o}{B} \tag{8.85}$$

where B is the desired bandwidth in radians per second. This is the very same problem which was solved for the tapped tuned circuit. In that circuit, the inductance in the collector circuit was found to be

$$L_1 = \frac{R_o}{\omega_o}\left(\frac{1}{2Q} - \frac{1}{Q_o}\right) \tag{8.75}$$

After determining the proper values of L_2 and L_1, we may determine the proper coupling coefficient k by the use of Eq. 8.84. A preferable solution would be to determine experimentally the maximum realizable value of coupling coefficient k for the particular coupling coil under consideration. Then the required value of secondary inductance L_2 could be determined from Eq. 8.84. This procedure would yield the minimum value of L_2 and hence the minimum reactance coupled into the tuned circuit.

It may be seen from Eq. 8.75 that L_1 must be very small if the required bandwidth is narrow and the desired circuit Q approaches the Q_o of the coil. Then the required tuning capacitance will be very large. The inductance L_1 may be increased and the tuning capacitance decreased if a tapped tuned circuit is inductively coupled to the load as shown in Fig. 8.13.

PROB. 8.9. A transistor which has $R_o = 20$ KΩ is to be coupled to a transistor which has $R_i = 1$ KΩ. The center frequency is 1 MHz and the desired bandwidth is 20 KHz. Using an inductively coupled single tuned circuit (without tapping), calculate suitable values for L_1, L_2, and C. The Q_o of the coil is 150 Assume $k = 0.8$.

PROB. 8.10. Calculate suitable values for L_1, L_2, and C when the collector of the transistor of Prob. 8.9 is connected to a center tap on the primary coil. ($Q_o = 150$.) Assume that k remains 0.8. *Answer: $L_1 = 42.5$ μhen, $L_2 = 2.5$ μhen, $C = 597$ pf.*

The inductively coupled and tapped circuits could be utilized in vacuum tube circuits as well as transistor circuits. In this case the grid circuit is the higher impedance. Therefore, the untuned winding is normally in the plate circuit. Since the tuned winding may be used as a d-c grid return, R_i is essentially infinite. Then the ohmic resistance of the coil cannot be neglected. Instead, it provides the load resistance of the coupling circuit.

The plate resistance for a pentode tube is so large that an impedance match cannot usually be obtained with practical values of coupling. Satisfactory power gain may be obtained, however, with realizable coupling values.

8.4 DOUBLE-TUNED CIRCUITS

Two tuned circuits may be used as a *double-tuned* circuit to couple two amplifying devices. The tuned circuits may be coupled by either mutual inductance or mutual admittance, as shown in Fig. 8.14. The mutual admittance may be provided by either a capacitor or an inductor as shown. In any case, the degree of coupling or coupling coefficient is usually small in comparison with the values used in the single-tuned circuits previously discussed. The gain-bandwidth product may be higher in the double-tuned circuit and the designer has greater freedom in the frequency response characteristics as compared with the single-tuned circuit. These features will be discussed in the following paragraphs.

To simplify writing of the equations, let

$$G + sC + \frac{1}{sL} = Y \tag{8.86}$$

and for the inductance coupled circuit,

$$\frac{1}{sL_m} = Y_m \tag{8.87}$$

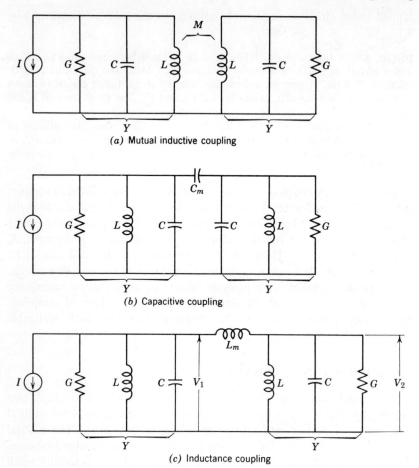

(a) Mutual inductive coupling

(b) Capacitive coupling

(c) Inductance coupling

Fig. 8.14. Typical double-tuned circuit coupling techniques.

Then the two nodal equations for the circuit are

$$-I = (Y + Y_m)V_1 - Y_m V_2 \qquad (8.88a)$$

$$0 = -Y_m V_1 + (Y + Y_m)V_2 \qquad (8.88b)$$

These equations are solved simultaneously for V_2. Thus

$$V_2 = \frac{-Y_m I}{(Y + Y_m)^2 - Y_m^2} = \frac{-Y_m I}{Y(Y + 2Y_m)} \qquad (8.89)$$

When the values of Y and Y_m are substituted into Eq. 8.89, V_2 is

$$V_2 = \frac{-\dfrac{I}{sL_m}}{\left(G + sC + \dfrac{1}{sL}\right)\left(G + sC + \dfrac{1}{sL} + \dfrac{2}{sL_m}\right)} \qquad (8.90)$$

If we let $L/L_m = k$, Eq. 8.90 becomes

$$V_2 = \frac{-\dfrac{I}{sL_m}}{\left(G + sC + \dfrac{1}{sL}\right)\left(G + sC + \dfrac{1 + 2k}{sL}\right)} \qquad (8.91)$$

or,

$$V_2 = \frac{-kIs^2L^2}{sL^3C^2\left(s^2 + \dfrac{G}{C}s + \dfrac{1}{LC}\right)\left(s^2 + \dfrac{G}{C}s + \dfrac{1 + 2k}{LC}\right)} \qquad (8.92)$$

When the common terms have been cancelled, Eq. 8.92 can be written as

$$\frac{V_2}{-I} = \frac{k\omega_n^2}{C}\frac{s}{(s - p_1)(s - p_2)(s - p_3)(s - p_4)} \qquad (8.93)$$

where $\omega_n^2 = 1/LC$

$$p_1, p_2 = -\frac{G}{2C} \pm j\left(\frac{1}{LC} - \frac{G^2}{4C^2}\right)^{1/2} = \sigma_1 \pm j\omega_o \qquad (8.94a)$$

$$p_3, p_4 = -\frac{G}{2C} \pm j\left(\frac{1 + 2k}{LC} - \frac{G^2}{4C^2}\right)^{1/2} \qquad (8.94b)$$

$$= -\sigma_1 \pm j\omega_o(1 + 2k)^{1/2} \qquad (8.95)$$

The pole-zero plot of the transfer function V_2/I is shown in Fig. 8.15a. As noted in Chapter 7, the magnitude of the transfer function V_2/I is equal to the distance from a given ω to the zero, divided by the product of the distances from the given ω to each of the poles. For a high Q-tuned circuit, interesting and useful values of ω occur only in the vicinity of the poles p_1 and p_3 near the $+j\omega$ axis. In this vicinity, the distances to the zero and to the poles p_2 and p_4 near the $-j\omega$ axis are large and almost constant for small variations of ω. Therefore, when ω is restricted to the region shown in Fig. 8.15b, the transfer function can be written for steady state sinusoidal signals as

$$V_2/I = \frac{-K}{(j\omega - p_1)(j\omega - p_3)} \qquad (8.96)$$

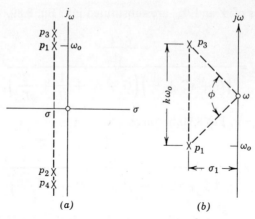

Fig. 8.15. A plot of the poles and zeros for the function V_2/I of Eq. 8.93.

where K is a constant to be evaluated. The frequency is approximately ω_o in this region. When this value of ω is substituted into Eq. 8.93, and it is recognized that $\omega_n \simeq \omega_o$ and $(j\omega_o - p_2) \simeq (j\omega_o - p_4) \simeq 2\omega_o$, Eq. 8.93 becomes

$$\frac{V_2}{I} \simeq -\frac{k\omega_o}{4C} \frac{1}{(j\omega - p_1)(j\omega - p_3)} \qquad (8.97)$$

The expression for the pole $p_3 = -\sigma_1 + j\omega_o\sqrt{1 + 2k^2}$ can be simplified by the use of the binomial theorem. Since in practical double-tuned circuits, $k \ll 1$, only the first two terms of the binomial expansion are significant and $\sqrt{1 + 2k^2} \simeq 1 + k$. Then, $p_3 \simeq -\sigma_1 + j\omega_o(1 + k)$, and the two poles are separated by $k\omega_o$ (Fig. 8.15b). Also, since the area of the triangle $\omega p_1 p_3$ (Fig. 8.15b) is $\frac{1}{2}\sin \phi \, |j\omega - p_1| \, |j\omega - p_3|$ and this area is also $\frac{1}{2}\sigma_1 k\omega_o$,

$$|j\omega - p_1| \, |j\omega - p_3| = \frac{\sigma_1 k\omega_o}{\sin \phi} \qquad (8.98)$$

Substituting Eq. 8.98 into Eq. 8.97, the magnitude of the transfer function is

$$\left|\frac{V_2}{I}\right| = \frac{\sin \phi}{4\sigma_1 C} = \frac{\sin \phi}{2G} \qquad (8.99)$$

Equation 8.99 shows that maximum output voltage V_2 is obtained when $\phi = \pi/2$ and $\sin \phi = 1$. Then (since $I = g_m V_{gk}$) the reference voltage gain of a tube amplifier is

$$K_v = \frac{g_m R}{2} \qquad (8.100)$$

The locus of points which gives $\phi = \pi/2$ is a semicircle with $k\omega_o$ as a diameter (Fig. 8.16). Observe that there may be two frequencies (values of $j\omega$) which yield maximum voltage output and hence maximum power transfer. These are the frequencies at which the maximum voltage locus crosses the $j\omega$ axis. There will be a single maximum power frequency when the maximum voltage locus is tangent to the $j\omega$ axis. Then

$$\frac{k_c \omega_o}{2} = \sigma_1 = \frac{G}{2C} \qquad (8.101)$$

where k_c is the value of k which produces this single maximum power frequency and is called the *critical coupling*. Then

$$k_c = \frac{G}{\omega_o C} = \frac{1}{Q} \qquad (8.102)$$

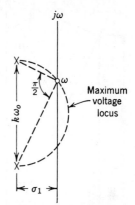

Fig. 8.16. Details of the pole-zero plot of Fig. 8.15 near P_1 and P_3.

When the coupling is less than critical, there is no frequency at which theoretical maximum power transfer occurs. When the coupling is greater than critical, there are two frequencies at which maximum power transfer occurs, as previously discussed. The coefficient of coupling is often given in terms of the critical coupling k_c. For example $k = bk_c$. A sketch of the frequency response for several values of b is given in Fig. 8.17. Note that one pole remains fixed at ω_o and the other pole moves. The separation between poles is $bk_c\omega_o$ and the center of the pass band is

$$\omega_c = \omega_o + \frac{bk_c\omega_o}{2} = \omega_o\left[1 + \frac{bk_c}{2}\right] \qquad (8.103)$$

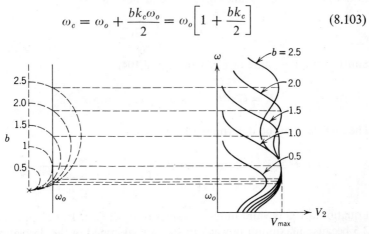

Fig. 8.17. A sketch of the frequency response for several values of relative coupling b.

The bandwidth may be determined as a function of b with the aid of Fig. 8.18. Since the output voltage is proportional to $\sin \phi$, as shown in Eq. 8.99, the half-power frequencies ω_H and ω_L will occur when $\sin \phi = 0.707$ or $\phi = \pi/4$ radians (Fig. 8.18). In this figure, the base of the trapezoid is $\omega_H - \omega_L =$ bandwidth B. To determine the bandwidth, we note that from Eq. 8.101:

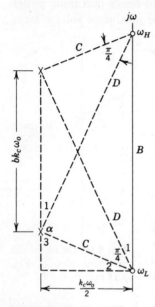

$$\sigma_1 = \frac{k_c \omega_o}{2} \qquad (8.101)$$

From Eqs. 8.98 and 8.101 the product of the two sides C and D of the triangles shown in Fig. 8.18 is

$$CD = \frac{b k_c{}^2 \omega_o{}^2}{\sqrt{2}} \qquad (8.104)$$

Observe that the area of the triangle with sides B, C, and D (Fig. 8.18) is, using Eq. 8.101,

$$A = \tfrac{1}{2}\sigma_1 B = \frac{k_c \omega_o B}{4} \qquad (8.105)$$

Fig. 8.18. The configuration used to determine the bandwidth of a double tuned circuit.

where B is the bandwidth $\omega_H - \omega_L$. Also the area of this triangle may be determined from the following relationship:

$$A = \tfrac{1}{2}CD \sin \alpha \qquad (8.106)$$

Equating Eqs. 8.106 and 8.105, the bandwidth is

$$B = \frac{2CD \sin \alpha}{k_c \omega_o} \qquad (8.107)$$

Substituting the value of CD from Eq. 8.104,

$$B = (2)^{\frac{1}{4}}b \sin \alpha\, k_c \omega_o = (2)^{\frac{1}{4}}b \sin \alpha\, \frac{\omega_o}{Q} \qquad (8.108)$$

The angle α may be determined from Fig. 8.18

$$\alpha = 225° - 2 \sin^{-1} \frac{1}{\left(b\left[\dfrac{b+1}{2} - \left(\dfrac{b^2 + b - 1}{4} \right)^{\frac{1}{2}} \right] \right)^{\frac{1}{2}}} \qquad (8.109)$$

Equation 8.109 is valid only for values of b between 1 and approximately 2.5 because maximum power transfer was assumed in the derivation, and the pass band splits in two at $b \simeq 2.5$ (Fig. 8.17). Since the angle α is rather tedious to evaluate, the values for $b = 1, 1.5,$ and 2.0 are given in Table 8.1. Interpolation may be used to obtain $\sin \alpha$ for other commonly used values of b.

TABLE 8.1

b	α	$\sin \alpha$
1.0	90°	1.0
1.5	104°	0.96
2.0	113°	0.92

Note that the term $(2)^{1/2}b \sin \alpha$ represents the improvement in the gain-bandwidth product of the double-tuned amplifier over the single tuned.

It should be observed that the Q used in Eq. 8.108 is the loaded Q of each tuned circuit, *not* considering the coupled resistance. This is in contrast to the single-tuned circuit where the Q must include all loading, including the coupled resistance.

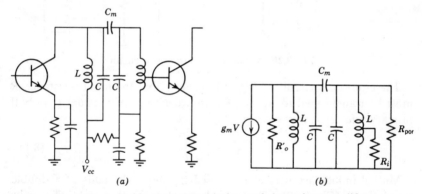

Fig. 8.19. A double-tuned capacitively coupled transistor amplifier.

The double-tuned circuit which uses the coupling inductance $L_m = L/k$ yields readily to analysis, but it is not the most convenient type of coupling. A capacitor C_m which has mutual admittance $j\omega C_m$ is smaller and less expensive then the inductor and has the additional advantage of blocking direct current. The circuit diagram of a capacitively coupled double-tuned transistor amplifier is given in Fig. 8.19a. Because of the similarity of capacitive coupling to the inductive coupling previously discussed, we can see that the relationship between the coupling capacitance and the tuning capacitance is

$$C_m = kC = bC/Q \tag{8.110}$$

The analysis of the capacitively coupled circuit will show that the fixed pole is at ω_o, but the movable pole is below ω_o and moves downward. The band center is, therefore, below ω_o. However, the bandwidth is usually so small in comparison with ω_o that the band center can be considered to be at ω_o in most applications. The movable pole does not move parallel to the $j\omega$ axis when capacitive coupling is used. Therefore, the analysis of this circuit is somewhat more complex than the analysis of the inductor coupled circuit. However, in the high Q case, the pole motion is approximately parallel to the $j\omega$ axis and the preceding analysis of the inductor coupled circuit is applicable to the capacitively coupled circuit.

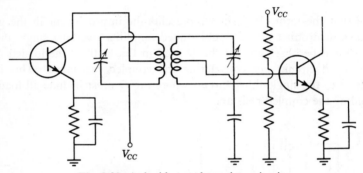

Fig. 8.20. A double-tuned transistor circuit.

The equivalent circuit of Fig. 8.19b shows that the input resistance R_i must be transformed to R_o, *not* R'_o, in order to provide equal Q in both primary and secondary circuits. Therefore

$$\frac{n}{n_2} = \left(\frac{R_o}{R_i}\right)^{1/2} \tag{8.111}$$

Mutual inductance may also be used to couple the coils of a double-tuned circuit (Fig. 8.20). The mutual impedance is then $j\omega M$. The value of critical coupling coefficient k_c is $1/Q$ and, in general, $k = bk_c = b/Q$ or $M = bL/Q$.

The mutually coupled circuit is most easily analyzed if both primary and secondary circuits are converted to equivalent series circuits and loop equations are used. The complex poles are then symmetrically located on either side of ω_o and they both move away from ω_o as k is increased. The poles do not move parallel to the $j\omega$ axis. However, the analysis of the inductively coupled circuit is adequately applicable to the mutually coupled circuit.

When the coil Q is high in comparison with the circuit Q, the major portion of source energy is transferred to the load. This follows from the fact that the effective series resistance caused by source and load resistances is large in comparison with the series ohmic resistance. When an impedance match is obtained, the power delivered to a specific load impedance is essentially independent of the type of coupling circuit, provided the coupling efficiency is high. The various circuits described in this chapter will each produce about the same reference gain under matched conditions. The double-tuned circuit will have the largest gain-bandwidth product because of the bandwidth ratio expressed in Eq. 8.108. In addition, the frequency response characteristics of the double-tuned circuit have steeper

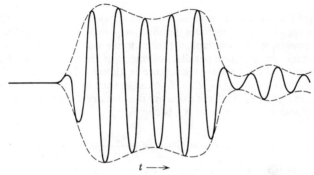

Fig. 8.21. Typical time domain response of a double-tuned amplifier driven by a rectangular pulse of frequency ω_0.

sides and a flatter top than the single-tuned circuit. Also the designer has some control on the shape of the response curve by his choice of b. The best choice would depend on the application. Values for b of the order of 1.0 to 1.7 look promising for cases where uniform frequency response is desired over most of the pass band.

The development of the transient or time domain response of a double tuned amplifier is beyond the scope of this book. However, Martin[2] has shown that the double-tuned amplifier (or actually its staggered pair equivalent) has an overshoot in the envelope response which is comparable with the overshoot of a transformer coupled amplifier. Thus, the improved gain-bandwidth product or gain-rise time ratio of the double-tuned amplifier is obtained at the expense of overshoot in the envelope response. This overshoot is illustrated in Fig. 8.21 where it is assumed that the excitation is a pulse-modulated sinusoid. Martin showed that the critically or transitionally coupled amplifier has a 4.3% overshoot. It has also been shown that the overshoot increases as the degree of coupling increases.

[2] Thomas L. Martin, Jr., *Electronic Circuits*, Sec. 6.6, Prentice-Hall, Englewood Cliffs, N.J., 1955.

Therefore, the degree of coupling b which provides the optimum frequency response characteristic does not, in general, provide optimum time domain response.

The procedure for designing a double-tuned circuit might be as follows:

1. Choose b for the best response characteristics.
2. With ω_o and the desired bandwidth known, calculate the circuit Q from Eq. 8.108.
3. Calculate the coefficient of coupling

$$k = bk_c = \frac{b}{Q}$$

4. Determine the primary inductance from the relationship $Q = R'_o/\omega_o L$, where the output resistance R'_o includes the effective parallel resistance of the primary coil. However, as for the tapped tuned circuit and the inductively coupled tuned circuit, the effective parallel resistance of the primary coil cannot be determined until the primary inductance is known. Therefore, the relationship stated previously $(Q = R'_o/\omega_o L)$ must be used in addition to the relationship $R'_o = R_p R_o/(R_p + R_o)$ to calculate the primary inductance. Using these two relationships, the value of R'_o becomes

$$R'_o = Q\omega_o L = \frac{R_p R_o}{R_p + R_o} \tag{8.112}$$

But $R_p = Q_o \omega_o L$. Then

$$Q\omega_o L = \frac{Q_o \omega_o L R_o}{Q_o \omega_o L + R_o} \tag{8.113}$$

Simplifying,

$$Q(Q_o \omega_o L + R_o) = Q_o R_o \tag{8.114}$$

$$Q Q_o \omega_o L = R_o(Q_o - Q) \tag{8.115}$$

$$L = \frac{R_o}{\omega_o}\left(\frac{Q_o - Q}{Q Q_o}\right) = \frac{R_o}{\omega_o}\left(\frac{1}{Q} - \frac{1}{Q_o}\right) \tag{8.116}$$

The secondary inductance would, of course, be the same as the primary inductance if this suggested design technique is used.

5. Calculate the value of capacitance required to resonate with the inductance calculated in step 4.
6. Determine the necessary tap points on the coil to provide proper loading of the tuned circuits.

An example of an inductively coupled double-tuned transistor amplifier will be given to illustrate this outlined procedure.

Example 8.1. A double-tuned circuit is to be used to couple a transistor which has $R_o = 40$ KΩ to a transistor which has $R_i = 1$ KΩ. The center frequency is 500 KHz and the desired bandwidth is 12 KHz. The foregoing suggested procedure will be used in designing the coupling circuit.

1. The coupling coefficient $1.5 \, k_c$ will be considered optimum ($b = 1.5$).

2. $B = 12 \, \text{KHz} = 1.41 \times 1.5 \times 0.98 \dfrac{500 \, \text{KHz}}{Q}$

3. $Q = \dfrac{2.06 \times 500 \, \text{KHz}}{12 \, \text{KHz}} = 86$

$\quad k = \dfrac{b}{Q} = \dfrac{1.5}{86} = 0.0175$

4. Assuming the coil $Q_o = 150$.

$$L_1 = L_2 = \frac{40 \times 10^3}{3.14 \times 10^6} \left(\frac{1}{86} - \frac{1}{150} \right) = 63 \, \mu\text{h}$$

5. $C = \dfrac{1}{(3.14 \times 10^6)^2 (63 \times 10^{-6})} = 1610 \, \text{pf}$

6. The tap on the secondary coil is

$$n_2 \simeq n \left(\frac{1}{40} \right)^{1/2} = 0.158n$$

The inductance could be increased and the tuning capacitance reduced from the values just calculated by tapping the primary as well as the secondary. The problem would then proceed as before but with a transformed value of R_o.

PROB. 8.11. A transistor having $R_o = 20 \, \text{K}\Omega$ is to be coupled to a transistor having $R_i = 1 \, \text{K}\Omega$. The desired bandwidth is 20 KHz and $f_o = 460 \, \text{KHz}$. Design a double-tuned circuit using $b = 1.2$ and $Q_o = 100$.

PROB. 8.12. Use pentode tubes with $r_p = 1$ megohm for the amplifier of Prob. 8.11. For good frequency stability assume $C = 100 \, \text{pf}$. Use loading resistors to reduce the load resistance of both primary and secondary. *Answer: Q = 38.3, L = 1.2 mh, R = 215 K\Omega.*

PROB. 8.13. The circuit of Fig. 8.19 is used with $f_o = 460 \, \text{KHz}$ and bandwidth $= 20 \, \text{KHz}$. Using $b = 1.5$ and $G'_o = G'_i = 50 \, \mu\text{mhos}$ determine $Q_1 = Q_2$ and C_m for the circuit. The Q_o of each coil is 100.

8.5 NEUTRALIZATION

It was learned in Chapter 7 that amplifiers such as triode tubes and transistors which have appreciable capacitance between their input and output circuits may be unstable at high frequencies. This instability occurs when the input and output circuits are inductive. Since a parallel-tuned circuit is inductive at frequencies below resonance, tuned amplifiers which use triodes or transistors are especially susceptible to oscillation.

In addition to being unstable, amplifiers which have appreciable coupling between their input and output circuits are difficult to design, as previously mentioned. Also, in the tuned amplifier, the reactance of the tuned circuit in the output affects the resonant frequency of a tuned circuit in the input and vice versa. Thus, tuning becomes very difficult.

As was previously mentioned, a process known as neutralization may be used to eliminate the effects of coupling between the input and output circuits of an amplifier. Neutralization is accomplished by providing a feedback current of opposite polarity and equal magnitude to that feedback through the amplifier. These two feedback currents cancel or neutralize each other, thus the name neutralization. A neutralized tuned triode amplifier is shown in Fig. 8.22. When the coil in the tuned plate circuit is center tapped, the neutralizing capacitor C_n should have the same capaci-

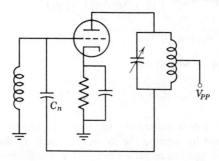

Fig. 8.22. A neutralized triode amplifier.

tance as the grid to plate capacitance. When the coil is tapped at a point other than the center, the required neutralizing capacitance will be changed by the ratio of the signal voltages at the top and bottom of the tapped tuned circuit. The neutralizing voltage could have been obtained from the secondary of an inductively coupled circuit utilizing the phase reversing capabilities of the circuit.

The neutralization of a transistor is not as straightforward as that of the vacuum tube because of the base spreading resistance in the transistor.

To neutralize the transistor, a series R-C combination may be needed in the neutralizing circuit as shown in the hybrid-π circuit of Fig. 8.23. In this circuit r_c has been omitted as it frequently may be. It may be seen that neutralization will occur if $I_n = I_b$. Then there will be no current flow and hence no voltage V_1 in the input circuit resulting from an output voltage V_2. Assuming the voltage to be sinusoidal, the current I_b will first be determined. Considering the circuit to be neutralized so that $V_1 = 0$, we find that

$$I_b = \frac{V_{b'e}}{r_b} \qquad (8.117)$$

but

$$V_{b'e} = \frac{I_f}{g_e/(h_{fe} + 1) + g_b + j\omega C_1} \tag{8.118}$$

where

$$g_e = \frac{1}{r_e} \quad \text{and} \quad g_b = \frac{1}{r_b}$$

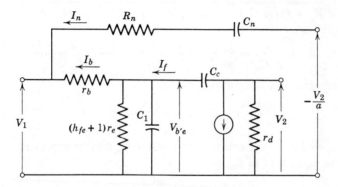

Fig. 8.23. A neutralizing circuit for the common emitter configuration.

Fig. 8.23 shows that the feedback current is

$$
I_f = \frac{V_2}{\dfrac{1}{g_e/(h_{fe} + 1) + g_b + j\omega C_1} + \dfrac{1}{j\omega C_c}}
$$

$$
= \frac{j\omega C_c \left(\dfrac{g_e}{h_{fe} + 1} + g_b + j\omega C_1 \right) V_2}{j\omega C_c + \dfrac{g_e}{h_{fe} + 1} + g_b + j\omega C_1} \tag{8.119}
$$

Substituting Eq. 8.119 into Eq. 8.118, we have

$$V_{b'e} = \frac{j\omega C_c V_2}{j\omega C_c + g_e/(h_{fe} + 1) + g_b + j\omega C_1} \tag{8.120}$$

and, using Eq. 8.117, we have

$$
I_b = \frac{j\omega C_c V_2}{r_b[j\omega C_c + j\omega C_1 + g_b + g_e/(h_{fe} + 1)]}
$$

$$
= \frac{j\omega C_c V_2}{j\omega r_b(C_c + C_1) + 1 + r_b g_e/(h_{fe} + 1)} \tag{8.121}
$$

Solving for I_n (see Fig. 8.23), we see that

$$I_n = \frac{V_2/a}{R_n + (1/j\omega C_n)} \tag{8.122}$$

where a is the ratio of the output voltage V_2 to the voltage applied to the neutralizing circuit. Equating I_b and I_n, we have

$$\frac{V_2/a}{R_n + (1/j\omega C_n)} = \frac{j\omega C_c V_2}{j\omega r_b(C_c + C_1) + 1 + r_b g_e/(h_{fe} + 1)} \tag{8.123}$$

Then

$$R_n + \frac{1}{j\omega C_n} = \frac{1}{a}\left[r_b\frac{(C_c + C_1)}{C_c} + \frac{1 + r_b g_e/(h_{fe} + 1)}{j\omega C_c}\right] \tag{8.124}$$

Equating reals and imaginaries, we have

$$R_n = \frac{r_b(C_c + C_1)}{aC_c} \simeq \frac{r_b C_1}{aC_c} \tag{8.125}$$

Since $\omega_\alpha = 1/r_e C_1$, the neutralizing resistor R_n may be expressed in terms of r_e and ω_α instead of C_1.

$$C_n = \frac{aC_c}{\left(1 + \dfrac{r_b g_e}{h_{fe} + 1}\right)} \tag{8.126}$$

Transistors such as the drift-field type which are designed especially for high-frequency applications often have a low value of ohmic base resistance and also a small collector-base junction capacitance. This combination may permit satisfactory neutralization with $R_n = 0$. The neutralizing capacitance C_n is then equal to aC_c where C_c is approximately equal to the C_{ob} listed by transistor manufacturers.

PROB. 8.14. A 2N384 transistor is used as an amplifier at 10 MHz. Inductive coupling is used in the output with a ratio of two primary turns to each secondary turn. The coefficient of coupling approaches unity. Determine the neutralizing components for the amplifier, using the secondary voltage as the neutralizing voltage. *Answer: $R_n = 1.75$ K, $C_n = 2.5$ pf.*

PROB. 8.15. Could a parallel R-C or R-L combination be used in the neutralizing circuit of the amplifier of Prob. 8.14? If so, would it be as satisfactory as the series R-C combination? Why?

8.6 THE RELATIONSHIP BETWEEN GAIN AND STABILITY IN A NONNEUTRALIZED TUNED AMPLIFIER

Any amplifier will be stable if its power gain is sufficiently low. Therefore, neutralization will not be needed in a tuned amplifier if the amplifier gain is sufficiently restricted. The maximum usable value of gain for a nonneutralized amplifier may be approximately determined as a function of the feedback capacitance C_c and the frequency of operation. The equivalent circuit of Fig. 8.24 will be used in this determination. This circuit represents either a tuned tube circuit or a tuned transistor circuit in which r_b is negligible. The circuit components L, C, and G include the shunt device parameters, and the input circuit values are initially assumed

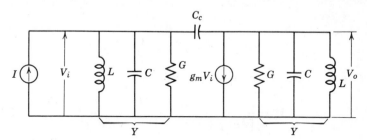

Fig. 8.24. Equivalent circuit used for determination of maximum nonneutralized gain.

to be equal to the output circuit values. Writing nodal equations for the circuit,

$$I = (Y + sC_c)V_i - sC_cV_o \qquad (8.127)$$

$$-g_mV_i = -sC_cV_i + (Y + sC_c)V_o \qquad (8.128)$$

Solving these equations simultaneously, the value of V_o is

$$V_o = \frac{(sC_c - g_m)I}{(Y + sC_c)^2 - sC_c(sC_c - g_m)} \qquad (8.129)$$

Simplifying,

$$V_o = \frac{(sC_c - g_m)I}{Y^2 + 2sC_cY + sC_cg_m} \qquad (8.130)$$

Poles of V_o (and thus possible oscillation) will exist when the denominator of Eq. 8.130 is equal to zero. Therefore, the roots of the denominator will be found. Using the quadratic formula, the roots Y_1 and Y_2 are

$$Y_{1,2} = -sC_c \pm \sqrt{(sC_c)^2 - sC_cg_m} = -sC_c \pm \sqrt{sC_c(sC_c - g_m)} \qquad (8.131)$$

In order for the amplifier to have appreciable power gain, the forward transconductance g_m must be large in comparison with the passive mutual admittance sC_c. Therefore, Eq. 8.131 may be simplified to

$$Y_{1,2} \simeq -sC_c \pm j\sqrt{sC_cg_m} \qquad (8.132)$$

and

$$V_o \simeq \frac{-g_mI}{(Y + sC_c + j\sqrt{sC_cg_m})(Y + sC_c - j\sqrt{sC_cg_m})} \qquad (8.133)$$

Substituting the value of $Y = sC + G + 1/sL$ into Eq. 8.133,

$$V_o = \frac{-g_m I}{\left(sC + G + \dfrac{1}{sL} + sC_c + j\sqrt{sC_c g_m}\right)\left(sC + G + \dfrac{1}{sL} + sC_c - j\sqrt{sC_c g_m}\right)}$$

(8.134)

or

$$V_o = \frac{-g_m I}{\left[s(C + C_c) + G + \dfrac{1}{sL}\right]^2 + sC_c g_m}$$

(8.135)

Let $C + C_c = C_t$. Then Eq. 8.135 becomes

$$V_o = \frac{-g_m I s^2 L^2}{[s^2 L C_t + sLG + 1]^2 + s^3 L^2 C_c g_m}$$

(8.136)

or

$$V_o = \frac{-g_m I s^2}{C_t^2 \left[s^2 + \dfrac{G}{C_t} s + \dfrac{1}{LC_t}\right]^2 + s^3 C_c g_m}$$

(8.137)

Poles of V_o occur when the denominator becomes zero, or

$$\left[s^2 + \frac{G}{C_t} s + \frac{1}{LC_t}\right]^2 = -\frac{s^3 C_c g_m}{C_t^2}$$

(8.138)

and

$$\left[\left(s + \frac{G}{2C_t} + j\omega_o\right)\left(s + \frac{G}{2C_t} - j\omega_o\right)\right]^2 = -\frac{s^3 C_c g_m}{C_t^2}$$

(8.139)

where $\omega_o = \left(\dfrac{1}{LC_t} - \dfrac{G^2}{4C_t^2}\right)^{1/2}$

This fourth-order equation may be reduced to a second-order equation if the circuit Q is high. Then the values of s which are of interest lie in the passband near ω_o. Since ω_o is much larger than $G/2C_t$, $j\omega_o$ may be substituted for either s or $(s + G/2C_t)$ in the sum or product terms. Then

$$(2j\omega_o)^2 \left(s + \frac{G}{2C_t} - j\omega_o\right)^2 = -\frac{(j\omega_o)^3 C_c g_m}{C_t^2}$$

(8.140)

or

$$s + \frac{G}{2C_t} - j\omega_o = \pm \sqrt{-\frac{j\omega_o C_c g_m}{4C_t^2}}$$

(8.141)

Equation 8.141 involves the poles of V_o which lie near the $+j\omega$ axis near ω_o. The locus of these poles may be determined as the product

$C_c g_m$ is varied. Rearranging Eq. 8.141, we have

$$s + \frac{G \pm (\omega_o C_c g_m)^{1/2} e^{-j45°}}{2C_t} - j\omega_o = 0 \qquad (8.142)$$

The pole-zero plot of Eq. 8.142 is given in Fig. 8.25. Observe that a double pole occurs at $s = -G/2C_t + j\omega_o$ when $C_c = 0$, but as C_c is increased the poles move in opposite directions along a locus line which forms an angle of $-45°$ with the real axis.

As seen from either the root-locus plot or Eq. 8.142, a pole will lie on the $j\omega$ axis (an undamped natural response will occur) when the real part of the lower pole vanishes. Then

$$G = (\omega_o C_c g_m)^{1/2} \cos 45° \qquad (8.143)$$

or

$$g_m = \frac{2G^2}{\omega_o C_c} \qquad (8.144)$$

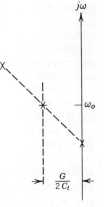

Fig. 8.25. The poles of V_o which lie near the $+j\omega$ axis.

The value of transconductance determined by Eq. 8.144 is the upper limiting value for a shunt load conductance G, coupling capacitor C_c, and band center frequency ω_o. Any smaller value of g_m will result in stable operation. However, Fig. 8.25 shows that the frequency response will be that of a nonsymmetrical double tuned circuit. The lower pole will appear as a higher-Q pole (nearer the $j\omega$ axis) than the upper pole. In fact, as the lower frequency pole approaches the $j\omega$ axis it will almost completely dominate the frequency characteristics and the amplifier will appear as a very narrow band amplifier. Therefore, if uniform, broadband amplification is desired, the conductance G should be adjusted so that the value of g_m actually provided by the tube or transistor is much lower than the limiting value.

The values of G seen from the input and output terminals of a transistor usually differ widely. Since both G's are equally important in determining the limiting value of g_m, it is reasonable to replace G^2 in Eq. 8.144 with $G'_i G'_o$. Making this substitution, the limiting value of g_m is

$$g_m = \frac{2G'_i G'_o}{\omega_o C_c} \qquad (8.145)$$

PROB. 8.16. A given high-frequency transistor has $C_c = 10$ pf. The total shunt resistances of the input and output circuits are $100\ \Omega$ and $1\ K\Omega$, respectively. Assuming $G'_o G'_i = G^2$, determine the limiting value of g_m and the upper limit of collector Q-point current for stable operation at $f_o = 10$ MHz. Assume the transistor temperature to be 25°C. *Answer:* $g_m = 3.18 \times 10^{-2}$, $I_{cmax} = 0.8\ ma$.

PROB. 8.17. A given transistor amplifier which has a quiescent collector current of 5 ma and a center frequency of 2.0 MHz is driven by a 200 Ω source at the resonant frequency. The transistor has a collector-base capacitance of 5 pf. Assume $T = 300°K$.

(*a*) What is the limiting value of output conductance G'_o?

(*b*) If, for stability and desirable frequency response characteristics, the output conductance G'_o is increased to three times the limiting value, what will be the approximate voltage gain of the amplifier? Assume that $r_b \simeq 0$.

PROB. 8.18. A single-tuned circuit is to be used, along with other necessary components, to couple two pentode tubes. Both pentodes are of the same type, having $g_m = 3000\ \mu$mhos and $r_p = 1$ megohm at the chosen Q point. Also these tubes have $C_{in} = C_{out} = 10$ pf and $C_{gp} = 0.003$ pf. The resonant frequency of the amplifier is 1 MHz. The tubes provide the total tuning capacitance. Calculate the voltage gain and the bandwidth of the stage if the coil $Q_o = 100$ and all grid resistors $= 1$ megohm.

PROB. 8.19. A transistor having an output resistance of 20 KΩ is inductively coupled to a transistor having 1 KΩ input resistance. The transformer primary is tuned to 1 MHz. The coefficient of coupling $k = 0.7$ and the primary coil $Q_o = 150$ at the resonant frequency of 1 MHz. Calculate the values of primary and secondary inductance required to provide maximum power transfer and 25 KHz bandwidth.

PROB. 8.20. A 1 MHz carrier is applied to the input of the amplifier of Prob. 8.19 at $t = 0$. Sketch the time response for the first few microseconds and determine the envelope rise time (10%–90%).

PROB. 8.21. A double-tuned 460-KHz transistor i-f amplifier is to have a 20-KHz bandwidth. The desired relative coupling $b = 1.4$. The coil $Q_o = 120$ (both primary and secondary). The output resistance of the driving transistor is 20 KΩ, and the transformer secondary is tapped so $Q_1 = Q_2$. Determine the coefficient of coupling k and the coil inductance $L_1 = L_2$ required to provide the desired bandwidth and the desired shape of the frequency-response curve.

9

Cascaded Amplifiers

Most practical amplifiers require more gain than can be obtained from a single stage. Consequently, it is common practice to feed the output of one amplifier stage into the input of the next stage (Fig. 9.1). When amplifiers are connected in this fashion, they are called *cascaded amplifiers*. There are a few concepts, unique to cascaded amplifiers, which will be considered in this chapter.

9.1 GAIN AND BANDWIDTH CONSIDERATIONS IN CASCADED AMPLIFIERS

Most of the cascaded amplifier stages are used to obtain either a voltage gain or a current gain. However, in most cascaded amplifiers, it is ultimately the power gain that is important. When the proper level of signal has been obtained, a power amplifier stage (to be discussed in Chapter 10) is used to produce sufficient power to activate the required load device (loud speaker—servo motor—antenna, etc.). If a voltage gain is required, we can calculate the total gain by using the equation for voltage gain of one stage. Thus, from Fig. 9.1, the voltage gain for stage 1 is

$$G_1 = \frac{V_2}{V_1} \qquad (9.1)$$

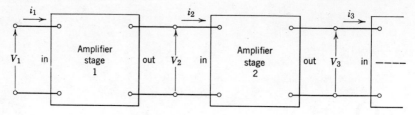

Fig. 9.1. Cascaded amplifier stages.

In addition, the voltage gain for stage 2 is

$$G_2 = \frac{V_3}{V_2} \qquad (9.2)$$

The gain for additional stages can be written in a similar manner. Then, the total amplifier voltage gain G_A for n cascaded stages is

$$\frac{V_2}{V_1} \times \frac{V_3}{V_2} \times \frac{V_4}{V_3} \times \cdots \frac{V_{n+1}}{V_n} = \frac{V_{n+1}}{V_1} \qquad (9.3)$$

or

$$G_A = G_1 \times G_2 \times G_3 \times \cdots G_n \qquad (9.4)$$

Obviously, a similar derivation could have been achieved for current gains or for power gains. In either of these cases, the total amplifier gain is equal to the product of the individual stage gains as indicated by Eq. 9.4. In general, the individual stage gains are functions of s and, consequently, the amplifier gain G_A is also a function of s. For steady-state sinusoidal signals, s becomes $j\omega$ and G_1, G_2, etc., become magnitudes at given phase angles. Then, G_A will be equal in magnitude to the products of all the magnitudes with a phase angle equal to the sum of the individual stage phase shifts.

Most amplifiers are fundamentally band-pass amplifiers. Even the R-C coupled amplifiers are actually band-pass amplifiers since they do not pass frequencies all the way down to zero. (Amplifiers which do pass d-c signals and, therefore, can be considered as low-pass amplifiers will be considered in more detail in Section 9.5.) In these band-pass amplifiers, a reference gain K has been defined. Using this reference gain, an amplifier reference gain K_A can be defined as

$$\pm K_A = (\pm K_1) \times (\pm K_2) \times (\pm K_3) \times \cdots (\pm K_n) \qquad (9.5)$$

The term $\pm K_A$ will be positive if the total number of phase inversions is even and negative if the number of inversions is odd. Since K is a magnitude only, this relationship does not involve s.

We have previously defined ω_1 and ω_2 as the lower and upper cut-off frequencies, respectively. These are the frequencies at which the voltage or current gain of one stage has been reduced to 0.707 of its reference value. (Power gain is reduced to 0.50 of its reference value for resistive loads.) Now, if we have an amplifier with two identical stages of amplification, the voltage gain at ω_1 will be reduced by a factor of 0.707 in each stage. Thus, the amplifier gain at ω_1 (and also ω_2) will be

$$0.707(-K_{v1}) \times 0.707(-K_{v2}) = 0.5K_A \tag{9.6}$$

In fact, for n-identical cascaded stages of amplification, the gain at ω_1 and ω_2 will be $(0.707)^n K_A$.

To re-establish a meaningful amplifier bandwidth, let us define ω_L as the lower cutoff frequency of the cascaded amplifier and ω_H as the upper cutoff frequency of the cascaded amplifier. At these frequencies, the gain of the amplifier will be $0.707K_A$. In order to arrive at some relationship between ω_1 and ω_L and also between ω_2 and ω_H, consider an R-C coupled amplifier containing n identical cascaded stages. The voltage gain per stage is given for the low frequencies by Eq. 7.19 as

$$G = -K \frac{s}{s + \omega_1} \tag{7.19}$$

For sinusoidal steady state, $s = j\omega$. Then, Eq. 7.19 can be written as

$$G = -K \frac{j\omega}{j\omega + \omega_1} \tag{9.7}$$

or

$$G = -K \frac{1}{1 - j\dfrac{\omega_1}{\omega}} \tag{9.8}$$

The magnitude of this function can be written as

$$|G| = K \frac{1}{[1^2 + (\omega_1/\omega)^2]^{\frac{1}{2}}} \tag{9.9}$$

If there are n cascaded stages, the magnitude of the amplifier gain from Eq. 9.4 is

$$|G_A| = |G|^n = K^n \left(\frac{1}{[1 + (\omega_1/\omega)^2]^{\frac{1}{2}}} \right)^n \tag{9.10}$$

Since $K^n = K_A$, we can write

$$|G_A| = K_A \frac{1}{[1 + (\omega_1/\omega)^2]^{n/2}} \tag{9.11}$$

Now, if ω is to be equal to ω_L, the term multiplying K_A must be equal to 0.707 or $1/(2)^{1/2}$. Then

$$2^{1/2} = \left[1 + \left(\frac{\omega_1}{\omega_L}\right)^2\right]^{n/2} \tag{9.12}$$

or

$$2^{1/n} = 1 + \left(\frac{\omega_1}{\omega_L}\right)^2 \tag{9.13}$$

This equation is solved for $\omega_L{}^2$ to yield

$$\omega_L{}^2 = \frac{\omega_1{}^2}{2^{1/n} - 1} \tag{9.14}$$

or

$$\omega_L = \frac{\omega_1}{[2^{1/n} - 1]^{1/2}} \tag{9.15}$$

A similar solution of Eq. 7.55 yields

$$\omega_H = \omega_2[2^{1/n} - 1]^{1/2} \tag{9.16}$$

PROB. 9.1. Derive Eq. 9.16 from Eq. 7.55.
PROB. 9.2. Determine the value of ω_L/ω_1 for $n = 1$, $n = 2$, $n = 4$, $n = 8$, and $n = 16$. Make a plot of ω_L/ω_1 vs n. *Answer: For $n = 4$, $\omega_L/\omega_1 = 2.3$.*
PROB. 9.3. Determine the value of ω_H/ω_2 for $n = 1$, $n = 2$, $n = 4$, $n = 8$, and $n = 16$. Make a plot of ω_H/ω_2 vs n.

From these equations, ω_L will be greater than ω_1 if n is greater than one and ω_H will be less than ω_2 is n is greater than one. Thus, the bandwidth of the amplifier decreases as the number of cascaded stages increases. Or, if the amplifier bandwidth is to remain constant, the stage bandwidth must increase as the number of cascaded stages increases. This last statement leads to an interesting dilemma. If a high-gain very wide band amplifier is desired, stages must be cascaded to obtain the higher gain. However, as more stages are cascaded, the bandwidth of each stage must be increased. Unfortunately, as noted in Section 7.7, the gain-bandwidth product *may be* a constant. Under these conditions, the increased bandwidth results in reduced gain per stage. Thus, in order to compensate for the reduced gain per stage, more stages of greater bandwidth are required. This process can be carried so far that the total *amplifier gain* (for a given bandwidth) *may actually decrease as additional cascaded stages are added.* (This statement is only true when we are actually utilizing the maximum gain bandwidth possible from an amplifier stage. In most amplifiers, the bandwidth can be increased without decreasing the gain.)

From the foregoing analysis, a relationship between total reference amplifier gain and bandwidth is highly desirable. In a typical R-C coupled stage, $\omega_1 \ll \omega_2$. Thus, the bandwidth $\omega_2 - \omega_1 \approx \omega_2$. The gain-bandwidth product (or figure of merit for the stage) GB, can then be written as

$$GB \approx K\omega_2 \qquad (9.17)$$

or

$$K = \frac{GB}{\omega_2} \qquad (9.18)$$

When an amplifier contains n identical cascaded stages, the *reference amplifier gain* K_A is equal to

$$K_A = K^n = \frac{(GB)^n}{\omega_2{}^n} \qquad (9.19)$$

However, from Eq. 9.16, we note that

$$\omega_2 = \frac{\omega_H}{[2^{1/n} - 1]^{\frac{1}{2}}} \qquad (9.20)$$

When this value of ω_2 is substituted into Eq. 9.19, K_A is

$$K_A = \frac{(GB)^n [2^{1/n} - 1]^{n/2}}{\omega_H{}^n} \qquad (9.21)$$

A plot of K_A as a function of n for a given value of GB and ω_H is given in Fig. 9.2. It is possible to extend the gain-bandwidth product of vacuum tube amplifiers and some transistor amplifiers through the use of compensated circuits.[1] However, in the interest of compactness, this treatment is not included in this edition.

PROB. 9.4. If $GB = 409 \times 10^6$ radians/sec, and $f_H = 12$ MHz, calculate K_A for 3, 7, and 8 cascaded stages. Determine the bandwidth per stage (f_2) and gain per stage for each amplifier. *Answer: For n = 7, K_A = 136, f_2 = 32 MHz, K = 2.03.*

When n identical singly tuned (or double tuned with critical coupling) amplifiers are cascaded, it can be shown[2] that

$$B_n = B(2^{1/n} - 1)^{\frac{1}{2}} \qquad (9.22)$$

[1] Compensated circuits are treated in the following texts: *Electronic Circuits* by T. L. Martin, Prentice-Hall, Englewood Cliffs, N.J., pp. 123–149 and 169–171, 1955. *Pulse and Digital Circuits* by J. Millman and H. Taub, McGraw-Hill, New York, pp. 67–85, 1956. *Fundamentals of Television Engineering* by G. M. Glasford, McGraw-Hill, New York, pp. 163–197, 1955.

[2] For derivations of this equation see *Electronic Circuits* by T. L. Martin, Prentice-Hall, Englewood Cliffs, N.J., pp. 171–174, 1955.

where B_n is the bandwidth of the total amplifier and B is the bandwidth of each stage in the amplifier. The behavior of these tuned circuits is much the same as the behavior of the R-C coupled amplifier just considered. In fact, Eq. 9.22 indicates the bandwidth per stage must increase with an increasing number of stages if a given total amplifier bandwidth is to be maintained. Thus, an optimum gain exists for a given transistor or tube and a given bandwidth.

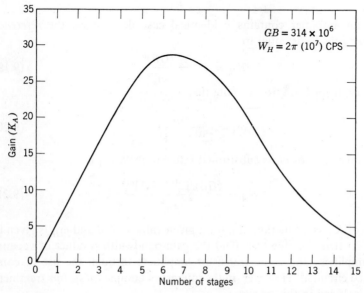

Fig. 9.2. A plot of Eq. 9.21.

Tuned circuits do have a rather unique advantage if the cascaded stages are *not* tuned to the same resonant frequencies. Tuned amplifiers of this type are known as stagger-tuned amplifiers. Again, the treatment of these amplifiers is deleted in the interest of compactness. However, excellent and detailed treatments exist in the literature.[3]

So far, the work on cascaded amplifiers has been primarily concerned with gain and bandwidth of the amplifier. If a step function is applied to a single stage amplifier, the rise time was given in Chapter 7 as being approximately equal to $2.2/\omega_2$. If this same concept is to be applied to

---

[3] The design of stagger-tuned circuits will not be included here. However, excellent derivations exist in *Vacuum Tube Amplifiers* by G. E. Valley and Wallman, Vol. 18 of the MIT Radiation Lab series, McGraw-Hill Book Co., New York, pp. 176–200, 1948, or *Electronic Circuits* by T. L. Martin, Prentice-Hall, Inc., Englewood Cliffs, N.J., pp. 186–205, 1955.

cascaded stage amplifier, the expected rise time will be about $2.2/\omega_H$. In addition, Martin[4] has used a work by Elmore[5] to show that the overall rise time of the cascaded amplifier T_{AR} is

$$T_{AR} = (T_{R1}{}^2 + T_{R2}{}^2 + T_{R3}{}^2 + \cdots)^{1/2} \qquad (9.23)$$

where

T_{R1} is the rise time of stage one
T_{R2} is the rise time of stage two, etc.

Thus, if n identical stages with a rise time of T_{RS} are cascaded, the rise time of the total amplifier T_{AR} will be

$$T_{AR} = T_{RS}(n)^{1/2} \qquad (9.24)$$

These two equations assume no overshoot in the rise waveform and are accurate to within 10 per cent when as few as two stages are involved.

PROB. 9.5. Design a video amplifier with a bandwidth of 30 Hz to 4 MHz. The total voltage gain must be at least 1000. Use 6AU6 tubes and assume the following data applies:

$$C_i = 5.5 \text{ pf}$$
$$C_{gp} = 0.003 \text{ pf}$$
$$C_o = 5 \text{ pf}$$
$$g_m = 5200 \text{ } \mu\text{mhos}$$
$$\max R_g = 1 \text{ megohm}$$
$$r_p = 1 \text{ megohm}$$

Assume wiring capacitance per stage is 3 pf.

(a) Determine the figure of merit for one stage.
(b) Determine how many stages are required.
(c) Determine ω_1 and ω_2.
(d) Determine R_L and C_c.
(e) Determine R_k, R_{sg}, C_{sg}, and C_k (see the 6AU6 curves in Appendix III).
(f) Draw the diagram for the total amplifier. List all values.

PROB. 9.6. Design a video amplifier with a bandwidth of 30 Hz to 4 MHz. The total current gain must be at least 1000. Use 2N384 transistors (characteristics are given in Appendix III) and assume the interstage wiring capacitance is 3 pf.

9.2 *db* GAIN

Power gain in bel units is defined as

$$b = \log \frac{P_2}{P_1} \qquad (9.25)$$

---

[4] *Op. cit.*, Martin, pp. 222–224.
[5] W. C. Elmore, "Transient Response of Damped Linear Networks with Particular Regard to Wideband Amplifiers," *J. Appl. Phys.*, Vol. 19, pp. 55–62, January 1948.

where "log" is the logarithm to the base 10 and b is in bels. P_2/P_1 is the power ratio between the points in question.

The bel unit is convenient because it reduces a multiplication problem in the case of the gain of a cascaded amplifier to an addition problem. Nevertheless, the bel is an inconveniently large unit because a power gain of 10 is only 1 bel. Therefore, the decibel (db) has been accepted as the practical unit. The db unit has the additional advantage that a power change of 1 db in an audio system is barely discernible to the ear, which has a logarithmic response to intensity changes.

$$db = 10 \log \frac{P_2}{P_1} \tag{9.26}$$

Also

$$db = 10 \log \frac{V_2^2/R_2}{V_1^2/R_1} \tag{9.27}$$

If the resistance is the same at the two points of reference,

$$db = 10 \log \left(\frac{V_2}{V_1}\right)^2 = 20 \log \frac{V_2}{V_1} \tag{9.28}$$

Similarly,

$$db = 20 \log \frac{I_2}{I_1} \tag{9.29}$$

The impedance levels are frequently of secondary importance in a voltage or current amplifier. Therefore, the Eqs. 9.28 and 9.29 are sometimes loosely used without regard to the relative resistance levels.

PROB. 9.7. An amplifier consists of four stages, each of which has a voltage gain of 20. What is the db gain of each stage? What is the total gain in db? Assume that the resistance levels of each stage are the same.

PROB. 9.8. What is the db level at the half-power frequencies, f_1 and f_2, compared with the mid-frequency or reference level?

It is often convenient to express a power level in db with regard to a certain reference level. One commonly used reference level is 6 mw. Another commonly used reference level is 1 mw. When this (1 mw) reference level is used, the db units are usually called "volume units" (vu). On the other hand, the open-circuit output voltage of a microphone is usually rated in db with reference to 1 v when the standard excess acoustical pressure is 1 micro bar, or one millionth of standard barometric pressure.

PROB. 9.9. What is the power level of 40 db? 40 vu? *Answer: 60 w, 10 w.*

PROB. 9.10. What is the open-circuit output voltage of a microphone which has −56 db level? Assume the excess acoustical pressure to be 1 micro bar.

9.3 STRAIGHT LINE APPROXIMATIONS OF GAIN AND PHASE CHARACTERISTICS (BODE PLOTS)

The analysis given in Section 9.1 is sufficient for the analysis and design of identical cascaded stages. This section will present a method of analysis which can be used on any amplifier. However, as an introduction, we will apply this method to a single R-C coupled stage. The transfer function of a single R-C stage was given by Eq. 7.56 as

$$G = -K \frac{s\omega_2}{(s + \omega_1)(s + \omega_2)} \qquad (7.56)$$

For a-c steady state, $s = j\omega$. Now, if ω is assumed to be small in comparison with ω_1, the term $(s + \omega_1)$ becomes essentially ω_1. In addition, since $\omega_1 \ll \omega_2$ in a typical amplifier, the term $(s + \omega_2)$ becomes essentially ω_2. Then, Eq. 7.56 becomes

$$G = -K \frac{j\omega}{\omega_1} \qquad (9.30)$$

Thus, the gain of the amplifier is proportional to frequency and the phase angle of G is $270°$. An interesting method of expressing the magnitude relationship exists. In musical terms, the frequency doubles every octave. Thus, from Eq. 9.30, the gain doubles for every octave increase in frequency. When Eq. 9.28 or 9.29 is used, 20 log 2 is approximately six. Thus, we can also state *the gain increases 6 db per octave frequency increase.* A plot of db gain vs frequency over the range where Eq. 9.30 applies will be a straight line if frequency is plotted on a logarithmic scale. As noted, Eq. 9.30 is valid for $\omega \ll \omega_1$. However, as ω approaches ω_1, the accuracy of this approximation decreases. Nevertheless, as an approximation let us assume that Eq. 9.30 is valid for $\omega \leq \omega_1$. Then, the plot of G vs ω and phase angle vs ω will be as shown (for $\omega \leq \omega_1$) in Fig. 9.3.

Now, if $s = j\omega$ and $\omega_1 \ll \omega \ll \omega_2$, then $(s + \omega_1) \approx j\omega$ and $(s + \omega_2) \approx \omega_2$. Then, Eq. 7.56 becomes

$$G = -K \qquad (9.31)$$

In this case, the gain is a constant and is independent of frequency while the phase angle remains constant at 180. If this condition is assumed to exist (again, this is a rough approximation) for $\omega_1 \geq \omega \geq \omega_2$, the plots will have the form given in Fig. 9.3.

Finally, if $s = j\omega$ and $\omega \gg \omega_2$, then, $(s + \omega_1) \approx j\omega$ and $(s + \omega_2) \approx j\omega$. Under these conditions, Eq. 7.56 becomes

$$G = -K \frac{\omega_2}{j\omega} \qquad (9.32)$$

In this case, G is reduced by one-half for each octave frequency increase or G decreases by 6 db per octave frequency increase. In addition, the phase angle becomes $90°$. If these conditions are assumed to be present for $\omega \geq \omega_2$, the plots will be as shown (for $\omega \geq \omega_2$) in Fig. 9.3.

The actual plots of gain and frequency (Fig. 7.16) are plotted as dashed lines in Fig. 9.3. The straight-line approximations are seen to be fairly good approximations. In fact, with a correction factor which can be

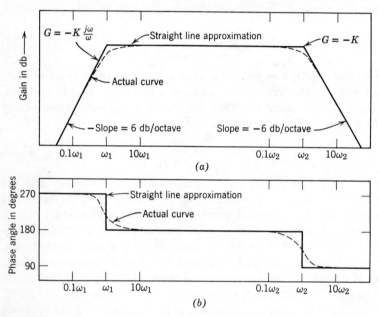

Fig. 9.3. Straight-line approximations for $G = -K[s\omega_2/(s + \omega_1)(S + \omega_2)]$. (*a*) Gain; (*b*) phase shift.

applied near the singularities, accurate plots can be obtained. With the insight gained from the straight-line analysis of the *R-C* coupled stage, we are now ready to derive some general rules which can be applied in plotting gain and phase curves.

The total amplifier gain G_A was given in Eq. 9.4 as

$$G_A = G_1 \times G_2 \times G_3 \times \cdots G_n \qquad (9.4)$$

In general, the stage gains (G_1, G_2, etc.) are functions of s. Consequently, G_A is also a function of s and will have the form

$$G_A = H \frac{s^n + a_1 s^{n-1} + a_2 s^{n-2} + \cdots a_n}{s^m + b_1 s^{m-1} + b_2 s^{m-1} + \cdots b_m} \qquad (9.33)$$

In actual circuits, any number of the coefficients a_1, b_1, a_2, b_2, etc. may be zero. The polynomial in the numerator and the polynomial in the denominator can be factored. When these polynomials are factored, the terms will have the following three forms:

$$\text{Form 1} = s^k \tag{9.34}$$

$$\text{Form 2} = (s + a)^k \tag{9.35}$$

$$\text{Form 3} = (s^2 + 2\zeta\omega_n s + \omega_n{}^2)^k \tag{9.36}$$

where k is an integer 1, 2, 3, etc. which differs from one if repeated roots are present. Thus, Eq. 9.33 can be factored (in fact, since G_A is usually written as the product of the individual stage gains, the terms are usually already factored) and written as

$$G_A = Hs^h \frac{(s + Z_1)(s + Z_2) \cdots}{(s + P_1)(s + P_2) \cdots} \tag{9.37}$$

where h can have a value of zero, a positive integer, or a negative integer, and Z_1, Z_2, P_1, P_2, etc. may be complex numbers if they are derived from terms such as those of Eq. 9.36. Now, if we take the logarithm[6] of Eq. 9.37 we have

$$\log G_A = \log H + h \log (s) + \log (s + Z_1) + \log (s + Z_2) + \cdots$$
$$- \log (s + P_1) - \log (s + P_2) - \cdots \tag{9.38}$$

Thus, if we work with logarithms of the different factors in Eq. 9.37, the responses of the different factors can be added or subtracted to obtain the response of the total amplifier.

The $\log H$ is a constant and is independent of frequency. However, for the steady-state solution, s becomes $j\omega$ and

$$h \log (s) = h \left[\log \omega + j \frac{\pi}{2} \right] \tag{9.39}$$

As already noted, the term $\log \omega$ is equal to a gain increase of 6 db/octave. The effect of $h \log (s)$ on G_A is plotted in Fig. 9.4 for several values of h.

When considering factors of the form given by Eq. 9.35, it is convenient to draw, first of all, a straight-line approximation for the gain and phase characteristics and then correct this approximation in order to arrive at the actual gain and phase curves. Thus, we note that when $s = j\omega$, Eq. 9.35 can be written as

$$\log [(j\omega + a)^k] = k \log (j\omega + a) \tag{9.40}$$

---

[6] In taking the logarithm of a complex number, the complex number should be reduced to a magnitude and a phase angle such as M^θ. Then, $\log M^\theta = \log M + j\theta$ where θ is in radians.

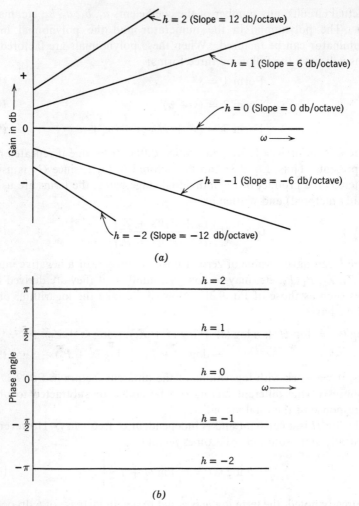

Fig. 9.4. A plot of $h \log (s)$ for several values of h. (a) Gain plot, (b) phase angle plot.

If $\omega \ll a$, Eq. 9.40 reduces to $(k \log a)$ which is a constant. Thus, for a straight-line approximation, the gain and phase curves will be as shown in Fig. 9.5 (by the dashed lines) for values below $\omega = a$. However, if $\omega \gg a$, Eq. 9.40 becomes $k \left[\log \omega + j \dfrac{\pi}{2} \right]$. In this case, the slope is $(k \times 6 \text{ db/octave})$ and the phase angle is $\dfrac{k\pi}{2}$. For the straight-line approximation, these curves hold for $\omega > a$ (Fig. 9.5). The two straight lines for the gain curve must intercept at $\omega = a$. When actual values

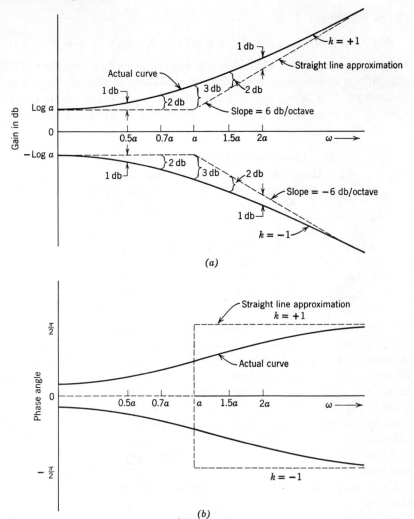

Fig. 9.5. A plot of $k \log (j\omega + a)$ for $k = +1$ and -1. (a) Gain; (b) phase angle.

near $\omega = a$ are calculated, the curves are as shown by the solid lines. Table 9.1 lists the actual error between the straight-line approximation and the actual curves for a few significant values of ω. Note that k will be positive if the term $(s + a)^k$ is in the numerator of Eq. 9.37 and will be negative if the term is in the denominator.

When conjugate poles or zeros exist (as in tuned amplifiers) the factors have the form given by Eq. 9.36. Again, a straight-line approximation can be used to simplify the plotting procedure. When $s = j\omega$, Eq. 9.36

can be written as

$$\log(-\omega^2 + 2j\zeta\omega_n\omega + \omega_n^2)^k = k \log(-\omega^2 + 2j\zeta\omega_n\omega + \omega_n^2) \quad (9.41)$$

Now, if $\omega \ll \omega_n$, Eq. 9.41 becomes $2k \log \omega_n$ which is a constant. This straight-line approximation is used for all values of $\omega < \omega_n$ (Fig. 9.6). In contrast, if $\omega \gg \omega_n$, Eq. 9.41 becomes $2k \log \omega + kj\pi$. Note that if k is one, the slope of the straight-line approximation will be 12 db/octave.

TABLE 9.1
Correction Factor for Log $[(j\omega + a)^k]$

ω	Magnitude Correction To Be Added to the Linear Approximation	Phase Angle Correction To Be Added to the Linear Approximation
$0.5a$	$k \times 1$ db	$k \times 26.6°$
$0.707a$	$k \times 2$ db	$k \times 35.3°$
a	$k \times 3$ db	$k \times 45°$
$1.414a$	$k \times 2$ db	$-k \times 35.3°$
$2a$	$k \times 1$ db	$-k \times 26.6°$

The interception of the two straight-line gain curves occurs at $\omega = \omega_n$. The straight-line approximations and the actual curve for a typical case is shown in Fig. 9.6. However, since Eq. 9.41 contains ζ as well as ω_n, the exact shape of the curve near ω_n is a function of ζ. Curves which can be used to determine the proper correction for different values of ζ are given in Fig. 9.7. The corrections listed by these curves should be multiplied by k to obtain the exact corrections to be used. The curves extend only to $\omega/\omega_n = 1.0$. However, the attenuation curves are also valid for ω_n/ω when $\omega > \omega_n$. With a change of sign, the phase shift curves are also valid for ω_n/ω when $\omega > \omega_n$.

The concepts just developed will now be used in an example to clarify their use.

Example 9.1. The gain equation for an amplifier is given by the following equation:

$$G_A = 10^4 \frac{s^2}{(s + 100)(s + 200)(s + 100,000)^2} \quad (9.42)$$

Plot the amplitude and phase of G_A as a function of frequency.

As a first step, find the gain at some frequency which can be used as a reference. For example, assume $s = j\omega = j10$. When this value is substituted into Eq. 9.42, it becomes

$$G_A = 10^4 \frac{-100}{(j10 + 100)(j10 + 200)(j10 + 100,000)^2} \quad (9.43)$$

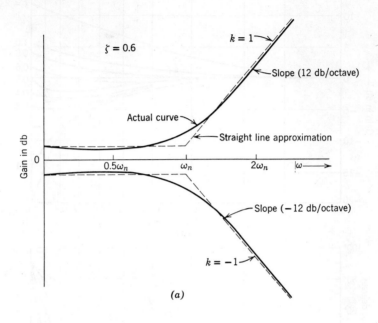

(a)

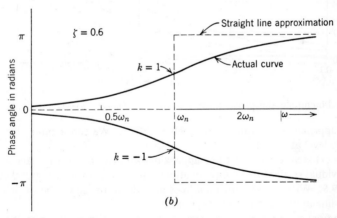

(b)

Fig. 9.6. A plot of $k \log(-\omega^2 + 2j\zeta\omega_n\omega + \omega_n^2)$ for $k = +1$ and $k = -1$. (a) Magnitude; (b) phase angle.

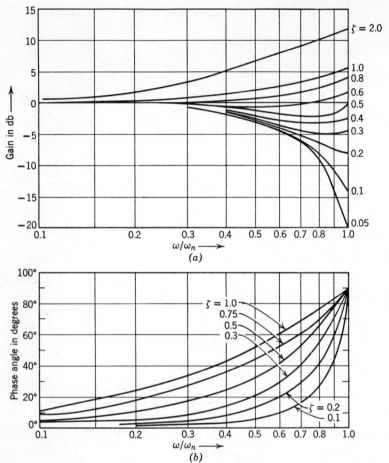

Fig. 9.7. Magnitude and phase of $(s^2 + 2\zeta\omega_n s + \omega_n^2)/\omega_n^2$. (a) Magnitude, (b) phase.

This is approximately equal to $G_A = 0.5 \times 10^{-8}$. We can assume this is our reference level at $\omega = 10$.

As a next step, the straight-line approximations can be drawn. Accordingly, the individual straight-line approximations will be as shown by the dashed lines in Fig. 9.8. When these individual lines are added, the solid line (which is the straight-line approximation for G_A) results.

In the final step, a correction table is tabulated as shown on page 355.

When these total corrections are applied to the straight-line approximation (shown dashed in Fig. 9.9), the actual gain and phase curves shown as solid lines in Fig. 9.8 result. These are the required curves.

The foregoing example indicates the process to be used in plotting gain and phase characteristics for any amplifier whose characteristic equation

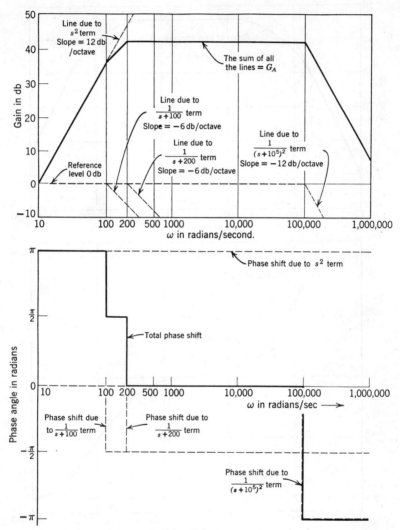

Fig. 9.8. The straight-line approximations for Eq. 9.42.

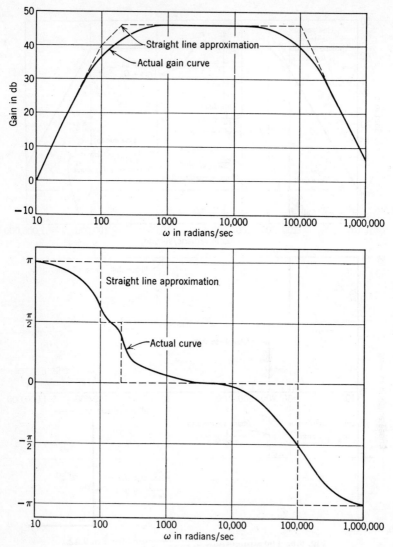

Fig. 9.9. The actual gain and phase curves for Eq. 9.42.

TABLE 9.2

Correction Values to be Used on Fig. 9.8

Frequency	Correction for $\frac{1}{s + 100}$ term		Correction for $\frac{1}{s + 200}$ term		Correction for $\frac{1}{(s + 100,000)^2}$ t		Total Correction	
	db	Phase	db	Phase	db	Phase	db	Phase
50	−1	−26.6°					−1	−26.6°
70	−2	−35.3°					−2	−35.3°
100	−3	45.0°	−1	−26.6°			−4	+18.4°
140	−2	+35.3°	−2	−35.3°			−4	0°
200	−1	+26.6°	−3	45.0°			−4	+71.6°
280			−2	35.3°			−2	+35.3°
400			−1	+26.6°			−1	+26.6°
50,000					−2	−53.2	−2	−53.2°
70,700					−4	−70.6°	−4	−70.6°
100,000					−6	−90.0°	−6	−90.0°
141,400					−4	+70.6°	−4	+70.6°
200,000					−2	+53.2°	−2	+53.2°

is known. In fact, it is often possible to start from a known gain curve and synthesize an amplifier which will have this gain curve.

PROB. 9.11. (a) Draw the straight-line approximation curves (gain and phase) for an amplifier whose gain is given by the equation

$$G_A = \frac{s^3}{(s + 100)(s + 1000)^2(s^2 + 6 \times 10^4 s + 10^{10})(s + 10^5)}$$

(b) Draw the actual gain phase curves for this amplifier.

PROB. 9.12. Repeat Prob. 9.11 if the gain equation is

$$G_A = \frac{s(s + 200)^2}{(s + 100)(s + 400)(s + 800)(s + 10^6)^3}$$

PROB. 9.13. Three identical stages are cascaded. The gain equation for one stage is

$$G_s = \frac{s}{(s + 100)(s + 10^6)}$$

(a) Plot gain vs frequency curves for the total amplifier. From this curve, find ω_L and ω_H for the total amplifier.

(b) Use the method outlined in Section 9.1 to determine ω_L and ω_H. How do these values compare with those in part a?

PROB. 9.14. It is desirable to construct an amplifier which has a gain vs frequency curve with the same shape as the one given in Fig. 9.10.

(a) Find a gain function G_A which would give this type of response.

(b) Break this function up into functions which represent R-C coupled stages.

(c) Transistors are available which have the following characteristics:

$$h_{ie} = 2000 \text{ ohms}$$

$$h_{re} \approx 0$$

$$h_{fe} = 50$$

$$h_{oe} = 2 \text{ } \mu\text{mhos}$$

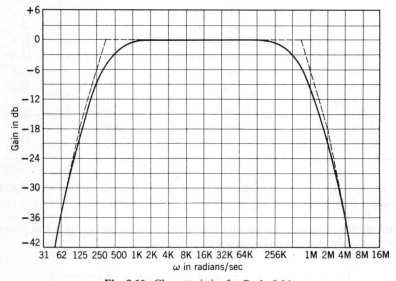

Fig. 9.10. Characteristics for Prob. 9.14.

If the total shunt and wiring capacitance per stage is assumed to be 250 pf and β cutoff is assumed to be much greater than ω_2, design the amplifiers which will produce the required response. *Answer:* (b) $G_A = [K_1 s/(s + 125)(s + 2 \times 10^6)] \times [K_2 s/(s + 350)(s + 7 \times 10^5)] \times [K_3 s/(s + 350)(s + 7 \times 10^5)]$.

9.4   CASCADING INTERACTING STAGES

In most transistor and in some high-frequency tube applications, the input impedance of one stage depends on the load of this stage. In fact, as found in Chapter 5, the input impedance of a common emitter amplifier was given as

$$R_i = h_{ie} - \frac{h_{re}h_{fe}}{h_{oe} + g_L} \tag{5.16}$$

This equation was developed for a common emitter circuit, but the solution is actually general and applies to the h parameters in any configuration. Thus, the input impedance can be written as

$$Z_i = h_i - \frac{h_r h_f}{h_o + Y_L} \qquad (9.44)$$

When stages are cascaded, the Y_L of one stage includes the input impedance to the next stage as well as the coupling network. Thus, Y_L will usually be a function of s and, if many stages are present, may be a rather complex function of s. In addition, the output admittance of a stage is given by the relationship

$$Y_o = h_o - \frac{h_r h_f}{h_i + Z_g} \qquad (9.45)$$

where Z_g is the impedance of the driving generator. From this relationship, we note that we not only have interaction from the output stages of a cascaded amplifier back toward the input stages, but also the input stages will interact with the output stages.

Obviously, the design of even a three- or four-stage amplifier can be very complex unless something is done to reduce the effects of the interaction. Two methods of reducing the effects of interaction have already been discussed in Chapter 8. The first of these methods (Section 8.5) was to neutralize each stage. When a stage is neutralized, h_r is reduced to zero. Under these conditions, $Z_i = h_i$ (also $Z_o = h_o$) and the stages are completely noninteracting. Unfortunately, it may be difficult or inconvenient to neutralize a stage completely (especially over a wide range of frequencies), since the magnitude and phase angle of h_r are both frequency sensitive.

The second method of reducing interaction is to deliberately mismatch the load[7] as outlined in Section 8.6. Note in Eq. 9.44 that if $Y_L \ll h_{oe}$, the second term on the right side becomes $\approx h_r h_f / h_o$ and a change of Y_L will have very little effect on Z_i. In the other extreme, if Y_L becomes quite large, the second term on the right of Eq. 9.44 can be made so much smaller than h_i that Z_i becomes essentially equal to h_i. In order to be more quantitative, let us define an interacting parameter δ_i as the fractional change of Z_i with a change of Y_L.

$$\delta_i = \frac{\partial Z_i / \partial Y_L}{Z_i / Y_L} = \frac{\dfrac{h_r h_f}{(h_o + Y_L)^2} Y_L}{h_i - \dfrac{h_r h_f}{h_o + Y_L}} \qquad (9.46)$$

[7] J. F. Gibbons, "The Design of Alignable Transistor Amplifiers," *Technical Report* 106, Stanford Electronics Laboratories, May 7, 1956.

A straightforward reduction of this equation yields

$$\delta_i = \frac{h_r h_f Y_L}{[h_i(h_o + Y_L) - h_r h_f](h_o + Y_L)} \tag{9.47}$$

Now, if Y_L is much greater than h_o, the term $(h_o + Y_L) \approx Y_L$. Then, Eq. 9.47 can be written as

$$\delta_i = \frac{h_r h_f Y_L}{h_i Y_L{}^2 - h_r h_f Y_L} = \frac{h_r h_f}{h_i Y_L - h_r h_f} \tag{9.48}$$

The interaction between stages is reduced as δ_i is reduced. For example, if δ_i is equal to 0.1, a 10 per cent change of load impedance is reflected back to the input as a 1 per cent (0.1 × 10 per cent) change of input impedance. Thus, for low interaction, δ_i should be small. Now, if δ_i is much less than unity, $h_i Y_L \gg h_r h_f$ in Eq. 9.48. If this is the case, the equation for δ_i becomes

$$\delta_i \approx \frac{h_r h_f}{h_i Y_L} \tag{9.49}$$

For the other extreme, Y_L will be much less than h_o. In this case, the term $(h_o + Y_L) \approx h_o$ and Eq. 9.47 can be written as

$$\delta_i = \frac{h_r h_f Y_L}{(h_i h_o - h_r h_f)h_o} \tag{9.50}$$

For a given value of δ_i, the appropriate value of Y_L can be determined from either Eqs. 9.49 or 9.50. The exact equation to use will be determined by the circuit configuration. For example, the value of Z_i is usually much less than Z_o in a common-emitter amplifier. Therefore, it is usually desirable to make $Y_L > h_{oe}$ and Eq. 9.49 would be applied if common-emitter stages are used. On the other hand, if an emitter follower is to be used to drive a high input impedance circuit, it would be desirable to let $h_{oe} > Y_L$, and Eq. 9.50 would be used.

The problem of interaction between stages is usually more pronounced in tuned amplifiers. In fact, just *aligning* a tuned-multistage-interacting amplifier can be a very tedious task. Of course, designing such an amplifier can be complex and difficult. Consequently, an example in the design of a multistage amplifier will be given.

Example 9.2. A three-stage I.F. amplifier is to be designed as shown in Fig. 9.11. The desired center frequency is 500 KHz and a bandwidth of 10 KHz is required. Determine all pertinent parameters in this circuit if δ_i is to be restricted to a magnitude of 0.1. The transistor has the following measured parameters at 500 KHz:

$$h_{ie} = 1000 \ \Omega$$
$$h_{re} = j10^{-3}$$
$$h_{fe} = 25$$
$$h_{oe} = (8 + j30)10^{-6} = (31 \times 10^{-6})\angle\underline{75°} \text{ mhos}$$

First, let us determine the required magnitude of Y_L from Eq. 9.49.

$$|Y_L| = \left| \frac{h_r h_f}{h_i \ \delta} \right| = 25 \times 10^{-5} \text{ mhos} \qquad (9.51)$$

In order to determine the real and reactive components of Y_L, a knowledge of the output admittance of the transistor must be known. The output admittance can be calculated from Eq. 9.45 if the total generator impedance is known. If

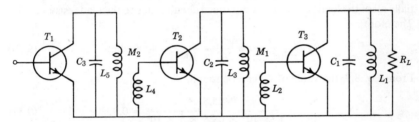

Fig. 9.11. An a-c circuit of a three-stage I.F. amplifier. (The d-c bias circuits are not shown.)

we assume the coupling circuit is adjusted so the input of the transistor is matched, the generator impedance of Eq. 9.45 is equal to Z_i of Eq. 9.44. When this substitution is made, Y_o is equal to

$$Y_o = h_o - \frac{h_r h_f}{h_i + h_i - \dfrac{h_r h_f}{h_o + Y_L}} \qquad (9.52)$$

Then

$$Y_0 = (8 + j30)10^{-6} - \frac{25 \times 10^{-3}\angle\underline{90°}}{2 \times 10^3 - J\dfrac{25 \times 10^{-3}}{(8 + J30)10^{-6} + (25 \times 10^{-5})\angle\underline{?}}}$$

While the phase angle associated with Y_L is not known, the effect of Y_L on Y_o is essentially negligible in this example. (In fact, the effect of Y_L becomes smaller as δ_i becomes smaller.) If the effect of Y_L is not negligible, assume a value for Y_L and substitute this value in Eq. 9.52. Use the value of Y_o so obtained to determine a tentative value for Y_L. Now use the value of Y_o obtained from this tentative value of Y_L in Eq. 9.52 to arrive at a final value for Y_L. The value of Y_o for this example is

$$Y_o \approx (8 + J17.5) \times 10^{-6} \qquad (9.53)$$

Maximum transfer of energy from a generator with an admittance of $G + jB$ is possible when the load has an admittance of $G - jB$. In this example, the magnitude of Y_L must be 250 micromhos. However, maximum power will be delivered to the load if the reactive term of Y_o is cancelled by the load admittance. Thus, $Y_L = (249 - j17.5) \times 10^{-6}$ or $250 \times 10^{-6}\angle{-4°}$ mhos.

The desired bandwidth for this amplifier is 10 KHz. However, since there are three stages, Eq. 9.22 is used to find the required bandwidth per stage:

$$B = \frac{B_n}{(2^{1/n} - 1)^{½}} = \frac{10 \text{ KHz}}{(2^{⅓} - 1)^{½}} = 19.6 \text{ KHz} \tag{9.54}$$

From Eq. 8.50, the Q of the output tuned circuit must be

$$Q = \frac{\omega_0}{B} = \frac{500 \text{ KHz}}{19.6 \text{ KHz}} = 25.5 \tag{9.55}$$

Now, if the unloaded Q of L_1 and C_1 in Fig. 9.11 is much higher than 25, essentially all of the loading on the output tuned circuit is due to the load resistance R_L. Therefore

$$R_L = \frac{1}{Re(Y_L)} = \frac{1}{249 \times 10^{-6}} \approx 4000 \text{ ohms} \tag{9.56}$$

From Eq. 8.9, the value of C_1 can be found.

$$C_1 = \frac{Q}{R\omega_0} = \frac{25.5}{4 \times 10^3 \times 6.28 \times 5 \times 10^5} = 0.00203 \ \mu\text{fd} \tag{9.57}$$

The admittance of C_1 at ω_0 is $j6.28 \times 5 \times 10^5 \times 2.03 \times 10^{-9}$ or 6.37×10^{-3} mhos. The desired reactive component for Y_L is $-J17.5 \times 10^{-6}$. Therefore, the total admittance of L_1 is $-j6370 \times 10^{-6} - j17.5 \times 10^{-6} = -j6.387 \times 10^{-3}$. Thus,

$$L_1 = \frac{1}{\omega_0 B_L} = \frac{1}{6.28 \times 5 \times 10^5 \times 6.387 \times 10^{-3}} = 49.9 \ \mu\text{hen.} \tag{9.58}$$

With the output circuit designed, we are now ready to consider the interstage coupling network L_2, L_3, and C_2. The input impedance to the output transistor (from Eq. 9.44) is

$$Z_i = 10^3 - \frac{J10^{-3} \times 25}{(8 + j30)10^{-6} + (249 - j17.5)10^{-6}} \approx 1000 - J100 \tag{9.59}$$

The output admittance of transistor T_2 is the same as the output admittance of transistor T_3. Thus $Y_o \simeq (8 + J17.5) \times 10^{-6}$. The desired load on T_2 will be the same as the load on T_3 or $(249 - j17.5) \times 10^{-6}$ mhos.

Hence, as noted in Eq. 9.56, the equivalent parallel resistance R_p for the circuit $C_2 L_3$ would be 4000 ohms. Using Eq. 9.57, the value of C_2 will be equal to 0.00203 μfds. The desired loaded admittance of the coil L_3 is given by Eq. 8.80 as

$$Z_{in} = R_{L3} + j\omega_0 L_3 + \frac{(\omega_0 M)^2}{R_{L2} + Z_i + j\omega L_2} \tag{9.60}$$

Now Z_i is over 1000 ohms, so it is much larger than R_{L2} or R_{L3}. In addition, $j\omega L_2$ can be used to cancel the $-j100$ component (see Eq. 9.59) of Z_i. Then

$$L_2 = \frac{100}{6.28 \times 5 \times 10^5} = 31.8 \ \mu \text{ henries} \qquad (9.61)$$

Under these conditions, L_3 furnishes all of the reactance in the primary circuit. The admittance of L_3 must be equal to the admittance of C_2 which is $-j6370$ μmhos plus the $-j17.5$ μmhos of the required Y_o. Thus, L_3 must have the same admittance as L_1. Hence

$$L_3 = 49.9 \ \mu \text{ henries} \qquad (9.62)$$

The value of M can be determined by using Eq. 8.83. For this example

$$R_p = \left(\frac{L_3}{M}\right)^2 Re(R_i) = 4000 = \left(\frac{49.9 \times 10^{-6}}{M_1}\right)^2 1000 \qquad (9.63)$$

or

$$M_1 = \frac{49.9}{2} = 25\mu \text{ henries}$$

The value of the coupling coefficient k_1 will be

$$k_1 = \frac{M_1}{(L_2 L_3)^{1/2}} = \frac{25 \times 10^{-6}}{(31.8 \times 49.9) \times 10^{-6}} = 0.63 \qquad (9.64)$$

All of the components in the second coupling circuit have now been determined.

The coupling circuit between T_1 and T_2 is coupling exactly the same impedances as the coupling circuit between T_2 and T_3. Consequently, $C_3 = C_2$, $L_5 = L_3$, $L_4 = L_2$, $M_2 = M_1$, and $k_2 = k_1$.

The foregoing example used impedance mismatching as the means of reducing interaction between stages. Of course, other interstage connections and other approaches[8] to the problem are also used. When impedance mismatching is used, the total power gain is reduced below that which can be obtained with a properly matched and neutralized stage. If too much power gain is lost through impedance mismatching and the circuit is extremely difficult to neutralize, a combination of the two processes may be used. A simple feedback circuit is employed to produce partial neutralization and impedance mismatching is employed to reduce the interaction to the desired level.

PROB. 9.15. Determine the total power gain at $\omega = 500$ KHz of the three-stage amplifier of Example 9.2.

[8] A graphical approach to the design of transistor (or tube circuits) is given in Chapters 11 and 18 of *Transistors and Active Circuits* by J. G. Linvill and J. F. Gibbons, McGraw-Hill, New York, 1961.

PROB. 9.16. Design a three-stage neutralized amplifier using the transistors of Example 9.2. The amplifier should be designed to produce maximum power gain and still have the same bandwidth and the same center frequency as in Example 9.2. Use inductively coupled circuits to couple the three stages.

9.5 *D-C* AMPLIFIERS

The need frequently arises for an amplifier that will amplify signals which vary so slowly that capacitors of practical size cannot be used for either coupling or bypass. Transformers are also useless in this application. Therefore, one amplifier must be directly coupled to another and the bias currents may not be separable from the signal currents. This type of

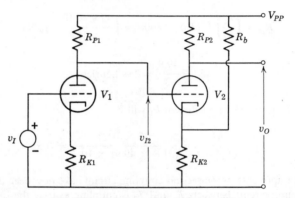

Fig. 9.12. One type of d-c tube amplifier.

amplifier is called a *direct coupled* or *d-c amplifier*. Special problems arise in these amplifiers because of the restricted freedom in the choice of bias potentials and techniques. Transistors offer some advantages when compared with tubes because of the availability of both *p-n-p* and *n-p-n* types. However, the transistor thermal currents may present a serious problem in a high-gain d-c amplifier because the thermal currents may be amplified along with the signal currents and therefore the thermal currents, or their variations, must be kept small in comparison with the signal currents. Some typical d-c amplifier circuits will be discussed in this section to illustrate the special problems in d-c amplifier design and some techniques which may lead to satisfactory solutions of these problems.

Although vacuum tubes are seldom used in present-day d-c amplifier design, this type of amplifier will be discussed here as an introduction to some of the problems encountered in d-c amplifiers. One type of tube amplifier is shown in Fig. 9.12. The first stage of this amplifier may have fairly high voltage gain even though the cathode bias resistor is unbypassed because the bias resistor R_{K1} may be small in comparison with the plate load resistor R_{P1}. The voltage gain is the same order of magnitude as R_{P1}/R_{K1} because the output voltage is $i_P R_{P1}$ and the input voltage v_I is the same order of magnitude as $i_P R_{K1}$. However, a problem arises in the second amplifier V_2 because the grid of this amplifier is at the same d-c potential as the plate of V_1. This high-positive grid potential with respect to ground requires an even higher positive cathode potential in order to provide negative grid bias. One way to provide this high-positive cathode potential is to use a large cathode resistor R_{K2}, but then the voltage gain of the amplifier V_2 is very small because R_{K2} is the same order of magnitude as

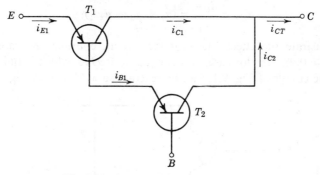

Fig. 9.13. A Darlington transistor circuit.

R_{P2} and the input voltage $v_{I2} = i_P R_{K2} + v_{GK}$ must be of the same order of magnitude as the output voltage. A bleeder resistor R_b may be used to increase the current through R_{K2} and therefore, to reduce its value. But in order to reduce the value of R_{K2} sufficiently to provide good voltage gain, the bleeder current must be large and the resulting heat generation and power supply drain may be serious disadvantages. A high-gain d-c amplifier may require several stages and since the plate potential of each tube must be of the order of 100 volts positive with respect to its grid, and hence the plate of the preceding tube, the supply voltage V_{PP} may be very large in comparison with that required for an R-C coupled amplifier. Another disadvantage of the amplifier of Fig. 9.12 may be the large d-c bias voltage which is associated with the signal voltage in the output v_O. Batteries could be used to buck out the undesirable d-c potential rises, but batteries are bulky, produce a large shunt capacitance and habitually run down and require replacement. Gas diodes could be used instead of batteries, but these tubes generate noise which may mask the signal.

The problems encountered in the tube amplifier may be minimized or avoided by the use of transistors. One commonly used transistor arrangement is shown in Fig. 9.13 and is known as the *Darlington* connection. From the common-base configuration,

$$i_{C1} = \alpha_1 i_{E1} \qquad (9.65)$$

Consequently,

$$i_{B1} = i_{E1} - i_{C1} = i_{E1}(1 - \alpha_1) \qquad (9.66)$$

In transistor 2

$$i_{C2} = \alpha_2 i_{B1} = \alpha_2 i_{E1}(1 - \alpha_1) \qquad (9.67)$$

and

$$i_{CT} = i_{C1} + i_{C2} = (\alpha_1 + \alpha_2 - \alpha_2\alpha_1)i_{E1} \qquad (9.68)$$

Hence, the effective α of the entire circuit is

$$\alpha_{eff} = \frac{i_{CT}}{i_{E1}} = (\alpha_1 + \alpha_2 - \alpha_2\alpha_1) \qquad (9.69)$$

To illustrate the effectiveness of the circuit, consider the case when $\alpha_1 = \alpha_2 = 0.98$. In this case, α_{eff} is equal to 0.9996, which is quite close to 1. The circuit of Fig. 9.13 can be rearranged as shown in Fig. 9.14.

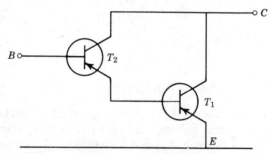

Fig. 9.14. The "common-emitter" configuration of the circuit of Fig. 9.13.

From Chapter 5,

$$h_{fe} = \frac{\alpha}{1 - \alpha} \qquad (5.44)$$

the value of h_{fe} for Fig. 9.14 ($\alpha_1 = \alpha_2 = 0.98$) would be

$$h_{fe} = \frac{0.9996}{1 - 0.9996} = 2499$$

A single conventional common-emitter circuit containing a transistor with an α of 0.98 would have an h_{fe} of 49. (The actual gain of one conventional stage would be less than h_{fe}.) Thus, if two conventional common-emitter stages are cascaded, the maximum possible gain would be h_{fe}^2. For the transistors with h_{fe} of 49, the maximum possible gain would accordingly be 2401. The Darlington configuration not only obtains a higher current gain, but also eliminates a number of circuit components.

In addition to the current gain characteristics, the input impedance characteristics of the Darlington connection are also of interest. For example, if the input impedance of transistor 1 is Z_{i1}, the input impedance of transistor 2 can be found from Eq. 7.132 of Chapter 7.

$$R_{in} = h_{ie} + (1 + h_{fe})R_L \qquad (7.132)$$

This equation was derived for a transistor with a load R_L in the emitter circuit and $R_L \ll R_d$. These conditions are satisfied by transistor 2 of Fig. 9.14. The load R_L in the emitter circuit of transistor 2 is Z_{i1}. Therefore, Eq. 7.132 becomes

$$Z_{i2} = h_{ie2} + (1 + h_{fe2})Z_{i1} \qquad (9.70)$$

where the subscript 2 denotes the parameters of transistor 2. In effect, the input impedance has been increased by a factor h_{fe}. Of course, the value of load impedance connected to the output terminals will also influence Z_{i2} and even Z_{i1} as well as the total current gain. Nevertheless, the circuit of Fig. 9.14 is a very high current gain circuit and also has a high input impedance.

The circuit given in Fig. 9.13 can be extended to include more than two transistors. Some manufactures include two or three separate transistors, connected in a Darlington configuration, in a single case.

One problem that may arise in the Darlington connection results from the thermal current I_{CO} of transistor T_2 which is multiplied by the stability factor of T_2, then enters the base of T_1, and is again multiplied, this time by the current gain of T_1. If germanium transistors are used, the component of thermal current in the output may be prohibitively large.

The thermal current which reaches the output may be greatly reduced if the linear stabilization circuit of Fig. 9.15a is used. Then parts of the thermal currents are shunted through the base resistors as discussed in Chapter 5 and are not amplified by the transistors. The stabilizing resistors reduce the gain of the amplifier because signal currents are also shunted through the base resistors. However, since the dynamic input resistance h_i of a transistor is much lower than its static input resistance h_I over the useful operating range (Fig. 9.15b), the thermal currents can be effectively reduced without a serious reduction of signal gain.

The circuit of Fig. 9.16 uses reversed biased diodes to conduct the thermal currents. The signal currents are not shunted appreciably because the dynamic resistance of a reverse-biased diode is very high. The diodes should be chosen so that their reverse bias (saturation) currents are essentially equal to the transistor thermal current I_{CO} which should flow through its associated diode. Good thermal conduction should be maintained between the transistor and the diode in its base circuit so compensation will be maintained over a wide ambient temperature range, and

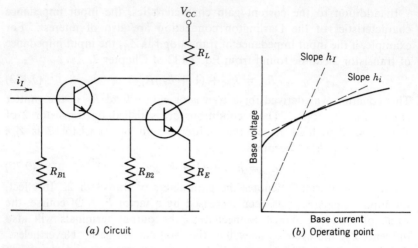

Fig. 9.15. A linearly stabilized Darlington-connected amplifier. (*a*) Circuit; (*b*) operating point.

with varying transistor dissipation. Positive, zero, or negative values of current stability factor may be obtained with diode stabilization, depending upon the characteristics of the diodes and the effectiveness of the thermal conduction.

In some applications, the high input resistance may be a disadvantage of the Darlington connection. A very high input resistance, as well as very high current gain, may be obtained if three transistors are used in conjunction with thermal compensating diodes.

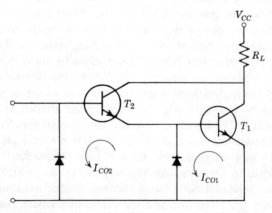

Fig. 9.16. A diode-stabilized Darlington circuit.

PROB. 9.17. A 2N1905 and a 2N1415 are used in the Darlington circuit shown in Fig. 9.15a. Let the base resistors R_B draw half as much current as the respective bases at maximum current. The load resistance R_L is 10 ohms and the supply voltage $V_{CC} = -20$ v. Using $R_E = 0.5$ ohm, determine suitable values for the other resistors in the circuit. Determine the magnitude of input current i_I required to drive the output transistor into saturation. Determine the approximate input resistance of the circuit. *Answer: $R_{B1} = 4\ K\Omega$, $R_{B2} = 150\ \Omega$, $i_I = 0.425\ ma$, $R_{in} \simeq 1.6\ K\Omega$.*

Another type of d-c amplifier is illustrated in Fig. 9.17. In this amplifier the transistor types alternate from *n-p-n* to *p-n-p*. Although only two

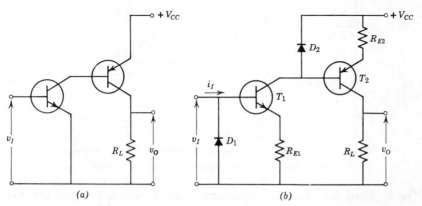

(a)   (b)

Fig. 9.17. A d-c amplifier using *n-p-n* and *p-n-p* transistors. (a) Basic circuit; (b) stabilized and linearized circuit.

stages are shown in Fig. 9.17, any desired number can be used. The collector current of the first amplifier is the base current of the second and so on, so the total current gain may be approximately equal to the product of the beta's of the transistors used. In contrast to the Darlington configuration, the input resistance of this amplifier is that of a single transistor and does not increase with the number of stages used. The thermal currents of each transistor are multiplied by all the transistors which follow. Therefore, at least the low-level stages should use silicon transistors.

The thermal currents can be shunted through reverse-biased diodes (Fig. 9.17b). In the circuit given, diode D_1 should have a saturation current equal to the I_{CO1} of transistor T_1 and similarly the saturation current of diode D_2 should match the I_{CO2} of transistor T_2. However, if the saturation current of diode D_2 were equal to the sum of I_{CO2} and $S_I I_{CO1}$ where S_I is the current stability factor of the first stage, the diode D_1 could be eliminated. Then the thermal currents of both stages would be shunted through D_2. The main problem may be locating a diode with the desired saturation current.

An alternate solution to the thermal stability problem is given in Fig. 9.18. In this circuit, the stabilizing diode has been replaced by transistor T_3. The thermal current which will flow through this transistor is $S_I I_{CO3}$, where S_I is the current stability factor of the circuit of T_3. But this stability factor can be adjusted over a wide range by varying the base circuit resistance R_B, as discussed in Chapter 5. Therefore, resistor R_B can

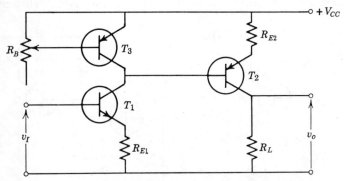

Fig. 9.18. A transistor thermal-stabilization circuit.

be adjusted for optimum temperature compensation, the resistors R_{E1} and R_{E2} are used to maintain fairly constant gain and input resistance over a wide range of input signal levels.

PROB. 9.18. A 2N1905 and a 2N2712 transistor are used in the circuit of Fig. 9.17b. The load resistance $R_L = 10\ \Omega$ and the emitter resistor $R_{E2} = 0.5\ \Omega$ and $V_{CC} = 20$ v. Determine a suitable value for R_{E1} and specify the desired saturation currents of diodes D_2 and D_1 at 25°C. Determine the values of the input current i_I and the input voltage v_I required to drive transistor T_2 into saturation.

The final type of d-c amplifier to be considered is the differential amplifier shown in Fig. 9.19. There are two basic types, balanced and unbalanced. In the balanced amplifier, the input signal comes from a symmetrical source such as a strain gage, a bridge circuit, a balanced transmission line and so forth, where one side of the signal is not referenced to ground. With this type of signal, the forward bias on one base is increased while the forward bias on the other is decreased. If the two transistors are matched and linear, the increase of emitter current in the one transistor will equal the decrease in the other and the total emitter current through R_E will be constant. Therefore, R_E, although very large, will not cause degeneration of the input signal since the emitter potential remains constant. In fact, if the transistors are not well matched, the emitter resistance R_E will tend to degenerate the higher gain transistor and regenerate the lower gain transistor so that their respective emitter currents will match. Of course the collector potential of one transistor decreases while the collector potential of the other increases. The output voltage, which is the difference between the collector potentials, may be fed to a balanced load or to another balanced amplifier. The balanced amplifier which follows should use the opposite type transistors (*p-n-p* to follow *n-p-n* etc.) for easy attainment of proper bias potentials.

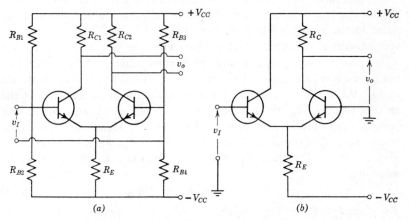

Fig. 9.19. A differential amplifier. (*a*) Balanced; (*b*) unbalanced.

From the foregoing observations and inspection of Fig. 9.19*a*, we can see that in comparison with a single transistor (similarly biased and with zero emitter circuit resistance) the balanced amplifier provides:

(a) The input resistance of the balanced amplifier is twice as high.
(b) The output resistance of the balanced amplifier is twice as high.
(c) The current and voltage gains are the same in both amplifiers.

The main advantage of the balanced amplifier in a d-c application is that common mode input signals do not alter the output signal. That is, any signal which causes the collector currents of both transistors to increase or decrease equally and simultaneously will have no effect on the output voltage, which is the difference of the collector potentials. Therefore, changes in I_{CO} and V_{BE} owing to temperature change do not affect the output, providing that the transistors are matched and maintained at the same temperature. Thus thermal currents are not passed from stage to stage. In addition, the individual transistors have excellent thermal stability because the emitter resistance R_E can be very large. Sometimes a transistor is used in place of R_E to provide very high dynamic resistance while permitting the desired Q-point currents to flow.

The circuit of Fig. 9.19a may be used to obtain an unbalanced output voltage, (or voltage with reference to ground) from either collector terminal. However, the output voltage is then reduced by a factor of two and the thermal component of collector current will not be cancelled in the output. However, the effect of variation of v_{BE} with temperature will tend to cancel and the current stability factor of the amplifier may be very good (low) because of the large usable value of R_E.

The circuit of Fig. 9.19b has both unbalanced input and output. The base of one transistor is used as the ground reference, although any other point in the circuit could have been grounded, providing that the d-c voltage shift at the input could be tolerated. The base bias of transistor T_1 is obtained through the driving source conductance. If the source does not have a conducting path, base bias resistors must be provided as shown in Fig. 9.19a. At first glance, the impression might be gained that the current through R_E will not be constant in the unbalanced circuit and serious degeneration will occur. However, the dynamic emitter-base resistance (h_{ib2}) of transistor T_2 is in parallel with R_E. Since h_{ib2} is normally very much smaller than R_E, the input resistance of the amplifier is, assuming $R_C \ll r_d$,

$$R_{in} \simeq h_{ie1} + (h_{fe1} + 1)h_{ib2} \qquad (9.71)$$

But if the transistors are alike $(h_{fe1} + 1)h_{ib2} = h_{ie1}$ and

$$R_{in} \simeq 2h_{ie1} \qquad (9.72)$$

Thus the input resistance of the unbalanced and balanced amplifiers is the same.

A balanced output could be obtained from the circuit of Fig. 9.19b if the collector circuits were arranged as shown in Fig. 9.19a. Since h_{ib} is very small in comparison with R_E, $\Delta i_{E2} \simeq -\Delta i_{E1}$ and equal collector circuit resistors would produce approximately balanced voltages of opposite polarity.

In the unbalanced circuit of Fig. 9.19b, the voltage and current gains are only one-half those of the balanced amplifier for the same collector circuit resistance because only one half of the available output is utilized. The thermal currents do not cancel in the output but the stability factor may be very good because of the large value of R_E and small value of R_B. As before, the effects of the thermal variation of V_{BE} tend to cancel. For example, if V_{BE1} and V_{BE2} decrease by equal amounts, the potential of the base of T_1 with respect to ground does not change. Observe that the unbalanced amplifier of Fig. 9.19b is a common collector amplifier directly coupled to a common-base amplifier.

An index of goodness for the difference amplifier is the *common mode rejection ratio*

$$CMRR = \frac{\text{Voltage Gain for Difference Signals}}{\text{Voltage Gain for Common Mode Signals}} \qquad (9.73)$$

Assuming that $R_C \ll 1/h_{oe}$ so that $G_i \simeq h_{fe}$, then the voltage gain for difference signals in the balanced amplifier is

$$G_{vD} \simeq G_i(2R_C/2h_{ie}) \simeq h_{fe}R_C/h_{ie} \qquad (9.74)$$

As previously discussed, the voltage gain of an amplifier with a large unbypassed emitter resistor ($R_E \gg r_e$) is approximately R_C/R_E. In the difference amplifier the effect of R_E is doubled because both emitter currents flow through R_E. Therefore, the common mode gain is

$$G_v = 2R_C/2R_E = R_C/R_E \qquad (9.75)$$

Substituting Eqs. 9.75 and 9.74 into Eq. 9.73.

$$CMRR = \frac{h_{fe}R_E}{h_{ie}} \qquad (9.76)$$

Transistor manufacturers provide two transistors in one case for use as difference amplifiers. In fact, these transistors are etched on a single silicon wafer so their characteristics will match and their temperatures will be as nearly the same as possible. Very low-drift difference amplifiers can be made from these units.

PROB. 9.19. Two 2N2712 transistors are used in the unbalanced differential amplifier circuit of Fig. 9.19b. The load resistor $R_C = 2.0$ KΩ and the supply voltage, $+V_{CC}$ to $-V_{CC}$, is 20 v.
(a) Determine suitable values for the emitter resistor R_E if V_{CC} to ground is 10 volts. *Answer:* $R_E = 2$ KΩ.
(b) Determine the approximate voltage gain, current gain, and current stability factor for the circuit.
(c) What is the common mode rejection ratio of this amplifier?

In addition to the foregoing d-c amplifier configurations, a circuit known as a "chopper" is also used. The crudest form of the chopper is shown in Fig. 9.20a. The switch S_1, which may be either motor driven, a vibrating reed, or an electronic switch, is switched very rapidly between positions 1 and 2. Switch S_1 must operate much faster than the highest frequency of the incoming signal v_I. As a result, the output signal is transformed into a series of pulses whose amplitude is determined by v_I (Fig. 9.20b). These pulses are amplified by conventional a-c amplifiers and then "detected" or rectified (see Chapter 14) to restore the low-frequency or d-c signal. The chopper eliminates most of the stabilization problems mentioned but introduces some new problems.

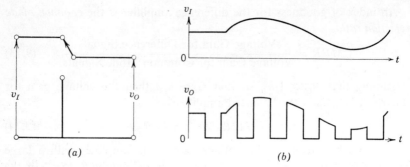

Fig. 9.20. A very crude chopper circuit. (*a*) Chopper circuit; (*b*) voltage waveforms.

The chopper circuits are beyond the scope of this text and consequently are introduced here so the reader will be aware of their existence. For a more detailed analysis the reader is referred to the literature.

9.6 NOISE IN AMPLIFIERS

Except in very broad band amplifiers where the available gain is determined by the gain-bandwidth product of the stage, the maximum useful power gain of an amplifier cascade is ultimately determined by the noise generated in the amplifier. For example, the question may arise as to whether an amplifier can be built that will amplify a 1-mv signal, with a specified source resistance, to a sufficiently high power level to operate a loud speaker or a pen recorder. Certainly enough cascaded stages can be used to provide any theoretical power gain. Excellent shielding and elimination of undesired coupling may be required to obtain stability at the required gain, but this requirement can almost always be met. The answer to the problem hinges basically on whether an amplifier is available which has sufficiently low internally generated noise so that the noise will not mask or obscure the signal.

Since the first stage of an amplifier amplifies its own noise as well as the input signal, the combined noise and signal power available as an input signal to the second stage is usually large in comparison with the noise power generated by the second stage. Therefore, the first stage is the crucial one in considering noise contribution in an amplifier. Inductive reasoning shows that if the stages of a cascade amplifier each generate equal noise power and have equal power gains, the contribution of a given stage to the total noise power in the output of the amplifier is $N_c = N_o/G_p^{(n-1)}$, where N_o is the noise generated in the amplifier, G_p is the power gain of each amplifier stage, and n is the numbered position of the stage (Fig. 9.1).

The purpose of this section is to discuss the sources of noise, associate these sources with tube and transistor amplifiers, and gain some insight into the design of low-noise amplifiers. A figure of merit for amplifier noise will be defined. Noise sources are usually classified in three categories: Thermal noise, diode noise, and $1/f$ noise.

Thermal noise, sometimes called Johnson noise, results from the random motion of charge carriers in a conductor. These random carriers produce a small net current in one direction one instant and in another direction the next instant. If these thermal currents are resolved into frequency components, they represent a continuous spectrum of essentially uniform

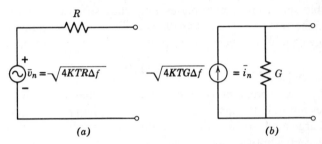

Fig. 9.21. Equivalent circuits for a thermal noise source. (*a*) Thévenin's; (*b*) Norton's.

amplitude from very low frequencies through the microwave range. Therefore, if a thermal noise signal were amplified by a noiseless amplifier, the noise power in the output of the amplifier would be proportional to the bandwidth of the amplifier.

Nyquist[7] postulated that the maximum noise power which can be transferred from a normal (noisy) resistor to a noiseless resistor is

$$p = kT \, \Delta f \qquad (9.77)$$

where k is Boltzmann's constant and Δf is the bandwidth in cycles persecond. This relationship has been verified experimentally and is not surprising since kT is the energy equivalent of absolute temperature T. Since maximum energy transfer occurs when the load resistance is equal to the source resistance, the noise equivalent circuits of Fig. 9.21 can be drawn. A simple calculation will show that either circuit will transfer the maximum power (under matched conditions) given by Eq. 9.77. Of course, there are no such things as noiseless resistors (unfortunately) and when two resistors of equal temperature are connected together there is no net transfer of energy. The equivalent noise source voltage of a

[7] H. Nyquist, "Thermal Agitation of Electric Charge in Conductors," *Phys. Rev.*, Vol. 32, p. 110, 1928.

resistor is, therefore

$$\bar{v}_n = \sqrt{4kTR\,\Delta f} \qquad (9.78)$$

where $\bar{v}_n$ is the rms value of the sum of all the noise voltage components in the frequency band Δf.

A diode (either thermionic or semiconductor) is a noise source because each emitted electron or injected carrier is a random event and small random fluctuations occur in the diode current which we have heretofore considered constant if the bias is fixed. These current fluctuations, like thermal noise, have a uniform and continuous frequency spectrum and therefore both diode and thermal noise are known as *white* noise. (In the visible spectrum, a continuous frequency spectrum produces white light.) Schottky postulated that the rms diode noise current in a given frequency band Δf can be represented by a current generator of magnitude

$$\bar{i}_n = \sqrt{2qI\,\Delta f} \qquad (9.79)$$

where I is the average or Q-point value of the diode current. Equation 9.79 does not hold for space-charge limited thermionic diodes because the space charge tends to smooth out or alter the randomness with which the electrons were emitted from the cathode.

The third type of noise is known as $1/f$ noise because its magnitude is approximately inversely proportional to frequency. This type of noise is effective only at lower audio frequencies, hundreds of Hertz or less. This $1/f$ noise is caused by a phenomenon known as *cathode flicker* in vacuum tubes, and results primarily from surface leakage in transistors and semiconductor diodes. This type of noise varies quite widely among units of the same type device and has not been theoretically characterized. Recent improvements in transistor surface treatment have greatly reduced the $1/f$ noise in comparison with earlier models. In applications which require a low noise amplifier the transistor or tube should be hand picked for low $1/f$ noise.

A noise figure of merit for an amplifier is the *spot noise figure F*, which is the ratio of the noise power delivered by an amplifier (over a narrow frequency band) to a load to the noise power that would be delivered if the only noisy component were the source resistance R_s at $T_o = 290°K$ (i.e., 290°K is defined as the standard reference temperature). Thus an amplifier which contributes no noise to the signal being amplified has a noise figure $F = 1$ (or $F = 0$ db). The amplifier always contributes some noise; therefore, F is always greater than 1, or greater than 0 db.

The noise contributed by an amplifier can be represented by an equivalent rms noise voltage $\bar{v}_n$ at the input of the amplifier, as shown in Fig. 9.22. The equivalent noise voltage $\bar{v}_n$ includes the noise generated by the source resistance R_s. Therefore, the resistance R_s in Fig. 9.22 is noiseless. The rms noise voltage $\bar{v}_n$ can be characterized as the noise voltage produced by a resistance R_n at 290°K. Then the noise figure of the amplifier is R_n/R_s, as is shown by the following relationships. First, the rms input noise current is

$$\bar{i}_n = \frac{\bar{v}_n}{R_s + R_i} = \frac{\sqrt{4kTR_n\,\Delta f}}{R_s + R_i} \tag{9.80}$$

where R_i is the input resistance of the transistor. The rms noise output voltage is

$$\bar{v}_{no} = i_n G_i R_L = \frac{\sqrt{4kTR_n\,\Delta f}}{R_s + R_i} G_i R_L \tag{9.81}$$

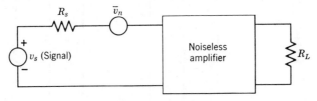

Fig. 9.22. The representation of amplifier noise by an equivalent noise source.

The rms noise voltage in the output which results only from the resistance of the source is

$$\bar{v}_{nos} = \frac{\sqrt{4kTR_s\,\Delta f}}{R_s + R_i} G_i R_L \tag{9.82}$$

The noise power in the load is $\bar{v}_{no}{}^2/R_L$, whereas if the amplifier were noiseless the noise power in the load would be $(\bar{v}_{nos})^2/R_L$. By definition, the spot noise figure is the ratio of these two noise powers. Then (using Eqs. 9.82 and 9.81, the spot noise figure is

$$F = \frac{\bar{v}_{no}{}^2}{(\bar{v}_{nos})^2} = \frac{R_n}{R_s} \tag{9.83}$$

Observe from Eq. 9.83 that the noise figure F is independent of the load resistance R_L. Also, the input resistance R_i does not appear explicitly in the equation. However, the equivalent noise resistance R_n is a function of the transistor input resistance.

The noise sources of a transistor will be considered next, then a relationship for the equivalent noise resistance R_n will be obtained. There are two major sources of noise in a transistor—the diode noise of the emitter current which is injected into the base region and the effective ohmic base resistance r_b. The emitter diode current divides into the collector

current I_C and the base current I_B as discussed in Chapter 4. Thus three
noise generators are shown in the hybrid-π equivalent circuit of Fig. 9.23
to represent these major noise sources. The equivalent noise voltage of
the driving source is also shown. Minor noise sources which are not
shown include the ohmic resistance of the emitter and collector regions
and the saturation (diode) currents I_{C0} and I_{E0} which flow across the
collector and emitter junctions, respectively. These sources are all
negligible, providing that the Q-point currents are large in comparison
with the thermal saturation currents, which may not be the situation in a
germanium transistor at moderate or high temperatures.

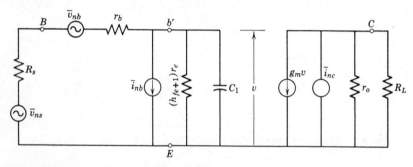

Fig. 9.23. The hybrid-π equivalent circuit of a transistor showing the major noise
sources.

Observe from Fig. 9.23 that the source noise voltage $\bar{v}_{ns}$, as well as the
transistor noise sources $\bar{v}_{nb}$ and $\bar{i}_{nb}$, must be amplified by the transistor
before their noise contributions can be compared with the collector
current noise component $\bar{i}_{nc}$. Also, Eq. 9.78 showed that a noise voltage
is proportional to the square root of a resistance and Eq. 9.79 showed that
a noise current is proportional to the square root of a quiescent diode
current. Therefore, the following conclusions can be drawn:

   (a) The contribution of the collector current noise component $\bar{i}_{nc}$ is
      small if I_C is small and the transistor current gain is high.
   (b) The contribution of the base current noise component $\bar{i}_{nb}$ is small
      if the transistor current gain is high (thus permitting small I_B) and
      I_{EO} is small.
   (c) The contribution of the base resistance noise component is small
      if r_b is small in comparison with the source resistance R_s.

From these conclusions, it seems clear that a silicon transistor with high
h_{FE} at a low value of I_C would have a low noise figure when driven from
a high-resistance source ($R_s \gg r_b$).

In order to determine the noise figure for a specific transistor operated at a given Q point and driven by a specified source, a relationship will be developed for the equivalent noise resistance R_n. First, an equivalent noise voltage $\bar{v}_n$ in series with R_s (see Fig. 9.22) will be determined which will produce the same effect at the output as all the noise generators of Fig. 9.23 combined. In combining noise sources, it should be noted that independent sources are uncorrelated (that is, there is no fixed relationship between the phases of their relative frequency components) and, therefore, the total rms voltage is the square root of the sum of the squares of the individual rms contributions. Then

$$\bar{v}_n{}^2 = \bar{v}_{ns}{}^2 + \bar{v}_{nb}{}^2 + (\bar{v}'_{nb})^2 + (\bar{v}'_{nc})^2 \qquad (9.84)$$

The voltage source $(\bar{v}'_{nb})$ results from the current source i_{nb} of Fig. 9.23. This current source can be transformed to an equivalent voltage source to

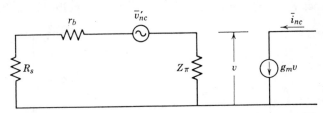

Fig. 9.24. An equivalent circuit used to determine $\bar{v}'_{nc}$ in terms of $\bar{i}_{nc}$.

the left of the imaginary terminals $b'E$ in Fig. 9.23 by obtaining the open circuit voltage at the terminals $b'E$ with the other voltage sources turned off. Then,

$$\bar{v}'_{nb} = \bar{i}_{nb}(r_b + R_s) \qquad (9.85)$$

The voltage source $(\bar{v}'_{nc})$ is the voltage required to produce $\bar{i}_{nc}$ in the output. Figure 9.24 is drawn as an aid in determining this equivalent voltage. From this circuit is it seen that

$$\bar{i}_{nc} = \frac{\bar{v}'_{nc} Z_\pi g_m}{R_s + r_b + Z_\pi} \qquad (9.86)$$

where Z_π is the parallel combination of $(h_{fe} + 1)r_b$ and $1/j\omega C_1$. Then

$$\bar{v}'_{nc} = \frac{\bar{i}_{nc}(R_s + r_b + Z_\pi)}{Z_\pi g_m} \qquad (9.87)$$

Substituting Eqs. 9.87 and 9.85 into Eq. 9.84, $\bar{v}_n{}^2$ becomes

$$\bar{v}_n{}^2 = \bar{v}_{ns}{}^2 + \bar{v}_{nb}{}^2 + \bar{i}_{nb}{}^2(r_b + R_s)^2 + \frac{\bar{i}_{nc}{}^2(R_s + r_b + Z_\pi)^2}{(g_m Z_\pi)^2} \qquad (9.88)$$

The equivalent resistances and diode Q-point currents can be substituted for the voltage and current sources. Then Eq. 9.88 becomes

$$4kTR_n\,\Delta f = 4kTR_s\,\Delta f + 4kTr_b\,\Delta f$$
$$+ 2qI_B\,\Delta f(r_b + R_s)^2 + \frac{2qI_C\,\Delta f(R_s + r_b + Z_\pi)^2}{(g_m Z_\pi)^2} \quad (9.89)$$

and

$$R_n = R_s + r_b + \frac{q}{2kT}I_B(r_b + R_s)^2 + \frac{q}{2kT}I_C\frac{(R_s + r_b + Z_\pi)^2}{(g_m Z_\pi)^2} \quad (9.90)$$

Then,

$$F = 1 + \frac{r_b}{R_s} + \frac{q}{2kT}I_B\frac{(r_b + R_s)^2}{R_s} + \frac{q}{2kT}I_C\frac{(R_s + r_b + Z_\pi)^2}{R_s(g_m Z_\pi)^2} \quad (9.91)$$

The right-hand term of Eq. 9.91 is a function of frequency because Z_π, which includes $1/j\omega C_1$, is a function of frequency. As the frequency approaches f_β and Z_π decreases significantly, the noise factor begins to

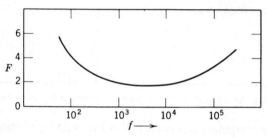

Fig. 9.25. Transistor noise as a function of frequency.

increase, since Z_π is in the denominator. However, since Z_π also appears in the numerator as a sum with R_s and r_b, the noise factor will not increase appreciably until Z_π becomes smaller than $R_s + r_b$, which may be at a frequency considerably above f_β, depending on R_s. A sketch of noise figure as a function of frequency for a typical transistor is given in Fig. 9.25. The $1/f$ noise accounts for the rise at low frequencies. Equation 9.91 shows that although the noise contribution of r_b is decreased as R_s is increased, the contributions from both the base and collector components of emitter current increase as R_s is increased. Therefore, there is an optimum value of R_s for a given set of transistor parameters. This optimum source resistance is the same order of magnitude as the input resistance of the transistor. Note also that the last term of Eq. 9.91 has the product $g_m Z_\pi$ in its denominator. At frequencies below f_β, Z_π is approximately equal to $(h_{fe} + 1)r_e$, and r_e is approximately $1/g_m$. Therefore, an improvement in noise factor will occur as I_C is reduced until a point is reached where $(h_{fe} + 1)^2$ decreases as rapidly as I_C.

Transistor manufacturers frequently supply constant noise figure contours for their low-noise transistor types. These contours give optimum values of quiescent current as a function of driving source resistance (Fig. 9.26).

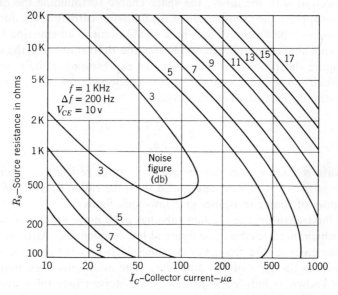

Fig. 9.26. Constant noise-figure contours for a typical low-noise transistor (2N2443).

PROB. 9.20. A given silicon transistor has $r_b = 200\ \Omega$, $h_{fe} = 150$, $h_{FE} = 100$ at the Q point $V_{CE} = 5$ volts, $I_C = 1$ ma and the frequency 1 KHz. Determine the 1 KHz spot noise figure at this Q point if the driving source resistance is 2 KΩ. Assume that the temperature is 300°K. The beta cutoff frequency is 100 kc. *Answer: F = 1.6.*

PROB. 9.21. The transistor of Prob. 9.20 has the Q-point collector current reduced to 0.1 ma, at which $h_{fe} = 90$ and $h_{FE} = 60$. Assuming all other parameters remain unchanged, determine the 1 KHz noise figure at this Q point.

PROB. 9.22. Determine the spot noise figure of the transistor of Prob. 9.20 at the $I_C = 1$ ma Q point at $f = 500$ KHz.

The field-effect transistor has only the channel resistance and surface leakage as principal sources of noise, since the only diode current is the thermal saturation current of the reverse biased gate diode. Therefore, the noise figure of a silicon FET may be very low. Since the diode current is very small, the medium frequency (1 KHz) noise figure is determined primarily by the ratio r_{ch}/R_s where r_{ch} is the channel resistance. A typical value for F is 1.1 for high values of source resistance (of the order of 1 megΩ). The $1/f$ noise is present, however, and the noise figure rises at low frequencies. Also, there is some diode current, so the noise figure increases as the power gain decreases at high frequencies.

The triode vacuum tube has primarily diode noise which results from the random electron emission from the cathode. However, as mentioned in connection with the diode, the space charge surrounding the cathode tends to suppress the randomness of the emission current and reduces the tube noise well below the value which would occur in an emission limited tube. This smoothing effect complicates the derivation of a theoretical noise figure determination. However, an expression for the equivalent grid circuit noise resistance has been developed[8] for the triode and experimentally verified. This expression is

$$R_n = \frac{2.5}{g_m} \qquad (9.92)$$

This noise resistance does not include the source resistance. Therefore, the noise figure F would be determined from the ratio $(R_s + R_n)/R_s$, and high values of source resistance give low-noise figures.

Like the transistor, the vacuum tube has a $1/f$ noise known as cathode flicker which increases the noise figure at low frequencies. Also, the noise figure increases as the frequency becomes high and the electron transit time reduces the gain of the amplifier. The additional high frequency noise is known as induced grid noise. Low-noise triode tubes and low-noise transistors have noise figures of approximately equal magnitude.

The tetrode or pentode tube has a source of noise in addition to those found in triodes. This noise, known as *partition noise*, results from the random division of the space current between the screen grid and the plate. The noise of a tetrode or pentode can be expressed as an equivalent grid circuit resistance by the following equation

$$R_n \simeq \frac{2.5}{g_m} + \frac{20I_{G2}}{I_K g_m} \qquad (9.93)$$

where I_K is the average cathode current. The second term on the right-hand side of Eq. 9.93 accounts for the partition noise.

The noise generated by a vacuum tube may be much higher than the values obtained by the foregoing equations because of defects in an individual tube or circuit. For example, gas in a tube causes random collisions which increase the noise. Also, faulty electrode contacts may generate noise. Heater-cathode interaction may cause noise and hum unless the bias between the heater and the cathode prevents an exchange

---

[8] K. R. Spangenberg, *Vacuum Tubes*, McGraw-Hill, New York, 1948, pp. 310–312.

of charge carriers between the two. Usually low-noise tubes are hand picked after noise tests have been made.

A noise test may be easily conducted on an amplifier if a noise diode is used as a signal source. The noise diode is connected in parallel with the desired source resistance as shown in Fig. 9.27a. The noise diode must have a high internal impedance compared with R_s in order to act as a true current source. Therefore, a temperature limited vacuum diode is usually used. First the noise output voltage V_{no} is measured with an rms activated meter while the noise diode is turned off. Then the output noise power results only from the equivalent amplifier noise

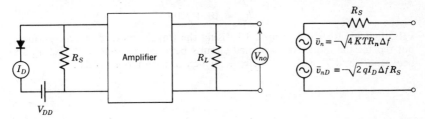

Fig. 9.27. A circuit used to determine the noise figure of an amplifier. (a) Block diagram; (b) equivalent input circuit.

source $\bar{v}_n$ (Fig. 9.27b). Next, the diode current is increased by adjusting the supply voltage V_{DD} until the output voltage increases by a factor of $\sqrt{2}$, which indicates that the noise power in the output has doubled and the Thévenin's equivalent voltage of the diode noise source $\bar{v}_{nD}$ is equal to equivalent noise voltage $\bar{v}_n$. Then, from Fig. 9.27b,

$$2qI_D \, \Delta f R_s^2 = 4kTR_n \, \Delta f \qquad (9.94)$$

and

$$R_n = \frac{qI_D R_s^2}{2kT} \qquad (9.95)$$

But the noise figure F is

$$F = \frac{R_n}{R_s} = \frac{qI_D R_s}{2kT} \qquad (9.96)$$

At the standard reference temperature $T = 295°K$, $q/2kT = 20$, and

$$F = 20I_D R_s \qquad (9.97)$$

The noise figure obtained by the procedure described will give an integrated noise figure over the pass band of the amplifier or meter, whichever is less. A filter can be placed in series with the output meter to determine the spot noise figure in the pass band of the filter.

PROB. 9.23. A given dynamic microphone has the following specifications: $R_o = 10 \text{ K}\Omega$; output voltage = -56 db below 1 v open circuit; frequency response = 40 to 15,000 Hz. Design an amplifier, using 2N2712 transistors, that will provide 1.0 v rms across a 10 KΩ load. Provide a pass band of approximately 20 to 20,000 Hz in the amplifier. Determine the approximate signal to noise ratio for your amplifier and express the noise as a number of db below the signal. Neglect $1/f$ noise.

PROB. 9.24. Repeat Example 9.2 for transistors with the following characteristics:

$$h_{ie} = 2000 \ \Omega$$
$$h_{re} = j5 \times 10^{-3}$$
$$h_{fe} = 50$$
$$h_{oe} = 10 + j20$$

PROB. 9.25. Repeat Example 9.2 (using the transistors listed in the example) but replace the inductively coupled circuits between transistors T_1 and T_2 and between T_2 and T_3 with tuned circuits which contain tapped coils.

10

Large-Signal Amplifiers

A typical amplifier consists of several stages of amplification. Most of these stages are small-signal, low-power devices. For these stages efficiency is usually not of major importance, distortion is negligible, and the equivalent circuits accurately predict their behavior (Chapters 7 to 9). In contrast, the final stage of an amplifier (and in some cases additional driver stages) is usually required to furnish appreciable signal power to its load. Typical loads include loudspeakers, antennas, positioning devices, and so on. These amplifiers are commonly called power amplifiers. Because of this relatively high power level, the efficiency of the power amplifier is important. Also, distortion becomes a problem because the amplifier parameters vary appreciably over the signal cycle. For this reason, the equivalent circuits are only rough approximations and graphical methods assume increased importance.

10.1 CLASSIFICATION OF LARGE-SIGNAL AMPLIFIERS

Many of the large-signal amplifiers are driven so hard by the input signal that amplifier current is either cut off or in the saturation region during a large portion of the input cycle. Consequently, a system for designating various operating conditions has been evolved. This designating system is

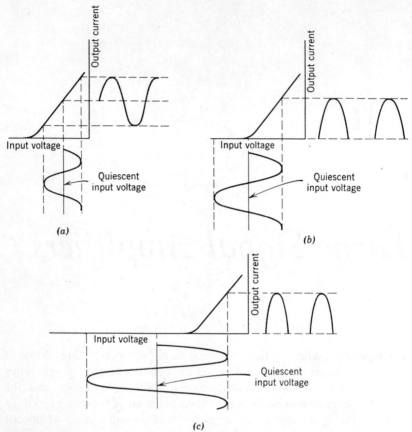

Fig. 10.1. Classification of large-signal amplifiers. (*a*) Class *A* amplifier; (*b*) class *B* amplifier; (*c*) class *C* amplifier.

illustrated in Fig. 10.1. In this diagram, the input signal is assumed to have a sinusoidal waveform. The dynamic transfer characteristics are used to relate the input voltage and output current. Thus, if the output current flows for 360° of the input cycle as shown in Fig. 10.1*a*, the device is designated as a class *A* amplifier. Similarly, if output current flows for more than 180° but less than 360° of the input cycle, the device is called a class *AB* amplifier (not shown). When the output current flows for approximately 180° of the input cycle as shown in Fig. 10.1*b*, the device is biased at cutoff and is designated as a class *B* amplifier. Finally, if the output current flows for less than 180° of the input cycle as illustrated in Fig. 10.1*c*, the device is referred to as a class *C* amplifier.[1] In addition to

[1] The class *C* amplifier is normally used only in tuned amplifiers and therefore will not be considered in this chapter. However, the chapter on large-signal tuned amplifiers will discuss class *C* amplifiers.

the foregoing designations, the subscript 1 is given to a vacuum tube circuit if the control grid is never driven positive. If the control grid is driven positive, a subscript 2 is given to the designation. Obviously, the subscripts have no meaning when applied to transistors, since the transistor base always draws current unless the transistor is cut off.

From the foregoing designations, the amplifiers that have been considered in the small-signal devices are class A_1 amplifiers for vacuum tubes and class A amplifiers for transistors. These amplifiers are usually referred to as class A with the subscript understood. Similarly, a vacuum tube that is biased at cutoff but that has a large enough input signal to drive the control grid positive is referred to as a class B_2 amplifier. For class B amplifiers with no subscripts, the amplifier is *assumed* to be class B_2.

PROB. 10.1. A 6J5 tube is connected through a resistive load with $R_L = 20,000$ Ω to a 300-v V_{PP} supply. What class of operation does this tube exhibit if (a) $v_I = -6 + 5 \sin \omega t$; (b) $v_I = -6 + 7 \sin \omega t$; (c) $v_I = -18 + 16 \sin \omega t$; (d) $v_I = -30 + 34 \sin \omega t$.

PROB. 10.2. Sketch the output waveforms for the input signals listed in Prob. 10.1. The characteristic curves of a 6J5 tube with positive as well as negative control grid voltage is given in Fig. 10.2.

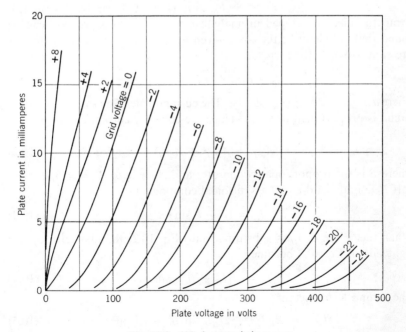

Fig. 10.2. 6J5 characteristic curves.

10.2 DISTORTION AND POWER OUTPUT CONSIDERATIONS

As already noted, the equivalent circuits provide accurate solutions to transistor and vacuum tube problems when the signal magnitudes are small. Unfortunately, as the magnitude of the signal increases, the accuracy of the equivalent circuits decreases. This loss of accuracy is due to the fact that the circuit parameters (r_p, g_m, h_{ie}, h_{fe}, etc.) are *not linear*. (This nonlinear behavior has been emphasized by Figs. 5.22 and 5.26.) As a result of these nonlinear elements, graphical solutions must be used if accurate results are desired and a large signal is present.

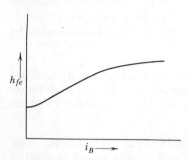

Fig. 10.3. A typical curve of h_{fe} vs i_B.

In order to gain a clearer insight into the effects of nonlinear parameters, we will consider the collector current of a transistor which has a nonlinear h_{fe}. Curves depicting the variation of the h parameters with emitter current or collector voltage (similar to those in Fig. 5.22 or Fig. 3.2) are often given by the transistor manufacturer. Since i_C depends on base current, a curve of h_{fe} vs i_B (Fig. 10.3) can be determined. From the ideas developed in analytical geometry, an expression can be found that will describe the curve given in Fig. 10.3. In general, this expression will have the form

$$h_{fe} = a_0 + a_1 i_B + a_2 i_B{}^2 + a_3 i_B{}^3 + \cdots \tag{10.1}$$

where a_0, a_1, a_2, etc. are constants. The current which flows in the collector circuit is proportional to $h_{fe} i_B$. Thus, the collector current can be written as

$$i_C = B h_{fe} i_B = A_0 i_B + A_1 i_B{}^2 + A_2 i_B{}^3 + A_3 i_B{}^4 + \cdots \tag{10.2}$$

where B is the proportionality constant and $A_0 = a_0 B$, $A_1 = a_1 B$, etc.

If i_B contains a d-c and a sinusoidal component

$$i_B = I_B + I_b \sin \omega t \tag{10.3}$$

When this value of i_B is substituted into Eq. 10.2, the first term on the right side of Eq. 10.2 becomes

$$A_0 i_B = A_0 I_B + A_0 I_b \sin \omega t \tag{10.4}$$

The second term becomes

$$A_1 i_B{}^2 = A_1 (I_B{}^2 + 2 I_B I_b \sin \omega t + I_b{}^2 \sin^2 \omega t) \tag{10.5}$$

However, a trigonometry identity states

$$\sin^2 x = \frac{(1 - \cos 2x)}{2} \tag{10.6}$$

Thus, Eq. 10.5 can be written as

$$A_1 i_B{}^2 = A_1 \left(I_B{}^2 + \frac{I_b{}^2}{2} + 2I_B I_b \sin \omega t - \frac{I_b{}^2}{2} \cos 2\omega t \right) \tag{10.7}$$

From Eq. 10.4, the $A_0 i_B$ term produces a d-c component and a sinusoidal component in the collector current. From Eq. 10.7, the $A_1 i_B{}^2$ term produces a d-c component, a sinusoidal component, and *a second harmonic component* in the collector current. The $A_2 i_B{}^3$ term will produce d-c, sinusoidal, second-harmonic, and third-harmonic terms. It follows that the higher terms will produce higher harmonics. The production of these harmonic terms is referred to as *distortion*. The effect of second harmonic distortion on the output waveform is shown in Fig. 10.4. Notice how the output signal has been modified or *distorted* from the original sine wave.

If h_{fe} (or g_m of a tube) were the only nonlinear parameter, it would be possible to use an equivalent circuit with a nonlinear h_{fe} (or g_m) and still to obtain results without too much complication. However, since not only h_{fe} and g_m but also h_{ie}, h_{oe}, h_{re}, μ, and r_p are nonlinear, the equivalent circuits become too complex to be useful. Thus, it is usually much easier to use a graphical solution for nonlinear operation.

It is interesting to note that some of the nonlinearities in tubes and transistors are of compensating nature. Thus, for a vacuum tube amplifier (Fig. 5.26), g_m decreases as the control grid becomes more negative. However, note that r_p increases as the control grid becomes more negative. Thus, the shunting effect of r_p decreases and a larger portion of the current from $g_m v_g$ goes through the load resistor. These effects do not completely cancel, but at least the gain does not decrease as much as the decreasing g_m may indicate. Similar compensating effects will also be noted in transistor amplifiers in the next section.

PROB. 10.3. Find an expression similar to Eq. 10.7 for the term $A_3 i_B{}^4$. Assume $i_B = I_B + I_b \sin \omega t$.

As indicated, the output current waveform may contain a number of harmonics in addition to the fundamental component. Also, if the load is a pure resistance, the output voltage has the same waveform and hence the same harmonic content as the output current. Thus the output current (or voltage) may be expressed as a Fourier series. This series will

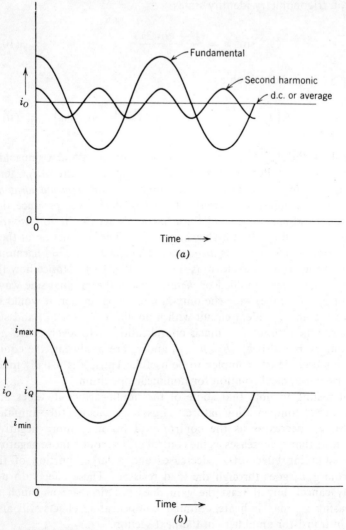

Fig. 10.4. The effect of second harmonic distortion. (*a*) Frequency components; (*b*) Total current.

have only cosine terms if the time reference ($t = 0$) is chosen at a point of symmetry as shown in Fig. 10.4. Then

$$i_O = I_0 + I_1 \cos \omega t + I_2 \cos 2\omega t + I_3 \cos 3\omega t + \cdots \qquad (10.8)$$

The values of I_0, I_1, I_2, etc. can be determined from a graphical plot of the output waveform. In fact, some of the harmonics may be deduced to be negligible by an examination of the output waveform. For example, waveforms with the general shape shown in Fig. 10.4 can be considered to have predominantly second harmonic distortion because successive half cycles are dissimilar. Thus waveforms of this general shape can be approximately represented by the equation

$$i_O = I_0 + I_1 \cos \omega t + I_2 \cos 2\omega t \tag{10.9}$$

where I_1 represents the peak value of the fundamental component and I_2 represents the peak value of the second harmonic component. Now there are three unknown quantities I_0, I_1, and I_2 which must be determined, so three independent equations involving these three unknowns must be found. For example, at time $t = 0$, (Fig. 10.4) $i_O = i_{max}$ and Eq. 10.9 becomes

$$i_{max} = I_0 + I_1 + I_2 \tag{10.10}$$

Similarly, at time $t = \pi/2\omega$, $i_O = i_Q$ and Eq. 10.9 becomes

$$i_Q = I_0 - I_2 \tag{10.11}$$

Also, at time $t = \pi/\omega$, $i_O = i_{min}$ and Eq. 10.9 becomes

$$i_{min} = I_0 - I_1 + I_2 \tag{10.12}$$

These three equations can now be solved simultaneously to yield the values of I_0, I_1, and I_2 in terms of the graphically determined values of i_{max}, i_Q, and i_{min}.

$$I_1 = \frac{i_{max} - i_{min}}{2} \tag{10.13}$$

$$I_2 = \frac{i_{max} + i_{min} - 2i_Q}{4} \tag{10.14}$$

$$I_0 = \frac{i_{max} + i_{min} + 2i_Q}{4} \tag{10.15}$$

The percentage of second harmonic distortion in the amplifier is

$$\% \sec = \frac{I_2}{I_1} \times 100 \tag{10.16}$$

PROB. 10.4. Obtain Eqs. 10.13, 10.14, and 10.15 from Eqs. 10.10, 10.11, and 10.12.

PROB. 10.5. One section of a 12AT7 triode is connected as a common emitter amplifier with a load resistance R_L of 20 KΩ. The V_{PP} supply is +300 volts. If $v_I = -2 + 2 \sin \omega t$, find the percentage of second harmonic distortion in this amplifier. *Answer: 9.45% second harmonic.*

A second type of distortion which commonly occurs in push-pull amplifiers (which are discussed later in this chapter) is shown in Fig. 10.5. In this type, successive half cycles are similar, so even harmonics are negligible, but the peaks of the wave are flattened, so the third harmonic may be assumed to be the principal distortion component as shown. Then, with the time reference selected as shown in Fig. 10.5, only sine terms appear and the output current may be represented approximately by the series

$$i_O = I_0 + I_1 \sin \omega t + I_3 \sin 3\omega t \tag{10.17}$$

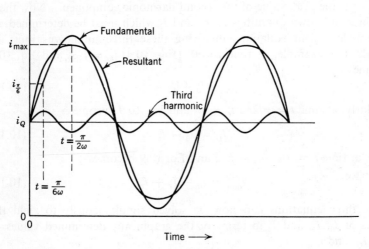

Fig. 10.5. Typical third harmonic distortion.

Again, there are three unknowns, so three equations must be written. At time $t = 0$, $i_O = i_Q$ and Eq. 10.17 becomes

$$i_Q = I_0 \tag{10.18}$$

At $t = \pi/6\omega$, $i_O = i_{\pi/6}$ (See Fig. 10.5) and Eq. 10.17 becomes

$$i_{\pi/6} = I_0 + \frac{I_1}{2} + I_3 \tag{10.19}$$

where $i_{\pi/6}$ is the output current that flows when the input quantity is one-half its maximum value, which occurs at $\pi/6$ radians since $\sin \pi/6 = \frac{1}{2}$. At $t = \pi/2\omega$, $i_O = i_{\max}$ and Eq. 10.17 becomes

$$i_{\max} = I_0 + I_1 - I_3 \tag{10.20}$$

Equation 10.18 determines the value of I_0. When this value is substituted into Eqs. 10.19 and 10.20, these equations can be solved simultaneously for I_1 and I_3. Thus

$$I_1 = \frac{2(i_{max} + i_{\pi/6} - 2i_Q)}{3} \tag{10.21}$$

and

$$I_3 = \frac{2i_{\pi/6} - i_{max} - i_Q}{3} \tag{10.22}$$

PROB. 10.6. Derive Eqs. 10.21 and 10.22 from Eqs. 10.18, 10.19, and 10.20.

The foregoing method of analysis can be used to obtain any given number of harmonics in the output of an amplifier. Of course, the number of independent equations found must be equal to the number of significant frequency components in the output current (or voltage) waveform. Equations which include all components through the fourth harmonic may be found in the literature.[2]

The ideal large-signal amplifier should have high-power output and low signal distortion. Unfortunately, these two characteristics are not compatible. Hence, a compromise must be reached between maximum power output and minimum distortion. Typical plots of power output and distortion vs load resistance R_L for vacuum tube amplifiers are shown in Fig. 10.6. (As will be found in Section 10.3, the distortion of a transistor amplifier depends on the impedance of the current source driving the transistor as well as on the load resistance.) In both cases in Fig. 10.6, the distortion is quite high for maximum power output. However, the distortion can be reduced to acceptable levels by a modest reduction of the power output.

Figure 10.7a and Fig. 10.7b show why the power output and the distortion of vacuum tube amplifiers vary with the load resistance in the manner given in Fig. 10.6. The assumption is made that the grid voltage varies between zero volts and the cutoff voltage. Also, the plate voltage V_{PP} is assumed fixed. Since the signal power output is proportional to the product of the plate voltage variation and the plate current variation, the power delivered to the load is proportional to the area of the right triangle which has the load line as its hypotenuse. Thus, for the smallest load resistance shown in Fig. 10.7, the power output is represented by the area of the triangle $V_{PP} - A - A'$. Notice that for the tube amplifiers, the power output increases as the load resistance is increased, and the load line is shifted from the position $V_{PP} - A$ to the position $V_{PP} - B$. A further increase of load resistance causes the load line to shift toward the position $V_{PP} - C$ and the power output decreases accordingly.

[2] F. E. Terman, *Radio Engineers Handbook*, McGraw-Hill, New York, 1943.

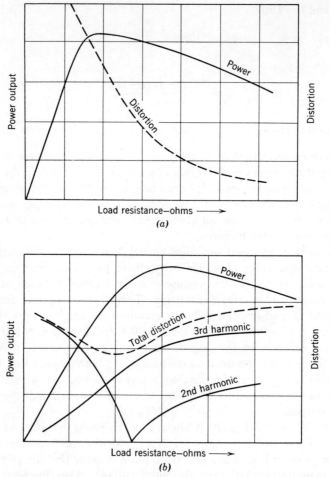

Fig. 10.6. Power output and distortion vs R_L for some electronic devices. (*a*) Triode tube; (*b*) beam power tube.

For the triode tube the plate current swing continually decreases as the load resistance increases. Therefore, the variation of the tube parameters and hence the distortion continually decreases as the load resistance increases. On the other hand, the plate current swing of the pentode does not decrease appreciably until the load line passes through the knee of the $v_G = 0$ curve. However, the second harmonic distortion does decrease as the knee is approached because the spacing of the plate characteristic curves becomes more uniform. The second harmonic actually approaches zero as the load line approaches the knee of the $v_G = 0$ curve. The dynamic transfer characteristic would appear as a slightly *s*-shaped, almost symmetrical curve for this value of load resistance. As the load resistance of the pentode is further increased, the distortion increases while the power output decreases, because the output wave is severely flattened on the positive half-cycle of the grid voltage swing.

An upper current limit for the transistor amplifier is often specified, but this limit is usually so high that the collector dissipation determines the

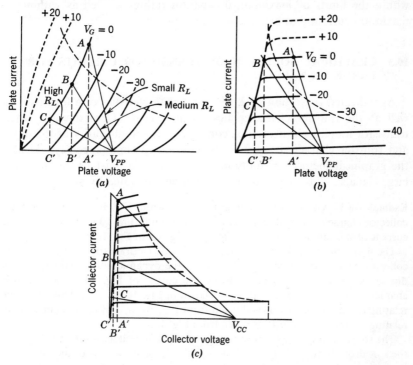

Fig. 10.7. The effect of R_L on distortion and power output. (*a*) Triode tube; (*b*) pentode tube; (*c*) transistor.

minimum value of load resistance that can be used. Therefore, the power output of the transistor amplifier increases as the load resistance is decreased, the limit being set by the dissipation capabilities of the transistor. This increasing power output with decreasing load resistance appears to be contrary to the maximum power transfer theorem. However, this theorem is not being violated because the power of the driving source must be increased to obtain the higher power output. The power gain, which *is* maximum under matched conditions, actually decreases as the load resistance is decreased. Methods of analyzing distortion in transistor amplifiers will be given in Section 10.4.

When power output as a function of load resistance is considered, the tube and transistor cases differ primarily because of the maximum positive grid voltage limit imposed in the vacuum tube case. If the grid could be driven positive as far as desired, the upper plate current limit would be determined only by the plate dissipation capability of the tube. This statement may be verified by the observation of Fig. 10.7a and Fig. 10.7b.

In all amplifiers, care should be exercised to confine the operation within the limits of maximum dissipation ratings as well as within the maximum current and maximum voltage ratings.

10.3 GRAPHICAL SOLUTION OF TRANSISTOR CIRCUITS FOR LARGE SIGNALS

As indicated in Section 10.2, the input characteristics of a transistor as well as the transfer characteristics are nonlinear. Consequently, when transistor amplifier distortion is considered, the nonlinearity of the input and transfer characteristics must be considered simultaneously. Hence, the graphical method of solution previously used must be modified for large signals. This modified method will be illustrated by an example.

Example 10.1. A transistor is connected as shown in Fig. 10.8. The input and collector characteristics of this transistor are given in Fig. 10.9. Plot the output current of this circuit if the input signal is as given in Fig. 10.8.

The first step in the solution of this problem is to draw the load line on the collector characteristics of Fig. 10.9. Then the dynamic input characteristic is drawn as shown in Fig. 10.9b. From the curves of Fig. 10.9, the dynamic characteristic curves can be drawn as shown in Fig. 10.10. The dynamic curve relating i_C and i_B (curve A) is derived from Fig. 10.9a, and the dynamic curve relating i_B and v_B (curve B) is taken from Fig. 10.9b.

The source voltage v_I is shown in Fig. 10.10. This voltage must be reduced by the $i_B R$ drop through R_{gen} to find the actual voltage at the base of the transistor.

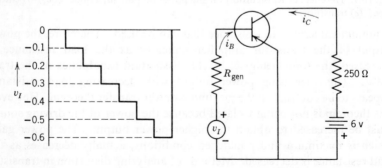

Fig. 10.8. A transistor amplifier.

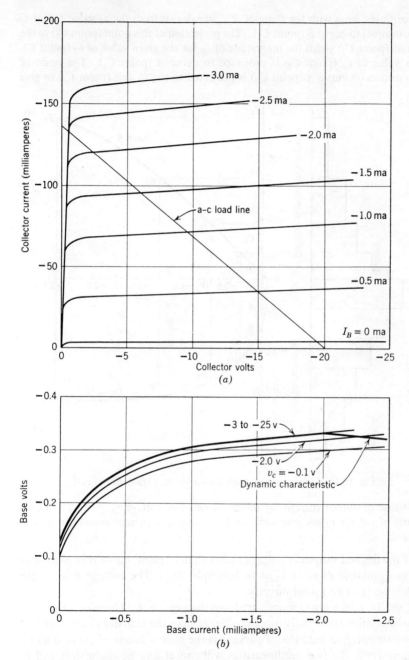

Fig. 10.9. Transistor characteristic curves.

Accordingly, lines with the slope of R_{gen} are drawn from the v_I value (point C for example) to curve B (point C_1). The projection of this point (point C_1) to the i_B axis (point C_2) yields the magnitude of i_B for the given value of v_I (point C). This value of i_B (point C_2) is projected to curve A (point C_3). The point of intersection on curve A (point C_3) is projected to the i_C axis (point C_4) to give

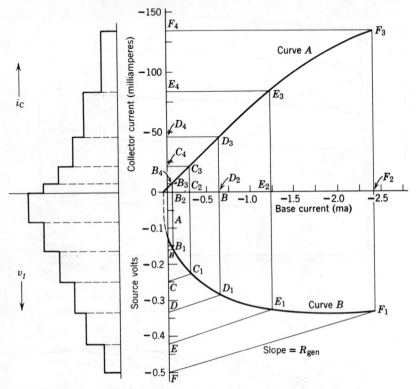

Fig. 10.10. Large-signal graphical solution of a transistor circuit.

the value of output current for the given value of voltage v_I (point C). Other values of voltage v_I are projected until the required current waveform can be drawn.

If the desired output is voltage rather than current, curve A is plotted as v_C vs i_B instead of i_C vs i_B as in Example 10.1. The voltage gain of the stage can thus be found directly.

Usually, curve B has more curvature than curve A. Therefore, the *input* characteristics are usually more nonlinear than the transfer characteristics. It is interesting to note that if curve A is the mirror image of curve B and if R_{gen} is zero, the two nonlinearities will cancel and no distortion will be present in the circuit. Even though the two nonlinearities do not cancel, at least the curvature is such so as to *minimize* distortion. This compensating effect is, therefore, similar in action to the compensating effect of r_p and g_m in the triode tube which was mentioned in Section 10.2.

It is interesting to note that the internal resistance (R_{gen} in Fig. 10.8) of the signal source has an important effect on the distortion of a transistor amplifier. The effect of this source resistance is illustrated in Fig. 10.11.

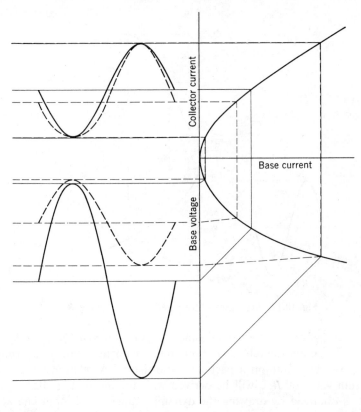

Fig. 10.11. The effect of signal source impedance on distortion in a transistor.

In this figure, the solid lines show the solution for a large value of R_{gen}. For large R_{gen}, the collector current swing from minimum current to quiescent current is *greater* than the current swing from quiescent current to peak current. In contrast to this case, the dashed lines of Fig. 10.11 show the solution if R_{gen} is small. For small R_{gen}, the current swing from minimum current to quiescent current is *smaller* than the current swing from quiescent current to peak current. Obviously, some value of R_{gen} must exist such that the distortion is very small. In fact, the second harmonic component may be zero. Thus, in case the driving source resistance is not optimum, the distortion of a transistor may be decreased by adding a resistor in series with the base (to increase the effective R_{gen}) or in parallel with the base (to decrease the effective R_{gen}). True, these resistors decrease the power gain of the circuit, but this price must be paid for low distortion.

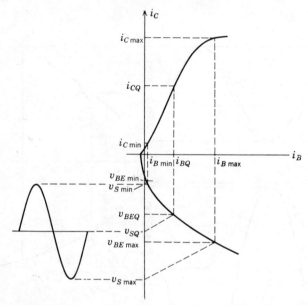

Fig. 10.12. Arrangement for determining optimum R_{gen}.

The value of driving source resistance R_{gen} that will give $(i_{C\,\max} - i_{CQ}) = (i_{CQ} - i_{C\,\min})$, and therefore near-minimum distortion, can be determined for a given load line on a particular transistor. A relationship for this optimum value of R_{gen} will be derived with the aid of Fig. 10.12. This figure is obtained by drawing the dynamic transfer and input characteristics for a given a-c load resistance as previously discussed. The values for $i_{C\,\max}$ (at or near saturation) and $i_{C\,\min}$ (at or near $i_B = 0$) are established next. The value of i_{CQ} is set at the mid-point between $i_{C\,\text{MAX}}$ and $i_{C\,\text{MIN}}$. The corresponding values of $i_{B\,\text{MAX}}$, $i_{B\,\text{MIN}}$, i_{BQ} and $v_{BE\,\text{MAX}}$, $v_{BE\,\text{MIN}}$ and v_{BEQ} are then graphically determined (Fig. 10.12). Also, the corresponding source potentials may be determined as follows:

$$v_{S\,\text{MAX}} = v_{BE\,\text{MAX}} + i_{B\,\text{MAX}}R_{\text{gen}} \qquad (10.23)$$

$$v_{SQ} = v_{BEQ} + i_{BQ}R_{\text{gen}} \qquad (10.24)$$

$$v_{S\,\text{MIN}} = v_{BE\,\text{MIN}} + i_{B\,\text{MIN}}R_{\text{gen}} \qquad (10.25)$$

But v_S is assumed to be a sinusoidal (or symmetrical) signal. Therefore

$$v_{S\,\text{MAX}} - v_{SQ} = v_{SQ} - v_{\text{MIN}} \tag{10.26}$$

Substituting Eqs. 10.23, 10.24, and 10.25 into Eq. 10.26

$$v_{BE\,\text{MAX}} + v_{BE\,\text{MIN}} + R_{\text{gen}}(i_{B\,\text{MAX}} + i_{B\,\text{MIN}}) = 2(v_{BEQ} + i_{BQ}R_{\text{gen}}) \tag{10.27}$$

Solving for R_{gen},

$$R_{\text{gen}} = -\frac{v_{BE\,\text{max}} + v_{BE\,\text{min}} - 2v_{BEQ}}{i_{B\,\text{MAX}} + i_{B\,\text{MIN}} - 2i_{BQ}} \tag{10.28}$$

If the calculated value of R_{gen} is zero or negative, and therefore unrealizable, a minimum practical value of R_{gen} should be used.

PROB. 10.6. Sketch v_C for the transistor in Example 10.1 by drawing curve A as v_C vs i_B. What other system could be used when i_C is known?

PROB. 10.7. If R_L in Example 10.1 is changed from 250 Ω to 1000 Ω, sketch i_C.

PROB. 10.8. Graphically find the per cent of second harmonic distortion in the output current of the transistor in Example 10.1. Assume the input voltage, v_I, is a sine wave with the same peak-to-peak value as the voltage v_I used in Example 10.1. *Answer: % sec = 35.2.*

PROB. 10.9. Repeat Prob. 10.8 if R_{gen} is changed to 5000 Ω.

10.4 EFFICIENCY OF CLASS A AMPLIFIERS

The *plate or collector efficiency* of a power amplifier can be found by dividing the output signal power by the input plate or collector source power. The average input power to the collector of a transistor $P_{C\,\text{in}}$ is equal to the collector supply voltage V_{CC} times the average collector current I_C or

$$P_{C\,\text{in}} = V_{CC}I_C \tag{10.29}$$

Similarly, the average input plate power to a tube amplifier ($P_{P\,\text{in}}$) is

$$P_{P\,\text{in}} = V_{PP}I_P \tag{10.30}$$

In both cases of efficiency, the instantaneous signal power to the load is given by the instantaneous voltage times the instantaneous current. If the signal is a sine wave and the load is purely resistive, the signal power is

$$P_{\text{out}} = \frac{V_o^2}{R_L} = I_o^2 R_L \tag{10.31}$$

where V_o and I_o are the rms value of the output signal. Now, if v_{MAX} is the maximum voltage across the load and v_{MIN} is the minimum voltage across the load, the peak-to-peak signal voltage is $v_{MAX} - v_{MIN}$. Therefore, if no distortion is present,

$$V_o = \frac{v_{MAX} - v_{MIN}}{2(2)^{\frac{1}{2}}}$$ (10.32)

Hence,

$$P_{out} = \frac{(v_{MAX} - v_{MIN})^2}{8R_L} = \frac{(v_{MAX} - v_{MIN})(i_{MAX} - i_{MIN})}{8}$$ (10.33)

An example can help illustrate the procedure for calculating efficiency.

Example 10.2. A circuit is connected as shown in Fig. 10.13. If the transistor is assumed to have no distortion, what is the maximum collector efficiency of a class A amplifier when a sinusoidal signal is applied?

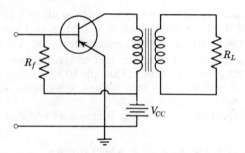

Fig. 10.13. The circuit for Example 10.2.

Since the collector circuit power input is constant (Eq. 10.29), maximum efficiency occurs when the collector voltage swing is maximum (Eq. 10.33). Since the quiescent collector voltage is V_{CC}, the maximum collector voltage swing occurs when the collector is driven to zero as a minimum and $2V_{CC}$ as a maximum. (See Fig. 10.14.) Actually, the collector cannot be driven completely to zero but zero is the limiting value.

For maximum efficiency, let i_C be 0 when v_C is equal to $2V_{CC}$. The maximum collector current will then be

$$i_{C\ MAX} = \frac{2V_{CC}}{n^2 R_L}$$ (10.34)

where n is the turns ratio of the transformer N_1/N_2. The quiescent collector current is

$$I_C = \frac{V_{CC}}{n^2 R_L}$$ (10.35)

Therefore, the input power is

$$P_{in} = V_{CC} I_C = \frac{V_{CC}^2}{n^2 R_L}$$ (10.36)

The rms value of the output voltage across the transformer is $0.707\,V_{CC}$,

$$P_{\text{out}} = \frac{V_{CC}^2}{2n^2R_L} \tag{10.37}$$

Consequently, the *maximum* class A collector circuit efficiency is

$$\eta_C = \frac{P_{\text{out}}}{P_{\text{in}}} = \frac{V_{CC}^2/2n^2R_L}{V_{CC}^2/n^2R_L} = 50\% \tag{10.38}$$

As the foregoing example illustrates, the maximum efficiency for a class A amplifier is only 50%. This example used a transistor, but identical

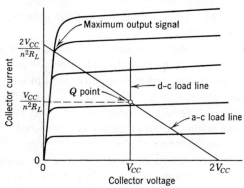

Fig. 10.14. Relations of voltage and current in Example 10.2.

results are obtained for plate efficiencies of vacuum tubes. Since an actual amplifier cannot be driven from 0 to $2\,V_{CC}$, the efficiency of actual class A amplifiers is *never* as high as 50%. However, an examination of typical transistor characteristic curves will show that the transistor can be driven almost to $v_C = 0$ before current saturation occurs. Hence, transistor amplifiers can *approach* 50% efficiency.

Pentodes have characteristic curves similar to the transistors but plate current saturation occurs at a relatively higher potential. Accordingly, the *plate circuit efficiency* of a pentode is usually lower than the efficiency of a transistor. When the input power to the screen and filament is considered, *the overall efficiency* of a pentode is considerably lower.

The characteristic curves of a typical triode tube indicate that the plate voltage is usually quite high when the control grid is at 0 potential. Accordingly, the plate circuit efficiency of a class A_1 triode is much lower than the plate circuit efficiency of a pentode. Again, when the filament power is also considered, the overall efficiency of a triode is quite low. Note that the plate circuit efficiency of a triode can be increased if the control grid is driven positive.

The foregoing discussion assumed a sinusoidal input signal. If other input waveforms are assumed, the collector circuit efficiency can be much higher than the 50% indicated. In fact, the sinusoidal input signal has one of the *lowest* efficiencies possible. When the input signal is a square wave, the efficiency of a class *A* transistor amplifier may approach 100%. This very high efficiency is obtained when the transistor is driven to cutoff during one half-cycle and into saturation during the other half cycle. The collector dissipation is then very low during both half cycles because the product $v_{CE}i_C$ is very low during both half cycles. This mode of operation is used in switching applications. In this mode of operation the collector dissipation increases greatly during the switching time. Therefore, the efficiency may be very high only in case the switching time is very short in comparison with the period.

Strictly speaking, the excitation or driving power as well as the power loss in the bias source should be included when *overall efficiency* is considered. However, the driving power is usually small in comparison with the collector or plate power input. On the other hand, the power loss in the bias resistors, especially emitter circuit resistors, may not be negligible and must be included when overall efficiency is considered.

Collector or plate circuit efficiency is usually of much greater importance than overall amplifier efficiency because the plate or collector circuit efficiency determines the amount of power output which can be obtained from the amplifier. The relationship between the collector or plate efficiency and the power output will be derived in a following section.

PROB. 10.10. Show that the maximum efficiency for a class *A* transistor amplifier with a resistive load in the plate circuit is 25%.

PROB. 10.11. Although a 6J5 is not primarily intended as a power amplifier device, calculate P_{in} and P_{out} as well as overall efficiency if $V_{PP} = 300$ v and $R_L = 10,000 \, \Omega$. Assume class A_1 operation and keep the output relatively linear.

PROB. 10.12. The characteristics of a 6V6 are given in Appendix 3. Calculate P_{in} and P_{out} for a 6V6 if $V_{PP} = 300$ v and $R_L = 15 \, \Omega$. What is the maximum plate circuit efficiency? The load is transformer coupled with $n = 20$. The grid to cathode voltage is $(-10 + 10 \sin \omega t)v$. *Answer: $P_{in} = 17.4$ w, $P_{out} = 4.4$ w, $\eta_P = 25.2\%$.*

10.5 PUSH-PULL AMPLIFIERS

The preceding paragraphs have indicated that the large-signal amplifier can produce considerable distortion of the excitation waveform. For example, the amplifier output signal may not be symmetrical even though the input signal is symmetrical, such as a sinusoid. This situation results because the changing parameters cause the amplifier to have different values of gain on alternate half cycles. A Fourier analysis shows that this unsymmetrical waveform is rich in even harmonics. (Actually odd harmonics may also be present.) On the other hand, any periodic wave which is symmetrical about a neutral axis contains no even harmonics. Thus an amplifier which flattens the input wave equally on both half cycles produces odd harmonics but no even harmonics.

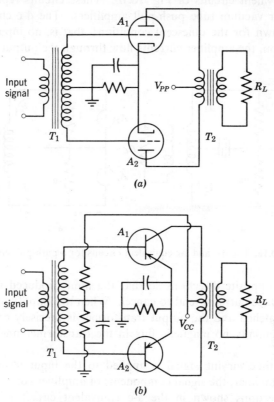

Fig. 10.15. Typical push-pull amplifier circuits.

A type of amplifier known as a push-pull amplifier can *eliminate* even harmonic distortion (generated in the amplifier) by providing a symmetrical output signal. Of course, any second harmonic present in the input signal will be reproduced in the output. Some typical push-pull circuits are given in Fig. 10.15. In these circuits, the input signal current introduces a voltage into the secondary winding of the transformer T_1. Since the center of this secondary winding is grounded, one end of the secondary will become positive while the other end is going negative. Therefore, the input signal to the amplifier A_1 will be inverted in relation to the input signal to the amplifier A_2. This polarity inversion between the two exciting signals is necessary for proper operation of the push-pull amplifier. These two input signals should also be equal in magnitude. If interstage transformer coupling is undesirable, the transformer T_1 may be replaced by one of the phase inverter circuits of Section 10.8.

The basic operating principles of the push-pull amplifier are illustrated by the equivalent circuits of Fig. 10.16. These circuits represent either transistor or vacuum tube push-pull amplifiers. The d-c circuit of Fig. 10.16 is drawn for the quiescent condition; that is, no input signal. In this condition, the amplifier currents flow through the output transformer

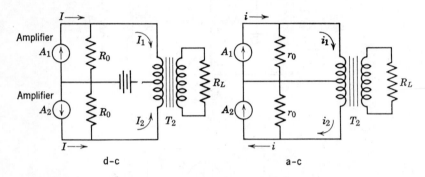

Fig. 10.16. The d-c and a-c equivalent circuits for a push-pull amplifier.

primary in opposite directions so that the mmf produced in the transformer by these currents tend to cancel. When the amplifying devices are perfectly matched and the output transformer is precisely center-tapped, there is essentially no magnetic flux in the transformer under quiescent conditions.

When a time-varying signal is applied to the input terminals of the push-pull amplifier, the signal components of amplifier current flow in the relative directions shown in the a-c equivalent circuit of Fig. 10.16. Observe that the signal current in the lower amplifier A_2 is reversed in comparison with the signal current in the upper amplifier A_1. These relative current relationships, as mentioned before, occur because the excitation of amplifier A_2 is of opposite polarity to the excitation of amplifier A_1. The a-c equivalent circuit shows that the signal current components produce mmf which add in the output transformer. Therefore, the total transformer mmf is the product of the signal current and the total number of primary turns. Hence, the power furnished to the load is the *sum* of the signal powers from the two tubes or transistors. Note that the signal current components do not pass through the power supply or the emitter biasing circuit.

The even harmonic distortion is cancelled in the push-pull amplifier output (assuming the circuit is balanced) because the negative half cycle of one tube or transistor adds to the positive half cycle of the other. Figure 10.17 illustrates the manner in which the even harmonics are cancelled. In this figure, the input signal is assumed to be sinusoidal. This cancellation of even harmonic distortion can also be shown mathematically if the output current is represented as a Fourier series. The input signal voltage source is assumed to be $v_1 = V \sin \omega t$. Then the output signal current of amplifier A_1 is

$$i_1 = B_1 \sin \omega t + B_2 \sin (2\omega t + \phi_2)$$
$$+ B_3 \sin (3\omega t + \phi_2)$$
$$+ \cdots B_n \sin (n\omega t + \phi_n) \quad (10.39)$$

Since the input voltage of amplifier A_2 is inverted (180° out of phase) when compared with that of A_1, $v_2 = V \sin (\omega t + \pi)$. Then the output current of amplifier A_2 is

$$i_2 = B_1 \sin (\omega t + \pi)$$
$$+ B_2 \sin [2(\omega t + \pi) + \phi_2]$$
$$+ B_3 \sin [3(\omega t + \pi) + \phi_3]$$
$$+ \cdots B_n \sin [n(\omega t + \pi)$$
$$+ \phi_n] \quad (10.40)$$

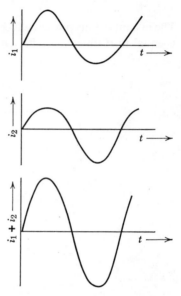

Fig. 10.17. Illustration of the cancellation of even harmonic distortion in the output of a balanced push-pull amplifier.

Re-writing Eq. 10.40 and recognizing that an even multiple of π radians, when added to an angle, does not change the angle, we see that

$$i_2 = B_1 \sin (\omega t + \pi) + B_2 \sin (2\omega t + \phi_2) + B_3 \sin (3\omega t + \pi + \phi_3)$$
$$+ \cdots B_n \sin (n\omega t + n\pi + \phi_n) \cdots . \quad (10.41)$$

By comparing Eqs. 10.41 and 10.39, we can see that only the fundamental and odd harmonics have *opposite polarities* in the output currents and thus *add* in the output transformer. Conversely, the even harmonics are *in phase* and therefore *cancel* in the output transformer.

The push-pull circuit can be analyzed by the use of the a-c equivalent circuit of Fig. 10.16. However, the two amplifying devices A_1 and A_2 appear to be in series insofar as the signal components of output current are concerned. Therefore, the analysis is made easier by replacing the current sources of Fig. 10.16 with voltage sources as shown in Fig. 10.18. In this circuit, N_1 is the number of turns in half of the primary and N_2 is the number of secondary turns. Then, assuming the circuit to be balanced, we see that

$$i_1 = i_2 = \frac{2v}{2r_o + (2N_1/N_2)^2 R_L} \cdot \qquad (10.42)$$

The instantaneous power delivered to the primary of the power transformer is equal to i^2 times the reflected load resistance, or

$$P_{\text{out}} = \left[\frac{2v}{2r_o + (2N_1/N_2)^2 R_L}\right]^2 \left(\frac{2N_1}{N_2}\right)^2 R_L \qquad (10.43)$$

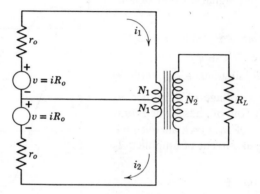

Fig. 10.18. A voltage source equivalent circuit for the push-pull amplifier.

Equation 10.43 can be rewritten as

$$P_{\text{out}} = \left[\frac{4v}{2r_o + 4(N_1/N_2)^2 R_L}\right]^2 \left(\frac{N_1}{N_2}\right)^2 R_L \qquad (10.44)$$

Dividing both the numerator and denominator of the bracketed term by 4, we have

$$P_{\text{out}} = \left[\frac{v}{(r_o/2) + (N_1/N_2)^2 R_L}\right]^2 \left(\frac{N_1}{N_2}\right)^2 R_L \qquad (10.45)$$

An equivalent circuit which will yield the power of Eq. 10.45 is given in Fig. 10.19a. The current source equivalent circuit is shown in Fig. 10.19b. These equivalent circuits represent a fictitious tube or transistor which has the same characteristics as a push-pull configuration. This fictitious tube is known as the *composite tube*. Similarly, the transistor represented by the equivalent circuit of Fig. 10.19b is known as a *composite transistor*.

The composite collector or plate characteristics may be obtained from the respective individual characteristics as illustrated in Fig. 10.20. The

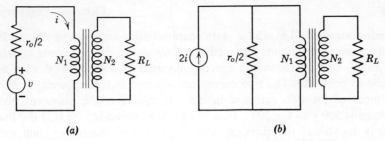

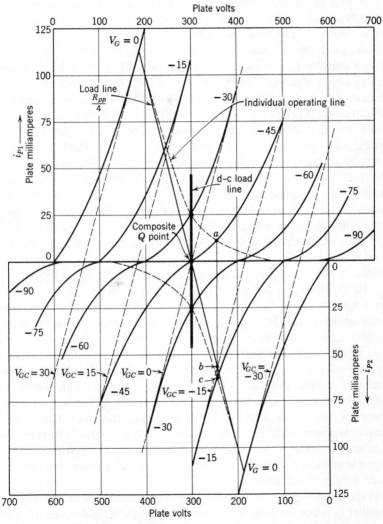

(a)　　　　　　　　　　　　　　　(b)

Fig. 10.19. Equivalent circuits for the composite tube or transistor.

Fig. 10.20. Composite characteristics and load lines for push-pull tubes.

triode-connected 6L6, whose plate characteristics are given in Fig. 10.20, will be used to illustrate the method of obtaining the composite characteristics. One characteristic curve is inverted and the $i_P = 0$ axes are made to coincide. The two curves are adjusted until the quiescent plate voltages of the two curves coincide. In this case, the quiescent plate voltage is 300 v so the 300-v lines are made to coincide. Next, a d-c load line is drawn and the quiescent operating point is chosen for each individual tube. In this example, the d-c resistance of the transformer primary is assumed to be negligible. Therefore the d-c load lines are drawn vertically and the quiescent operating point is chosen at the intersection of this d-c load line and the $v_G = -30$ curve.

Now, since the two plate currents subtract in the output transformer, the two currents can be subtracted graphically. For example, if no time-varying signal is present, both control grids will have -30 v applied and the dashed curve for $v_{GC} = 0$ (Fig. 10.20) results. This curve is seen to be the difference between the two $v_G = -30$ curves. Similarly, if the v_G of tube 1 is -15 v, the v_G of tube 2 is -45 v. The difference between these two curves is the $v_{GC} = +15$ v composite curve. Similarly, the $v_{GC} = +30$ v composite curve is the difference between the $V_G = 0$-v curve of tube 1 and the $V_G = -60$-v curve of tube 2. Since the circuit is symmetrical, the composite curves for $v_{GC} = -15$ v and -30 v are mirror images of the $+15$- and $+30$-v composite curves. Note that the slope of the composite characteristics is about twice as great as the slope of the individual characteristic at the Q point, thus verifying that r_p (composite) $= r_p/2$.

Observe that the quiescent operating point for the composite tube of Fig. 10.20 is at $v_P = 300$ v and $i_P = 0$. The a-c load line for the composite tube is drawn through this Q point. The slope of this load line should be determined from power output, power gain, and plate dissipation considerations in the same manner as discussed for the single tube. The slope of the composite load line for a triode can frequently be made the negative of the slope of the composite characteristic, thus providing maximum power gain at maximum power output. This impedance matching provides somewhat more than twice the power output for the composite tube than could be obtained from the individual tube at acceptable distortion levels. The slope of the composite load line represents a resistance which is one-fourth of the plate-to-plate resistance of the output transformer, because the composite amplifier works into one-half of the output transformer.

As shown in Fig. 10.20, the operating path of each tube in the push-pull amplifier is a curved path which passes through the individual Q point. The composite tube current is

$$i_{PC} = i_{P1} - i_{P2} \qquad (10.46)$$

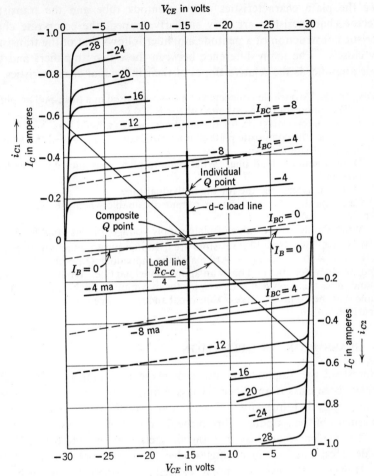

Fig. 10.21. Composite characteristics and load lines for push-pull transistors.

Therefore, the plate current in the individual tube may be determined at a particular value of grid voltage from the relationship

$$i_{P1} = i_{PC} + i_{P2} \qquad (10.47)$$

Then, if a vertical line is drawn through the intersection of a composite characteristic with the load line, the intersection of this vertical line with the corresponding individual tube characteristics will provide a point on the operating line for the individual tube. This construction is illustrated by the points a, b, and c on Fig. 10.20.

Figure 10.21 shows that the construction techniques illustrated for the push-pull triode amplifier also apply to the push-pull transistor amplifier.

Since the plate characteristics of the pentode tube and the transistor collector characteristics are very similarly shaped, the composite characteristic construction of a pentode amplifier follows that of the transistor very closely. The main difference between these two amplifiers and the triode amplifier is the relative slopes of their individual characteristics.

PROB. 10.13. Two triode-connected 6L6 tubes are used in a push-pull amplifier circuit. The quiescent plate-cathode voltage is 300 v.

(*a*) Draw a circuit diagram for the amplifier, using cathode bias.

(*b*) Construct the composite plate characteristics, using $V_G = -30$ v as the Q point of the individual tube.

(*c*) Draw a suitable load line. What plate-to-plate resistance does this load line represent?

(*d*) Draw the operating line for the individual tube.

(*e*) Calculate the maximum power output obtainable when the excitation is sinusoidal.

(*f*) What should be the value of plate-supply voltage for this amplifier?

PROB. 10.14. Two 2N2147 transistors are used in a push-pull amplifier circuit with $V_{CC} = -20$ v and $I_B = -10$ ma at the individual Q point. Sketch the composite characteristics and draw an appropriate load line. What value of load resistance does this represent? Determine the maximum available power output. Assume that the exciting source is sinusoidal and the source resistance is large in comparison with h_{ie}.

10.6 CLASS *B* OR *AB* OPERATION

Almost all the amplifiers considered in the preceding portion of this text have been class *A* amplifiers. Class *A* amplifiers were used because it was assumed that linearity, or minimum waveform distortion, was a requirement of the amplifier. From the definition of the classes of operation, it is evident that class *A* is the only class of operation which can provide good linearity in a single-ended (non push-pull) audio amplifier. However, the even-harmonic cancelling property of a push-pull amplifier permits class *B* or *AB* operation for this type of amplifier.

If the amplifying device, such as a tube or transistor, were linear during the time current flowed through the device, the push-pull amplifier would be linear even though the individual amplifier were operated class *B* (biased at cutoff). In this case, the output current and power would be furnished by one of the individual amplifiers during the first half of the input cycle and the other individual amplifier would furnish the output current and power during the second half of the input cycle. The addition of the two individual currents would produce a distortionless output cycle.

The no-signal output current for a class *B* amplifier is zero. Therefore, when the excitation is zero, there is no drain on the collector or plate power supply. This feature of the class *B* amplifier is very attractive because of the large reduction of collector supply power in the class B amplifier compared with the class A amplifier when equal output power capabilities are considered.

In addition to the greatly increased small-signal efficiency, the class B amplifier is considerably more efficient than the class A amplifier at maximum signal levels. The maximum theoretical efficiency of the class B amplifier, for sinusoidal excitation, may be readily computed by assuming the amplifier operation to extend from the voltage axis along the load line to the current axis. This technique was used to calculate the maximum theoretical efficiency of the class A amplifier, which is 50% with sinusoidal excitation.

Load lines are drawn on the output (collector or plate) characteristics of typical transistor and tube amplifiers in Fig. 10.22. When the operation is assumed to swing from axis to axis along the load line, the peak value of input current is I_A. Now, the average current for one half of a sine wave with a peak value of I_A is $(2/\pi)I_A$. Thus, if the transistor is used as an example the collector power input P_{in} is equal to V_{CC} times the average, collector current or

$$P_{in} = \frac{2I_A V_{CC}}{\pi} \tag{10.48}$$

where I_A is the current axis intercept value of i_C. This P_{in} is the average power into one transistor for one half-cycle or for two push-pull transistors for the full cycle. For the push-pull configuration, the characteristics of Fig. 10.22 represent the top half of the composite characteristics. Here, the average power output for either the half cycle or full cycle is

$$P_{out} = \frac{I_A V_{CC}}{2} \tag{10.49}$$

The *maximum theoretical collector circuit efficiency* is

$$\eta_C = \frac{P_{out}}{P_{in}} \times 100 = \frac{\pi}{4} \times 100 = 78\% \tag{10.50}$$

This value of efficiency is closely approached by the transistor amplifier and reasonably approached by the pentode amplifier. It is interesting to note that the triode amplifier is quite inefficient, compared with the other two, when the maximum permissible grid voltage is zero volts. However, when the grid is driven appreciably into the positive region, the efficiency of the triode may be as high as that of the pentode amplifier.

The collector or plate dissipation capability of an amplifier usually limits the amount of power that can be obtained from this amplifier. Thus, a given amplifier can deliver much more power when operated in the

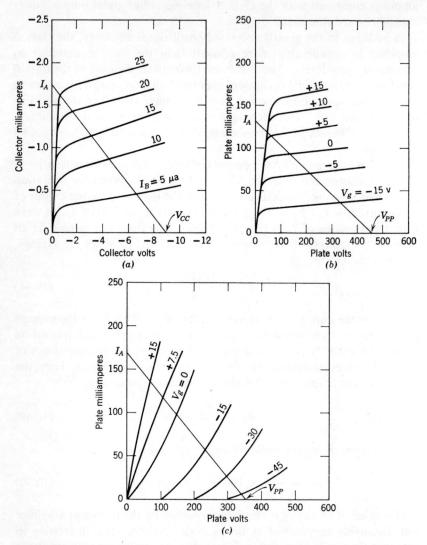

Fig. 10.22. Load lines are drawn on the output characteristics to determine the maximum theoretical efficiency and to compare the efficiency of transistor and tube amplifiers under various situations. (*a*) Transistor; (*b*) pentode; (*c*) triode.

class B mode than when operated in the class A mode. The relationship between the maximum possible power output and the efficiency is derived as follows. The collector or plate dissipation is

$$P_d = P_{in} - P_{out} \qquad (10.51)$$

But

$$P_{in} = \frac{P_{out}}{\eta_C} \qquad (10.52)$$

Then

$$P_d = P_{out}\left(\frac{1}{\eta_C} - 1\right) \qquad (10.53)$$

and

$$P_{out} = \frac{\eta_C P_d}{1 - \eta_C} \qquad (10.54)$$

PROB. 10.15. A certain transistor can safely dissipate 10 w in a given environment. Determine the power output which can be obtained from a push-pull amplifier using two of these transistors when the transistors are operated (*a*) class A, (*b*) class B. Assume the excitation to be sinusoidal and the efficiencies to be 50% and 75% respectively.

As in class A operation, the class B efficiency is a function of waveform as well as magnitude of excitation. In fact, as mentioned, the efficiency may approach 100% when the excitation is rectangular.

The realizable increased power output of the class B mode as compared with the class A mode is not obtained automatically as the bias is changed. This maximum power output can result only from increased collector power input. The collector power input can be increased by either increasing the collector supply voltage or increasing the output current or a combination of the two. In case the collector supply voltage has already been set at the maximum permissible value, the output current can be increased by reducing the load resistance and increasing the excitation. For the vacuum tube, this means that to realize the maximum dissipation capabilities of the tube the grid must be driven into the positive region. The triode tube looks quite promising when driven into the positive grid voltage region because the efficiency as well as the power output is then increased appreciably.

Actually, either the tube or the transistor push-pull amplifier has intolerable distortion when biased strictly at cutoff. This high distortion results from the high degree of nonlinearity of the characteristics near zero collector or plate current. This high distortion which occurs near plate current cutoff is known as *cross-over* distortion. This distortion can be eliminated by biasing the amplifier at *projected cutoff* rather than at actual cutoff. The meaning of projected cutoff is illustrated by Fig. 10.23. The relatively straight portion of the transfer or input characteristic curve is extended until it intercepts the zero plate current or base current line as the case may be. This intersection is at the projected cutoff value of bias voltage as shown in Fig. 10.23*a*. The composite transfer characteristic may be drawn by inverting the second transfer curve and aligning the projected cutoff bias points as shown in Fig. 10.23*a*.

The composite transistor input characteristic can be drawn for the case of projected cutoff bias, as shown in Fig. 10.23*b*. The second set of

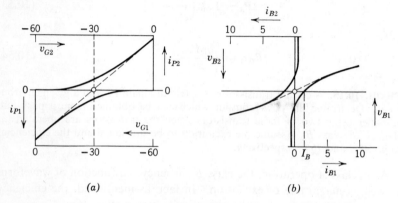

(a)   *(b)*

Fig. 10.23. Illustration of the method of determining projected cutoff for the *(a)* vacuum tube, *(b)* transistor.

characteristics is inverted and the projected cutoff bias *voltage* values of the two curves is aligned. The extensions of the relatively straight portions of the curves then join and form the composite characteristic. The addition of the second curve is really unnecessary because no additional information is added. The extended linear portion of the curve becomes the composite characteristic for one-half of the input cycle and the second half cycle is merely a repetition of the first half cycle if the amplifiers are balanced.

Operation at projected cutoff is sometimes called class *B* operation in the literature. However, it is more correctly known as class *AB* operation. The efficiency of class *AB* is less than that of class *B*, of course, but is still much higher than that of class *A*. Push-pull amplifiers are usually operated at projected cutoff. The chief disadvantage of this mode of operation in comparison with class *A* is the increased importance of maintaining good amplifier balance.

The composite characteristics and composite load line can be drawn for the class *AB* push-pull amplifier in the manner described for the class *A* amplifier. The only difference in the two amplifiers is the selection of the bias point. However, the construction of the composite curves is much easier for the class AB amplifier because the composite curves follow the individual curves over most of the region of operation. In fact, the composite curves are not required for a class AB amplifier because the composite quiescent operating point is fixed independently of the composite curves, and the composite curves are identical with the individual characteristic curves at the extremities of the region of operation. Also, as previously mentioned, one set of collector characteristics is sufficient to

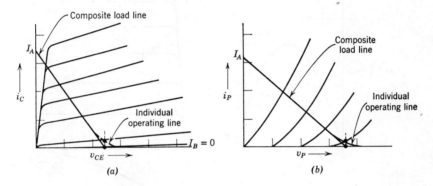

Fig. 10.24. Graphical analysis of the class AB push-pull amplifier. (*a*) Transistor; (*b*) triode tube.

define the operation over one-half of the output cycle, and the second half of the output cycle is assumed to be identical (although inverted) to the first half. Therefore, only one set of output characteristics needs to be used. These simplifications in the graphical analysis are illustrated in Fig. 10.24. The maximum positive grid voltage of a vacuum tube operating in the class 1 (no grid current) condition is established at zero volts. Then the optimum composite load line can be drawn, using the guiding principles discussed for the single ended amplifier. However, the maximum permissible excursion of either input voltage or output current is not so clearly defined for the class AB_2 tube amplifier or for the class AB transistor amplifier. The maximum permissible output current can be determined as a function of the permissible plate or collector dissipation and the quiescent value of output current. This maximum permissible value of output current then establishes the upper extremity or current axis intercept of the load line.

A method of determining the maximum permissible output current for a class B transistor amplifier is illustrated in Fig. 10.25. Initially, the amplifier is assumed to operate class B so the quiescent current is approximately zero. Then with sinusoidal excitation, the average power dissipation for one half-cycle is

$$P_d = P_{in} - P_{out} = \frac{2}{\pi} I_{max} V_{CC} - \frac{I_{max}^2 R_L}{2} \qquad (10.55)$$

The value of signal current I_{max} which causes maximum dissipation may

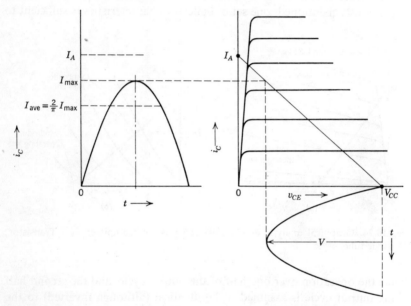

Fig. 10.25. Illustration of the method used to determine the maximum permissible collector current for a class B transistor.

be obtained by differentiating Eq. 10.55 with respect to I_{max} and equating the derivative to zero.

$$\frac{dP_d}{dI_{max}} = 0 = \frac{2}{\pi} V_{CC} - I_{max} R_L \qquad (10.56)$$

$$I_{max} = \frac{2}{\pi} \frac{V_{CC}}{R_L} = \frac{2}{\pi} I_A \qquad (10.57)$$

Substituting this value of I_{max} into Eq. 10.55 will yield the maximum power dissipation.

$$P_{d\,max} = \frac{4}{\pi^2} I_A V_{CC} - \frac{2}{\pi^2} I_A{}^2 R_L \qquad (10.58)$$

Substituting $I_A R_L = V_{CC}$ into Eq. 10.58 we have

$$P_{d\,max} = \frac{2}{\pi^2} I_A V_{CC} \tag{10.59}$$

For purposes of comparison, sketches of power dissipation and power output as functions of I_{max} are given in Fig. 10.26 for both class B and class A.

Equation 10.59 will determine the value of I_A for a class B amplifier when V_{CC} (or V_{PP}) and the maximum permissible dissipation are known.

$$I_A = \frac{P_{d\,max}}{(2/\pi^2)V_{CC}} = \frac{\pi^2 P_{d\,max}}{2V_{CC}} \simeq \frac{5P_{d\,max}}{V_{CC}} \tag{10.60}$$

This equation was derived for one transistor operating over one half-cycle. However, when a complete cycle is considered, the average power

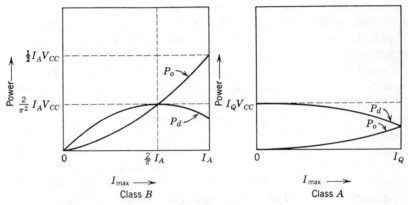

Fig. 10.26. Power output and power dissipation as functions of I_{max} (sinusoidal signal).

input and the average power output remain the same as in the preceding equations, but the power dissipation is the total dissipation capability of the two transistors (or tubes). A more general equation which would be valid for class AB operation, and thus include I_Q, would be more useful than Eq. 10.60. Such an equation is difficult to derive. Equation 10.60 can be altered, however, to include I_Q and to provide approximate values of I_A for class AB (or even class A) operations. The altered equation is

$$I_A \simeq \frac{5P_{d\,max}}{V_{CC}} - 3I_Q \tag{10.61}$$

Although the foregoing relationships were developed for sinusoidal signals, they are also safe design values for random signals.

PROB. 10.16. A particular transistor can safely dissipate 5 w with a given heat sink. The projected cutoff bias of this transistor provides a quiescent collector current of 20 ma. Calculate the maximum permissible collector current I_A, the collector-to-collector load resistance, and the maximum power output when two of these transistors are operated in class AB push-pull. The excitation is sinusoidal and V_{CC} is 15 v. *Answer: $I_A = 3.27\,a$, $R_L = 18.4\,\Omega$, $P_o = 24\,w$.*

10.7 THERMAL CONDUCTION AND THERMAL RUNAWAY

As noted in Chapter 4, small-signal transistors have collector-junction dissipation ratings which are based on an ambient air temperature, usually 25°C. These transistors, like small (receiving) tubes rely on air convection to transfer the heat, which results from the dissipated power, to the surrounding atmosphere. The small-signal transistors must be derated as the ambient temperature rises above the reference temperature. Convection-cooled tubes should also be derated as the ambient temperature increases, but the normal changes of ambient temperature are usually negligible in comparison with the operating temperature of the tube. Therefore, little attention is usually given to derating vacuum tubes, although the need for derating should not be overlooked.

Forced air (or even water) cooling is frequently recommended by the manufacturer for high-power tubes such as transmitting tubes. In contrast, the heat from a power transistor is usually transferred by conduction to a heat sink. Therefore, the power dissipation rating of a power transistor is specified for a given case temperature, usually 25°C. The actual power which can be dissipated by the transistor depends on the thermal conductivity between the transistor case and the surrounding air or environment, as well as on the ambient temperature of the surroundings. The power transistor (500 mw and above) is usually fastened securely to a large metal plate or chassis, which serves as the heat sink. The collector of the power transistor is usually electrically and mechanically connected to the transistor case. Maximum thermal conductivity to the heat sink is obtained when the transistor case is electrically and mechanically fastened to the heat sink. However, an insulator is frequently required to electrically isolate the collector from the heat sink.

Every transistor has a maximum permissible junction temperature T_j, which ranges from 85 to 110°C for germanium transistors and is about 175°C for silicon transistors. *Thermal resistance* Θ_T has been defined as the ratio of temperature rise in degrees centigrade to the power conducted in watts.[3] Therefore, the junction temperature T_j can be related to the power being dissipated P_d, the thermal resistance Θ_T, and the ambient temperature

---

[3] The symbol Θ_T may not seem to be an appropriate symbol for thermal resistance. However, this symbol is commonly used by the transistor industry.

T_a by the equation

$$T_j = \Theta_T P_d + T_a \tag{10.62}$$

The thermal resistance Θ_T actually consists of three parts; the thermal resistance between the collector junction and the case Θ_{jc}, between the case and the heat sink Θ_{cs}, and between the heat sink and the ambient environment Θ_{sa}. The equivalent circuit of Fig. 10.27 represents *the thermal relationships* of the transistor and its heat sink. The capacitors shown represent the *thermal capacitance* of the three parts of the circuit. The thermal capacitance C_j of the collector junction is very small. Therefore,

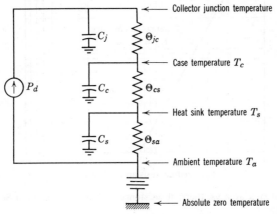

Fig. 10.27. An equivalent circuit which relates the various temperatures of a heat-conducting system to the power being dissipated and the thermal resistance.

the thermal time constant $\Theta_{jc}C_j$ is of the order of milliseconds. The significance of this time constant is that the load line can cross the maximum dissipation line of a transistor without damaging the transistor, *providing that the excessive dissipation does not continue for more than a few milliseconds.* The thermal capacitance C_c of the case is much greater than that of the junction. Therefore, the transistor which is designed to operate with a heat sink can operate for at least several seconds without the heat sink before the transistor is damaged. Similarly, the thermal capacity of a heat sink is usually much larger than that of the transistor case. Therefore, the transistor may operate several minutes with an inadequate heat sink.

The thermal resistance Θ_{jc} from the collector junction to the case is usually given by the manufacturer for each type of power transistor. Also, thermal resistance data are available for the various transistor mounting systems.[4] The thermal resistance Θ_{sa} of a $\frac{1}{8}$-in. thick bright aluminum

[4] See *Motorola Power Transistor Handbook*, First edition, p. 23, Motorola Semiconductor Products Division, Inc., Phoenix, Arizona.

plate as a function of area (both sides) is given in Fig. 10.28. This chart is for vertical orientation. When the heat sink is horizontal, the thermal resistance increases by the order of 10 % because of the reduced convection. On the other hand, black painting or anodizing of the heat sink could lower its thermal resistance.

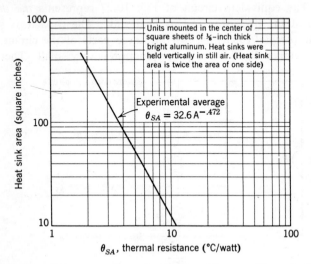

Fig. 10.28. Heat sink area vs. thermal resistance. (Courtesy Motorola Semiconductor Products Division.)

PROB. 10.17. A particular power transistor which has $\Theta_{jc} = 0.5°C/w$ is mounted on a vertical $\frac{1}{8}$-in. aluminum 200-in.^{2} heat sink. The maximum junction temperature is 90°C and the mounting system has $\Theta_{cs} = 0.8°C/w$. How much power can be dissipated when the ambient temperature is 25°C? What is the dissipation rating of the transistor?

The transistor is not completely protected when the heat sink is adequate for the required dissipation; the transistor can be destroyed by *thermal runaway*. This thermal runaway results from the increasing collector current, caused by the increasing I_{CO} which occurs as the junction temperature rises. Thus, thermal stability is dependent on the current stability factor S_I as well as on the heat sink.

Thermal runaway occurs when the rate of increase of collector junction temperature exceeds the ability of the heat sink to remove the heat. The rate of increase of junction temperature is obtained by differentiating Eq. 10.62,

$$\partial T_j = \Theta_T \, \partial P_d \qquad (10.63)$$

where $\Theta_T = \Theta_{jc} + \Theta_{cs} + \Theta_{sa}$. At quiescent operating conditions, the power dissipation P_d is equal to the collector power input $V_C I_C$. Then

$$\partial T_j = \Theta_T \, \partial(V_C I_C) = \Theta_T V_C \, \partial I_C \qquad (10.64)$$

or,

$$\frac{\partial T_j}{\partial I_C} = V_C \Theta_T \qquad (10.65)$$

Then,

$$\left(\frac{\partial T_j}{\partial I_{CO}}\right)\left(\frac{\partial I_{CO}}{\partial I_C}\right) = V_C \Theta_T \qquad (10.66)$$

But $\partial I_C / \partial I_{CO} = S_I$, the current stability factor noted (Chapter 5). Thus,

$$\frac{\partial T_j}{\partial I_{CO}} = S_I V_C \Theta_T \qquad (10.67)$$

In a germanium transistor, I_{CO} theoretically *doubles* for each 10°C temperature increase, as previously mentioned. Then I_{CO} increases about 7% for each °C increase of junction temperature. This relationship can be expressed mathematically as follows:

$$\frac{\partial I_{CO}}{\partial T_j} = 0.07 I_{CO} \qquad (10.68)$$

where I_{CO} is determined at the operating junction temperature T_j. Substituting Eq. 10.68 into Eq. 10.67, we have

$$0.07 I_{CO} = \frac{1}{S_I V_C \Theta_T} \qquad (10.69)$$

$$0.07 I_{CO} S_I V_C \Theta_T = 1 \qquad (10.70)$$

Equation 10.70 expresses the parameter relationship at the transition between the stable condition and thermal runaway. The left side of this equation must be *less* than unity to assure stability. After the collector supply voltage V_C is set and the heat sink is designed, the maximum value of stability factor which will provide thermal stability may be calculated.

$$S_I < \frac{14.3}{I_{CO} V_C \Theta_T} \qquad (10.71)$$

The constant in the numerator of Eq. 10.71 is theoretically appropriate for germanium transistors. However, the rate of change of I_{CO} with temperature varies quite widely among different types of transistors. The actual rate of increase is less than the theory predicts. This is especially true of silicon transistors because the surface leakage, the carriers generated within the depletion region and so on, which account for the discrepancy, cause a larger portion of I_{CO} in the silicon transistor. Therefore the constant in the numerator of Eq. 10.71 should be determined for each particular transistor. This constant can usually be determined from the data furnished by the manufacturer. For example, if I_{CO} is given for two different temperatures, Eq. 10.72 can be used to find the constant which represents the rate of increase of I_{CO} with temperature.

$$I_{CO2} = I_{CO1}(1 + r)^{\Delta T_j} \qquad (10.72)$$

where r is the rate of increase, and $1/r$ is the numerator of Eq. 10.71.

The I_{CO} in Eq. 10.71 must be determined at the *maximum* junction temperature, which is equal to the maximum ambient temperature plus the maximum d-c collector dissipation times the total thermal resistance. The maximum collector dissipation is a function of the junction temperature because $S_I I_{CO}$ is a significant part of the collector current. The maximum junction temperature is $T_{j\ max} = T_{a\ max} + (P_{in} - P_{out})\theta_T$. Then

$$T_{j\ max} = T_{a\ max} + (I_C + S_I I_{CO\ max})V_C\Theta_T - P_{out}\theta_T \qquad (10.73)$$

where I_C is the average value of collector current determined at maximum dissipation conditions but neglecting I_{CO}. Then

$$I_C V_C = \frac{T_{j\ max} - T_{a\ max}}{\Theta_T} - S_I V_C I_{CO\ max} + P_{out} \qquad (10.74)$$

where $I_C V_C$ is the permissible collector power input with I_{CO} neglected.

When the permissible collector power input is determined from Eq. 10.74 and the maximum stability factor is determined from Eq. 10.71 (using $I_{CO\ max}$), the junction temperature will not exceed the design value. The ohmic resistance in the collector circuit provides a safety factor because V_C normally decreases as the total collector current increases. The R-C coupled amplifier does not present a thermal runaway problem because of the comparatively large value of ohmic resistance in the collector circuit.

PROB. 10.18. Two transistors of the the type used in Prob. 10.17 have $I_{CO} = 1.5$ ma at 25°C and $I_{CO} = 30$ ma at 90°C measured at $V_C = -30$ v. What is the maximum permissible stability factor for a transformer coupled amplifier with $V_C = -30$ v, using these transistors? Both transistors are mounted on a $\frac{1}{8}$-in thick aluminum heat sink of 200 in² area on one side. *Answer: $S_I = 5.24$.*

PROB. 10.19. The transistor amplifier of Prob. 10.18 is operated class AB. If $I_{C\ max}$ and $I_{C\ ave}$ are determined with the aid of the typical collector characteristics, as discussed in the preceding problem, what is the maximum permissible value of $I_{C\ ave}$?

10.8 PHASE INVERTER CIRCUITS

In some instances, a transformer may be undesirable in the input of a push-pull amplifier. For this reason, phase inverter circuits which provide balanced voltages of opposite polarity have been devised. One rather simple type of phase inverter circuit is shown in Fig. 10.29. This phase inverter makes use of the inversion characteristics of a conventional amplifier. The tube V_1 inverts the signal of grid G_1 and applies this inverted signal to the grid G_2. The tap on resistor R_{g1} is adjusted until the magnitudes of the signals on G_1 and G_2 are equal. In fact, this circuit can even

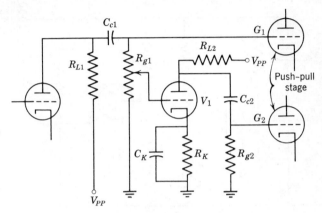

Fig. 10.29. A simple type of phase inverter circuit.

be adjusted to compensate for differences in the amplification of the push-pull tubes.

PROB. 10.20. A vacuum tube amplifier is to be used in the circuit of Fig. 10.29. If $R_{g1} = R_{g2} = 500$ KΩ and R_{L2} is 50 KΩ, find where the tap on R_{g1} must be located. Assume g_m of the triode is 2000 μmhos and r_p of the triode is 10,000 Ω. *Answer: 30.5 KΩ from ground.*

A transistor counterpart exists for the phase inverter circuit of Fig. 10.29. This transistor phase inverter is shown in Fig. 10.30. This circuit contains stabilized bias in each stage. Accordingly, a large number of circuit elements are required. However, by the proper choice of bias currents, several of the circuit elements may be eliminated. For example, if the bias current to transistor T_1 is less than the bias current of transistor T_2, resistors R_3 and R_2 may be removed and capacitor C_1 replaced by a short circuit. Bias for transistor T_1 is supplied by R_8 and R_7. Obviously, the adjustment of R_1 controls the output current of transistor T_1.

The greater complexity of the transistor circuit (Fig. 10.30) as compared to the vacuum tube circuit (Fig. 10.29) results from the bias requirements. In vacuum tube circuits, the bias circuit can be located in the cathode of each tube. Hence, isolation of the grid circuits are not required. In contrast, the bias circuits of transistor amplifiers are located in the base circuits. Consequently, isolation of the base circuits must be maintained.

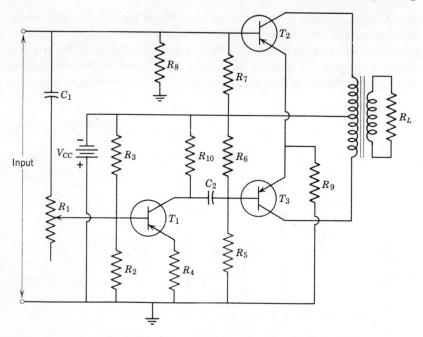

Fig. 10.30. A transistor phase inverter circuit.

PROB. 10.21. A transistor circuit is connected as shown in Fig. 10.30. All three transistors are the same type (transistor T_1 is usually a lower current rating device than transistors T_2 and T_3). $h_{ie} = 250\ \Omega$; $h_{re} \simeq 0$; $h_{oe} = 10^{-5}$ mhos; h_{fe} or $\beta = 50$. The desired quiescent conditions are $I_B = 1$ ma and $I_C = 50$ ma. Let the currents through R_2, R_8, and R_5 be 3 ma each. Now, if $R_9 = 10\ \Omega$ and $R_4 = 20\ \Omega$, find the value of the other circuit elements including R_1. Assume R_{10} is 300 Ω and V_{CC} is 20 v. The lowest frequency to be amplified is 30 Hz.

A second type of phase inverter circuit which has proven very popular is shown in Fig. 10.31. In this circuit, R_{L1} and the vacuum tube act as a cathode follower. Accordingly, the signal in grid G_2 is *in phase* with the signal v_i. In contrast, the signal on grid G_1 is developed across the conventional plate load resistance R_{L2} and is *inverted* in relation to the signal v_i. Hence, if $R_{L1} = R_{L2}$, the two signals will be equal in magnitude (the same current flows through both R_{L1} and R_{L2}) and inverted in phase.

PROB. 10.22. Show how the phase inverter of Fig. 10.31 can be directly coupled to the plate of the amplifier which precedes it. Use triodes for both the phase inverter and the preceding amplifier. A single duo-triode would serve both functions.

Since the cathode circuit acts as a cathode follower, the total voltage gain in the cathode circuit is less than one. Similarly, since the voltage gain in the plate circuit is equal to the voltage gain in the cathode circuit,

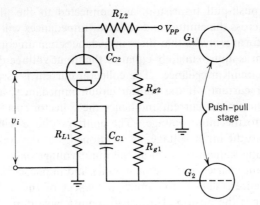

Fig. 10.31. A split-load phase inverter circuit.

the total voltage gain in the plate circuit is less than one. However, since the voltage in the cathode is inverted in relation to the voltage in the plate, the *grid-to-grid voltage* on the push-pull stages may have a gain greater than one (but never greater than two).

The transistor version of the phase inverter of Fig. 10.31 is shown in Fig. 10.32. The operation of this circuit is the same as for a vacuum tube. However, in this version, the *currents* flowing in the base circuits of T_2 and T_3 must be equal. As for the vacuum tube, the voltage across R_{L1} will be equal to the voltage across R_{L2} if transistors T_2 and T_3 are not present.[5]

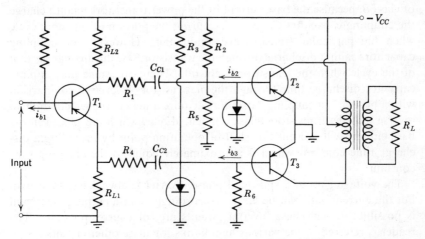

Fig. 10.32. The transistor version of Fig. 10.30.

[5] R_{L1} passes a slightly greater current ($I_C + I_B$) than the current through R_{L2}, (I_C). This current difference is usually negligible but can be compensated for by making R_{L1} less than R_{L2}.

When the push-pull transistors are connected to the phase inverter, the voltages across the emitter and collector impedances will be equal and of good waveform *provided* that these impedances remain equal. The total emitter current is approximately equal to the input voltage divided by the total emitter circuit impedance. The collector current is essentially equal to the emitter current. If the emitter circuit impedance varies over the signal cycle, the emitter current and hence the collector current will not be proportional to the input voltage. The emitter voltage will be approximately equal to the input voltage, as mentioned, but the collector voltage *will not* have the same waveform as the input voltage *unless* the collector circuit impedance varies in the same manner and in phase with the emitter circuit impedance. This is too much to expect of the collector circuit impedance, since the push-pull transistors must have opposite polarities. Therefore, the emitter and collector circuit impedances must be essentially linear, or nonvarying.

The load impedances of the split load phase inverter can be linearized by making the shunt fixed resistances, such as R_{L1} and R_{L2}, small in comparison with the input resistance to the transistor. Linearization can also be accomplished by placing fixed resistance in series with the transistor input resistance. This method is used in the circuit of Fig. 10.32. A much smaller resistance in the emitter circuits of the push-pull transistors would accomplish the same purpose, providing that they are not bypassed.

The two diodes shown in the base circuits of transistors T_2 and T_3 (Fig. 10.32) are needed when the push-pull amplifier is operated class AB or class B, because the base current of the power transistors tend to charge the coupling capacitors C_{C1} and C_{C2} during the portion of the input cycle when the particular transistor is conducting. However, the coupling capacitors cannot discharge through the transistor base during that portion of the cycle when the transistor is cut off. Therefore, since the coupling capacitor discharge time through the bias resistors is large in comparison with a period, the coupling capacitors acquire a net charge which tends to reverse bias the transistors (class C). The diodes which are placed in the base circuits will prevent this shift of operating point by providing a discharge time constant which is approximately equal to the charging time constant.

The voltage gain of a split load phase inverter is always less than two, but the current gain can be large. Accordingly, considerable power gain is possible. Other phase inverter circuits are, of course, possible. The reader is referred to the various handbooks for these other circuits.

PROB. 10.23. A circuit is connected as shown in Fig. 10.31. (*a*) If $R_{L1} = R_{L2} = 5000\ \Omega$, what is the grid-to-grid voltage if v_i is a sine wave with 1 v peak. Assume g_m is 5000 μmhos and r_p is 10,000 Ω. (*b*) How would you modify the circuit if the desired quiescent point for the phase inverter tube is $V_G = -4$ v when $I_P = 8$ ma? *Answer:* (a) *1.85 v peak.*

PROB. 10.24. A circuit is connected as shown in Fig. 10.32. (a) Find i_{b2} if the signal i_{b1} is 1 ma peak. Assume $R_{L1} = R_{L2} = 1000 \ \Omega$. The input impedances of T_2 and T_3 are each 200 Ω. The characteristics of transistor T_1 are $h_{ie} = 250 \ \Omega$, $h_{re} = 0$, $h_{oe} = 10$ micromhos, h_{fe} or $\beta = 50$. R_2 and R_3 are much larger than 200 Ω. (b) What value should R_{L1} have if R_{L2} is 1000 Ω and perfect balance is desired? Assume $R_5 = R_6 = 500 \ \Omega$ and $R_1 = R_4 = 1000 \ \Omega$.

10.9   GRID DRIVE REQUIREMENTS FOR CLASS B_2 (or AB_2) VACUUM TUBE OPERATION

A rather drastic change occurs in the control grid circuit of a tube when the control grid is driven positive. The positive control grid intercepts electrons from the cathode and current flows in the control grid circuit.

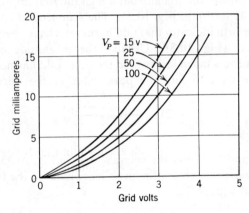

Fig. 10.33. Control-grid current as a function of positive control grid voltage.

The curves of control grid current vs the control grid potential are given in Fig. 10.33. These curves indicate that the control grid current follows the same pattern as does plate current in a diode. In contrast to a diode, the triode plate voltage does have an effect on grid current, but this effect is quite small.[6] Hence, the positive control grid can be roughly represented as a resistor from grid to cathode. The size of this resistor is usually in the order of 1000 Ω or less.

As a result of the action of the positive control grid, the input characteristics of a push-pull class B_2 (or AB_2) vacuum tube amplifier has the form indicated in Fig. 10.34. The voltage $A0$ (and $B0$) represents the bias

---

[6] Plate voltage can have a big effect on grid current if the plate voltage approaches the magnitude of the control grid voltage.

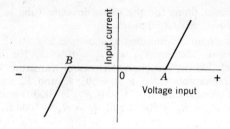

Fig. 10.34. Input characteristics of a class B_2 (or AB_2) vacuum tube push-pull amplifier.

potential of the push-pull grids. As soon as this bias potential is exceeded, the control grid begins to draw current. This control grid current causes a load to be applied to the driver stage which supplies the signal voltage for the push-pull tubes. As a result of this load, *which is only present for the peaks of the input signal*, the signal from a high internal impedance driver stage is distorted as shown in Fig. 10.35. The symmetrical appearance of the distorted waveform indicates that odd harmonics have been introduced into the waveform (Fig. 10.5). Usually, the magnitude of the third harmonic component is much larger than the other odd harmonics. Thus, Eq. 10.22 can be used to find the peak value of the third harmonic component, V_3.

$$V_3 = \frac{2V_{\pi/6} - V_{max} - V_Q}{3} \tag{10.75}$$

where V_{max}, V_Q, and $V_{\pi/6}$ have the values shown in Fig. 10.35. Similarly, Eq. 10.21 may be used to obtain the peak magnitude of the fundamental component of grid voltage V_1.

$$V_1 = \frac{2V_{max} + 2V_{\pi/6} - 4V_Q}{3} \tag{10.76}$$

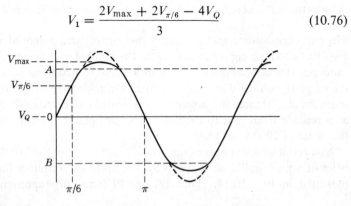

Fig. 10.35. Distortion in the input signal of a class B_2 (or AB_2) push-pull vacuum tube amplifier.

The foregoing analysis reveals the special requirements a driver stage must have to properly operate a class B_2 (or AB_2) stage.

1. The driver stage must be capable of supplying the power required by the positive control grids of the push-pull stage.
2. The output impedance of the driver stage must be much less than the minimum grid circuit impedance for low distortion.

The first condition determines the required size of driver tube. The second condition determines the type of circuit which produces least distortion. Because of the low value of positive grid-to-cathode impedance, transformer coupling is almost always used. (The cathode follower could also be used as a push-pull driver.) This transformer coupling allows the high output impedance of the driver stage to be lowered to meet the low grid-cathode impedance requirement. In addition, the phase inversion for the push-pull grids is achieved by the transformer.

PROB. 10.25. The output impedance of a driver tube is 10,000 Ω. This driver tube is coupled through a transformer to a set of push-pull tubes which have a bias voltage of -25 v. The transformer has 500 turns in the driver plate winding and 1000 turns (center tapped) in the grid-to-grid circuit. The positive grid-to-cathode impedance of the push-pull tubes is approximately 1000 Ω. The magnitude of the signal from the driver stage is 35 v peak when the push-pull tubes are removed from the circuit. (a) What is the peak value of driver voltage with the push-pull tubes in the circuit? (b) What percentage of third harmonic signal is present under these conditions? (c) What is the maximum output power required in the driver stage? *Answer:* (a) *25.9 v,* (b) *10.5%, and* (c) *23.3 mw peak inst. power.*

PROB. 10.26. Repeat Prob. 10.25 if the signal out of the driver tube is tripled and the number of turns on the driver side of the transformer is tripled (1500 turns). The number of turns on the grid side of the transformer are the same as in Prob. 10.25.

10.10   COMPLEMENTARY SYMMETRY AMPLIFIERS

Because of the availability of both *p-n-p* and *n-p-n* configurations, the transistor allows more versatility of design than does the vacuum tube. One interesting circuit arrangement that does not have a vacuum tube counterpart is the *complementary symmetry amplifier*. This amplifier employs one *p-n-p* and one *n-p-n* transistor of similar characteristics in a push-pull arrangement as shown in Fig. 10.36. The two transistors are actually driven in parallel, thus no phase inverter is needed. When the transistors are biased at projected cutoff, the resistor R_1 is very small in comparison with the resistors R_2 and R_3. Therefore, R_1 does not materially increase the input impedance of the amplifier, even though it is not by-passed. The resistor R_1 may be a potentiometer and thus be used to improve the balance of the amplifier.

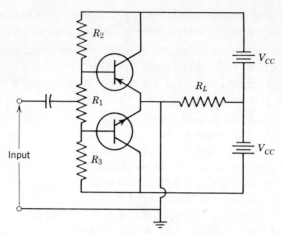

Fig. 10.36. A complementary symmetry push-pull amplifier.

Observe from Fig. 10.36 that the positions of the load resistance and the power supply have been reversed in the complementary symmetry amplifier as compared with the conventional push-pull amplifier. Thus, the signal currents add in the load, but the d-c currents do not pass through the load when the load is placed in the common branch. Therefore, no output transformer is required in this push-pull amplifier. However, a transformer may be needed for impedance matching when the available load is not a suitable impedance for the transistors. Fortunately, the popular loud-speaker impedances are suitable as loads for power transistors.

An h-parameter equivalent circuit of the complementary symmetry amplifier is given in Fig. 10.37. Inspection of this circuit shows that the

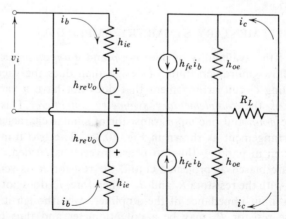

Fig. 10.37. An h-parameter circuit for the complementary symmetry amplifier of Fig. 10.36.

composite h-parameter circuit of Fig. 10.38a is also valid. In both of these circuits, class A operation is assumed. In fact, the equivalent circuit of Fig. 10.37 is valid only for class A operation because the individual transistors must operate linearly for the h parameters to be meaningful. However, the composite equivalent circuit may be applicable to class AB operation as well as class A, providing that the composite characteristics are linear. The composite h parameters for class AB operation are equivalent to the class A, h parameters of the individual transistor, as previously discussed, because essentially only one transistor is conducting during each half cycle. The class AB h-parameter circuit is shown in Fig. 10.38b. Observe that the actual load resistance R_L is the *composite* load

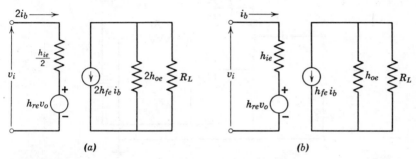

(a) (b)

Fig. 10.38. The h-parameter equivalent circuit of the composite transistor (a) class A, and (b) class AB.

resistance. Therefore, the composite load line has a slope equal to the reciprocal of R_L not $R_L/4$ as in the conventional push-pull amplifier. Composite characteristics may be obtained and graphical analysis performed for the complementary symmetry amplifier in the same manner as for the conventional push-pull amplifier.

The possible elimination of the output transformer with its cost, weight, and response characteristic disadvantages are very enticing in favor of the complementary symmetry amplifier. However, this circuit also has disadvantages. First, two power supplies are needed, as shown in Fig. 10.36. Also, in the common emitter circuit of Fig. 10.36 the power supplies cannot be at ground signal potential because the output signal voltage appears between the power supplies and ground. The shunt capacitance which exists between the power supplies and ground makes this circuit undesirable. Also, the power supplies are not usable for other amplifiers in the system unless a common ground exists.

A circuit which places the power supplies at signal ground potential is shown in Fig. 10.39. This circuit differs only from the common emitter circuit of Fig. 10.36 in that the ground or common point has been moved to the power supply end of the load resistor. However, this change in ground point changes the amplifier to the common collector configuration. In addition to the desirable ground point, this configuration provides very good linearity because the load voltage is almost identical to the input voltage. However, this common collector configuration has high-input impedance and for this reason requires comparatively high-voltage excitation, thus reducing the power gain and increasing the excitation problems.

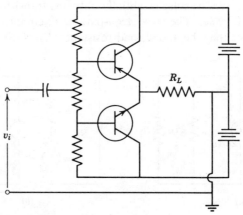

Fig. 10.39. A common collector configuration of the complementary symmetry amplifier.

A final disadvantage of the complementary symmetry configuration is the limited availability and high cost of complementary symmetry pairs of transistors. A circuit which provides the advantages of the complementary circuit but employs two power transistors of the same type is shown in Fig. 10.40. This circuit is known as a *quasi-complementary circuit*. The main difference between this circuit and the complementary symmetry circuit is the input circuit. Although the power transistor T_4 is in the common emitter configuration, the input impedance of the *n-p-n* driver T_2 matches that of the *p-n-p* driver T_1 because the effective resistance in the emitter circuit of the *n-p-n* driver is $R_L i_L / i_{E2}$ and is therefore $(h_{fe4} + 1)R_L$. Although a complementary symmetry pair of transistors is used to drive the power transistors, these transistors do not need to be closely matched. Therefore, there is little difficulty in obtaining this complementary pair. Both driver transistors operate in the common collector mode. They have very high (and about equal) input impedances.

Note that diodes are not needed in the base circuit of the complementary symmetry or quasi-complementary amplifiers included here because no coupling capacitors are required. When the thermal stability

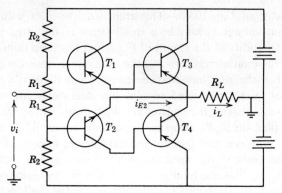

Fig. 10.40. A quasi-complementary circuit which uses power transistors of the same type.

requirements are stringent, it may become necessary to place thermistors or reversed biased diodes in the base circuits, as will be discussed, in order to provide adequate thermal stability.

A quasi-complementary circuit which uses a single power supply is shown in Fig. 10.41. The capacitor C in series with the load resistor R_L permits the load resistor to return to one end of the power supply rather than to a center point. Also the transistor T_1 has replaced the lower

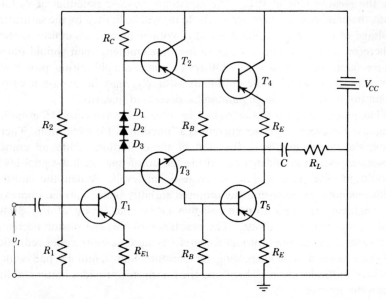

Fig. 10.41. A quasi-complementary circuit which uses a single power supply.

biasing resistor of Fig. 10.40. This transistor provides voltage gain so that the input voltage v_I may be a small signal of the order of one volt. The thermal stability of the circuit of Fig. 10.41 has been improved by the addition of the emitter resistors R_E, the base circuit resistors R_B, and the replacement of the inter-base biasing resistors with diodes D_1, D_2 and D_3. These diodes must be selected so that the total quiescent voltage drop across them is equal to the sum of the V_{BE} drops across transistors T_2, T_3, and T_4 plus the $I_E R_E$ drop in the emitter circuit of T_4 at quiescent conditions. However the Q-point emitter current is normally very near zero and the resistor R_E must be small in comparison with the load resistance R_L so that the load power will not be decreased appreciably. Therefore the $I_E R_E$ drop may usually be neglected at the low temperature Q point.

As the input signal v_I goes positive (Fig. 10.41), the current through transistor T_1 decreases, and the forward bias of transistor T_2 increases. When transistor T_1 reaches cutoff, transistors T_2 and T_4 should reach saturation so maximum voltage is available across the load. Since the saturation value of base current for T_2 must flow through R_C, the value of R_C should be chosen so that the voltage drop across R_C does not exceed one or two volts when this maximum base current flows through it. As the input voltage v_I goes negative and transistor T_1 is driven toward saturation, the base potential of transistor T_3 approaches ground potential on the positive side of V_{CC}. The maximum positive potential of T_3 (and thus the maximum voltage across the load) will be limited by the saturation voltage of transistor T_1 plus the $i_E R_{E1}$ voltage drop in its emitter circuit. Therefore this maximum voltage drop in the emitter circuit should not be more than one or two volts. Otherwise the available output power will be seriously reduced. The emitter resistor R_{E1} may be bypassed with a resulting increased voltage gain and a decreased linearity.

The emitter circuit resistor *cannot* be bypassed in the class *AB* amplifier because the average emitter current is a function of the excitation. Therefore, the bias would be a function of the excitation. Thus an emitter resistance which would provide projected cutoff bias at low-signal levels would provide class *C* bias at large-signal levels. When the stability requirements are stringent, the required stability factor may be improved by replacing the base-to-base resistors (R_1 in the circuit of Fig. 10.41) with a thermistor or diode. The resistance of this thermistor decreases with increasing temperature and therefore causes a more rapid reduction of base current with increasing temperature than could be had with a resistor in this location. Therefore, the thermistor provides better stability than the resistor.

The circuits included in this chapter are intended to be representative, not all inclusive. Many additional circuits may be found in the literature.[7]

PROB. 10.27. Two 2N1905 transistors are to be used in a quasi-complementary circuit with an 8-Ω loudspeaker as a load. Select a suitable value for V_{CC}. Draw the load line and calculate the maximum sinusoidal power output available. V_{CE} max for the 2N1905 is -40 v. Assume the maximum dissipation with the available heat system is 10 w per transistor. Use projected cutoff bias. *Answer: With $V_{CC} = -20$ v, $P_O = 22.3$ w.*

PROB. 10.28. Two 2N2147 power transistors are used in the circuit of Fig. 10.41. The *n-p-n* driver is a 2N3705 and the other two transistors are type 2N3703. The total power supply voltage is 30 v. The 2N2147's are mounted on one 9 in. × 12 in. aluminum chassis with transistor sockets which have 0.6°C/w thermal resistance. Using projected cutoff, determine:

1. Minumum permissible load resistance if the maximum ambient temperature is 40°C.
2. Maximum permissible stability factor S_I when an 8 Ω load is used (40°C maximum ambient).
3. Determine suitable values of all components with $R_L = 8$ Ω.
4. Determine maximum sinusoidal power output and required driving voltage V_i for your amplifier.

PROB. 10.29. The typical operation for *two* 6L6 tubes operating in push-pull class AB, is listed in the tube manual as:

Plate voltage = 360 v
Screen voltage = 270 v
Grid voltage = -22.5 v
Peak grid-to-grid voltage = 45 v
Zero signal plate current = 88 ma (44 ma/tube)
Maximum signal plate current = 132 ma
Zero signal screen current = 5 ma (2.5 ma/tube)
Maximum signal current = 15 ma
Effective plate-to-plate load resistance = 6600
Maximum signal power output = 26.5 watts

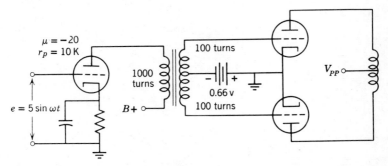

Fig. 10.42. The configuration for Prob. 10.30.

[7] One excellent circuits handbook is Seymour Schwartz, Ed., *Selected Semiconductor Circuits Handbook*, Wiley, New York, 1960.

Draw the circuit and determine the magnitude of all resistors and capacitors. Assume the lowest frequency to be amplified is 50 Hz. Prove the maximum signal power output would be 26.5 watts for the conditions listed.

PROB. 10.30. A circuit is connected as shown in Fig. 10.42. Plot the voltage waveform on the grids of the push-pull circuit. If only third harmonic distortion is assumed to be present, find the magnitude of third harmonic component. Assume the resistance from cathode to positive control grid is 1000 Ω.

PROB. 10.31. A 2N174 transistor has $T_{j\,max} = 100°C$ and Θ_{jc} (junction to case) $= 0.5°C/w$. If the thermal resistance from case to ambient $\Theta_{ca} = 0.5°C/w$ also, determine the current stability factor required to prevent thermal runaway if:

(a) the transistor is transformer coupled and $V_{CC} = 40$ v.

(b) the transistor must dissipate 30 w.

(c) the maximum ambient temperature is 35°C.

(d) $I_{CO} = 3$ ma at 25°C and doubles for each 10°C temperature increment. What is the maximum power dissipation rating of this transistor (case temperature 25°C)?

11

Amplifiers with Negative Feedback

The performance characteristics of amplifiers may be altered by the use of feedback, that is, by adding part or all of the output signal to the input signal. If there are an even number of polarity reversals (or no polarity reversals) in the closed loop[1] so the feedback signal re-enforces the input signal in the mid-frequency range, the feedback is said to be positive. This type of feedback is usually employed in oscillator circuits, which are treated in Chapter 13. On the other hand, if there are an odd number of polarity reversals in the closed loop so the feedback signal tends to cancel the input signal in the mid-frequency range, the feedback is said to be negative. This negative feedback is the subject of this chapter. Feedback affects the driving point impedances as well as the transfer function of the amplifier. These effects are considered in the following paragraphs.

[1] The closed loop is the signal path from the input through the amplifier and the feedback system back to the input.

11.1 THE EFFECTS OF FEEDBACK ON GAIN, DISTORTIƆN, AND NOISE

The block diagram of an amplifier with negative feedback is given in Fig. 11.1. The signal is indicated at the various points by the symbol x. It may be seen from the diagram and from the definition of a transfer function

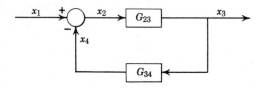

Fig. 11.1. The block diagram of an amplifier with negative feedback.

that the following relations exist.

$$x_3 = x_2 G_{23} \tag{11.1}$$

$$x_4 = x_3 G_{34} \tag{11.2}$$

$$x_2 = x_1 - x_4 \tag{11.3}$$

To obtain the transfer function of the feedback amplifier, x_3 is needed in terms of x_1. Then, combining the foregoing equations, we have

$$x_3 = (x_1 - x_4)G_{23} = (x_1 - x_3 G_{34})G_{23} \tag{11.4}$$

rearranging terms,

$$x_3(1 + G_{23}G_{34}) = x_1 G_{23} \tag{11.5}$$

and

$$G_{13} = \frac{x_3}{x_1} = \frac{G_{23}}{1 + G_{23}G_{34}} \tag{11.6}$$

or when mid-frequency amplification is considered, the mid-frequency reference gain K_{13} of the feedback amplifier may be written from Eq. 11.6 as

$$K_{13} = \frac{K_{23}}{1 + K_{23}\beta} \tag{11.7}$$

where K_{23} is the reference gain of the amplifier without feedback and β is the mid-frequency value of G_{34}. This β is frequently known as the feedback factor.[2] In electronic amplifiers, β is almost always less than unity. In

[2] The symbol β has been used in previous chapters to represent the current amplification factor of the common emitter transistor. However, β is also commonly used in the literature to represent the feedback factor, determined at mid-frequency. Therefore, β will be used as the feedback factor in this chapter and the common emitter current amplification factor will be exclusively h_{fe}.

fact, G_{34} is usually a voltage dividing network, as will be seen in the examples which follow. Notice that the reference gain is reduced by the factor $1 + K_{23}\beta$.

Negative feedback may be used to stabilize the gain of an amplifier. With reference to Eq. 11.6, the product $G_{23}G_{34}$ may be large in comparison with unity. Under these conditions the transfer function with feedback becomes

$$G_{13} \simeq \frac{G_{23}}{G_{23}G_{34}} = \frac{1}{G_{34}} \qquad (11.8)$$

Similarly, the reference gain of the amplifier becomes

$$K_{13} \simeq \frac{1}{\beta} \qquad (11.9)$$

Again, G_{34} may be the ratio of two resistances in a voltage-dividing network, and thus the transfer function, or gain, is almost wholly independent of the characteristics of the amplifying device which may change with

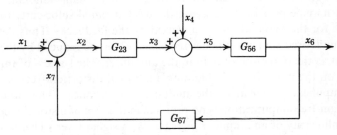

Fig. 11.2. A feedback amplifier with two input signals.

temperature, age, and power supply voltage. For example, the transconductance of a vacuum tube decreases with age. However, the gain of the amplifier will remain essentially constant as long as $G_{23}G_{34}$ (or $K_{23}\beta$) remains large in comparison with unity.

More than one signal may be introduced into an amplifier, as is shown in Fig. 11.2. This feedback amplifier has two input signals, x_1 and x_4. The plus signs indicate that x_3 is added to x_4; however, these two signals may have different waveforms or frequencies and the instantaneous polarity would then vary from time to time.

If the amplifiers are linear, the law of superposition may be applied to the signals in the amplifier of Fig. 11.2. That is, the part of the output signal x_6 which results from input signal x_1 may be determined as though signal x_4 were not present. Likewise, the part of the output signal x_6 which results from input signal x_4 may be determined by considering x_1 to be nonexistent. The sum of these two output signals would actually be x_6. Equation 11.6 may be used to obtain the transfer functions with feedback.

$$G_{16} = \frac{G_{23}G_{56}}{1 + G_{23}G_{56}G_{67}} \tag{11.10}$$

Also

$$G_{46} = \frac{G_{56}}{1 + G_{23}G_{56}G_{67}} \tag{11.11}$$

With no feedback (using again the principle of superposition), $G_{16} = G_{23}G_{56}$ and $G_{46} = G_{56}$. Therefore, it is evident by inspection of Eq. 11.10 and 11.11 that the negative feedback reduces the transfer function from each input by the same amount; namely, the total loop gain of the system plus one.

Now, consider the case where the signal x_4 is distortion[3] or noise generated within the amplifier. The application of negative feedback would reduce the amount of the undesirable signal appearing in the output. The desired signal from x_1 would also be reduced by the same amount. However, it may be possible to increase the desired signal sufficiently to compensate for the reduction in gain caused by the feedback. Thus the ratio of the undesired signal to the desired signal could be reduced by the same amount as the reduction of gain in the amplifier. The success of this plan hinges on the possibility of obtaining additional distortion-free, or noise-free amplification ahead of the undesired disturbance. This additional distortion-free amplification is no problem in the case of distortion because the nonlinearity of an amplifier increases with signal level. Therefore, the final or output stage of an amplifier is usually the chief contributor of distortion. Conversely, the reduction of noise by feedback is not so fruitful because the noise in the output of an amplifier is determined primarily by the noise generated in the first stage. For example, the noise generated in the input of the first amplifier will be amplified and then applied as a signal to the second amplifier, as discussed in Chapter 9. Therefore, the most noise-free amplifier should be used as the first, or input, amplifier. It is usually assumed that the signal input to the first amplifier is fixed. Thus the application of negative feedback will reduce both the signal and noise by the same amount and the signal to noise ratio will remain unchanged.

---

[3] The consideration that the signal x_4 might represent the amplifier distortion appears to be in conflict with the requirement that the amplifiers must be linear to validate the superposition theorem. However, the representation of the distortion as an external signal effectively removes this distortion source from the amplifier, thus creating a distortionless amplifier.

Returning to the reduction of distortion by negative feedback, we see that the ratio of distortion with feedback D_f, to distortion without feedback D_o, is

$$\frac{D_f}{D_o} = \frac{G_{56}/(1 + G_{23}G_{56}G_{67})}{G_{56}} = \frac{1}{1 + G_{23}G_{56}G_{67}} \tag{11.12}$$

But $G_{23}G_{56}$ is the transfer function from the desired signal input to the output or total forward transfer function. Therefore, in the symbolism of Fig. 11.1,

$$\frac{D_f}{D_o} = \frac{1}{1 + G_{23}G_{34}} \tag{11.13}$$

In the region of operation where the reference gain is applicable, Eq. 11.13 reduces to

$$D_f = \frac{D_o}{1 + K_{23}\beta} \tag{11.14}$$

11.2 THE EFFECT OF NEGATIVE FEEDBACK ON BANDWIDTH

The effect of negative feedback on the transfer function of a single stage R-C coupled amplifier will be investigated first. The transfer function which neglected the shunt capacitance was

$$G = -K \frac{s}{s + \omega_1} \tag{7.28}$$

The negative sign associated with K will be omitted in the remainder of this chapter. This sign indicates polarity reversal which has already been accounted for in the derivation of the feedback formula. Then, if it is assumed that the feedback is obtained from a resistive voltage divider so that $G_{34} = \beta$, the transfer function with feedback is

$$G_f = \frac{Ks/(s + \omega_1)}{1 + \dfrac{Ks\beta}{s + \omega_1}} = \frac{Ks}{s + \omega_1 + Ks\beta} \tag{11.15}$$

$$G_f = \frac{Ks}{(1 + K\beta)s + \omega_1} = \frac{K}{1 + K\beta} \frac{s}{s + \omega_1/(1 + K\beta)} \tag{11.16}$$

It may be observed from Eq. 11.16 that ω_1, as well as the reference gain, is reduced by the factor $1 + K\beta$. Since the transfer function of the transformer-coupled amplifier is of the same form as that of the R-C coupled amplifier when the shunt capacitances are neglected, the reduction in ω_1 would be the same in the two cases.

The effect of feedback on the large s or high-frequency performance of an R-C coupled amplifier will now be investigated. The transfer function of the R-C coupled amplifier without feedback follows:

$$G = -\frac{K\omega_2}{s + \omega_2} \qquad (7.50)$$

Again, it will be assumed that negative feedback is obtained from a resistive voltage dividing network so that $G_{34} = \beta$ is constant and real. Then

$$G_f = \frac{K\omega_2/(s + \omega_2)}{1 + K\beta\omega_2/(s + \omega_2)} = \frac{K\omega_2}{s + \omega_2 + K\beta\omega_2} \qquad (11.17)$$

$$G_f = \frac{K}{1 + K\beta}\frac{\omega_2(1 + K\beta)}{s + \omega_2(1 + K\beta)} \qquad (11.18)$$

Notice in Eq. 11.18 that ω_2 is multiplied by the factor $1 + K\beta$. Therefore, the upper cutoff frequency, and hence the bandwidth, of amplifier is increased by the same factor by which the reference gain is reduced.

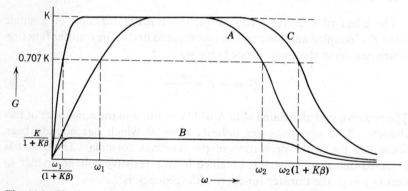

Fig. 11.3. The frequency response of a typical R-C coupled amplifier. Curve A is for the amplifier with no feedback. Curve B is taken with negative feedback but no increase of input gain. Curve C is for negative feedback and increased input signal.

Consequently *the gain-bandwidth product of the amplifier with feedback is the same as that of the amplifier without feedback.*

The effect which negative feedback has on the frequency response of an R-C coupled amplifier is illustrated in Fig. 11.3. The improvement of the frequency response characteristics is most evident when the input signal is increased to compensate for the decreased gain due to feedback, as shown by Curve C. The rise time and flat top response to a rectangular input signal are improved by the same factor as the frequency response, when feedback is applied. The relationships between frequency response and time response were discussed in Chapter 7.

The effect of negative feedback on the high-frequency performance of a transformer-coupled amplifier will be deferred to Section 11.7 in which the stability and performance characteristics are considered jointly.

In passing, the student should observe that the equations which have been developed for negative feedback also apply for the positive feedback if the sign of β is reversed. Then the factor $1 + K\beta$ becomes $1 - K\beta$ and the performance of the amplifier is modified in a manner opposite to that of negative feedback.

PROB. 11.1. A certain amplifier has a reference gain = 100. Negative feedback is applied to the amplifier. If the feedback factor $\beta = 0.1$, determine the reference gain of the amplifier with feedback.

PROB. 11.2. The amplifier of Prob. 1 delivers 10 w of power output at 10% distortion when 0.1 v signal is applied to the input without feedback. Determine the per cent distortion and required input voltage after the negative feedback has been applied, assuming that the power output is to remain at 10 w. *Answer: $D_f = 0.91\%$ and $V_i = 1.1$ volts.*

PROB. 11.3. A frequency response curve of the amplifier of Prob. 11.1, without feedback, indicates that $f_1 = 30$ Hz and $f_2 = 100$ KHz. The amplifier has R-C coupling. Determine f_1 and f_2 after the application of negative feedback. Sketch the frequency response with feedback and without feedback.

The equations in the preceding paragraphs of this chapter are completely general in regard to the types of signal and transfer function involved. For example, the transfer function could be a current ratio (current gain), a voltage ratio (voltage gain), or a ratio of current to voltage. However, the only transfer functions which have been considered for electronic amplifiers are current gain and voltage gain. Where current gain is being considered, the feedback factor must be a current ratio. Conversely, when the voltage gain is of prime concern, the feedback factor must be considered as a voltage ratio. Every amplifier has a voltage transfer function as well as a current transfer function. The relationship between these transfer functions is

$$G_v = \frac{V_o}{V_i} = \frac{I_o Z_L}{I_i Z_i} = \frac{G_i Z_L}{Z_i} \tag{11.19}$$

where G_v = the voltage transfer function
$\quad\quad G_i$ = the current transfer function
$\quad\quad Z_L$ = the s-domain load impedance
$\quad\quad Z_i$ = the s-domain input impedance

Similarly, every feedback network must provide a ratio of feedback current to output current as well as a ratio of feedback voltage to output voltage. These ratios will generally not be the same, as is demonstrated from the distortion relationship, Eq. 11.14. Consider first that the transfer functions are voltage ratios; then

$$D_f = \frac{D_o}{1 + K_v \beta_v} \tag{11.20}$$

Substituting the reference current gain for the reference voltage gain (Eq. 11.19), we find that

$$D_f = \frac{D_o}{1 + \beta_v K_i (R_L/R_i)} = \frac{D_o}{1 + \beta_i K_i} \tag{11.21}$$

But the distortion in the output current waveform is the same as the distortion in the output voltage waveform when the load is resistive. Also, a specific feedback network will provide a specific amount of distortion without regard to whether the total loop gain has been considered as a current ratio or a voltage ratio. Then, from Eq. 11.21,

$$\beta_i K_i = \beta_v K_i \frac{R_L}{R_i} \tag{11.22}$$

and

$$\beta_i = \frac{\beta_v R_L}{R_i} \tag{11.23}$$

11.3 THE EFFECT OF NEGATIVE FEEDBACK ON OUTPUT IMPEDANCE

Figure 11.4 will be used to investigate the effect of negative feedback on output impedance. The output resistance is determined by applying a

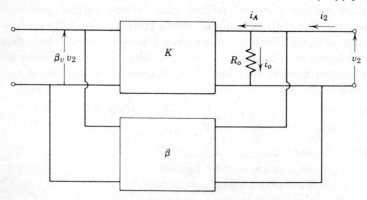

Fig. 11.4. A circuit used to determine the output impedance of an amplifier with voltage feedback.

voltage v_2 to the output terminals and by evaluating the current i_2 which results. The impedance will be determined in the mid-frequency range and will, therefore, be resistive. Note that the output resistance R_o of the amplifier without feedback is drawn external to the block representing the amplifier. Since the feedback voltage $\beta_v v_2$ is proportional to the output voltage, this type of feedback (parallel output connection) is known as *voltage feedback*. The input current is

$$i_i = \frac{\beta_v v_2}{R_i} \tag{11.24}$$

Since the amplifier must include an odd number of polarity reversals (negative feedback), the output current i_A is in the direction shown.

$$i_A = K_i i_i = \frac{\beta_v K_i v_2}{R_i} \tag{11.25}$$

If the feedback network draws negligible current in comparison with the output current, the total current provided by the source v_2 is

$$i_2 = i_o + i_A = \frac{v_2}{R_o} + \frac{\beta_v K_i}{R_i} v_2 \tag{11.26}$$

But, using Eq. 11.23, $\beta_v/R_i = \beta_i/R_o$. Then

$$i_2 = v_2 \left(\frac{1}{R_o} + \frac{\beta_i K_i}{R_o} \right) \tag{11.27}$$

and since $K_i \beta_i = K_v \beta_v = K\beta$, the output resistance with feedback is

$$R_{of} = \frac{v_2}{i_2} = \frac{R_o}{1 + K\beta} \tag{11.28}$$

In the second case to be considered, the feedback voltage v_f is proportional to the output current as shown in Fig. 11.5. This type of feedback is known as *current feedback*. The amplifier input current is

$$i_i = -\beta_i i_2 \tag{11.29}$$

Then the amplifier output current is

$$i_A = K_i i_i = -\beta_i K_i i_2 \tag{11.30}$$

The current i_2 as provided by the source v_2 is

$$i_2 = i_o + i_A = i_o - \beta_i K_i i_2 \tag{11.31}$$

If the voltage drop $i_2 R_f$ across the series feedback resistor is small in comparison with v_2, then $i_o \simeq v_2/R_o$ and

$$i_2(1 + K_i\beta_i) = \frac{v_2}{R_o} \qquad (11.32)$$

As a result, the output resistance with feedback is

$$R_{of} = \frac{v_2}{i_2} \simeq R_o(1 + K\beta) \qquad (11.33)$$

Thus the output impedance has been increased by the term $(1 + K\beta)$ as a result of current feedback.

Observe from Fig. 11.5 that the polarity of the amplifier input voltage

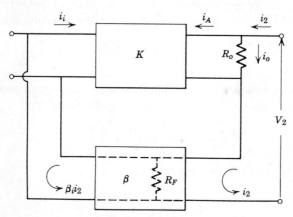

Fig. 11.5. A circuit used to determine the effect of current feedback on output impedance.

resulting from feedback is reversed in the current feedback case as compared with the voltage feedback of Fig. 11.4. Note, however, that the feedback is negative in each case, as can be verified by terminating the amplifier with a load resistance and by comparing the polarity of the feedback voltage with an assumed input voltage.

PROB. 11.4. The cathode follower may be considered as an amplifier with feedback since $v_{gk} = v_i - v_o$. In this case, $\beta_v = 1$. Derive expressions for the voltage gain and output impedance of the amplifier in terms of μ, r_p, and R_L.

PROB. 11.5. An amplifier with impedance in the emitter circuit may be treated as an amplifier with feedback. The feedback voltage is $i_L Z_E$ and $\beta_v = Z_E/Z_L$ where Z_E is the emitter impedance, Z_L is the load resistance, and i_L is the output current. Determine the voltage gain of a vacuum tube amplifier which has $\mu = 100$, $r_p = 50$ KΩ, $R_L = 100$ KΩ, and R_E (unbypassed resistance in the cathode circuit) $= 2$ KΩ. *Answer:* $G_f = 28.6$.

PROB. 11.6. Determine the output resistance of the amplifier of Prob. 11.5. Would you expect the bandwidth of this amplifier to be greater with the cathode resistance bypassed or unbypassed? Why?

11.4 THE EFFECT OF FEEDBACK ON INPUT IMPEDANCE

In the preceding discussion, there has been no concern about the method of mixing the feedback signal with the input signal. There are two basic ways of mixing these signals—the amplifier input and feedback ports may be connected either in series or parallel. The series connection

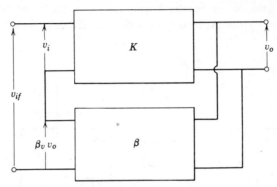

Fig. 11.6. A circuit used to determine the input resistance with the amplifier input and feedback ports in series.

of Fig. 11.6 will be considered first and the input impedance for this configuration will be determined. The input voltage with feedback is

$$v_{if} = v_i + \beta_v v_o = v_i(1 + K_v\beta_v) \tag{11.34}$$

But $v_i = i_i R_i$. Then, (using $K_v\beta_v = K\beta$)

$$v_{if} = i_i R_i(1 + K\beta) \tag{11.35}$$

Finally, the input resistance with feedback is

$$R_{if} = \frac{v_{if}}{i_i} = R_i(1 + K\beta) \tag{11.36}$$

The inquisitive reader will ask, "What effect does this increased impedance have on the gain of the amplifier which precedes the feedback amplifier?" The answer is, "If the increased impedance provides an improved impedance match between the two amplifiers, the power gain of the preceding amplifier will be increased and vice versa." For a vacuum tube amplifier, the input impedance of the tube at mid-frequencies is essentially infinite; therefore, the impedance match remains essentially unchanged and the reference gain of the preceding amplifier is unchanged. In a transistor amplifier, the input impedance without feedback is usually smaller than the output impedance of the driving amplifier. Under these conditions, the increased input impedance of the feedback amplifier will increase the power gain of the preceding amplifier for moderate amounts of feedback because the impedance match will be improved. As the input impedance of the transistor amplifier is increased, its input current will decrease and the current gain of the preceding amplifier will decrease accordingly. However, this is the actual mechanism by which the current gain of the feedback amplifier is reduced, and it has been accounted for by the previously derived transfer functions. The voltage

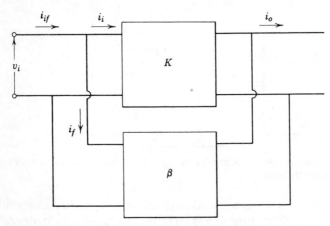

Fig. 11.7. A circuit used to determine the input resistance with the amplifier input and feedback ports in parallel.

gain of the preceding amplifier will increase more rapidly than its current gain decreases until the matched condition is obtained. This explanation accounts for the improved power gain.

The parallel port connection is shown in Fig. 11.7. From this configuration, the input current with feedback is

$$i_{if} = i_i + i_f \tag{11.37}$$

But $i_f = \beta_i i_o$ and $i_o = K_i i_i$. Therefore,

$$i_{if} = i_i + K_i \beta_i i_i = i_i(1 + K_i \beta_i) \tag{11.38}$$

Since $i_i = v_i Y_i$, where Y_i is the amplifier admittance without feedback, the input admittance with feedback is

$$Y_{if} = \frac{i_{if}}{v_{if}} = Y_i(1 + K\beta) \tag{11.39}$$

Observe that for the parallel connection the input impedance is reduced by the factor $1 + K\beta$.

Again, the effects of the reduced input impedance of the feedback amplifier on the gain of the preceding amplifier should be considered. In a transistor amplifier the current gain of the preceding amplifier is essentially unaltered, assuming the normally mis-matched *R-C* coupled case. Voltage and power gain will decrease, however. In a vacuum tube amplifier, the power gain of the driving amplifier will be increased for moderate amounts of feedback because of the improved impedance match. The feedback equations account for the reduction on voltage gain.

The feedback paths previously discussed have all been provided by resistors. It was assumed that the output should be a faithful reproduction of the input. Sometimes it is desirable to alter the waveforms or frequency response of the output as compared with the input. This alteration can be accomplished by including capacitive or inductive elements in the feedback path. For example, a series capacitance in the feedback circuit will provide a feedback factor of the form

$$G_{34} = \beta \frac{s}{s + \omega_f} \tag{11.40}$$

The feedback factor will then be essentially inversely proportional to *s* for values of *s* smaller than ω_f, where ω_f is the reciprocal of the time constant of the feedback circuit. This type of circuit could be used to provide a "bass boost" tone control.

Another interesting use of the feedback circuit to control the waveform of the output is the integrator version of the operational amplifier which is used so extensively in analog computers. The parallel-type feedback is used but the feedback path consists of a capacitor. This path causes the input impedance of the amplifier to be of the form $Y_i = 1/Cs$. Under these conditions the output waveform will be the integral of the input waveform.

PROB. 11.7. Show that the feedback factor G_{34} can be written as $\beta \dfrac{s}{s + \omega_f}$ when the feedback path consists of *R* and *C* in series.

PROB. 11.8. A given transistor amplifier has 2KΩ input resistance and 2KΩ output resistance without feedback. The output voltage polarity is opposite to that of the input. What type of input and output port connections (series or parallel) are needed for a negative feedback circuit which will permit this amplifier to be inserted in a 500 Ω (characteristic impedance) telephone line without causing a mis-match in the line in either direction? (i.e., make $Z_{in} = Z_{out} = 500\,\Omega$). What value of $K\beta$ will be required? *Answer: $K\beta = 3$.*

11.5 TYPICAL FEEDBACK CIRCUITS

Since low output impedance is usually desirable in an amplifier—at least a broadband amplifier—voltage feedback is much more common than current feedback. Figure 11.8 shows a common series voltage feedback arrangement for an *R-C* coupled amplifier. Since there is no polarity reversal between the emitter and collector of an amplifier, the second amplifier provides the only polarity reversal between the point of application of the feedback and the amplifier output. This polarity reversal is necessary to provide negative feedback. Notice that the feedback voltage

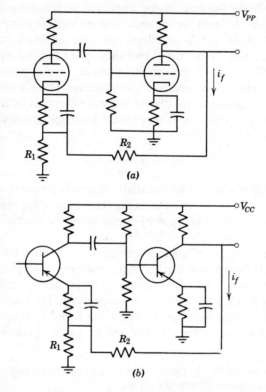

Fig. 11.8. Series-type voltage feedback for *R-C* coupled amplifiers.

tends to cancel the input voltage. It is usually desirable that R_1 be as small as possible to provide minimum degeneration and thus maximum gain for the input amplifier. Also, the resistance of R_2 should be large in comparison with the total shunt output impedance of the output amplifier. Otherwise R_2 would appreciably reduce the gain of the second amplifier due to loading. Consequently, a sensible design procedure might be to choose R_2 about ten times the total shunt resistance R_{sh} of the output amplifier. Then the resistance of R_1 could be calculated to give the desired amount of feedback.

A casual glance at Fig. 11.8 might cause us to conclude that the reference feedback factor is

$$\beta = \frac{i_f R_1}{i_f (R_1 + R_2)} = \frac{R_1}{R_1 + R_2} \tag{11.41}$$

However, the emitter current of the input amplifier in addition to the feedback current i_f flows through R_1. Moreover, these two currents are interdependent, which adds to the complexity of calculating an accurate value of R_1. An easy solution to the problem is to calculate R_1 from the relationship of Eq. 11.41 and then experimentally adjust R_2 after the amplifier has been constructed. An example of this procedure follows.

Example 11.1. For the purposes of stabilizing the transfer function, or gain, and improving the response of the tube amplifier of Fig. 11.8, it is desired to make the reference loop gain $K\beta = 10$. First, the reference gain K must be calculated without feedback. We will assume that the reference voltage gain is found to be 50 for each stage. Then the total reference gain of the amplifier is 2500. Consequently $\beta = 10/2500 = 0.004$.

The shunt resistance of the output stage would be somewhat less than r_p — perhaps 50 KΩ since high μ tubes were used. Then the resistor R_2 in the feedback circuit should be of the order of 500 KΩ. Using 470 KΩ for R_2 and the value of β above in Eq. 11.41, R_1 is calculated to be about 1.9 KΩ. This value is a typical value of cathode bias resistance for a triode amplifier. Therefore, the additional bypassed resistance shown in the figure will not be needed. Also a resistance of this magnitude would cause appreciable degeneration in the input amplifier.

The desired loop gain could be adjusted experimentally by measuring the open loop reference gain of the amplifier with the resistor R_2 disconnected. Then a value of R_2 could be selected experimentally which would reduce the gain of the amplifier by the factor $1 + K\beta = 1 + 10 = 11$.

In case there is no blocking capacitor in the feedback loop, as shown in Fig. 11.8, the direct current through R_2 must be added to the quiescent plate current of the input amplifier in determining the bias for that amplifier.

PROB. 11.9. Determine a feedback circuit for the transistor amplifier of Fig. 11.8b. Use 2N192 transistors and assume that the load resistance of the second transistor is 2 KΩ. Is your value of R_1 suitable for temperature stabilization of the input transistor? Use $K\beta = 10$.

A parallel voltage feedback arrangement for R-C coupled amplifiers is shown in Fig. 11.9. In this arrangement the feedback loop must include an odd number of stages to provide negative feedback. This statement is true only if each amplifier is a common emitter configuration. More correctly, an odd number of polarity reversals must be included within the feedback loop to provide negative feedback. Figure 11.9a shows three common emitter amplifiers within the loop whereas Fig. 11.9b includes

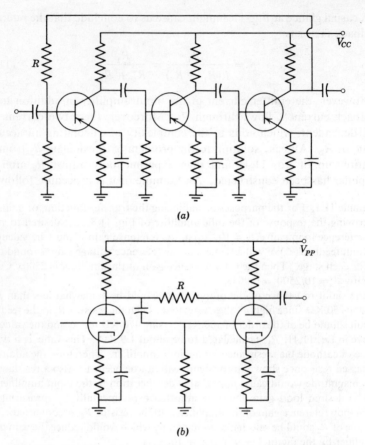

Fig. 11.9. Parallel voltage feedback applied to *R-C* coupled amplifiers.

only one common emitter stage within the loop. Since no blocking capacitor is included in the feedback path, there is d-c feedback as well as signal
feedback. In Fig. 11.9a this d-c feedback tends to stabilize the quiescent
operating point of the input transistor. For example, an investigation of
the relative polarities of the amplifiers with parallel feedback, such as those
of Fig. 11.9, will show that the d-c feedback tends to stabilize the *Q* point
of the input amplifier as well as the final amplifier. Thus, feedback can
improve the thermal stability of a transistor amplifier. However, in order
for the d-c feedback to affect any stage other than the first in the feedback
loop, the amplifier must be direct-coupled. In the series feedback arrangements of Fig. 11.8, the d-c feedback decreases the thermal stability of the
input amplifier. Therefore, a blocking capacitor would probably be

included in the feedback path, to prevent this degeneration in thermal stability.

In a transformer coupled amplifier, negative feedback can improve linearity and response characteristics but not to the same degree as that shown for the R-C coupled amplifier. The extent of the improvement will be seen more clearly in the following section on stability. Transformers are seldom used as coupling devices in untuned amplifiers except to couple the final amplifier to the load. However, the feedback loop should include the transformer so that the effective transformer characteristics will be improved by the feedback. A typical feedback loop which includes the output transformer is shown in Fig. 11.10. When a transformer is included, negative feedback may be obtained with an arbitrary number of stages of arbitrary connection within the loop because either end of the transformer secondary may be used as the reference, or grounded, end. Again, R_2 should be large in comparison with R_L, but R_1 should be small in order to minimize the degeneration in the first stage. Parallel feedback could have been used just as well as the series type shown. In the parallel circuit R_2 may serve as the biasing resistor R'_2, providing that it is a suitable value.

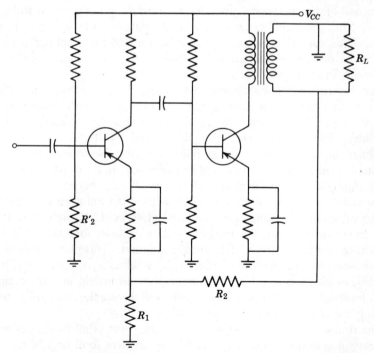

Fig. 11.10. A feedback circuit which includes the output transformer.

As the foregoing discussion indicates, many variations and applications of feedback circuits may be devised by the resourceful engineer.

11.6 STABILITY OF FEEDBACK CIRCUITS

In the beginning of this chapter it was shown that the transfer function of an amplifier with negative feedback is

$$G_{13} = \frac{G_{23}}{1 + G_{23}G_{24}} \tag{11.6}$$

where G_{23} is the forward transfer function of the amplifier and G_{34} is the s-domain feedback factor. The magnitude of the transfer function can be infinite (poles can exist) if there are values of s for which the denominator of Eq. 11.6 becomes zero. Then

$$1 + G_{23}G_{34} = 0 \tag{11.42}$$

or

$$G_{23}G_{34} = -1\underline{/0} = 1\underline{/180°} \tag{11.43}$$

If Eq. 11.43 can be satisfied at real frequencies ($s = j\omega$), a pole will lie on the $j\omega$ axis of the s plane and any transient initiated in the amplifier will not decay. Thus the amplifier can have a steady-state output when there is no input. This condition is known as oscillation and the amplifier is then said to be *unstable*. Oscillation is a "must" for an oscillator, but it is *intolerable* in an amplifier.

The instability, or oscillation, may occur in a feedback amplifier because of the inductances and capacitances in the circuit which may cause polarity reversal with reference to the mid-frequency (s) range of the amplifier. We can determine from the overall transfer function of the amplifier, Eq. 11.6, whether the amplifier will be stable or unstable. One way to determine the stability would be to replace s in the transfer function by $j\omega$ and then to test the denominator and find if it can become zero at real frequencies. A much more informative method is to plot on the s plane all the values of s for which Eq. 11.42 and 11.43 hold. If any part of this plot crosses the $j\omega$ axis, the amplifier will be unstable for values of loop gain which exceed a certain, determinable amount. This plot is known as a *root-locus plot*. In addition to determining whether a particular amplifier is stable or not, this root-locus technique gives an insight into the design of a feedback amplifier which not only will be stable, but which will provide the desired response characteristics.

The root-locus plot is actually a plot of the locus of all the values of s which will give the proper angle (180° for negative feedback) of $G_{23}G_{34}$ (see Eq. 11.43). We may gain the impression that tedious work would be required in plotting a root locus. On the contrary, simple rules have been developed which make it possible to sketch a sufficiently accurate locus with very little effort. Some of these rules are given in Appendix II. The derivation or formulation of all of these rules is too lengthy to be included in this work, but may be found in textbooks and literature primarily devoted to this technique.[4] A few of the basic rules will be stated in the paragraphs which follow.

A few examples will illustrate how the root-locus plot may be used to determine the stability and response characteristics of an amplifier. A single R-C coupled amplifier with a purely resistive feedback circuit as shown in Fig. 11.9 will first be considered. The transfer function derived in Chapter 7 for the R-C coupled amplifier follows:

$$G_{23} = \frac{K s \omega_2}{(s + \omega_1)(s + \omega_2)} \tag{11.44}$$

Then

$$G_{13} = \frac{\dfrac{K s \omega_2}{(s + \omega_1)(s + \omega_2)}}{1 + \dfrac{K \beta s \omega_2}{(s + \omega_1)(s + \omega_2)}} \tag{11.45}$$

Poles occur in the overall transfer function, G_{13}, at values of s which reduce the denominator of Eq. 11.45 to zero. This denominator will equal zero when the following equality holds.

$$\frac{K \beta s \omega_2}{(s + \omega_1)(s + \omega_2)} = -1 = 1\underline{/180°} \tag{11.46}$$

This equation is of the form

$$K' F(s) = 1\underline{/180°} \tag{11.47}$$

where K' is the constant part of $G_{23}G_{34}$, in this case $K\beta\omega_2$, and the function $F(s)$ is the part of $G_{23}G_{34}$ which varies with s. Then

$$F(s) = \frac{s}{(s + \omega_1)(s + \omega_2)} \tag{11.48}$$

A root-locus plot of $F(s)$ will now be made. First, the poles and zeros of $F(s)$ will be plotted on the s plane (see Fig. 11.11). Inspection of Eq. 11.48 shows that the angle of $F(s)$ can be 180° when s is real and is less than zero but greater than $-\omega_1$. Then the numerator is negative and the

[4] An excellent treatment is given in *Introduction to Feedback Systems*, L. Dale Harris, Wiley, New York, 1961.

denominator is positive. The same situation occurs when s is real and less than $-\omega_2$. In fact, the general rule given in Appendix II states that portions of the real axis lying to the left of an odd number of singularities are branches of the root locus in a negative feedback circuit. These plots are shown in Fig. 11.11. Another rule in Appendix II states that the number of infinite seeking branches is equal to the difference between the number of finite poles and finite zeros. Or, to invoke still another rule from Appendix II, all branches must begin on a pole and end on a zero. The number of infinite seeking branches in the example is one since there are two poles and one zero. The plot shown in Fig. 11.11 is the complete

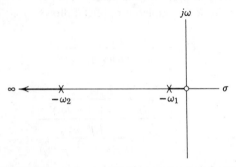

Fig. 11.11. The root-locus plot of an R-C coupled amplifier.

root locus because there is one infinite seeking branch on the negative real axis. Notice that the number of locus branches is the same as the order of the denominator of $F(s)$.

As previously mentioned, poles will occur in the overall transfer function when the angle of $K'F(s)$ is $180°$, which limits s to the root-locus branches, and when the magnitude of $K'F(s)$ is one. Then

$$K' = \frac{1}{|F(s)|} \tag{11.49}$$

If both of the foregoing conditions can be satisfied by a value of s which has a real part σ which is either zero or positive, the transient part of the output either remains constant or increases with time, respectively. Then the amplifier is unstable. Conversely, when the poles of the overall transfer function all lie in the left half of the s plane, the transients decay exponentially with time and the amplifier is said to be stable. In case the root-locus branches lie entirely within the left half plane, the amplifier is said to be *unconditionally stable*, which means it is stable for all finite values of gain.

It may not be obvious that the R-C coupled feedback amplifier whose root locus is plotted in Fig. 11.11 is unconditionally stable, since the root locus touches the $j\omega$ axis at the origin. But there is a zero of $F(s)$ at the origin; therefore K' must be infinite at the origin and the amplifier is stable for any finite gain. Thus this circuit is unconditionally stable.

It is also well to notice that the magnitude of $F(s)$ is infinite at a pole of $F(s)$. Therefore, from Eq. 11.49, K' must be zero at a pole of $F(s)$. Consequently, the value of K' and hence the magnitude of the loop gain must increase from zero to infinity as a root-locus branch is traversed from a pole to a zero.

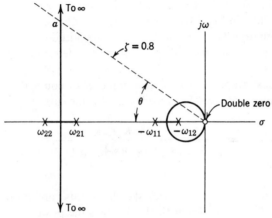

Fig. 11.12. Root-locus plot for a two-stage R-C coupled feedback amplifier.

The case of two R-C coupled stages included in the feedback loop will now be investigated. In this case,

$$G_{23}G_{45} = K'F(s) = \frac{K_1 K_2 \beta \omega_{21} \omega_{22} s^2}{(s + \omega_{11})(s + \omega_{12})(s + \omega_{21})(s + \omega_{22})} \quad (11.50)$$

where ω_{11} is ω_1 of the first amplifier, etc. A pole-zero plot of $F(s)$ is made in Fig. 11.12. The root locus is also sketched as shown with the aid of the basic rules in Appendix II. This locus is tangent to the $j\omega$ axis at the origin, but the point of tangency occurs at a double zero, so K' must be infinite at this point and the amplifier is unconditionally stable.

Each branch of the root locus [beginning on a pole of $F(s)$ and ending on a zero] contains all values of K' between zero and infinity, as previously mentioned. If a point which represents the same value of K' is found on each branch, these points are the poles of the overall transfer function G_{13} with the loop gain adjusted to give the value of K'. This condition follows from the fact that these points are all the zeros of the denominator of G_{13} at the value of K'. Thus it may be seen from Fig. 11.12 that a pair of complex conjugate poles may appear in the transfer function of the two-stage R-C coupled feedback amplifier. These poles cause the circuit to have a damped oscillatory transient response. As the total loop gain increases, the damping ratio ζ decreases since σ remains essentially constant and $j\omega$ increases with increasing K'. Thus the value of loop gain which provides optimum transient response can be found. For example a damping factor $\zeta = 0.8$ is near optimum for some applications. To determine the value of K' which will provide a predetermined value of ζ, the constant ζ line is drawn on the pole zero plot as shown in Fig. 11.12, where $\zeta = \cos\theta$. This constant ζ line intersects the root-locus branch as shown at point a in Fig. 11.12. The values of s at this point a is substituted into the equation $F(s)$. Then K' is the magnitude of $1/F(s)$. A device known as a spirule can also be used to determine K' at a given value of s.

A feedback amplifier which has three R-C coupled stages included within the loop will now be considered. In this case

$$G_{23}G_{34} = K'F(s) = \frac{K_1 K_2 K_3 \beta \omega_{21} \omega_{22} \omega_{23} s^3}{(s + \omega_{11})(s + \omega_{12})(s + \omega_{13})(s + \omega_{21})(s + \omega_{22})(s + \omega_{23})}$$

$$(11.51)$$

The pole-zero plot and root-locus sketch for this configuration is given in Fig. 11.13. Two branches of the locus cross the positive $j\omega$ axis at points a and b. This configuration is known as *conditionally stable*, which means that the feedback amplifier is stable for some values of loop gain but unstable for other values. The amplifier here will be stable for all values of K' less than the smaller of K'_a or K'_b, where $K'_a = \left|\dfrac{1}{F(a)}\right|$ and $K'_b = \left|\dfrac{1}{F(b)}\right|$, and $F(a)$ is the function $F(s)$ evaluated at point a, etc. If K'_a is less than K'_b the frequency of oscillation will be ω_a, and vice versa. The values of K'_a and K'_b could be evaluated either by substituting $j\omega_a$ and $j\omega_b$ respectively into $1/F(s)$ or by using the spirule.

Although Fig. 11.13 shows all the significant poles and zeros of the open loop transfer function, it is usually not practical to include both the poles near the origin and those far removed from the origin on the same plot. This follows from the fact that poles which result from the shunt capacitance occur at values of s which may be hundreds of times as large as the values of s at poles near the origin. Thus a scale which would permit the inclusion of the poles far removed from the origin would cause the poles and zeros near the origin to be compressed into an area about the size of a pinpoint. One solution to this problem might be the use of logarithmic scales for the s-plane plot, but then the root-locus rules as well as the spirule would be unusable. Fortunately, the singularities far removed from the origin have essentially no influence on the root-locus branches near the origin and vice versa, so the problem can be divided into two parts, as shown in Fig. 11.14. This solution is basically the same as the

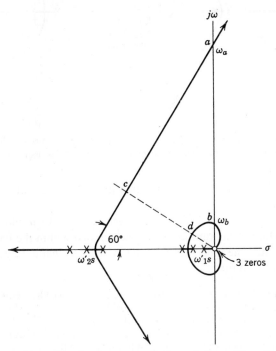

Fig. 11.13. Root-locus plot of a three-stage R-C coupled amplifier with feedback.

technique used in Chapter 7 whereby one equivalent circuit was used to represent the low-frequency range and another equivalent circuit was used to represent the high-frequency range.

Although the amplifier will be stable if the loop gain is adjusted so that all the poles of the overall transfer function G_{13} are in the left-half plane, the transient response of the amplifier may be unsatisfactory, as mentioned before, if the poles are too near the $j\omega$ axis. Again, the desired damping ratio may be obtained by adjusting the loop gain to give the value of K' which is found at the intersection of the root locus with the desired damping ratio line. Points c and d (Fig. 11.13) are both intersections with the $\zeta = 0.8$ line. The value of K' should be determined at both points,

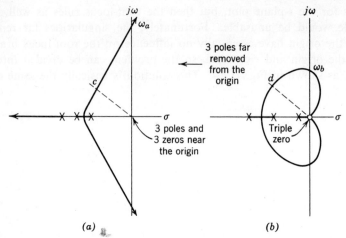

Fig. 11.14. The root-locus plot of a three-stage R-C coupled amplifier divided into two regions. (a) Singularities far from the origin; (b) singularities near the origin.

and, if very little overshoot can be tolerated, the lower value of loop gain should be used.

From the foregoing examples, a general trend should be noticed. That is, the larger the number of stages included within the feedback loop, the more limited the loop gain must be in order to maintain good transient response and stability.

PROB. 11.10. A three-stage R-C coupled tube amplifier has feedback from output to input. All amplifiers are identical and have $\omega_1 = 100$ and $\omega_2 = 0.5 \times 10^6$ radians/sec. Using a root-locus plot similar to the one in Fig. 11.12, determine the largest value of loop gain $K\beta$ which can be used without causing high-frequency oscillation in the amplifier. What would be the frequency of oscillation if oscillation does occur? *Answer: $K\beta < 8$, $\omega_0 = 8.66 \times 10^5$ rad/sec.*

PROB. 11.11. An R-C coupled transistor amplifier has two identical stages which have $f_2 = 100$ KHz, and $f_1 = 20$ Hz. Determine the loop gain which will give $\zeta = 0.8$ when feedback is applied around the amplifier.

11.7 THE CHARACTERISTICS AND STABILITY OF TRANSFORMER COUPLED FEEDBACK AMPLIFIERS

The stability of a feedback amplifier which consists of one transformer coupled stage will now be considered. The approximate transfer function of a transformer coupled amplifier was developed in Chapter 7 and is repeated as follows:

$$G = \frac{K\omega_n^2\omega_3 s}{(s + \omega_1)(s + \sigma + j\omega_2)(s + \sigma - j\omega_2)(s + \omega_3)} \qquad (11.52)$$

Then, from the poles and zeros of the open loop transfer function (Eq. 11.52) the root locus is drawn in Fig. 11.15. Observe that the single-stage transformer-coupled feedback amplifier is only conditionally stable. As the loop gain K' is increased, all the poles of the overall transfer function move away from the poles of the open loop transfer function shown in Fig. 11.15. The complex pair move in the direction of increasing ω and decreasing σ. This action increases the high-frequency response but decreases the damping ratio ζ. As the pole which leaves ω_1 moves toward the origin, the low-frequency response improves. In addition, the effect

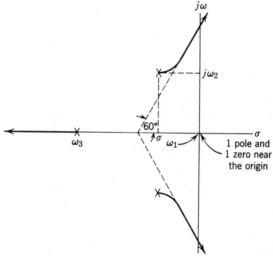

Fig. 11.15. The root-locus plot for a single-stage transformer-coupled amplifier.

of the pole moving from ω_3 toward $-\infty$ is to increase the magnitude of the transfer function at large values of s, or in other words, to improve the high-frequency response. In summary, then, the frequency characteristics of the amplifier are improved but the transient response may be deteriorated.

A paradox exists in the application of feedback to a transformer coupled amplifier: the transformer with poor frequency and transient response is less susceptible to improvement by feedback than is the high-quality transformer. Figure 11.15 shows that the damping ratio ζ generally decreases as the loop gain is increased. Therefore, the transient response of the amplifier deteriorates as the feedback is increased *unless* the damping ratio of the transformer itself is less than the optimum value. High-quality transformers usually have a comparatively high damping ratio. When negative feedback is applied to amplifiers using these transformers, the transient response, frequency response, and distortion are improved simultaneously by moderate amounts of feedback. However, when negative feedback is applied to the amplifier which incorporates a poor transformer with a damping ratio of 0.8 or less, the frequency response can be modestly improved at the expense of impaired transient response. Therefore, those amplifiers which are in greatest need of improvement are generally the least susceptible to improvement by feedback.

The root-locus plot for a feedback amplifier consisting of two typical transformer-coupled tube amplifier stages is shown in Fig. 11.16. Notice

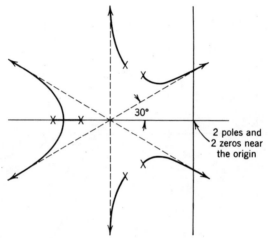

Fig. 11.16. The root-locus of a two-stage transformer-coupled feedback amplifier.

that a modest loop gain would improve the frequency response with little, if any, deterioration of the transient response. However, as K' is increased, the $j\omega$ axis is approached quite rapidly and poor transient response if not instability would result if a moderately large loop gain were employed. The magnitude of loop gain which could be tolerated would naturally depend on the characteristics of the transformers used. It is evident from Fig. 11.16 that the loop gain could be increased if the poles of the transformers were moved to the left. This could be accomplished by reducing the leakage inductance and distributed capacitances of the transformers. Also, the transient response of the amplifier would be improved if the transformer damping ratios were increased.

The sketch of the root locus for a typical transformer-coupled amplifier plus an *R-C* coupled amplifier is given in Fig. 11.17. The design of a transformer-coupled feedback amplifier is more difficult than the design of an *R-C* coupled feedback amplifier because the constants of the transformer are not usually known. Some experimentation will no doubt be necessary in optimizing the design. One satisfactory procedure might be to determine the desired loop gain in view of the distortion or other response requirements of the amplifier, then estimate the number and type of stages which might be included within the feedback loop without risking poor transient response or instability. A test of the amplifier after it has been constructed will either verify the assumptions or indicate the necessity for modifications. More than one stage should usually be included in the feedback loop for two reasons. First, the open loop gain should be large enough so that the

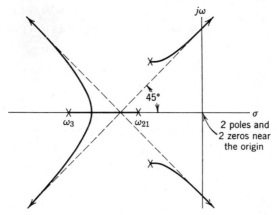

Fig. 11.17. The root-locus plot for a transformer-coupled amplifier and an R-C coupled amplifier.

feedback factor β may be small and the feedback network will not load the output amplifier. Second, the signal input to the feedback amplifier should be small so that the preceding amplifier will be a small-signal, low-distortion amplifier. Except for these two requirements, the application of negative feedback to each individual amplifier stage has some real advantages when compared with the inclusion of several stages within one feedback loop.[5]

PROB. 11.12. Sketch the root locus of a feedback amplifier which includes one typical transformer-coupled and two typical R-C coupled amplifiers.

11.8 COMPENSATING NETWORKS

The impression may have been gained while studying the stability of feedback amplifiers that some additional zeros would be invaluable for the

---

[5] An excellent discussion of single versus multiple feedback systems is given in *Introduction to Feedback Systems*, L. Dale Harris, Wiley, New York, 1961.

purpose of improving the stability of a feedback amplifier. Although zeros, by themselves, are difficult to buy at any price, a rather simple compensating network which provides an additional pole along with a zero will materially increase the loop gain which may profitably be used in a multistage feedback amplifier. This network is commonly known as a phase lead network and is shown in Fig. 11.18. The transfer function of the feedback network is

$$G_f = \frac{V_f}{V_o} = \frac{R_2}{R_2 + (R_1/sC)/(R_1 + 1/sC)} \tag{11.53}$$

$$G_f = \frac{R_2}{R_2 + R_1/(sCR_1 + 1)} = \frac{R_2(sCR_1 + 1)}{R_2(sCR_1 + 1) + R_1} \tag{11.54}$$

$$G_f = \frac{s + \dfrac{1}{R_1C}}{s + 1/R_1C + 1/R_2C} = \frac{s + \omega_a}{s + \omega_b} \tag{11.55}$$

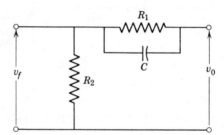

Fig. 11.18. A phase lead network.

where $\omega_a = 1/R_1C$ and $\omega_b = 1/R_1C + 1/R_2C$. Since R_1 is normally large in comparison with R_2, ω_b may be large in comparison with ω_a. In fact, since the feedback factor β is the value of G_f when s is small in comparison with both ω_a and ω_b, Eq. 11.55 may be used to obtain the relationship $\omega_b = \omega_a/\beta$. The manner in which this network may be used to advantage is illustrated in Figs. 11.19 and 11.20. In this case, a feedback amplifier including a transformer and two R-C coupled stages is considered. In Fig. 11.19 the root-locus plot is made for the amplifier with a purely resistive feedback network. Figure 11.20 is the root-locus plot of the same amplifier with phase lead compensation in the feedback network. Notice how the effect of the pole at ω_3 has been essentially neutralized by the zero of the compensating network at ω_a. The pole of the compensating network at ω_b is far to the left, and thus moves the intersection of the root-locus asymptotes quite a distance to the left compared with the point of intersection in the uncompensated case. Consequently, the root-locus

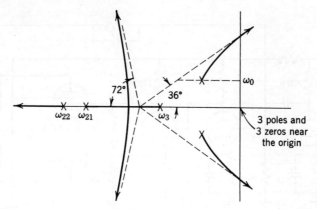

Fig. 11.19. Root-locus plot for a feedback amplifier consisting of two *R-C* coupled stages, one transformer-coupled stage, and resistive feedback.

branches which leave the complex poles depart in a more nearly vertical direction and traverse a much greater distance before crossing the $j\omega$ axis than they did in the uncompensated feedback amplifier. Therefore the amplifier would be stable at larger values of loop gain, or conversely, for a given value of loop gain the amplifier would have better transient characteristics when phase lead compensation is used in the feedback network.

Trial and error calculations will show that the ratio of ω_b to ω_a in the compensating network is more important than is the actual value of ω_a or ω_b. A practical upper limit of ω_b and ω_a results from the requirement that

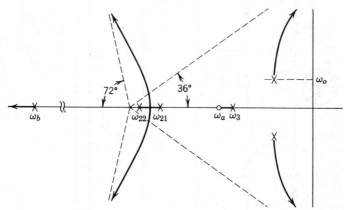

Fig. 11.20. The root-locus plot of the amplifier of Fig. 11.19 with phase lead compensation.

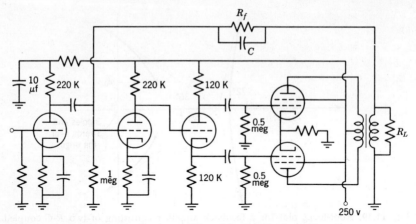

Fig. 11.21. A feedback amplifier with phase lead compensation.

the shunting capacitor be large in comparison with the stray capacitance in the feedback network.

The circuit diagram of a feedback amplifier with phase lead compensation is given in Fig. 11.21. The directly coupled phase inverter eliminates one pole-zero pair near the origin. This system is used in the popular "Williamson" amplifier.

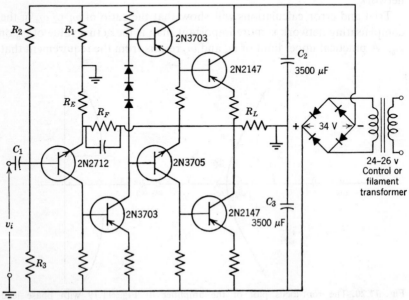

Fig. 11.22. A quasi-complementary symmetry transistor amplifier employing feedback.

The circuit diagram of a transistor feedback amplifier is given in Fig. 11.22. This circuit is basically the quasi-complementary symmetry circuit discussed in Chapter 10 (see Fig. 10.41). The 2N2712 transistor has been added to the previous circuit to allow the addition of negative feedback without increasing the input voltage requirement. The type feedback used also provides very high input resistance. Therefore, this amplifier is a desired load for a wide variety of sources such as radio tuners, phonograph and microphone pre-amplifiers, etc. An additional feature has been incorporated in this circuit. The filter capacitance in the power supply is provided by two equal capacitances, so that the mid-point of the power supply may be used as a signal reference or ground. This feature is desirable because the entire circuit appears as a bridge-type circuit with the power supply attached to one pair of the bridge terminals and the signal applied to the other pair. Therefore, the amount of power supply ripple voltage coupled into the desired signal is very small. Thus the hum level in this amplifier is very low even though the power supply filter is not very good. An additional bonus of this balanced power supply arrangement is the reduction in the number of capacitors required. Observe that the filter capacitor C_2 also bypasses the emitter circuit resistor R_1 in the 2N2712 circuit and the two filter capacitors block the direct current from the load resistor.

Note in designing the circuit of Fig. 11.22 that the emitter resistor R_E is chosen to give the desired voltage gain in the 2N2712 stage, since $G_v \simeq R_L/R_E$. Then the feedback resistor R_f is chosen to give the desired amount of feedback. Observe that the d-c feedback factor is much larger than the a-c feedback factor because R_1 is included in the d-c circuit but not in the a-c circuit, and R_1 is large in comparison with R_E. This large amount of d-c feedback provides very good Q-point stability for all the amplifiers in the circuit.

11.9 FEEDBACK DESIGN FROM GAIN-PHASE (BODE) PLOTS

The gain and phase plots, known as Bode plots, which were discussed in Section 9.3, can be conveniently used in the design of feedback amplifiers. Any feedback amplifier will become unstable if the feedback signal is in-phase with the input signal and has a magnitude equal to (or greater than) the input signal. Consequently, even a negative feedback circuit can be unstable (as the reader has already been shown) if the open-loop gain is equal to (or greater than) one and a total phase shift of 180° occurs in the open circuit loop. Since the Bode plots contain both gain and phase information, these plots can be used in the design of feedback circuits as shown in the following example.

Example 11.1 A three-stage R-C coupled amplifier has three zeros at $s = 0$; three poles at $s = j2\pi(10)$; and single poles at $s = j2\pi(10^4)$, $s = j2\pi(3 \times 10^4)$, and $s = j2\pi(9 \times 10^4)$. The total reference gain $K = 1000$. Investigate the conditions under which this circuit will be stable if it is used in a negative feedback configuration.

The power gain and phase plots of this amplifier are shown in Fig. 11.23. The amplifier will be unstable if the total loop gain magnitude is at least unity (0 db) at a frequency which produces 180° phase shift, relative to the mid-

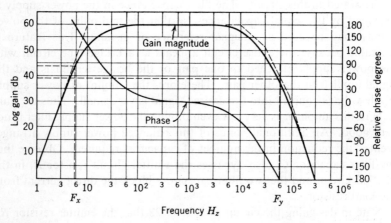

Fig. 11.23. Plots of power gain and phase (relative to mid-frequency phase) for the amplifier in Example 11.1.

frequency phase. Note that in this example there are two such frequencies, f_x and f_y. (Compare these frequencies with f_a and f_b, respectively, in the root-locus plot of Fig. 11.13 which represents a somewhat similar situation.) The gain magnitude of f_x is 44 db and at f_y is 39 db. Therefore, the feedback circuit, if purely resistive, must provide a gain less than −44 db or the amplifier will be unstable. In fact, the feedback gain must be considerably less than −44 db or poor transient response will result because the s-plane poles are too near the $j\omega$ axis. Most designers allow an extra 6 db to 10 db, known as *gain margin* in order to provide good transient response. In this example a 6-db gain margin will be considered adequate and the desired feedback factor is

$$20 \log \beta = -50 \text{ db}$$

$$\beta = \log^{-1}(-2.5) = 0.00316$$

$$K\beta = 3.16$$

This value of permissible loop gain is disappointingly low. However, the feedback factor and loop gain could be increased if at least one of the low frequency poles were eliminated by direct coupling. Then the gain at f_y would be the limiting gain (39 db) and the desired feedback factor would be

$$\beta = \log^{-1}(-2.25) = 0.0056$$

and $K\beta = 5.6$. This improvement results from the staggering of the upper cutoff frequencies, or poles, as compared with the triple pole at the low frequency. The permissible loop gain could again be greatly increased if a phase-lead compensating network were included to shift f_y to a much higher frequency.

PROB. 11.13 One stage of the amplifier in Example 11.1 is made direct coupled so one of the poles at $s = j2\pi(10)$ is eliminated. In addition, a phase-lead network (as shown in Fig. 11.18) is used as the feedback path with $R_1 = 10$ KΩ, $R_2 = 200$ Ω, and $C = 1100$ pf.

(a) Make an open-loop gain-phase plot for this circuit.
(b) Determine the value of $K\beta$.
(c) Find the frequency at which the relative phase shift is 180°.
(d) Find the gain margin for the closed-loop circuit. *Answer: (c) $f \approx 3 \times 10^5$ Hz (d) Gain margin $\simeq 16$ db.*

PROB. 11.14. The distortion of the amplifier of Fig. 11.22 without feedback is approximately 6% at maximum power output. Use the values you determined for the circuit of Prob. 10.28 and determine the additional components needed for the circuit of Fig. 11.22 to provide 0.6% distortion and 1-v peak input at maximum power output.

PROB. 11.15. The amplifier of Fig. 11.21 uses 12AX7 tubes for the voltage amplifiers and 6CM6 tubes for the power amplifier. The load resistance is a 16 Ω speaker. The transformer has complex poles at $\pm j\omega = 2\pi \times 20,000$ radians/sec, $\zeta = 0.9$, and a real pole at $\omega_3 = -2\pi \times 40,000$ radians/sec. The upper cutoff frequency of the R-C coupled stage is 100 KHz. With the aid of the tube manual, calculate the approximate open loop gain, then calculate the value of R_f which will reduce the distortion in the output to one-tenth of the value without feedback. Make a root-locus plot of the feedback amplifier, without the phase lead capacitor, and determine whether the amplifier will be stable at the desired value of total loop gain. If so, what will be the damping ratio ζ? (Refer to the locus branches from the complex pair.)

PROB. 11.16. Using a phase lead feedback network for the amplifier of Prob. 11.15, determine the value of C which will essentially cancel the pole of the transformer which lies on the real axis (ω_3). Make a root-locus plot of the amplifier and determine the maximum value of total loop gain which can be used without causing oscillation. Determine the damping ratio ζ (caused by the complex poles of the transformer) for the value of total loop gain required to reduce the distortion by a factor of ten.

PROB. 11.17. A single R-C coupled amplifier has a transfer function

$$G_{23}' = \frac{sK\omega_2}{(s + \omega_1)(s + \omega_2)}$$

(a) If ω_1 is 100 and ω_2 is 10^6 radians/sec, sketch a root-locus plot for a three-stage R-C coupled amplifier with negative feedback.

(b) If singularities far from the origin are ignored, what value of K is required for oscillation and what is the frequency of oscillation?

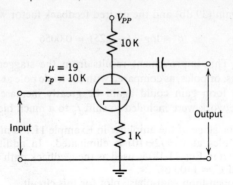

Fig. 11.24. The circuit to be used for Prob. 11.18.

PROB. 11.18. A circuit is connected as shown in Fig. 11.24. Find the gain of this circuit and determine the magnitude of the feedback parameter β.

PROB. 11.19. A feedback circuit contains one transformer-coupled amplifier and an R-C amplifier. If the transfer characteristics of these stages are as given below, sketch the root-locus plot. For what values of loop gain will the circuit be stable?

$$R\text{-}C \text{ Stage } G = \frac{sK\omega_2}{(s + \omega_1)(s + \omega_2)}$$

$$\text{Trans stage } G = \frac{sK\omega_3\omega_5^2}{(s + \omega_4)(s + \sigma + j\omega_5)(s + \sigma - j\omega_5)(s + \omega_3)}$$

$\omega_2 = 10^6$
$\omega_1 = 10^2$
$\omega_4 = 2 \times 10^2$
$\sigma = 10^6$
$\omega_5 = 10^6$
$\omega_3 = 2 \times 10^6$
$K = 500$

PROB. 11.20 Make a Bode plot of the amplifier of Problem 11.19 and determine the value of β if the gain margin is 6 db.

12

Large-Signal Tuned Amplifiers

In Chapter 10, the class B amplifier was found to have a higher theoretical efficiency than the class A amplifier. However, unless special circuits were used, the distortion was very high. In general, this distortion takes the form of adding harmonics to the desirable fundamental. Consequently, if a method can be found to eliminate the harmonics, a very desirable circuit is achieved. For broad frequency band amplification, the class B push-pull circuit achieves both high efficiency and even harmonic cancellation. However, if a narrow band of frequencies is to be amplified, a different approach is possible. A resonant circuit is used to pass the desired band of frequencies and to reject the harmonics.

In class B and class C amplifiers, the collector (or plate) current flows for only a portion of each cycle. Consequently, the collector current can be considered as a series of pulses with a pulse repetition rate equal to the frequency of the input signal. An insight into the behavior of this type of signal can be gained by considering the action of a linear tuned amplifier which is activated by a square wave.

471

The response of the tuned amplifier (Fig. 12.1) to a periodic pulse can be found by using the concepts already developed in Chapter 8. In Section 8.1 the response of a tuned amplifier stage to a step function (Fig. 8.4) was found to be

$$v_o = - \frac{g_m V}{\omega_o C} e^{-\zeta \omega_n t} \sin \omega_o t \qquad (8.18)$$

Now, if the input signal is composed of a square wave with a period of $1/f_o$, (Fig. 12.2a), this input signal can be synthesized from a series of

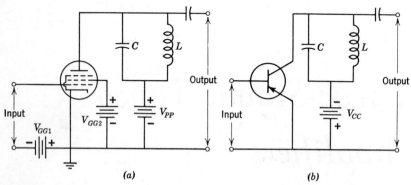

(a)   (b)

Fig. 12.1. A class B or C tuned amplifier. (a) Tube circuit; (b) transistor circuit.

positive and negative step functions as shown in Fig. 12.2c. The output signals (as given by Eq. 8.18) for the step functions are plotted in Fig. 12.2d. When these individual output signals are added together, the total output signal (Fig. 12.2b) results. Hence, sinusoidal output signals may be obtained when the input signals are square waves.

One way to visualize the behavior of the tuned amplifier is to reduce the square wave of Fig. 12.2a to a series of sinusoidal voltages. Fourier analysis allows the square wave to be reduced to a fundamental component and an infinite series of harmonic components. In the tuned amplifier, the tuned circuit in the output of the amplifier is tuned to the same frequency as the fundamental component in the square wave. Hence, the impedance of the tuned circuit is very high for the fundamental component. Since the gain of the amplifier is proportional to the plate or collector load impedance, the gain of the amplifier is high for the fundamental component. In contrast, the capacitor C (Fig. 12.1) has a low impedance for all harmonic components. Consequently, the gain of the amplifier at these harmonic frequencies is very low.

From the foregoing analysis, the tuned amplifier is able to amplify the fundamental component of a class B or class C amplifier while suppressing

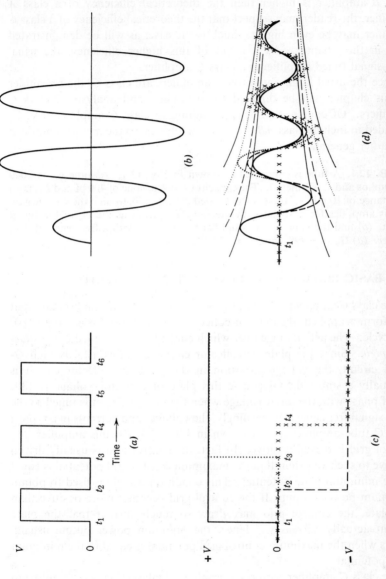

Fig. 12.2. The response of a tuned amplifier to a square-wave input. (*a*) Input signal; (*b*) the total output signal; (*c*) a series of step functions which can be added to produce the input signal; (*d*) the output signals from the step functions of part *c*.

the harmonics which are generated. Since the theoretical efficiency of a class B amplifier is higher than the theoretical efficiency of a class A amplifier, the reader may suspect that the theoretical efficiency of a class C amplifier may be even higher. Such is the case, as will be demonstrated later in this chapter. As a result of this higher efficiency, the usual large-signal tuned amplifier is a class C amplifier.

Since the usual large-signal tuned amplifiers are class C, the remainder of this chapter will be directed to the design and analysis of class C amplifiers. Of course, the ideas pertaining to class C amplifiers can be extended to include class AB or class B amplifiers, so the methods outlined are rather general.

PROB. 12.1. A tube is connected as shown in Fig. 12.1. Assume g_m is 2000 micromhos and r_p is 1 meg Ω. The capacitor C has a value of 400 pf and L has an inductance of 10 mh. If the Q of the tuned circuit is 50, (a) find the voltage gain of this amplifier for a signal with the same frequency as the ω_o of the tuned circuit; (b) find the gain of this amplifier for a signal with a frequency of $2\omega_o$. *Answer:* (a) $G_v = -400$, (b) $G_v = 6.67\underline{/90°}$.

12.1 BASIC BEHAVIOR OF CLASS C TUNED CIRCUITS

The class C amplifier is biased below cutoff. Hence, if a sinusoidal input waveform is applied, the plate or collector current flows for less than 180° of a cycle. The actual angle over which current flows is called the *conduction angle*. Since the plate or collector circuit contains a fairly high Q-tuned circuit, the voltage variation in the plate or collector circuit is essentially a sinusoid. Of course this plate or collector voltage is 180° out of phase with the input voltage when the output circuit is tuned to the input signal frequency. Accordingly, the voltages and currents in a typical class C tube amplifier are as shown in Fig. 12.3. In this amplifier, the control grid is driven positive. In fact, the control grid is usually driven positive to such an extent that the maximum control grid potential is equal to the minimum plate potential. This condition usually is used to obtain maximum power output. If the control grid becomes more positive than the plate, the control grid may draw so much current that the plate current actually *decreases*. Hence, the optimum power output usually occurs when the maximum control grid potential is equal to the minimum plate potential.

The class C amplifier requires a graphical analysis that is different from the methods employed previously in this text. The methods used in the preceding chapters assumed that the plate current was a fairly linear function of the input voltage. However, in the class C amplifier this linear relationship no longer holds. In fact, as will be shown in Section 12.2, the

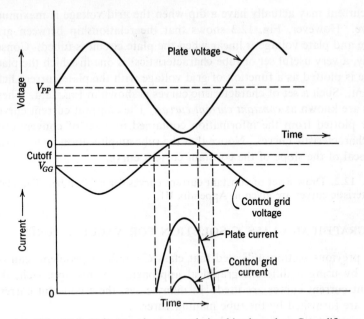

Fig. 12.3. Voltage and current relationships in a class C amplifier.

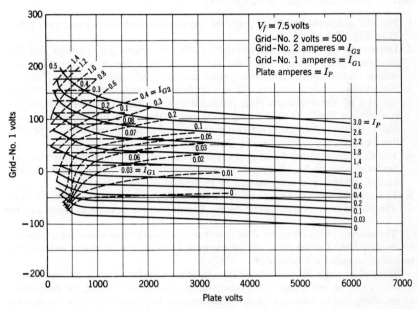

Fig. 12.4. Constant current curves for a 4-1000A tube. (Courtesy of Radio Corporation of America.)

plate current may actually have a dip when the grid voltage is maximum positive. However, Fig. 12.3 shows that the relationship between grid voltage and plate voltage *is* linear when the plate circuit is tuned. Consequently, a very useful set of tube characteristics[1] is one in which the plate voltage is plotted as a function of grid voltage with the plate current held constant. Such a set of characteristic curves is shown in Fig. 12.4. These curves are known as *constant current curves*. The constant current curves can be plotted from the information contained in a set of conventional plate characteristic curves. Notice that the tube amplification factor is the reciprocal of the slope of the constant current curve.

PROB. 12.2. Draw a set of constant current curves for a 6J5 tube. The plate characteristic curves are given in Appendix III.

12.2 GRAPHICAL CLASS *C* SOLUTION FOR VACUUM TUBES

The previous section indicated that class *C* amplifier problems can be solved by using a different graphical approach. In this approach, the constant current curves are used. In many cases, these constant current curves are furnished by the tube manufacturer.

The usual method of approach to a graphical solution for vacuum tube class *C* tuned amplifiers is as follows:

1. Plot the quiescent operating point on the constant current curves. (See point *Q* of Fig. 12.6.)
2. Determine the desired magnitudes of the maximum grid voltage and the minimum plate voltage. As these voltages occur at the same time this point is also plotted on the constant current curves. (See point *P* of Fig. 12.6.)
3. Since the a-c plate voltage is 180° out of phase with the control grid excitation, the plot of instantaneous plate potential vs the instantaneous grid potential is a straight line.[2] Thus, a straight line can be drawn on the constant current characteristics connecting the two points found in step 1 and step 2. (See the line between point *P* and point *Q* of Fig. 12.6.)
4. Values of plate current and grid current (also screen current for tetrodes and pentodes) can be found for given values of grid voltage. Thus, the waveform for all voltages and currents can be plotted as shown in Fig. 12.3.
5. The average values of these currents can be found by integrating the current waveforms over one complete cycle. In addition, a Fourier analysis can be

---

[1] The analysis of the transistor class *C* amplifier is more complex than the analysis of a tube amplifier. Consequently, the tube amplifier will be considered first and then the transistor amplifier will be treated.

[2] If the phase angle between two a-c voltages of the same frequency is different than 0° or 180°, a plot of one voltage vs the other voltage is an ellipse. In fact, the dimensions of the ellipse can be used as a means of determining the phase angle between the two voltages. For a more detailed analysis of this approach see F. E. Terman, *Radio Engineers Handbook*, McGraw-Hill, New York, pp. 947–949, 1943.

used to determine the fundamental components of these current waveforms.

6. When the average currents are known, the power requirements from the power supplies can be determined. In addition, with the fundamental current components known, the signal power input and the signal power output can be determined.

In order to find the average (d-c) currents and the fundamental components of the signal currents, integration must be performed. Usually, a graphical approach is necessary. Therefore, a review of graphical integration may be in order at this time. To integrate the area under the curve of Fig. 12.5, the base of the area is divided into a series of uniform lengths

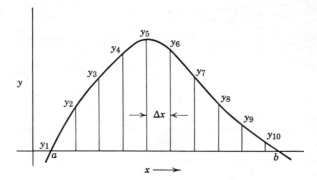

Fig. 12.5. A method of graphical integration.

Δx as shown. Now, since the integral of y from a to b is the total area under the curve or the sum of all the small areas,

$$\int_a^b y \, dx \simeq \Delta x \left[\left(\frac{y_1}{2} + \frac{y_2}{2} \right) + \left(\frac{y_2}{2} + \frac{y_3}{2} \right) + \left(\frac{y_3}{2} + \frac{y_4}{2} \right) + \cdots \right] \quad (12.1)$$

or

$$\int_a^b y \, dx \simeq \Delta x \left[\frac{y_1}{2} + y_2 + y_3 + y_4 + \cdots + y_{n-1} + \frac{y_n}{2} \right] \quad (12.2)$$

Of course, the smaller Δx becomes, the more accurate the graphical integration will be.

The method of solution for a class C amplifier can be further clarified by the use of an example.

Example 12.1. A 4-1000 A tube is to be used as a class C amplifier in a circuit similar to Fig. 12.1. The screen grid is maintained at a constant potential of 500 v. The characteristic curves of this tube are shown in Fig. 12.4. If a 5000-v plate supply and a −200-v bias supply is to be used, find the characteristics of the amplifier.

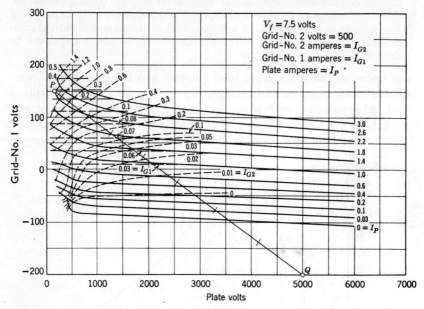

Fig. 12.6. Graphical solution of a class C amplifier. (Curves are Courtesy of Radio Corporation of America.)

TABLE 12.1

A List of Current and Voltage Values in a Class C Amplifier

Phase Angle θ	$\cos \theta$	Grid 1 Voltage	Plate Voltage	Plate Current	Grid 2 Current	Grid 1 Current
0°	1.000	+150 v	150 v	2.2 a	1.2 a	0.3 a
10°	0.985	+144.5	250	2.4	1.1	0.26
20°	0.940	+129	475	2.4	0.8	0.18
30°	0.866	+103	800	2.2	0.45	0.093
40°	0.766	+68	1275	1.85	0.18	0.048
50°	0.643	+25	1900	1.2	0.029	0.005
60°	0.500	−25	2550	0.47	0.005	0
70°	0.342	−80.4	3300	0.03	0	0
80°	0.174	−139.1	4150	0	0	0
90°	0.000	−200	5000	0	0	0

The constant current curves are reproduced in Fig. 12.6. The quiescent operating point is denoted in Fig. 12.6 as the point Q. The second point is taken where the control grid potential is maximum and the plate potential is minimum. As already mentioned, the usual optimum point occurs when the maximum grid potential is approximately equal to the minimum plate potential. Let the control grid swing to $+150$ v and let the plate swing down to $+150$ v. This value of grid and plate voltage is shown in Fig. 12.6 as point P. The line from P to Q of Fig. 12.6 is drawn and is known as the *operating line* and determines not only the relationship between the control grid voltage and the plate voltage, but also the relationship between the control grid potential and the various currents in the tube. Accordingly, the line PQ is marked for grid voltage intervals corresponding to Δt intervals. In this example, Δt is chosen so that $\omega \Delta t$ is equal to 10 electrical degrees.

From the operating line in Fig. 12.6, the values of voltages and currents in Table 12.1 are found. The values listed in Table 12.1 can be used to plot the various voltages and currents in the circuits. This plot is given in Fig. 12.7. Also from the values in Table 12.1, the magnitudes of the d-c currents and the fundamental components of the grid and plate signal currents can be found.

We can simplify the graphical Fourier analysis by choosing the proper value as reference. For example, in Fig. 12.6, if $t = 0$ or $\theta = 0$ at $v_{g\ max}$, only cosine terms will be present in the Fourier series because the value of the function at $+\theta°$ will be equal to the value of the function at $-\theta°$. Because of this simplification, the $v_{g\ max}$ point of Fig. 12.7 will be used as the reference ($\theta = 0$) in the following analysis. The 10° intervals along the operating line can be located by first determining the grid or plate voltage at these intervals.[3]

Now, from the Fourier analysis of Fig. 12.7, the d-c value of plate current I_P is given by

$$I_P = \frac{1}{2\pi} \int_{-\pi}^{\pi} i_P \, d\theta \qquad (12.3)$$

In Fig. 12.7, the value of $\Delta \theta$ is 10° or $\pi/18$ radians. Hence, the graphical integration from 0 to π becomes

$$\int_{0}^{\pi} i_P \, d\theta = \frac{\pi}{18} \left(\frac{i_{P1}}{2} + i_{P2} + i_{P3} + \cdots + i_{P7} + \frac{i_{P8}}{2} \right) \qquad (12.4)$$

where i_{P1}, i_{P2}, etc. have the values indicated in Fig. 12.7. Now, since the area under the curve (Fig. 12.7) from $-\pi$ to 0 is equal to the area under the curve from 0 to π (for the given reference), the average plate current is (Eq. 12.3)

$$I_P \simeq 2 \times \frac{1}{2\pi} \times \frac{\pi}{18} \left(\frac{i_{P1}}{2} + i_{P2} + i_{P3} + \cdots i_{P7} + \frac{i_{P8}}{2} \right) \qquad (12.5)$$

For the values in Table 12.1, the value of I_P is

$$I_P \simeq \frac{1}{18} \left(\frac{2.2}{2} + 2.4 + 2.4 + 2.2 + 1.85 + 1.2 + 0.47 + 0.03 + \frac{0}{2} \right)$$

---

[3] For example, at these intervals, $v_{G1} = -200 + 350 \cos(n \, \Delta \theta)$ where $\Delta \theta = 10°$ and $n = 0, 1, 2, 3$, etc. The values of v_{G1} at these intervals are listed in Table 12.1.

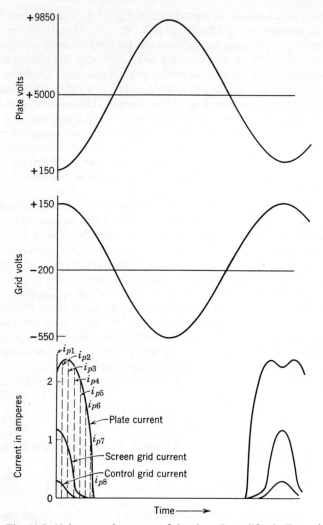

Fig. 12.7. Voltages and currents of the class C amplifier in Example 12.1.

or

$$I_P \simeq \frac{11.65}{18} = 0.647 \text{ amp}$$

By similar analysis, the direct or average current to the screen grid and to the control grid can be found. For the values in Table 12.1, the magnitude of I_{G1} (the average control grid current) is 44.5 ma and the magnitude of I_{G2} (the average screen grid current) is 175 ma.

The peak value of the fundamental component of the plate current is also needed. To find this value, the required Fourier expansion is

$$I_{p1} = \frac{1}{\pi} \int_{-\pi}^{\pi} i_P \cos \theta \, d\theta \tag{12.6}$$

Because of the symmetry involved, this can be written as

$$I_{p1} = \frac{2}{\pi} \int_0^{\pi} i_P \cos \theta \, d\theta \tag{12.7}$$

Accordingly,

$$I_{p1} \simeq \frac{2}{\pi} \times \frac{\pi}{18} \left[\frac{i_{P1} \cos 0°}{2} + i_{P2} \cos 10° + i_{P3} \cos 20° + i_{P4} \cos 30° \right.$$
$$\left. + \cdots + I_{P(n-1)} \cos (10n - 20)° + i_{Pn} \cos (10n - 10)° \right] \tag{12.8}$$

For the values in Table 12.1, the peak magnitude of the fundamental value of plate current, I_{p1}, is

$$I_{p1} \simeq \frac{10.059}{9} = 1.118 \text{ amp}$$

By similar analysis, the peak magnitude of the fundamental component of control grid current I_{g1}, is 81.7 ma. The magnitude of the fundamental component of screen current could also be found, but the screen has essentially no a-c component of voltage. Consequently, the power at the fundamental frequency is zero, and the magnitude of fundamental current is not required.

From the values of voltages and currents just derived, the power relationships of the tube can be established. The power drawn from the power supply by the plate of the tube is

$$P_I = V_{PP} I_P \tag{12.9}$$

For this example $P_I = 5000 \times 0.647 = 3235$ w.

The load impedance which the tuned plate circuit must offer at the fundamental frequency can now be found. Since the tuned circuit is at resonance, this impedance is purely resistive and has a value given by the relationship

$$R_L = \frac{V_p}{I_{p1}} \tag{12.10}$$

where V_p and I_{p1} are the peak values of fundamental voltage and current. In this case,

$$R_L = \frac{4850}{1.118} = 4340 \ \Omega$$

Now the signal power output P_o is

$$P_o = \frac{V_p I_{p1}}{2} = \frac{(V_{PP} - V_{p \min}) I_{p1}}{2} \tag{12.11}$$

For this example,

$$P_o = \frac{(5000 - 150)\,1.118}{2} = 2710 \text{ w}$$

The total power dissipated by the plate of the tube is

$$P_d = P_I - P_o \qquad (12.12)$$

Thus, $P_d = 3235 - 2710 = 525$ w. This value of plate dissipation is well within the limits of the tube, so operation at this level is permissible.

The plate efficiency η_p of the tube is given by the relationship

$$\eta_p = \frac{P_o}{P_I} \times 100 \qquad (12.13)$$

For this example,

$$\eta_p = \frac{2710}{3235} = 83.8\%$$

Other information which can be found is the effective input resistance. This resistance R_{in} is given by the relationship

$$R_{in} = \frac{V_{g1}}{I_{g1}} \qquad (12.14)$$

Thus,

$$R_{in} = \frac{350}{0.0817} = 4280\Omega$$

where V_{g1} and I_{g1} are the peak values of the control grid voltage and the fundamental component of grid signal current. The grid driving power P_g, can be found by the relationship,

$$P_g = \frac{V_{g1}I_{g1}}{2} \qquad (12.15)$$

In this example,

$$P_g = \frac{0.0817 \times 350}{2} = 14.3 \text{ w}$$

Since the maximum control grid dissipation for a 4-1000 A tube is 25 w, this grid power dissipation is permissible. However, the stage which supplies the signal for this stage must be capable of furnishing the grid power required by this stage.

The results of this example are tabulated below.

The peak signal voltage on the grid V_{g1} is 350 v.
The peak fundamental component of grid current I_{g1} is 81.7 ma.
The input resistance R_{in} is 4280 Ω.
The average d-c voltage in the grid circuit V_{GG} is -200 v.
The average d-c current in the grid circuit I_{G1} is 44.5 ma.

The input power to the grid circuit P_g is 14.3 w.

The average d-c current in the screen circuit I_{G2} is 175 ma.

The voltage on the screen grid V_{G2} is $+500$ v.

The average d-c current in the plate circuit I_P is 0.647 amp.

The average d-c voltage on the plate V_{PP} is 5000 v.

The peak signal voltage on the plate V_p is 4850 v.

The peak fundamental component of plate current I_{p1} is 1.118 amp.

The required value of plate load impedance R_L is 4340 Ω.

The power output P_o is 2710 w.

The plate power input P_I is 3235 w.

The plate dissipation P_d is 525 w.

The plate efficiency η_p is 83.8%.

The plate conduction angle θ is $17°$ to $(180° - 17°)$ or $146°$.

The foregoing example illustrates the method of approach to solve class C (or class B or class AB) problems. The list of known quantities at the end of the example indicates the effectiveness of the method. Unfortunately, if one bias or signal voltage level is changed, the entire process must be repeated for the new condition. Consequently, in order to optimize a circuit a number of solutions must be tried. Hence, a trial and error approach is indicated. On the brighter side, a little experience in the design of class C amplifiers reduces the trial and error to a minimum.

The waveform of the plate current in Fig. 12.7 deserves a word of explanation. At maximum grid voltage the control and screen grids are *robbing* the plate current from the plate. Since the control grid is so much nearer the cathode than the plate, this action is not unexpected. In addition, since the screen grid is so much more positive than the plate, the screen has a tendency to take a larger portion of the total space current. An examination of the constant current curves (Fig. 12.6) indicates the reason for this type of behavior. Over most of the range of the constant current curves, these curves are straight. However, at the end of the curves where the plate voltage is very low, the curves rise gradually at first and then more sharply. As the control grid potential becomes more positive, the plate potential for the beginning of the rise becomes more positive. If the plate does not swing low enough to shift the operating line into the rising portion, the plate current will have a waveform indicated by Fig. 12.8, curve a. If the plate swings low enough, the operating line of Fig. 12.6 may become parallel to the constant current curves over the low-plate voltage end of the operating line. If this condition occurs, the plate current is saturated for low-plate voltages. This condition is shown in Fig. 12.8, curve b. If the plate swings to an even lower potential, the operating line may actually recross one or more constant current curves. In this case, the plate current has the waveform shown in Fig. 12.8, curve c.

The curves of Fig. 12.7 were drawn to aid the reader in visualizing the operation of the amplifier and to illustrate the procedure of solution. However, in most solutions the sketch is not required. In fact, all the values required for the solution of the problem can be obtained from Table 12.1.[4]

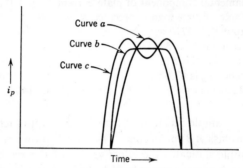

Fig. 12.8. Typical plate current waveforms in class C operation. In curve a, the minimum plate potential is much larger than the maximum grid potential. In curve b, the minimum plate potential is low enough to cause plate current saturation. In curve c, the maximum grid potential is high enough to rob the plate of current while the plate potential is minimum.

PROB. 12.3. A 6J5 tube is to be opeiated class C. V_{GG} is -30 v and V_{PP} is $+300$ v. Assume the peak magnitude of control-grid signal is 34 v and the peak magnitude of the plate signal is 260 v. Plot the plate current waveform. Use the curves from Prob. 12.2.

PROB. 12.4. Repeat Example 12.1 with $V_{GG} = -200$ v, $V_{PP} = 5000$ v, and $V_{G_2} = 500$ v. However, in this problem let the maximum control-grid potential be 145 v and the minimum plate potential be 250 v. Compare the results of this problem with the results of Example 12.

12.3 DETERMINATION OF THE TUNED-CIRCUIT PARAMETERS

In Example 12.1, many electrical quantities were found, but no attempt was made to determine the values of the tuned-circuit components except to note the magnitude of resistance the tuned circuit should offer at resonance. Actually, the configuration of the tuned circuit determines the method of approach that must be used. In general, all the ideas developed in Chapter 8 can be used for the large-signal tuned circuits. However,

[4] To aid in determining the values of Table 12.1, a plastic overlay is made by the Eitel-McCullough Tube Co. This overlay is known as the "No. 5 Tube Performance Computer" and is available from the Manager of Amateur Service Department, Eitel-McCullough, Inc., 301 Industrial Way, San Carlos, California.

there is one striking difference in the philosophy of design in large-signal as opposed to small-signal coupling circuits. In the small-signal amplifier, efficiency is not of prime concern. The power loss in the coupling circuit results in smaller stage gain than would be possible with lossless circuits, but the loss of a few decibels gain is not serious in a high-gain amplifier. As noted in Chapter 8, the bandwidth of the small-signal amplifier is of major importance because this type of amplifier is used in applications which normally require the selection of a specified band of frequencies and the rejection of all other frequencies. On the other hand, the large-signal tuned amplifier is usually used in radio transmitters or other applications where power output and waveform of the signal are important

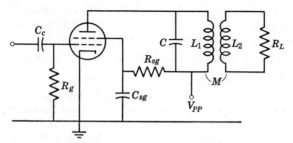

Fig. 12.9. A typical class C coupling circuit.

but frequency selection is *not*. In the tuned power amplifier the desired output is a sinusoid or modulated sinusoid and the Q's of the coupling circuits need be only high enough to adequately eliminate the harmonics. The coupling efficiency increases as the circuit Q decreases, as will be shown. The efficiency is important in high-power amplifiers where increased efficiency results in materially reduced operating costs.

Considering a single-tuned, inductively coupled circuit as shown in Fig. 12.9, the power loss in the tuned circuit is I^2R_o, where I is the current and R_o is the resistance of the primary coil at the resonant frequency. The power transferred to the secondary circuit is $I^2R'_L$ where R'_L is the resistance coupled into the tuned circuit as a result of the load current flowing in the secondary. As discussed in Chapter 8, the ohmic resistance of the secondary is usually very small in comparison with the load resistance. Then the efficiency of the coupled circuit becomes

$$\eta = \frac{\text{coupled power}}{\text{loss power} + \text{coupled power}} \times 100 = \frac{I^2R'_L}{I^2(R_o + R'_L)} \times 100$$

$$= \frac{R'_L}{R_o + R'_L} \times 100 \qquad (12.16)$$

The efficiency may be obtained in terms of the coil Q_o and circuit Q, since $R_o = \omega_o L / Q_o$ and $(R'_L + R_o) = \dfrac{\omega_o L}{Q}$ then

$$R'_L = \frac{\omega_o L}{Q} - R_o = \frac{\omega_o L}{Q} - \frac{\omega_o L}{Q_o} \tag{12.17}$$

$$\eta = \frac{\omega_o L (1/Q - 1/Q_o)}{\omega_o L (1/Q)} \times 100 = \frac{Q_o - Q}{Q_o} \times 100 \tag{12.18}$$

It may be seen from Eq. 12.18 that Q_o must be large in comparison with the circuit Q in order for the efficiency to approach 100%. This relationship generally holds for coupled circuits. The maximum practical efficiency can be obtained by selecting a coil with a Q as high as possible and then choosing a circuit Q which is just adequate to provide good waveform. Values of circuit Q between 12 and 20 are commonly used.

Example 12.2. The tube in Example 12.1 must operate at a frequency of 10^6 radians/sec. The tuned circuit has an actual Q_o of 200 and the desired loaded Q is 20. The actual value of load resistance is 100 Ω and the coupling circuit of Fig. 12.9 is selected to provide the power transfer.

To simplify the calculations, we will assume that the resistance of coil L_2 is much less than R_L and also that the reactance of L_2 at resonance is much less than R_L.

From Example 12.1, the resistance of the loaded tuned circuit at resonance is 4340 Ω. For a parallel tuned circuit, the Q is given by the relation

$$Q = \frac{R_p}{\omega_o L_1} = \frac{\omega_o C}{G} \tag{12.19}$$

where R_p is the parallel resistance, G is the conductance of the resonant circuit, and C is the capacitance of the tuned circuit. Hence, for this example

$$C = \frac{QG}{\omega_o} = \frac{20}{4340 \times 10^6} = 4.6 \times 10^{-9} \text{ fds}$$

The value of L_1 can be found from the relation

$$\omega_o = \frac{1}{\sqrt{L_1 C}} \tag{12.20}$$

In this case

$$L_1 = \frac{1}{10^{12} \times 4.6 \times 10^{-9}} = 2.18 \times 10^{-4} \text{ h}$$

The loaded tuned circuit parallel resistance R_p is 4340 Ω. Part of this resistance R'_L is coupled from the load back to the tuned circuit and the remainder of this resistance R_o is due to the resistance in the tuned circuit. Since the unloaded Q_o is known (200), Eq. 12.19 can be used to calculate R_o.

$$Q_o = \frac{R_o}{\omega_o L_1} = 200 = \frac{R_o}{10^6 \times 2.18 \times 10^{-4}}$$

or

$$R_o = 200 \times 2.18 \times 10^{-4} \times 10^6 = 43{,}400 \ \Omega$$

Now, the parallel combination of R_o and R'_L must be equal to R_p.

Thus we can write

$$R'_L = \frac{R_p R_o}{R_o - R_p} = \frac{4340 \times 43{,}400}{43{,}400 - 4340} = 4820\Omega$$

From Eq. 8.86, the magnitude of L_2 can be determined if the coefficient of coupling k is known. If k is assumed to be 0.7, L_2 is

$$L_2 = \frac{L_1 R_L}{k^2 R'_L} \tag{12.21}$$

For this example

$$L_2 = \frac{2.18 \times 10^{-4} \times 100}{0.49 \times 4820 \ \Omega} = 9.22 \ \mu h$$

From Eq. 12.18, the coupling efficiency is given as

$$\eta = \frac{Q_o - Q}{Q_o} \times 100 = \frac{200 - 20}{200} \times 100 = 90\%$$

Thus, in this example, 90% of the power output from the tube is coupled into the load and 10% of this power is lost in the coupling circuit.

PROB. 12.5. Repeat Example 12.2 if the Q of coil L_1 is 100. How much power would be coupled to the load under these conditions?

PROB. 12.6. The tube in Example 12.1 is connected to a coupling circuit which is shown in Fig. 12.10. If the resonant frequency is 1 MHz and the Q of the

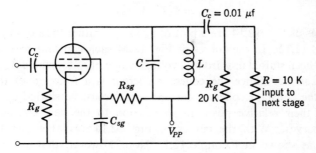

Fig. 12.10. The circuit for Prob. 12.6.

tuned circuit with load is 20, find the values of the tuned circuit components. The Q_o of coil L is 200 at resonance.

12.4   CLASS C TRANSISTOR AMPLIFIERS

When we arrived at the graphical solution of the class C amplifier by using constant current curves, we assumed that the input voltage and output voltage of the amplifier were both sinusoidal. This assumption is valid only if the effective output resistance of the stage which drives the amplifier is small in comparison with the lowest value of the input resistance of the amplifier. In either tube or transistor amplifiers this requirement may not always be met. In case the source resistance is not negligibly small, the input characteristics should be modified to include the effects of the source resistance, as was done in the determination of transistor distortion in Chapter 10. The effect of the source resistance will be included in the example of the transistor amplifier which follows.

The constant current curves for the transistor can be developed from the collector and input characteristic curves. The collector and input characteristic curves of a transistor are given in Fig. 12.11. From these curves, the constant current curves of Fig. 12.12 can be drawn. The curves of constant base current are found directly from the v_{BE} vs i_B curves of Fig. 12.11. When the constant base current curves have been drawn, the curves for constant collector current can be obtained from the i_C vs v_{CE} curves. The required values of i_B and v_{CE} are obtained from Fig. 12.11 and plotted in Fig. 12.12.

The curves of Fig. 12.12 can be used if the impedance of the voltage source which excites the base of the transistor is negligible. However, if the impedance of the source is *not* negligible, a modification must be made. For example, if the circuit of Fig. 12.13 is to be used, the curves of Fig. 12.12 must be modified to the form shown in Fig. 12.14. This modification is achieved by observing that (in Fig. 12.13) the open circuit generator voltage v_S is

$$v_S = i_B Z_S + v_{BE} \qquad (12.22)$$

The curves of Fig. 12.14 are a plot of v_S vs v_{CE} rather than of v_{BE} vs v_{CE} as in Fig. 12.12. In the curves of Fig. 12.14 each constant base current, curve has been shifted upward by a voltage value of $i_B Z_S$, where $Z_S = 10\,\Omega$ in this example. Since the collector current is a function of the base current, the constant collector current curves must be shifted upward to maintain their relative positions in relation to the new constant base current curves. With the curves of Fig. 12.14 available, the solution proceeds as shown in Example 12.1. Note, however, that a new set of curves must be drawn if the generator impedance is changed.

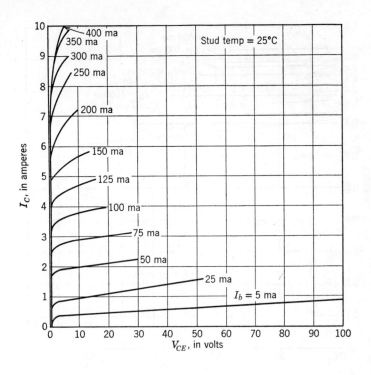

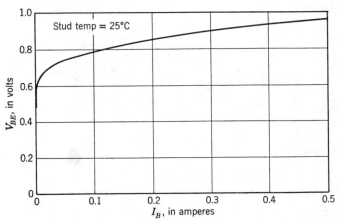

Fig. 12.11. The characteristic curves of a 2N1899 power transistor.

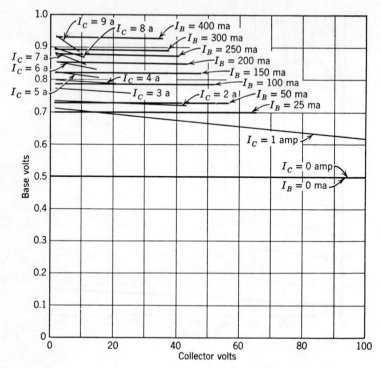

Fig. 12.12. Constant current curves for the transistor of Fig. 12.11.

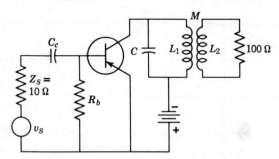

Fig. 12.13. A Class C transistor amplifier.

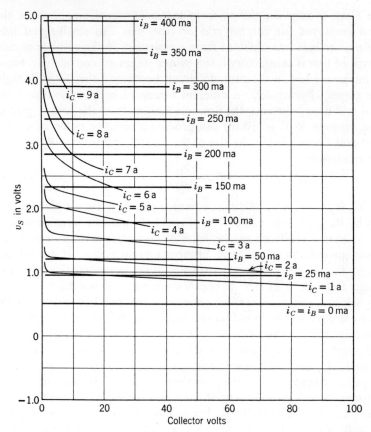

Fig. 12.14. Modified constant current curves for the transistor when the signal voltage source has an internal impedance of 10 Ω.

12.5 SELF-BIAS CIRCUITS FOR CLASS C AMPLIFIERS

The use of two or three batteries (Fig. 12.1) or power supplies is undesirable in class C amplifiers. Accordingly, means of self-bias for class C amplifiers was achieved at an early date. The circuits of Fig. 12.10 and Fig. 12.13 illustrate typical self-bias stages. The screen circuit of Fig. 12.10 operates in the same manner as described in Chapter 6. As before, the value of R_{sg} is given by the relationship

$$R_{sg} = \frac{V_{PP} - V_{G2}}{I_{G2}} \tag{6.13}$$

Also, the value of C_{sg} is chosen so X_{csg} is small at the operating frequency.

The class C amplifier differs from the small-signal amplifiers in the method employed for control grid or base bias. In small-signal *tube amplifiers*, the bias was obtained from a resistance in the cathode circuit. This type of bias is satisfactory if low-power stages are considered. However, the power lost in the cathode circuit becomes rather large in high-power stages. Fortunately, a different means of bias is possible if the control grid draws current; the flow of electrons from the control grid to ground through R_g (Fig. 12.10) can provide a negative potential on the control grid. Accordingly, the size of the control grid resistor R_g is found by the relationship

$$R_g = \frac{V_G}{I_G} \tag{12.23}$$

where V_G is the required grid bias potential and I_G is the d-c grid current drawn by the grid. The value of C_c (Fig. 12.10) must be large enough to store the charge produced by the pulse of grid current, so an essentially constant current flows through R_g between current pulses. If the old rule of thumb that X_c be equal to approximately $0.1R_g$ is applied, this condition is usually fulfilled. This type of bias is known as *grid-leak* bias.

The self-bias system described previously has one bad characteristic. If the a-c driving signal should be removed from the control grid, the bias on this stage will be reduced to zero. Zero bias will allow large currents to flow through the tube. These large currents usually destroy the tube in a short time. Consequently, protective circuits are usually incorporated in this type of circuit to remove the plate supply voltage if the excitation fails. Sometimes enough cathode bias or fixed bias is used in conjunction with grid-leak bias to protect the tube. Frequently an RF choke is connected in series with the grid-leak resistor so essentially no signal currents flow through the grid resistor. Otherwise signal power is wasted.

In the transistor amplifier, the current flowing through the base circuit resistance produces reverse bias in the same manner as grid-leak bias in the tube amplifier. Fortunately, the direction of base current is proper to produce the required polarity of bias voltage. Thus

$$R_b = \frac{V_B}{I_B} \tag{12.24}$$

where R_b is the magnitude of bias resistance required (Fig. 12.13). The voltage V_B is the quiescent base voltage and I_B is the average value of base current. However, in the transistor, zero bias is also cutoff bias. Therefore, no protective devices are necessary, since the collector current reduces to essentially zero when the excitation is removed.

The value of base bias required for class C operation of a transistor amplifier cannot be specified in terms of the cutoff bias (as for a vacuum tube) because the "cutoff" bias voltage of a transistor is actually a forward bias. However, the transistor class C bias can be determined in terms of the collector current conduction angle (Fig. 12.15). In this figure, an operating line is shown on a modified set of constant current characteristics (similar to those of Fig. 12.14). The desired bias voltage is V_B. The base-emitter voltage at which collector current begins to flow is V_X and the peak

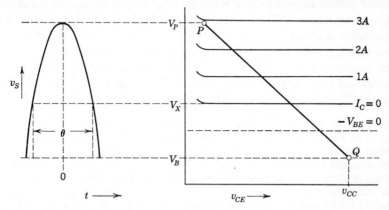

Fig. 12.15. The relationships used to determine the transistor base bias voltage as a function of conduction angle.

source voltage, which occurs at the collector saturation point P, is V_P. From Fig. 12.15 it can be seen that

$$\frac{V_X - V_B}{V_P - V_B} = \cos\frac{\theta}{2} = \frac{V_X - V_B}{(V_P - V_X) + (V_X - V_B)} \qquad (12.25)$$

where θ is the collector current conduction angle. Then, solving for $V_X - V_B$

$$V_X - V_B = \frac{(V_P - V_X)\cos\theta/2}{1 - \cos\theta/2} \qquad (12.26)$$

or

$$V_X - V_B = \frac{V_P - V_X}{\sec\theta/2 - 1} \qquad (12.27)$$

The potential difference $V_P - V_X$ may be determined from the input characteristics as well as from the modified constant current curves since $V_P = V_{BE\ \max} + i_{B\ \max}R_s$. After determining V_P, the conduction angle θ is then chosen and the potential difference between V_X and V_B is readily determined by the use of Eq. 12.27. For example, if the typical class C conduction angle $120°$ is chosen, $\cos 60° = 0.5$, $\sec 60° = 2$ and $V_X - V_B = V_P - V_X$.

In designing transistor Class C amplifiers, the emitter-to-base reverse breakdown voltage V_{EBO} must be considered. If the combination of bias potential V_B and peak base signal voltage V_b exceeds this breakdown voltage, steps must be taken to protect the transistor. While several configurations are possible, the simplest way to protect the transistor is to insert a diode in series with the base. The polarity of this diode should permit current to flow when forward bias is applied to the diode-base combination. Then, when reverse bias is applied, the diode will essentially prohibit the flow of reverse current in the base circuit. Of course, the reverse voltage breakdown of the diode should be greater than the maximum reverse bias applied to the diode-base combination. This method of transistor base protection is also used in some of the pulse circuits (for example, Fig. 16.53) in Chapter 16.

PROB. 12.7. The transistor in Fig. 12.13 is the one whose characteristics are shown in Fig. 12.11. The V_{CC} supply is 50 v and it is desired to swing the collector current to 8a with i_B of 300 ma. A conduction angle of 110° is desired. The resonant frequency is one MHz and the desired circuit Q is 15. Find the values of all pertinent voltages and currents (both a-c and d-c), the input power, the output power, the efficiency of the circuit and all circuit components. Neglect the loss resistance in the coils and assume $k = 0.7$. The signal source resistance is 10 Ω. *Answer: $P_o = 77.5\ w$, $P_I = 90.5\ w$, $P_b = 0.42\ w$, diode protection of the base is required.*

12.6 THE DESCRIBING FUNCTION

The technique of pole-zero plots and consequently of root-locus plots assumes that all the circuit elements are linear. However, as indicated in Section 10.2, large-signal amplifiers are usually not linear. When a nonlinear element was encountered, a graphical approach was used. We will now consider a technique which can be used to adapt the pole-zero method to circuits which contain nonlinear elements.

As noted previously, the nonlinear elements produce harmonics which are not present in the original waveform. Hence, if a fundamental sinusoidal waveform is applied to a nonlinear circuit, the output current waveform contains the fundamental signal plus various harmonics. The *describing function* approach is based on the premise that the harmonics may be neglected without introducing appreciable error. Since tuned amplifiers contain resonant circuits, the harmonics *are* effectively filtered out of the response. Consequently, the use of the describing function with tuned amplifiers is valid.

In using the describing function, the general transfer function of a network is divided into two components. One component represents the transfer function of the linear elements (a conventional function in *s*, or

$j\omega$ for steady-state alternating current). The second component is known as the describing function and represents the nonlinear characteristic. (If more than one nonlinearity is present, all nonlinearities are grouped together and are considered as a single nonlinear component.) The describing function simply relates the fundamental component in the output of the nonlinear device to the fundamental component of the input to the nonlinear device. Mathematically this concept (Fig. 12.16) is expressed as

$$G = G_l \mathscr{G} \tag{12.28}$$

where G is the total transfer function. G_l is the linear transfer function and is a function of radian frequency only. $\mathscr{G}$ is the describing function

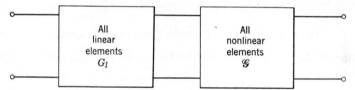

Fig. 12.16. A graphical representation of Eq. 12.28.

of the nonlinear element. As we have already found for the class C amplifiers, the ratio of the fundamental component of plate current to the fundamental component of grid voltage varies as the conduction angle (or signal amplitude) varies. Thus $\mathscr{G}$ is a function of signal amplitude. Fortunately, in most class AB, B, or C amplifiers, the relative phase between the fundamental component of output current and the fundamental component of input voltage does not change with frequency if the tuned circuit is always tuned to the fundamental. However, in some nonlinear elements the phase can change with frequency. Thus, although the describing functions with which we will be concerned are functions of signal amplitude only, the general describing function may be a function of amplitude and also of frequency. An example will be used to help clarify the describing function concept.

Example 12.3. Find the describing function for an ideal class C amplifier. The transfer function for an ideal amplifier is shown in Fig. 12.17.

A plot of the output current as a function of time is given in Fig. 12.18. The time when the output reaches its peak value will be used as the reference time for this analysis. The peak value of the fundamental component of current in the output signal can be found from a Fourier analysis of the output wave. Thus

$$I_{p1} = \frac{1}{\pi} \int_{-\pi}^{\pi} i \cos \omega t \, d(\omega t) \tag{12.29}$$

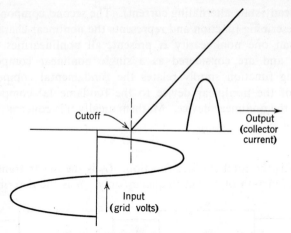

Fig. 12.17. Ideal Class C amplifier transfer characteristics.

By reason of the symmetry involved in Fig. 12.18, this equation can also be written as

$$I_{p1} = \frac{2}{\pi} \int_0^\pi i \cos \omega t \, d(\omega t) \qquad (12.30)$$

However, the current is zero from $\theta/2$ to π (Fig. 12.18), so Eq. 12.30 becomes

$$I_{p1} = \frac{2}{\pi} \int_0^{\theta/2} i \cos \omega t \, d(\omega t) \qquad (12.31)$$

The signal current is given by the expression $i = I \cos \omega t$. But since the axis of the current in Fig. 12.18 is displaced from $i = 0$ by the amount ($I \cos \theta/2$), the total expression for i is

$$i = I \cos \omega t - I \cos \theta/2 \qquad (12.32)$$

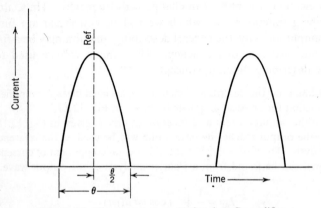

Fig. 12.18. The output current of a class C amplifier.

When this value of i is inserted into Eq. 12.31, I_{p1} is

$$I_{p1} = \frac{2}{\pi} \int_0^{\theta/2} (I \cos \omega t - I \cos \theta/2) \cos \omega t \, d(\omega t) \qquad (12.33)$$

This integral can be evaluated to yield

$$I_{p1} = \frac{2I}{\pi} \left[\frac{\theta}{4} - \frac{1}{4} \sin \theta \right] \qquad (12.34)$$

or

$$I_{p1} = I \frac{1}{2\pi} (\theta - \sin \theta) \qquad (12.35)$$

Note that if the operating point in Fig. 12.18 is moved until the device is operating class A, the ratio of I (the peak output current) to the peak input

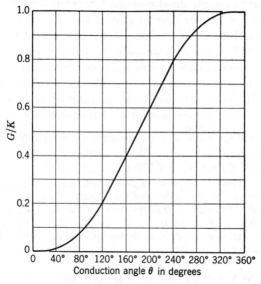

Fig. 12.19. A plot of $\mathscr{G}/K$ for the ideal Class C amplifier.

voltage V_i is the midband gain of the amplifier K. Thus, if both sides of Eq. 12.35 are divided by V_i, the equation becomes

$$\frac{I_{p1}}{V_i} = \mathscr{G} = \frac{K}{2\pi} (\theta - \sin \theta) \qquad (12.36)$$

A plot of $\mathscr{G}/K$ for various values of θ is given in Fig. 12.19.

From this example, we note that a class C amplifier can be treated much as a linear amplifier if

$$G = G_t \mathscr{G} \qquad (12.28)$$

where G is the total transfer function of a stage. The describing function

$\mathscr{G}$ is obtained from Eq. 12.36 and is used to replace the reference gain K of the amplifier. The term G_t contains the transfer function for the coupling circuits, including the tuned circuits. Thus, the treatment of large-signal amplifiers is similar to that of small-signal amplifiers except K is replaced by the describing function term $\mathscr{G}$.

One word of caution should be given at this time. The ideal class C amplifier output current given in Fig. 12.18, and the actual class C amplifier output current (Fig. 12.8) may not agree. When flattening or a dip occurs in the output current (due to a high amount of input drive), the actual value of $\mathscr{G}$ will be less than that shown in Fig. 12.19. However, if the waveform is known, (or can be determined), the correct value of $\mathscr{G}$ can be calculated.

The foregoing example developed the total transfer function I_p/V_g for a vacuum tube. When the current gain of a transistor is considered, an interesting situation occurs. Since both base current and collector current begin to flow at approximately the same base-to-emitter voltage, the conduction angle of base current and collector current is essentially the same. Thus, the $\mathscr{G}$ of current gain is ≈ 1 unless saturation occurs in the collector circuit. However, the $\mathscr{G}$ for the ratio of base current to base voltage *will* vary in a manner similar to that shown in Fig. 12.19.

PROB. 12.8. Find the value of $\mathscr{G}$ for the amplifier in Example 12.1.

PROB. 12.9. Find the value of $\mathscr{G}$ for the amplifier in Prob. 12.7. *Answer: $\mathscr{G}$ for I_c/I_b is 0.97, $\mathscr{G}$ for $I_c/V_s = 0.505$.*

PROB. 12.10. A class C amplifier is connected as shown in Fig. 12.13. The conduction angle is 120°, h_{fe} is 50, and the effective shunt resistance (including that coupled back from the 100 Ω resistor) for the L_1 and C circuit is 2 KΩ. Assume that $1/h_{oe} \gg 2$ KΩ. Find the current gain of this transistor. (Assume that the output current is the current through C and L_1 rather than the current in the 100 Ω resistor.)

12.7 EFFICIENCY OF CLASS C AMPLIFIERS

The high efficiency of the class C amplifier can be understood by reference to Fig. 12.20. The instantaneous power the plate or collector must dissipate is equal to the instantaneous value of plate (or collector) voltage times the instantaneous value of current. Since current only flows while the plate voltage is low, the plate or collector dissipation is relatively low. However, the total power into the stage is equal to the V_{PP} supply (or collector supply) voltage multiplied by the average current. The difference between the input power and the plate or collector dissipation is the useful output power.

The *theoretical maximum collector or plate efficiency* can be calculated in the following manner. From Fig. 12.20, the average power into the circuit is

$$P_i = \frac{1}{2\pi} \int_{-\pi}^{\pi} V_{CC} i(t) \, d(\omega t) \qquad (12.37)$$

where V_{CC} is the collector supply voltage. (This voltage would be V_{PP} for a tube circuit), and $i(t)$ is the current as a function of time. Since the waveforms are symmetrical about the reference point (Ref. of Fig. 12.20) Eq. 12.37 can be written as

$$P_i = \frac{2}{2\pi} \int_{0}^{\pi} V_{CC} i(t) \, d(\omega t) \qquad (12.38)$$

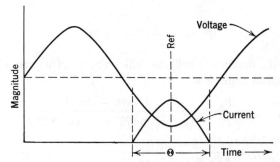

Fig. 12.20. A plot of plate or collector current and voltage in a Class C amplifier.

Now, if the current $i(t)$ is assumed to be a section of a sinusoid within the conduction angle θ, $i(t)$ can be written as

$$i(t) = I(\cos \omega t - \cos \theta/2) \qquad (12.39)$$

Notice that $I(1 - \cos \theta/2)$ is the peak value of current in the collector circuit and that $i(t)$ is zero at $\omega t = \theta/2$. Equation 12.38 can now be written as

$$P_i = \frac{V_{CC} I}{\pi} \int_{0}^{\theta/2} (\cos \omega t - \cos \theta/2) \, d(\omega t) \qquad (12.40)$$

or

$$P_i = \frac{V_{CC} I}{\pi} [\sin (\theta/2) - (\theta/2) \cos (\theta/2)] \qquad (12.41)$$

Although the actual collector (or plate) voltage cannot swing all the way to zero in an actual amplifier, this condition would still give the limiting value of power output. Accordingly, the average collector dissipation, P_d, can be written as

$$P_d = \frac{1}{2\pi} \int_{-\pi}^{\pi} (V_{CC} - V_{CC} \cos \omega t) i(t) \, d(\omega t) \qquad (12.42)$$

The term $(V_{CC} - V_{CC} \cos \omega t)$ is the relationship which describes the voltage on the collector. Now, if the point Ref. of Fig. 12.20 is taken as reference and it is observed that $i(t) = 0$ for $\pi > t > \theta/2$, Eq. 12.42 can be written as

$$P_d = \frac{1}{\pi} \int_0^{\theta/2} V_{CC}(1 - \cos \omega t)I(\cos \omega t - \cos \theta/2)\, d(\omega t) \qquad (12.43)$$

The power output P_o of the stage is given by the relationship

$$P_o = P_i - P_d = \frac{V_{CC}I}{\pi}\left[\int_0^{\theta/2} \cos^2 \omega t\, d(\omega t) - \cos \theta/2 \int_0^{\theta/2} \cos \omega t\, d(\omega t)\right]$$
$$(12.44)$$

or

$$P_o = \frac{V_{CC}I}{4\pi}(\theta - \sin \theta) \qquad (12.45)$$

Therefore, the maximum collector efficiency η_p of a class C amplifier with a conduction angle θ is

$$\eta_p = \frac{P_o}{P_i} = \frac{V_{CC}I/4\pi(\theta - \sin \theta)}{V_{CC}I/\pi(\sin \theta/2 - \theta/2 \cos \theta/2)} \qquad (12.46)$$

$$\eta_p = \frac{\theta - \sin \theta}{4 \sin \theta/2 - 2\theta \cos \theta/2} \qquad (12.47)$$

When θ is equal to π, the stage would be operating as a class B amplifier. As a check on Eq. 12.47, when $\theta = \pi$, the maximum efficiency is 0.785 or 78.5%. This is the value of maximum efficiency for a class B amplifier as found in Chapter 10. As another point of interest, note that as $\theta \to 0$, the $\sin \theta \to \theta$ and the $\sin \theta/2 \to \theta/2$. When these values of θ are substituted into Eq. 12.47, the result is an indeterminate form (0/0). However, when L'Hospital's rule is applied, the limit of Eq. 12.47 as $\theta \to 0$ is 1. Hence, the efficiency approaches 100% as $\theta \to 0$. However, as $\theta \to 0$, the power output also approaches zero for a finite collector or plate current. Accordingly, a compromise must be made between efficiency and output power.

In the usual design procedure, the collector or plate current is allowed to approach the permissible maximum. Then, a rough approximation can be found from Eq. 12.45.

The value of θ is made as small as possible to keep the efficiency high but still produce the required output power. The value of V_{CC} in Eq. 12.45 is made as high as practical to keep the conduction angle low and consequently the efficiency high. However, after all these preliminary calculations, solutions of the type indicated in Example 12.1 or Section 12.4 must be found to verify the behavior of the circuit.

In many design problems, the stage under development is required to produce a certain amount of power at a required voltage level to drive the next stage in the amplifier. In these problems, the type of coupling circuit must be considered as well as the operating voltages and currents of the tube or transistor. As a final word of caution, Eq. 12.47 gives the *maximum theoretical efficiency* of a circuit. Actual circuits will *always* have efficiencies *lower* than the values indicated by Eq. 12.47 for a given θ. (Actual amplifiers are not driven to 0 collector volts, and the collector current is usually not sinusoidal.)

PROB. 12.11. The characteristics of a 4-65A tube are given in Fig. 12.21. Design an amplifier using this tube to drive the tube of Examples 12.1 and 12.2. List all voltage and current requirements for this driver stage.

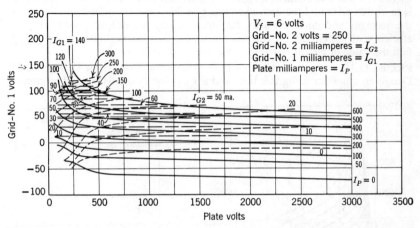

Fig. 12.21. Constant current curves for a 4-65A tube. (Courtesy of Radio Corporation of America.)

PROB. 12.12. Design a class C power amplifier to operate at 1 MHz, using a 2N1899 transistor with $V_{CC} = 50$ volts. The driving source resistance is 3 ohms. Use i_C max = 8a, i_B max = 0.3a and conduction angle = 120°. Determine power output, collector efficiency and driving power. Is base circuit protection required?

PROB. 12.13. A 4-1000A tube is to be used as a class *C* amplifier. Reference to a tube manual indicates the proper power output can be achieved if a control grid bias supply of −200 v and a plate supply of 5500 v is used. The screen is maintained at +500 v. If the grid signal is 325 v peak, find the values of currents, voltages, powers, and efficiency.

PROB. 12.14. A triode class *C* amplifier is analyzed and found to have the following voltages and currents;
Control grid supply −1000 v
Plate supply +10,000 v
Peak signal plate voltage 9000 v
Peak signal plate current 2 amp
Peak signal grid voltage 2000 v

Peak signal grid current 0.1 amp
Average plate current 1.2 amp
Average grid current 0.06 amp
(a) What is the signal power output?
(b) What is the plate power input?
(c) What is the plate efficiency?
(d) What is the signal power required to drive the grid circuit?
(e) If self-bias is used, what size of grid resistor is required?
(f) What impedance must the load in the plate circuit have?

PROB. 12.15. A circuit is connected as shown in Fig. 12.13. The characteristics of this transistor are given in Fig. 12.11. The internal resistance Z_g of the generator is 2000 Ω and V_{CC} is -20 v. The maximum collector current should not exceed 150 ma. A conduction angle of 120° is desirable. The resonant frequency is to be 500 KHz and the desired circuit Q is 20. Find the values of all a-c and d-c voltages and currents, also the input power, the output power, and the efficiency of the circuit. If the resistance of the coil is negligible and $k = 0.7$, find the value of circuit elements. Assume $f_\beta \gg 500$ KHz.

PROB. 12.16. The characteristics of a 9C21 triode are given in Fig. 12.22. Design an amplifier using this tube and a V_{PP} supply of 10,000 v. The control

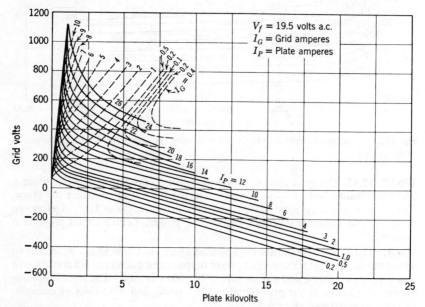

Fig. 12.22. Constant current curves for a 9C21 tube. (Courtesy of Radio Corporation of America.)

grid is to be biased at -500 v and to have a voltage swing of 960-v peak. The power output should be approximately 27 kw. List all voltages, currents, and power as well as efficiency. Sketch the circuit and give circuit element values if the resonant frequency is 2 MHz and the circuit Q is 20.

13

Oscillator Circuits

In this chapter, an electronic oscillator will be defined as a device that generates a sinusoidal voltage or current waveform. As with any electronic item, a source of d-c power is required for operation. In general, either one terminal pair devices such as klystrons, tunnel diodes, and so forth, or two-terminal pair devices such as conventional triodes, pentodes, transistors, etc., can be used as the active elements. The active elements must work in conjunction with passive (R, L, and C) networks. In some microwave devices, the values of R, L, and C are distributed over the circuit rather than being separate lumped elements. However, even in these instances equivalent circuits of R, L, and C elements can be developed to help visualize the action of the device.

13.1   OSCILLATORS WITH TWO-TERMINAL ACTIVE ELEMENTS

If the active element in an oscillator contains only two terminals, this active element must be connected either in series or in parallel with the passive elements of the circuit. Accordingly, the circuit can be represented as shown in Fig. 13.1. If the active element behaves as a negative conductance, oscillations can occur if this negative conductance of the active elements is greater than or equal to the positive conductance of the passive

503

circuit. To determine how oscillations can occur, and at which frequency and at what amplitude a given circuit will oscillate, the following procedure is followed. First, a polar plot is made *of the negative* of the admittance of the passive circuit as a function of frequency. Second a polar plot is made of the admittance of the active element as some circuit parameter is varied.

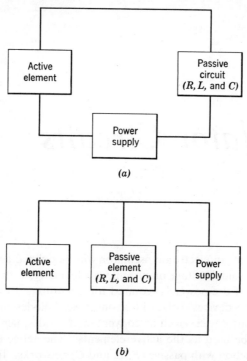

(a)

(b)

Fig. 13.1. A simplified block diagram of an oscillator with a two-terminal active element. (*a*) Series connections; (*b*) parallel connection.

This second polar plot is made on the same chart (and to the same scale) as the first polar plot. Usually, the circuit parameter which varies the admittance of the active element is the magnitude of the a-c signal in the circuit, although other circuit parameters can be used. Wherever the two plots intersect, the conditions are suitable for the circuit to oscillate. The frequency of oscillation and usually the magnitude of oscillation can be determined from the plot.

The reader was introduced to the tunnel diode in Chapter 3 (Section 3.8). To illustrate the method just discussed, an example will be given for a tunnel diode oscillator.

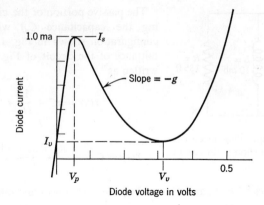

Fig. 13.2. The characteristic curve of a tunnel diode.

Example 13.1. The characteristic curve of a tunnel diode is given in Fig. 13.2. This tunnel diode is connected as shown in Fig. 13.3a. The diode specifications list a total shunt capacitance C_d of 7 pf. (An inductance of 6×10^{-9} h is also present but will be ignored in this example.) Find the frequency of oscillation and the magnitude of voltage across the tuned circuit for this configuration.[1] If the resistance of L is ignored, the tunnel diode will be biased at $+0.12$ v. Thus the tunnel diode can be replaced by an equivalent circuit (consisting of a negative conductance $-g$ and capacitance C_d) as shown in Fig. 13.3b.

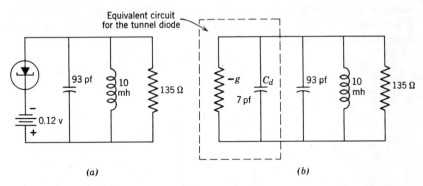

Fig. 13.3. A tunnel diode oscillator. (a) Actual circuit; (b) equivalent circuit.

[1] This circuit is idealized to the extent that a battery of 0.12 v is not practical. However, this voltage can be obtained from power supplies or resistor-battery-capacitor combinations. Unfortunately, great care should be taken or the diode will oscillate (or switch) with the battery circuit instead of with the tuned circuit. Additional tunnel diode oscillator circuits are given in "Designing Tunnel Diode Oscillators," by Wen-Hsiung Ko in *Electronics*, February 10, 1961; Vol. 34, No. 6, pp. 68–72.

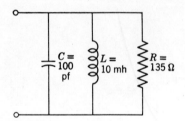

Fig. 13.4. The equivalent a-c circuit for the passive portion of the circuit in Fig. 13.3.

The passive portion of the circuit (including the capacitance C_d) will have the configuration shown in Fig. 13.4. The admittance of the circuit of Fig. 13.4 can be written as

$$Y(s) = sC + \frac{1}{sL} + \frac{1}{R} \tag{13.1}$$

or

$$Y(s) = C\frac{s^2 + s(1/RC) + (1/LC)}{s} \tag{13.2}$$

When the values of R, L, and C from Fig. 13.4 are substituted into Eq. 13.2,

$$Y(s) = 10^{-10}\frac{s^2 + s \times 7.4 \times 10^7 + 10^{12}}{s} \tag{13.3}$$

Now, for steady-state alternating current, the complex frequency s becomes $j\omega$ in Eq. 13.3. Accordingly

$$Y(j\omega) = 10^{-10}\frac{-\omega^2 + j(7.4 \times 10^7)\omega + 10^{12}}{j\omega} \tag{13.4}$$

Therefore, a polar plot of $Y(j\omega)$ as ω varies is as given in Fig. 13.5.

The next step requires the construction of a curve which represents the admittance of the tunnel diode. The characteristic curve of the tunnel diode has been reproduced in Fig. 13.6. Since the diode is biased at $+0.12$ v, the Q point would be located as shown in Fig. 13.6. The slope of the characteristic curve at Q is indicated by the line AB. *The slope of this line AB is the admittance of the diode with no a-c signal*

$$-g = \frac{0.6 \times 10^{-3}\,\text{a}}{0.08\,\text{v}} = 7.5 \times 10^{-3}\,\text{mhos}$$

This value of g is plotted as point A in Fig. 13.7.

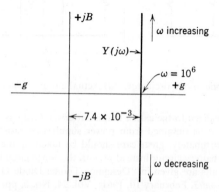

Fig. 13.5. A plot of $Y(j\omega)$ from Eq. 13.4.

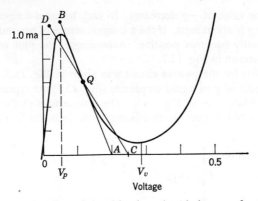

Fig. 13.6. The effect of signal level on the admittance of a tunnel diode.

If an a-c signal is superimposed on the voltage at Q, the voltage varies along the line AB (Fig. 13.6) for small signals. However, as the a-c signal increases in magnitude, the voltage must follow the characteristic curve. Accordingly, as the signal becomes larger, the voltage digresses from the AB curve. As the a-c voltage becomes larger, the *average slope*[2] *of* dI/dV decreases to the value indicated by the line CD. The slope of this line indicates that the average admittance of the diode with an a-c signal of 0.05 v is about

$$-g = \frac{1.2 \times 10^{-3} \text{ a}}{0.25 \text{ v}} = 4.8 \times 10^{-3} \text{ mhos}$$

This value of g is plotted on Fig. 13.7 as point B. As the magnitude of the a-c

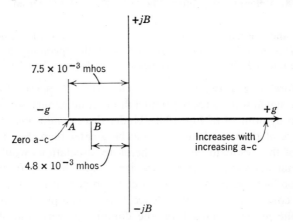

Fig. 13.7. A plot of g vs signal amplitude for the tunnel diode of Fig. 13.3.

[2] The idea of using the average slope may cause the reader to question the validity of this approach. However, this method is an extension of the *describing function* noted in Section 12.6.

signal increases, the value of $-g$ decreases. In fact, for an a-c signal of about 0.09 v, the average g is about zero. If the a-c signal increases beyond this value, the average g actually becomes positive. Accordingly, the plot of g for the tunnel diode is as shown in Fig. 13.7.

The plot of $Y(j\omega)$ for the passive circuit was given in Fig. 13.5. A plot of $-Y(j\omega)$ and the plot of g vs signal amplitude (Fig. 13.7) are reproduced on a single set of coordinate axes in Fig. 13.8. The intersection of the two plots, point P, is the required solution. In this example, the resonant frequency is 10^6

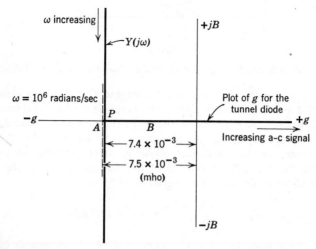

Fig. 13.8. A plot of $-Y(j\omega)$ from Fig. 13.5 and the plot $f(g)$ from Fig. 13.7.

radians/sec and the magnitude of signal for $-g = 7.4 \times 10^{-3}$ mhos is about 0.04 v. This is the value of a-c voltage for which the operating line just begins to leave the line A-B in Fig. 13.6. Hence g is just below 7.5×10^{-3} mhos.

In the foregoing example, if the circuit were at quiescent conditions and the a-c signal were zero, the tunnel diode conductance would have the value given by point A of Fig. 13.8. Under these conditions, the negative conductance of the tunnel diode would be greater than the positive conductance of this resonant circuit. Therefore, oscillations would build up in the circuit until the a-c signal was large enough to shift the value of negative conductance in the tunnel diode to point P of Fig. 13.8. At point P, the net conductance is zero. Hence, a pole-zero plot would show the poles on the $j\omega$ axis. Therefore, the damping is zero and steady-state oscillations occur. Under these conditions, the circuit is in equilibrium and will continue operation at this signal level.

The admittance plots of many devices are more complicated than the straight-line plot of Fig. 13.7. In addition, the plots of $Y(j\omega)$ for many passive circuits are more involved than the straight-line plot of Fig. 13.5. Even so, the method outlined in Example 13.1 can be applied to these more complicated circuits.

PROB. 13.1. Determine the slope of the characteristic curve of Fig. 13.2 at diode voltages of 0.05, 0.06, 0.07 ... 0.18, 0.19 v. Find the average of these slopes to determine the value of $-g$ when the a-c signal of Example 13.1 is 0.05 v rms.

13.2 OSCILLATORS WITH FOUR-TERMINAL ACTIVE ELEMENTS

Many oscillator circuits use triodes, pentodes, transistors, and so on as the active elements. In all these oscillators, energy of the proper magnitude and phase is fed from the output back to the input circuit. This type of

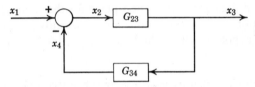

Fig. 13.9. A typical feedback circuit.

oscillator is a type of feedback amplifier. To visualize the requirements of an oscillator, consider the typical feedback circuit shown in Fig. 13.9.

The transfer function G_{13} was found in Chapter 11 to be

$$G_{13} = \frac{x_3}{x_1} = \frac{G_{23}}{1 + G_{23}G_{34}} \tag{11.6}$$

In this equation, the feedback was negative feedback. If the feedback is positive, Eq. 11.6 becomes

$$G_{13} = \frac{x_3}{x_1} = \frac{G_{23}}{1 - G_{23}G_{34}} \tag{13.5}$$

Whereas most oscillators use positive feedback, some oscillators actually require *negative feedback* for proper operation. In fact, as already noted in Chapter 11, an ordinary amplifier with negative feedback may become unstable and oscillate.

If the circuit is an oscillator, the signal x_1 must be zero and the signal x_3 must be finite. Accordingly, from Eq. 13.5,

$$\frac{G_{23}}{1 - G_{23}G_{34}} = \infty \tag{13.6}$$

or

$$1 - G_{23}G_{34} = 0 \tag{13.7}$$

Hence,

$$G_{23}G_{34} = 1 \qquad (13.8)$$

This criterion just establishes the instability of the circuit. In addition to this criterion, in order to fulfill our definition of an oscillator the output should be sinusoidal.

The root-locus plot, which was discussed in Chapter 11, is a solution of Eq. 13.7 as the gain K of the circuit is adjusted. (The rules for a root-locus plot with positive feedback are given in Appendix II.) Accordingly, the point of operation must lie on the root-locus plot. In addition, if the output of the circuit is to be a steady-state sinusoidal waveform, the point of operation must lie on the $j\omega$ axis of the s-plane. Consequently, the root-locus plot of a circuit must cross the $j\omega$ axis in the s-plane if the circuit is to be used as an oscillator. In addition to this restriction, no other poles of G_{13} can be in the right half of the s-plane for the value of K which produces oscillation. This restriction must be enforced to prevent the instability of a pole in the right half plane from "swamping" out the oscillation.

PROB. 13.2. Prove that if $x_2 = x_1 + x_4$ (positive feedback) in Fig. 13.9, then

$$G_{13} = \frac{G_{23}}{1 - G_{23}G_{34}}$$

13.3 TYPICAL *R-C* OSCILLATORS

Several types of *R-C* oscillators are in common use. The most common type of *R-C* oscillator (a circuit that is used in many commercial audio oscillators) is the type shown in Fig. 13.10. In effect, this circuit is a two-stage amplifier with the feedback loop composed of R_1, C_1, R_2, and C_2. Triode tubes have been shown, but pentode tubes or transistors could be used. With transistor circuits, the parallel combination of R_2 and R_{in} would be used in place of R_2 in the following derivation. The value of C_c is chosen large enough to pass the lowest frequencies to be generated with negligible phase shift.

The voltage feedback in this particular circuit is positive, since there are two polarity reversals in the amplifier. Accordingly, the circuit in Fig. 13.10 can be redrawn as shown in Fig. 13.11. In this figure, G_{23} is the gain of the two-stage amplifier. Hence, let G_{23} be given as K. The transfer function G_{34}, can be written as

$$G_{34} = \frac{x_4}{x_3} = \frac{R_2(1/sC_2)/[R_2 + (1/sC_2)]}{R_1 + 1/sC_1 + R_2(1/sC_2)/[R_2 + (1/sC_2)]} \qquad (13.9)$$

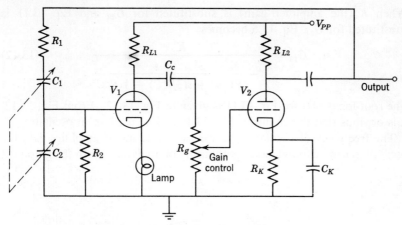

Fig. 13.10. An *R-C* bridge oscillator.

This equation can be simplified to

$$G_{34} = \frac{1}{R_1 C_2} \frac{s}{s^2 + s \dfrac{R_1 C_1 + R_2 C_2 + R_2 C_1}{C_1 C_2 R_1 R_2} + \dfrac{1}{C_1 C_2 R_1 R_2}} \qquad (13.10)$$

Equation 13.10 can be further simplified by letting $R_1 = R_2 = R$ and $C_1 = C_2 = C$. Then,

$$G_{34} = \frac{1}{RC} \frac{s}{s^2 + s \dfrac{3}{RC} + \dfrac{1}{R^2 C^2}} \qquad (13.11)$$

Since this circuit has positive feedback, Eq. 13.5 applies.

$$G_{13} = \frac{G_{23}}{1 - G_{23} G_{34}} \qquad (13.5)$$

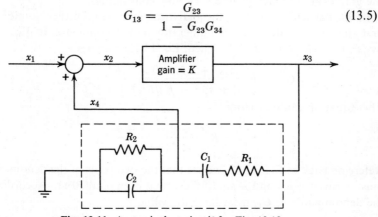

Fig. 13.11. An equivalent circuit for Fig. 13.10.

When K (the amplifier gain) is substituted for G_{23} and Eq. 13.11 is substituted for G_{34}, Eq. 13.5 becomes

$$G_{13} = \frac{K}{1 - \dfrac{K}{RC}\dfrac{s}{s^2 + s(3/RC) + 1/R^2C^2}} \tag{13.12}$$

The root-locus plot for Eq. 13.11 is given in Fig. 13.12. From Fig. 13.12, it is obvious that the circuit in Fig. 13.10 can be used as an oscillator.

The frequency of oscillation as well as the required amplifier gain for oscillation can be found either graphically or analytically. In the graphical

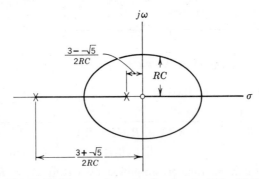

Fig. 13.12. The root locus for the circuit of Fig. 13.10.

analysis, careful construction of the root-locus plot is required. A spirule simplifies finding the required value of K. In some cases, the problem is so complicated that the analytical approach is rather difficult to evaluate. Hence, the graphical approach is the logical method of solution. However, the graphical approach can be very time consuming.

In this particular problem, the analytical approach is rather simple. The first step is to multiply both numerator and denominator of Eq. 13.12 by $(s^2 + s(3/RC) + 1/R^2C^2)$. Then, Eq. 13.12 becomes

$$G_{13} = K\frac{s^2 + s(3/RC) + 1/R^2C^2}{s^2 + s[(3 - K)/RC] + 1/R^2C^2} \tag{13.13}$$

This equation can be written as

$$G_{13} = K\frac{s^2 + 2\zeta_1\omega_n s + \omega_n{}^2}{s^2 + 2\zeta_2\omega_n s + \omega_n{}^2} \tag{13.14}$$

Referring back to Fig. 13.12, we see that the two roots of the denominator must occur at $+j\omega_1$ and $-j\omega_1$ (if the circuit is an oscillator). Accordingly, the denominator of G_{13} must have the value

$$(s + j\omega_1)(s - j\omega_1) = \text{denominator of } G_{13} \tag{13.15}$$

or

$$s^2 + \omega_1{}^2 = \text{denominator of } G_{13} \tag{13.16}$$

When Eq. 13.16 is equated to the denominator of Eq. 13.14, the following relationship results.

$$s^2 + \omega_1{}^2 = s^2 + 2\zeta_2\omega_n s + \omega_n{}^2 \tag{13.17}$$

Thus, if there are to be steady-state oscillations, the damping factor ζ_2 must have a value of zero. When the values of ζ_2 and ω_n from Eq. 13.13 are substituted into Eq. 13.17, the coefficients of like powers of s can be equated to yield

$$0 = \frac{3 - K}{RC} \tag{13.18}$$

$$\omega_1{}^2 = \frac{1}{R^2C^2} \tag{13.19}$$

From Eq. 13.18,

$$K = 3 \tag{13.20}$$

and from Eq. 13.19,

$$\omega_1 = \frac{1}{RC} \tag{13.21}$$

Figure 13.12 illustrates that the gain of the amplifier in an oscillator circuit must be maintained at a constant value. Figure 13.12 shows that a decrease of gain will shift the poles from the $j\omega$ axis into the left half plane. Under these conditions, the signal output will be an exponentially decaying sinusoidal wave. In contrast, an increase of gain will shift the poles from the $j\omega$ axis into the right half plane. In this case, the output waveform is an exponentially increasing sinusoidal wave. Consequently, it is important for the gain of the amplifier to be maintained at a constant level.

Many circuits have a sort of "built-in" gain stabilization factor. We can visualize this type of gain stabilization by referring to the typical dynamic transfer characteristic in Fig. 13.13. For small a-c signals, the operation is along the steepest part of the dynamic curve indicated by the line AB. However, as the a-c signal increases in magnitude, operation extends into the less steep portions of the dynamic transfer characteristic and the *average slope* decreases, as indicated by the line CD. Consequently, the average gain $\Delta V_p/\Delta V_g$ decreases as the a-c signal level increases.

The typical linear oscillator circuits are adjusted so the gain is slightly higher than the gain necessary for oscillations with very small signals. Hence, the poles in the root-locus plot are slightly to the right of the $j\omega$ axis (in the right half plane) when the oscillator is first turned on. Consequently, the level of signal increases. As the signal level increases, the gain

of the amplifier decreases and the poles of the root-locus plot slide back
to the $j\omega$ axis. If the signal increases or decreases beyond this value, the
gain of the circuit will change in such a direction as to return the operating
point back to the $j\omega$ axis. Unfortunately, this method of gain control
causes distortion in the output signal because of operation into the
non-linear portion of the plate characteristic curves.

The circuit of Fig. 13.10 has a device added to the circuit to maintain the
gain of the circuit at a nearly constant level. This device is the lamp in the
cathode circuit of the tube V_1. This lamp (with tungsten filament) acts as an

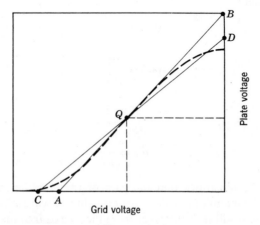

Fig. 13.13. A typical dynamic plate characteristic curve.

unbypassed cathode resistor. Hence, the lamp produces negative feedback
in the circuit. For low output, the current through the lamp is low. Because of the temperature dependence of the lamp filament resistance, the
low current through the filament allows the filament to present a rather low
resistance and consequently a low value of negative feedback. In contrast,
for high output, the current through the lamp filament is high. This high
current raises the temperature and consequently the resistance of the lamp
filament. Hence, increased output causes increased negative feedback in
the circuit to help stabilize the gain. Thus, the operation can be in the
linear portion of the tube characteristics and still have gain control.
Consequently, the signal output has very little distortion present.

The circuit of Fig. 13.14 is an improved version of the oscillator of
Fig. 13.10. In Fig. 13.14, the forward gain of the amplifier is completely
controlled by negative feedback. The negative feedback path consists of
the resistor R_f and the lamp which acts to stabilize the gain. In addition to
increased gain stability, the additional negative feedback improves the

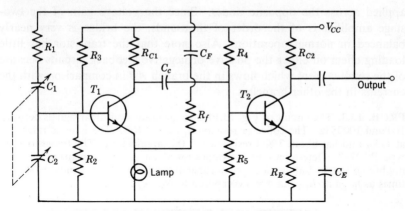

Fig. 13.14. An R-C oscillator with negative feedback gain control.

waveform of the output signal. The negative feedback circuit must be designed so that the gain $K_f = 3$ as given by Eq. 13.20.

The R-C oscillator configuration of Fig. 13.14 is commonly known as a Wein-Bridge oscillator because of its bridge characteristics, which are illustrated in Fig. 13.15. The biasing resistor R_3 has not been included in this figure because its resistance is (and needs to be) high in comparison with the impedance of the $R_1 C_1$ branch. Also, C_F has been omitted because its only purpose is to block direct current. Observe that the amplifier input is between nodes A and B and the amplifier output is

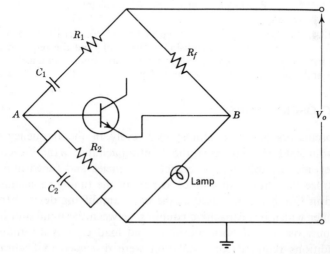

Fig. 13.15. Illustration of the bridge circuit arrangement of the oscillator of Fig. 13.15.

applied across the opposite nodes. Since the voltage gain of the two-stage amplifier is of the order of thousands, the bridge is very nearly balanced in normal operation. Also note that the transistor has little loading effect on either the positive or negative feedback circuits because of the small current which flows in the branch *AB* in comparison with the currents in the other branches.

PROB. 13.3. The circuit of Fig. 13.14 is to generate sinusoidal signals between 100 and 1000 Hz. The collector resistor R_{C2} is 2.2 KΩ. The lamp is rated 3 w at 115 v and has about 2 KΩ resistance in this application. The transistors are type 2N 2712. Determine suitable values for all circuit components which have not been given, including the range of capacitance $C_1 = C_2$. R_1 should be several times as large as R_{C2} but small compared to R_3. $V_{CC} = 20$ v.

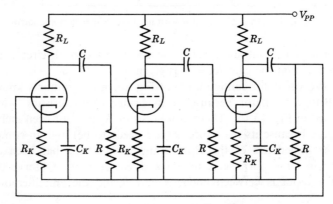

Fig. 13.16. A three-stage *R-C* oscillator.

PROB. 13.4. An *R-C* oscillator is shown in Fig. 13.16. (*a*) Find the required transfer function. (*b*) Draw the root-locus plot. (*c*) Find the required circuit gain and the resonant frequency. Neglect the stray shunt capitance. Assume each tube and load resistor forms an amplifier.

13.4 *L-C* OSCILLATORS

R-C oscillators are used almost exclusively in the frequency range below about 500 KHz. However, the shunt capacitance in the *R-C* coupled stages becomes troublesome at higher frequencies and tuned amplifiers which utilize this shunt capacitance as part of the tuning capacitance, as discussed in Chapter 8, are used as the basic amplifying device. In fact, an amplifier which has capacitive coupling between the input and output circuits may oscillate if both the input and load circuits are inductive. The conditions required for oscillation were discussed in Section 8.6. The oscillator which results when these conditions are intentionally met

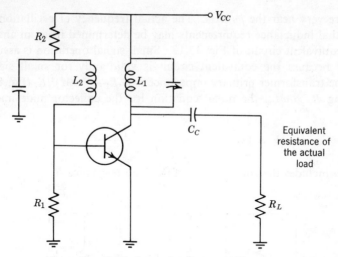

Fig. 13.17. A tuned-collector oscillator.

is known as a tuned-plate tuned-grid (or tuned-collector tuned-base) oscillator.

The single-tuned inductively coupled amplifier can be used as an oscillator if some of the energy in the output circuit is coupled back to the input circuit, as shown in Fig. 13.17.

The pole-zero plot for the voltage gain of the tuned-collector amplifier was developed in Chapter 8 and is given in Fig. 13.18. The root-locus plot for positive feedback is also given in this figure. Observe that the frequency of oscillation is very nearly the resonant frequency of the tuned circuit if the circuit Q is high because the amplifier (open-loop)

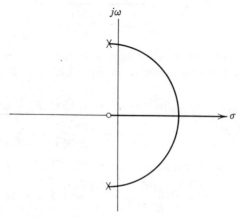

Fig. 13.18. Pole-zero and root-locus plot for the tuned-collector oscillator.

poles are very near the $j\omega$ axis. The actual frequency of oscillation and the mutual inductance requirements may be determined from an analysis of the equivalent circuit of Fig. 13.19. Small-signal operation is assumed initially because the equivalent circuit is valid only for small signals. Since the transformer primary impedance is $j\omega L_1 + (\omega M)^2/R_i$ (Eq. 8.82), assuming $R_i \gg \omega L_2$, the nodal equation for the collector node may be written

$$g_m V = \left[G + j\omega C + \frac{1}{j\omega L_1 + (\omega M)^2/R_i} \right] V_o \qquad (13.22)$$

where G includes the conductance of the load resistance R_L.

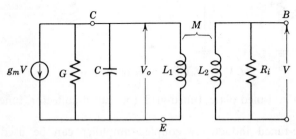

Fig. 13.19. An equivalent circuit for the tuned-collector oscillator.

For the hybrid-π equivalent circuit, the voltage V is approximately equal to the base-emitter voltage, providing that r_b is small and the frequency of operation is not appreciably above f_β. Also, if $R_i \gg \omega L_2$, as previously assumed, the base-emitter voltage is essentially $j\omega M I_p$, where I_p is the signal current through L_1. Then

$$V = \frac{j\omega M V_o}{j\omega L_1 + \dfrac{(\omega M)^2}{R_i}} \qquad (13.23)$$

The voltage gain with positive feedback may now be written using $G_{23} = V_o/V$, which is obtainable from Eq. 13.22, and $G_{34} = V/V_o$ from Eq. 13.23.

$$G_{13} = \frac{G_{23}}{1 - G_{23}G_{34}} = \frac{g_m/[G + j\omega C + R_i/(j\omega L_1 R_i + \omega^2 M^2)]}{1 - \dfrac{j\omega M g_m}{(j\omega L_1 + \omega^2 M^2/R_i)(G + j\omega C) + 1}} \qquad (13.24)$$

Oscillation occurs when the denominator of Eq. 13.24 is zero. Then

$$j\omega L_1 G - \omega^2 L_1 C + \frac{\omega^2 M^2 G}{R_i} + \frac{j\omega^3 M^2 C}{R_i} + 1 - j\omega M g_m = 0 \qquad (13.25)$$

Equating the real terms to zero

$$\omega^2 L_1 C = \frac{\omega^2 M^2 G}{R_i} + 1 \qquad (13.26)$$

or

$$\omega^2 = \frac{1}{L_1 C - \dfrac{M^2 G}{R_i}} \simeq \frac{1}{L_1 C} + \frac{GM^2}{L^2 C^2 R_i} \qquad (13.27)$$

Since $1/L_1 C = \omega_n{}^2$, where ω_n is the undamped resonant frequency of the tuned circuit,

$$\omega = \omega_n \sqrt{1 + \frac{(\omega_n M)^2 G}{R_i}} \qquad (13.28)$$

Equation 13.28 shows that the frequency of oscillation depends on the load conductance G, the input resistance R_i, and the coupling impedance $\omega_n M$. The oscillation frequency will be very nearly ω_n if $(\omega_n M)^2 G/R_i$ is small in comparison with unity, which is true if the circuit Q is high.

The required value of mutual inductance may be obtained by equating the imaginary terms of Eq. 13.25 to zero. Then

$$\frac{\omega^3 M^2 C}{R_i} - \omega M g_m + \omega L_1 G = 0 \qquad (13.29)$$

or

$$M^2 - \frac{g_m R_i M}{\omega^2 C} + \frac{L_1 G R_i}{\omega^2 C} = 0 \qquad (13.30)$$

Using the quadratic formula,

$$M = \frac{g_m R_i}{2\omega^2 C} \pm \sqrt{\left(\frac{g_m R_i}{2\omega^2 C}\right)^2 - \frac{L_1 G R_i}{\omega^2 C}} \qquad (13.31)$$

$$M = \frac{g_m R_i}{2\omega^2 C}\left(1 \pm \sqrt{1 - \frac{4\omega^2 L_1 C G}{g_m{}^2 R_i}}\right) \qquad (13.32)$$

If the circuit Q is high, $\omega^2 \simeq 1/L_1 C$. Then

$$M \simeq \frac{g_m R_i L_1}{2}\left(1 \pm \sqrt{1 - \frac{4G}{g_m{}^2 R_i}}\right) \qquad (13.33)$$

The solution which results from the positive sign preceding the radical in Eq. 13.33 may be discarded because it yields unrealizable values of M. Normally, $4G/g_m{}^2 R_i \ll 1$; therefore, the approximation $(1 - x)^{\frac{1}{2}} \simeq 1 - x/2$ can be used to simplify Eq. 13.33. Then,

$$M \simeq \frac{L_1 G}{g_m} \qquad (13.34)$$

Note that the required value of M is independent of frequency, provided that a variable capacitor is used and L_1 remains fixed. The value of M obtained from Eq. 13.34 results in class A operation. Larger values of M cause increased base drive and result in class B or class C operation, depending on M.

The Hartley oscillator circuit shown in Fig. 13.20 is similar to the tuned-collector circuit except a single, tapped coil is used and the tuning

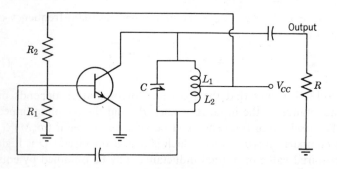

Fig. 13.20. A Hartley oscillator circuit.

capacitor tunes the entire coil. In this arrangement, the coupling between the collector and base circuits does not depend on the mutual inductance between L_1 and L_2 because an a-c voltage across L_1 is also applied across the series combination of C and L_2. Therefore, signal current will flow through L_2 and the voltage across L_2 is the feedback voltage to the base-emitter junction. The signal currents through L_1 and L_2 are essentially equal (because the tuned circuit current is large compared with the collector current), so that the ratio of collector voltage to base voltage is essentially L_1/L_2. This ratio is the voltage gain, and the reciprocal (L_2/L_1) is the feedback ratio. Thus $K\beta = 1$, provided that L_2/L_1 is large enough to cause oscillation. Note that one end of the tuned circuit is at the same signal potential as the collector, and the other end of the tuned circuit is the same signal potential as the base, and the coil tap is at the same signal potential as the emitter. This signal arrangement always holds for the Hartley oscillator. Since the input signal is not referenced to ground, any one of the three-coil or electrode terminals may be at signal ground potential. The oscillator operation is unaltered by the choice of ground point except, of course, that the output terminal must *not* be at the signal ground point. An example will be used to illustrate one method of designing a Hartley oscillator.

Example 13.2. A 2N 1613 transistor is to be used in the Hartley oscillator circuit of Fig. 13.20. Let us assume the load resistance R_L to be 10 KΩ, the transistor output resistance R_0 to be 40 KΩ, and the Q_0 of the coil to be 100. The oscillator frequency is to be 1.0 MHz. The circuit Q should be high to insure good frequency stability. In this example, we will design for $Q = 50$. The base driving power is very small in comparison with the power furnished to the load or dissipated in the tuned circuit and, therefore, its effect on the circuit Q will be neglected. Then the parallel combination of R_L and R_0 is $R_X = 8$ KΩ.

The inductance L_1 can be determined by the following method. The total shunt collector circuit resistance is (using Eq. 8.9):

$$R_{sh} = Q\omega_o L_1 \tag{13.35}$$

The portion of this shunt resistance contributed by the coil resistance in the tuned circuit is

$$R_{par} = Q_o\omega_o L_1 \tag{8.8}$$

But R_{sh} is the parallel combination of R_{par} and R_X. Then, using Eqs. 8.8 and 13.35

$$R_X = \frac{R_{par}R_{sh}}{R_{par} - R_{sh}} = \frac{Q_o Q}{Q_o - Q}\,\omega_o L_1 \tag{13.36}$$

and

$$L_1 = \frac{R_X(Q_o - Q)}{\omega_o(Q_o Q)} \tag{13.37}$$

In this example

$$L_1 = \frac{8 \times 10^3(50)}{6.28 \times 10^6(100)(50)} = 12.7\ \mu\text{h}$$

The class A voltage gain of the amplifier is approximately $g_m R_{sh}$, providing that $r_b \ll (h_{fe} + 1)r_e$ and the oscillator frequency is not appreciably above f_β. These constraints are met in this example. Now, R_{sh} is 8 KΩ in parallel with $Q_o\omega_o L_1 = 8$ KΩ, or 4 KΩ. The Q-point collector current will be chosen as 2.0 ma. Then

$$G_v \simeq g_m R_{sh} = \frac{q}{kT}I_C R_{sh} = 80 \times 10^{-3}(4 \times 10^3) = 320$$

The oscillator will operate class A if

$$L_2 = L_1/G_v = 12.7/320 = 0.04\ \mu\text{h}$$

However, a change in parameters or loading might stop the oscillation in this class A mode. The oscillator will be much more dependable if the inductance L_2 is increased by a factor of at least 4 or 5. The oscillator will then have much better amplitude stability and greater power output. Then

$$L_2 \simeq 5(0.04)\ \mu\text{h} = 0.2\ \mu\text{h}$$

The tuning capacitance can be found from the relationship

$$C = \frac{1}{\omega_o^2 L} = \frac{1}{(6.28 \times 10^6)^2(12.9 \times 10^{-6})} = 1960\ \text{pf}$$

The bias components are chosen to provide about 2.0 ma quiescent collector current and the blocking capacitor C should have reactance equal to approximately one-tenth of the bias resistance.

The Colpitts oscillator shown in Fig. 13.21 is almost identical to the Hartley except that the tuned circuit capacitance, instead of the inductance, is tapped. Also, an r-f choke has been added to permit the application of

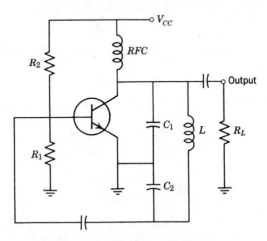

Fig. 13.21. A Colpitts oscillator.

direct current to the collector and to present a very high impedance at the oscillation frequency. The design of a Colpitts oscillator may follow the pattern given for the Hartley oscillator in Example 13.2 but with $j\omega L_1$ and $j\omega L_2$ replaced by $1/j\omega C_1$ and $1/j\omega C_2$ respectively.

PROB. 13.5. Design a Colpitts oscillator which uses a 2N1613 transistor and has the same specifications and load resistance as the Hartley oscillator of Example 13.2.

PROB. 13.6. Design a Hartley oscillator using a 2N2844 field effect transistor. Draw a circuit diagram and determine suitable circuit components if $f_o = 1$ MHz, $V_{DD} = -15$ volts and the external load resistance $R_L = 10$ KΩ. The coil $Q_o = 150$ and the desired circuit $Q = 100$. Design for class C operation. Specify the coil tap point n_2/n. *Answer: $L_1 = 5.3 \mu h$, $n_2/n \simeq 1/6$.*

13.5 CRYSTAL-CONTROLLED OSCILLATORS

A general class of oscillators which achieve very good frequency stability because of the exploitation of a high Q circuit is the *crystal-controlled* oscillator. In the "crystal" oscillator, the conventional L-C circuit is replaced by a quartz crystal. The crystal has the property of producing a potential difference between its parallel faces when the crystal is strained or deformed. Conversely, when a potential difference is applied across the faces of a crystal, it will deform or change shape. This property, which is known as the Piezo-electric effect after its discoverer, causes the crystal to behave as a very high Q-resonant circuit. The crystal will vibrate readily at its *mechanical resonant frequency*, but because of its associated electrical properties the crystal behaves as though it were an *L-C* circuit with extremely high Q (of the order of thousands). The crystal is cut into very thin slices and then carefully ground to the desired resonant frequency. The orientation of the slice, with reference to the crystal axes, determines the properties of the crystal, such as vigor of oscillation and variation of frequency with temperature.

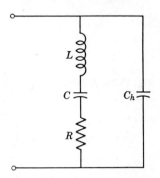

The equivalent electrical circuit of a crystal is given in Fig. 13.22. The crystal itself behaves as a series *R-L-C* circuit. However, the electrical connections must be made to the crystal faces by conducting electrodes or plates, known as a crystal holder. The crystal

Fig. 13.22. The equivalent circuit of a crystal mounted in a holder.

holder provides a capacitance, shown as C_h in Fig. 13.22, which is in parallel with the crystal circuit. Thus the crystal behaves as a series resonant circuit at its natural resonant frequency, but at a slightly higher frequency the net inductive reactance of the crystal resonates with the crystal holder capacitance to produce parallel resonance. The parallel resonant frequency is only slightly higher than the series resonant frequency because the equivalent inductance of the crystal may be of the order of henries. This extremely high equivalent inductance accounts for the extremely high Q of the crystal and provides a very impressive rate of change of reactance with frequency.

The reactance of a typical crystal in a holder is sketched as a function of frequency in Fig. 13.23. Note that the reactance is inductive only between the series resonant frequency ω_s and the parallel resonant frequency ω_p. These frequencies differ by a very small percentage (a few hundred Hz per MHz); therefore, the effective inductance changes very rapidly with frequency in this region.

The crystal can replace the tuning inductor in a conventional circuit as illustrated by the Colpitts-type circuit of Fig. 13.24. The oscillator may be designed as a conventional oscillator and the crystal will provide the proper inductance for operation very near its natural resonant frequency. A change of tuning capacitance changes the impedance of the tuned

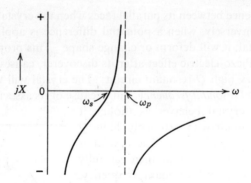

Fig. 13.23. A sketch of reactance as a function of frequency for a crystal in a holder.

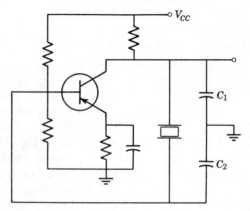

Fig. 13.24. A Colpitts oscillator with a crystal for a tuned circuit.

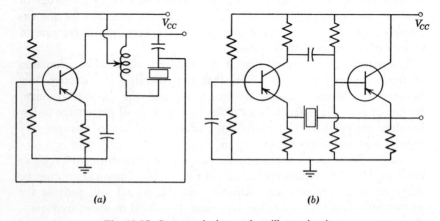

(a)   (b)

Fig. 13.25. Some typical crystal oscillator circuits.

circuit but has little influence on the frequency of oscillation because of the compensating change of effective inductance.

In the circuit of Fig. 13.25a, the crystal operates in its series mode. At the resonant frequency of the crystal, the oscillator operates as a Hartley circuit. The circuit of Fig. 13.25b uses the crystal in its series mode to couple two transistors, one of which is operating in the common base configuration and the other in the common collector configuration. Many other circuits may be devised or found in the literature.

The chief disadvantages of crystals are as follows:

1. They are fragile, especially the high-frequency crystals, and consequently can be used only in low-power circuits.
2. The oscillator frequency cannot be adjusted appreciably. However, the parallel or holder capacitance has some effect on the frequency in the parallel mode.

PROB. 13.7. A quartz crystal has the following electrical characteristics:

$$L = 3.2 \text{ henries}$$
$$C = 0.05 \, pf$$
$$R = 4000\Omega$$
$$C_h = 6 \, pf$$

(a) Determine the value of f_s and f_p for this crystal. (b) What is the Q of this crystal? (c) Design a Colpitts oscillator which uses this crystal and a 2N1613 transistor. The value of R_L is 10 KΩ and the transistor output resistance is 40 KΩ. *Answer:* (a) $f_s = 398 \, KHz, f_p = 401 \, KHz$. (b) $Q = 2000$.

PROB. 13.8. The phase shift oscillator shown in Fig. 13.26 is a rather common type of *R-C* oscillator. The tube and load resistor form an amplifier and the three capacitors C in conjunction with the three resistors R form the feedback path. Make a root locus plot for this circuit and determine the required amplifier gain and oscillation freq.

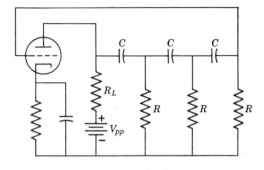

Fig. 13.26. A phase shift oscillator.

PROB. 13.9. A reflex klystron is used for generating microwave frequencies. A typical reflex klystron contains a built-in resonant cavity, which can be represented as a parallel-tuned circuit. (a) Determine the value of L, C, and R for this tuned circuit if the resonant frequency is 10^{10} Hz and the Q of the circuit is 1000. The conductance of the tuned circuit at resonance is 20 micromhos. (*b*) Make a plot of $-Y(j\omega)$ for this tuned circuit.

An electron beam passes through a gap in the resonant cavity. The electrons in this beam are stopped by the electric field of a negative "repeller" electrode and repelled back through the gap in the resonant cavity. The electron beam interacts with the electric field of the gap to produce a conductance g in parallel with the capacitor of the tuned circuit. A plot of the value of g as a function of N is shown in Fig. 13.27. The parameter N is the number of cycles the electric field

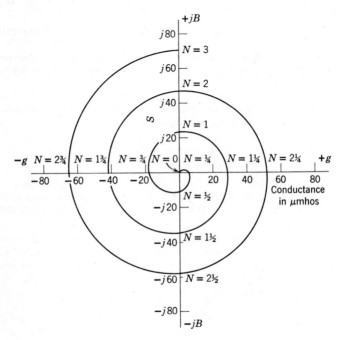

Fig. 13.27. A plot of electron beam conductance in a reflex klystron.

across the gap has completed between the time a given reference electron first passed through the gap to the time when this same electron returns to the gap. (*c*) At what value of N will oscillations first begin? (*d*) What is the frequency of these oscillations? The radius of the admittance spiral decreases as the a-c signal increases. (*e*) At what value of N (for $0 < N < 2$) will the a-c signal be maximum? (*f*) As N is increased above this value for maximum signal, the oscillations will cease. At what value of N will oscillations cease? (*g*) What frequency corresponds to the value of N in part *f*?

PROB. 13.10. Convert the amplifier of Prob. 12.8 into an oscillator. This oscillator will provide the excitation for the tube of Examples 12.1 and 12.2.

14

Amplitude Modulation and Detection

In the preceding chapters, the goal has been the development of basic principles whereby the process of signal amplification may be achieved by the use of electronic devices. In the amplifier it is usually desirable that the output quantity or response be the same form as the input quantity or excitation. This chapter will consider some electronic devices in which the form of the signal is *intentionally* changed. Generally, these devices are known as *modulators* and the process is known as *modulation*, which means "to change."

Modulators are needed in a great number of electronic systems. For example, in a radio transmitter an oscillator generates the basic radio frequency signal which is commonly known as the *carrier*. If this carrier were merely amplified and broadcast, there would be no intelligence transmitted and the system would be useless. Thus, somewhere in the transmitter the carrier must be changed or modulated by the intelligence which is to be transmitted. The intelligence can then be recovered at radio receivers by a device known as a *detector*. The carrier may be changed in any of several ways such as *in amplitude* or *in frequency*. In this chapter only *amplitude modulation* will be considered.

14.1   AMPLITUDE MODULATION

In order to gain some understanding of the fundamental principles of amplitude modulation, a simple special case will be considered in which a carrier with maximum amplitude A_c and natural frequency ω_c will be

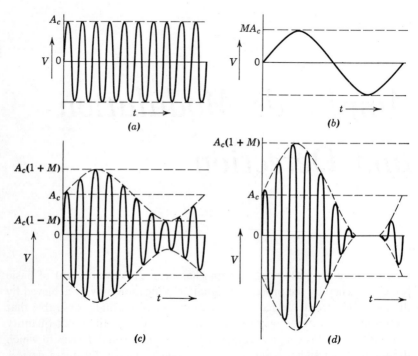

Fig. 14.1. Modulation (*a*) the carrier; (*b*) the modulating signal; (*c*) an amplitude modulated carrier; (*d*) an overmodulated carrier.

modulated by a sinusoidal (single-frequency) signal which has a natural frequency ω_m. A sketch of the modulated carrier voltage as a function of time, along with the carrier and the modulating signal, is given in Fig. 14.1. As shown in this figure, the maximum amplitude variation from the unmodulated value is MA_c, where M is known as the *modulation index*.

When M has a value of one, the amplitude of the modulated wave varies between $2A_c$ and zero. In this case, the carrier is said to be 100% modulated. When M has the value 0.5, the amplitude of the modulated carrier varies between $1.5A_c$ and $0.5A_c$. The carrier is then said to be 50% modulated, and so forth. Observe that if M exceeds unity, the carrier is completely interrupted for a time, the envelope (see Fig. 14.1) of the carrier no longer has the same form as the modulating signal, and the carrier is said to be *overmodulated*. Overmodulation naturally causes distortion in the system. It may be seen from Fig. 14.1 that the voltage of the modulated wave may be expressed by Eq. 14.1

$$v = A_c[1 + M \cos \omega_m t] \cos \omega_c t \tag{14.1}$$

This expression could have just as well been in terms of current instead of voltage. Also Eq. 14.1 would be more general if arbitrary phase angles were included in the expression. However, the results would not be altered by the increased generality. Expanding Eq. 14.1, we have

$$v = A_c \cos \omega_c t + MA_c \cos \omega_c t \cos \omega_m t \tag{14.2}$$

Substituting the trigonometric identity $\cos a \cos b = \frac{1}{2}[\cos(a+b) + \cos(a-b)]$ into Eq. 14.2, we see that

$$v = A_c \cos \omega_c t + \frac{MA_c}{2} \cos(\omega_c + \omega_m)t + \frac{MA_c}{2} \cos(\omega_c - \omega_m)t \tag{14.3}$$

It may be seen from Eq. 14.3 that the effect of the modulation is to *produce two new frequencies*, which are called side frequencies. The upper side frequency is the *sum* of the carrier frequency and the modulating frequency whereas the lower side frequency is the *difference* between the carrier and modulating frequencies. Therefore, a tuned amplifier which is called on to amplify a modulated carrier must have sufficient bandwidth to include the side frequencies. Notice that the modulating frequency *is not* included in the modulated wave. In case the modulating signal were derived from a symphony orchestra, each frequency component would produce a pair of side frequencies. Consequently, the highest frequency components present in the modulating signal would determine the required bandwidth of the tuned circuits in the radio transmitting and receiving equipment. If these tuned circuits have insufficient bandwidth, the highest modulating frequencies will not be reproduced by the receiver. Collectively, the upper side frequencies are known as the upper sideband and the lower side frequencies are known as the lower sideband.

Any modulating waveform which is represented as a function of time may be resolved into frequency components by Fourier analysis. Thus, the bandwidth requirements may be determined whenever the waveform of the modulating signal is known as a function of time.

Example 14.1. Consider the rectangular pulse shown in Fig. 14.2a to be the modulating signal. The pulse duration is t_d and the period is T. Using Fourier analysis the frequency components of the modulating signal are found as follows. The time reference is taken so that only cosine terms will appear in the Fourier series. Then

$$A_n = \frac{2}{T}\int_{-T/2}^{T/2} V \cos\left(\frac{2\pi n}{T}t\right) dt = \frac{4}{T}\int_{0}^{T/2} V \cos\left(\frac{2\pi n}{T}t\right) dt \qquad (14.4)$$

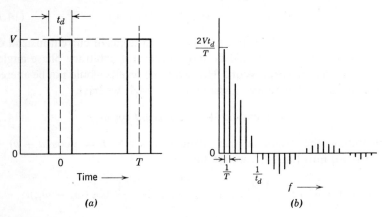

Fig. 14.2. (a) A rectangular pulse-modulating signal; (b) the frequency spectrum of a rectangular pulse.

Since the function V is zero from $t_d/2 < t < T/2$ Eq. 14.4 becomes

$$A_n = \frac{4}{T}\int_{0}^{t_d/2} V \cos\left(\frac{2\pi n}{T}t\right) dt = \frac{T4V}{2\pi Tn}\left[\sin\left(\frac{2\pi n}{T}\right)t\right]_{0}^{t_d/2} \qquad (14.5)$$

then

$$A_n = \frac{2V}{\pi n}\sin\left(\frac{\pi n t_d}{T}\right) \qquad (14.6)$$

Multiplying both the numerator and denominator of Eq. 14.6 by t_d and rearranging, we have

$$A_n = \frac{2Vt_d}{T}\frac{\sin(\pi n t_d/T)}{n\pi t_d/T} \qquad (14.7)$$

Thus, the frequency components of the modulating wave are an infinite series as shown below.

$$V_{(\omega)} = \frac{2Vt_d}{T}\left[\frac{\sin\left(\frac{\pi t_d}{T}\right)}{(\pi t_d)/T}\cos\left(\frac{2\pi}{T}t\right) + \frac{\sin\left(\frac{2\pi t_d}{T}\right)}{(2\pi t_d)/T}\cos\frac{4\pi}{T}t\cdots\right] \qquad (14.8)$$

The coefficients of these harmonically related frequency components are of the form $(\sin x)/x$. These frequency components, which are spaced at the interval

$f = 1/T$, are shown graphically in Fig. 14.2b. It was assumed in Fig. 14.2 that the period T is large in comparison with the pulse duration t_d. Of course, all the components cannot be shown because they form an infinite series. The frequency components of the amplitude modulated carrier are shown in Fig. 14.3 along with a sketch of the modulated wave. To include all the side frequencies, the bandwidth of the amplifiers which amplify this signal must be infinite. Of course, an infinite bandwidth is practically impossible to attain, so a compromise must be reached. Frequently the accepted compromise is that all the side frequencies up to the first zero amplitude component be included, since the frequency com-

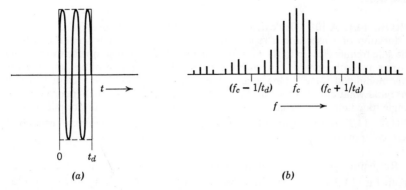

Fig. 14.3. (a) A pulse-modulated wave; (b) the frequency components of a pulse-modulated wave.

ponents beyond this point are of rather small amplitude. This choice would result in a modulated signal which departs considerably from the ideal rectangular shape, but nevertheless it provides a convenient reference point because the first zero amplitude modulating component occurs (from Eq. 14.7) at the lowest value of n for which

$$A_n = \frac{2Vt_d}{T} \frac{\sin (n\pi t_d/T)}{n\pi t_d/T} = 0 \tag{14.9}$$

The lowest value of n at which Eq. 14.9 will hold is

$$\frac{n\pi t_d}{T} = \pi \tag{14.10}$$

or

$$n = \frac{T}{t_d} \tag{14.11}$$

Since the frequency components are separated by the frequency $1/T$, the width of a single sideband would be (from Eq. 14.11)

$$\frac{B}{2} = n\left(\frac{1}{T}\right) = \frac{1}{t_d} \tag{14.12}$$

The bandwidth requirement would then be $2/t_d$. Wider bandwidth would naturally provide better waveform of the modulated signal.

The bandwidth requirement for a pulse-modulated wave can also be determined from the required rise time of the modulation envelope. The analysis of the time response of a tuned amplifier, given in Chapter 8, showed that the rise time of the modulation envelope is approximately $4.4/B$, where B is the bandwidth of the tuned amplifier in radians per second. Therefore, the bandwidth may be determined from the desired rise time.

PROB. 14.1. A 100 MHz carrier is modulated by a rectangular pulse which has a duration of 1 μsec and a repetition rate of 1000 pulses per second (pps). If the side frequencies up to the first zero magnitude component on each side of the carrier are to be included, what bandwidth will be required of an amplifier for this modulated wave? How many side frequencies would be included in this case and what circuit Q would be required of an amplifier which incorporates a single tuned circuit? What will be the envelope rise time of this amplifier?

PROB. 14.2. Repeat Prob. 14.1 but include all side frequencies up to the second zero component.

Returning to the case of a single modulating frequency, we can see from Eq. 14.3 that when the modulation index M is unity (100% modulation) the amplitude of either side frequency is one-half that of the carrier. Since power is proportional to the square of the amplitude, each side frequency will have one-fourth as much power as the carrier and the total side frequency power will be one-half as great as the carrier power. Again, this relationship holds only for 100% sinusoidal modulation.

14.2 MODULATING CIRCUITS

A large variety of circuits may be used to provide amplitude modulation. Only a few typical circuits will be included in this work for the purpose of illustrating the basic principles. One common method of accomplishing modulation is by using the modulating signal to vary the plate or collector voltage of a class B or class C amplifier as shown in Fig. 14.4. Since in class B or class C operation, the peak amplitude of the signal voltage in the output is very nearly equal to the supply voltage, the amplitude of the output voltage follows very closely the variation in voltage supplied from the modulator. The modulation is said to be *linear* when the envelope of the modulated wave has the same waveform as the modulating signal. Observe that the modulation may be linear even though the modulated amplifier may be very nonlinear so far as the waveform of each r-f cycle is concerned. The tuned coupling circuit essentially eliminates the harmonics of the carrier frequency as well as the modulating frequency so the output is a modulated wave of the form of Fig. 14.1c. The capacitor C provides a low impedance path to the carrier currents so these currents do not flow through the modulation transformer. On the other hand, the capacitor C must not bypass the modulating frequencies.

The power requirement of the modulator as well as the modulator load resistance may be determined from the basic current and voltage relationships of the modulated amplifier. To obtain 100% modulation, the maximum value of the modulating voltage V_m must be equal to the power

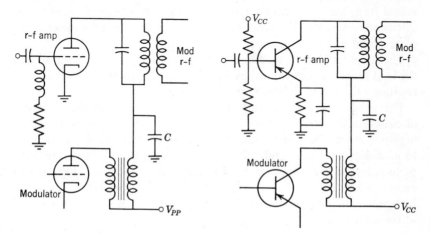

Fig. 14.4. Typical circuits for (a) plate and (b) collector modulation.

supply voltage (V_{PP} or V_{CC}). Under these conditions, the r-f output of the modulated amplifier is equal to zero at the negative peak of the modulating signal. Then, using the tube circuit as an example, we have

$$V_{m(\max)} = V_{PP} \qquad (14.13)$$

Also, since the average plate current of the modulated amplifier is reduced from I_P to zero during this negative half-cycle of the modulating signal, the maximum value of the modulating signal current is

$$I_{m(\max)} = I_P \qquad (14.14)$$

The modulator power output is

$$P_{\mathrm{mod}} = \frac{V_{m(\max)}I_{m(\max)}}{2} = \frac{V_{PP}I_P}{2} \qquad (14.15)$$

Thus, as shown by Eq. 14.15, the power output from the modulator must be equal to one-half the power supplied to the r-f amplifier by the power supply. Therefore, the power from the modulator provides the power for the sideband frequencies. It was previously shown that the power in the side frequencies is one-half the carrier power for this case.

The effective load on the modulator may be easily determined since the maximum amplitudes of both the modulator voltage and current are known.

$$R_L = \frac{V_{m(\text{max})}}{I_{m(\text{max})}} = \frac{V_{PP}}{I_P} \tag{14.16}$$

The value of supply voltage is known and the value of I_P may be determined from the graphical analysis of the class B or class C amplifier as discussed in Chapter 12. Also, I_P is easily measured by a d-c meter in the plate circuit of the r-f amplifier.

The turns ratio of the modulation transformer should be chosen so that the load resistance determined by Eq. (14.16) will present the desired load resistance for the modulating tube or transistor.

The modulator may typically be any of the power amplifier circuits discussed in Chapter 10. Push-pull circuits are usually used to modulate high-power amplifiers. For pentode and tetrode r-f amplifiers, it is helpful to modulate the screen grid voltage as well as the plate voltage, since the plate potential has a very small effect on the magnitude of plate current except at low values of plate voltage. Also, the screen current becomes high when the plate voltage is low, unless the screen voltage is reduced at the same time.

PROB. 14.3. A class C amplifier which has 1 Kw output and is 80% efficient is to be plate modulated. The plate supply voltage $V_{PP} = 2000$ v. Determine the required power output and load resistance for the modulator. The modulator is expected to provide 100% modulation. *Answer: $P_{mod} = 625$ w, $R_L = 3200\Omega$.*
PROB. 14.4. Draw the circuit diagram for a modulated pentode amplifier in which both plate and screen grid are modulated.

The linearity of plate or collector modulation is usually good. In the tube circuit, better linearity is attained when the modulated amplifier has grid leak bias rather than fixed bias. The improved linearity results from the variation of the bias over the modulation cycle. During the negative half of the modulation cycle, the grid draws more current because the plate potential is reduced. Thus, the bias is increased and assists in the reduction of plate current. Conversely, during the positive portion of the modulation cycle, the grid current is decreased because of the increased plate voltage. Consequently, the bias is decreased, thus enhancing the plate current increase. This varying bias tends to offset the tendency toward flattening of the peaks of the modulated wave due to saturation effects.

Collector modulation presents a special problem in the transistor circuit. The base drive must be large enough to saturate the transistor at the peak of the modulation cycle in order to provide linear modulation and high efficiency. Consequently, the transistor may be highly over-driven during the modulation troughs when the collector current should be comparatively small. However, excess charge is stored in the base during the time the transistor is in saturation and the collector current cannot decrease until this excess charge has been removed. As a result of this delay, the large values of collector current are not confined to the period during which the collector voltage is low and the collector dissipation is increased. In fact, the collector current may increase during the portion of the collector voltage cycle when the current would normally decrease. This enlarged, out-of-phase current may seriously decrease the efficiency of the amplifier. Grid leak type, or R-C bias, will curtail the excess stored charge because the base current increases rapidly when the transistor is driven into saturation and the resulting increased bias decreases the excessive base drive. A discussion of collector-saturation and excess stored charge is given in Chapter 16.

The main disadvantage of plate modulation is the large modulating power required when the modulated amplifier is of high power. Of course, a lower level stage could be modulated in a high-power transmitter and the modulated wave could then be amplified. But class C amplifiers are not suitable for amplifying modulated waves because the waveform of the modulation is not preserved. Of course, class B amplifiers are suitable, but their reduced efficiency is a serious handicap when the power level is high.

Fortunately, grid or base modulation requires much less modulating power than does plate modulation. Typical grid and base modulation circuits are given in Fig. 14.5. The r-f amplifiers could be operated either class B or class C. In these circuits, the modulating voltage varies the grid (or base) bias as shown in Fig. 14.6. The dynamic transfer characteristic for a typical vacuum tube is given in Fig. 14.6a, and the current transfer characteristics of a typical transistor are given in Fig. 14.6b. For the transistor, the effects of the driving source resistance R_g, as discussed in Chapter 10, are included. In this figure, the source resistances of the carrier and the modulator are assumed to be the same, and in practice these resistances should be adjusted to approximately the same value.

In the r-f amplifiers of Fig. 14.6 it is desirable to vary the output current from the maximum design value (point b') at the crest of the modulating signal to essentially zero (point c') at the trough of the modulating signal. Therefore, the r-f amplifier current peaks should be adjusted to the average of these two values (point a') when the carrier is unmodulated. It may be seen from Fig. 14.6 that the maximum amplitude of the modulating voltage should be the potential difference between point a and either point b or point c on the input voltage axis. This potential difference will be called V_m. Considering the transistor, we know that the bias current varies from the value obtained when the carrier is unmodulated (I_{Ba}) to zero as

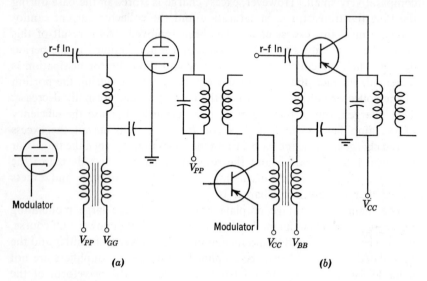

Fig. 14.5. (*a*) Grid-modulated and (*b*) base-modulated amplifiers.

the modulating voltage varies through its negative half-cycle. Therefore, the transducer[1] power required from the modulator is

$$P_m = \frac{V_m I_{Ba}}{2} \qquad (14.17)$$

As stated previously, the output resistance of the modulator and its associated circuits should be approximately the same as the output resistance of the carrier source and its associated circuits. These resistances should have the value which gives best linearity as determined by the technique discussed in Chapter 10.

In the tube amplifier, the grid draws no current when the carrier is unmodulated. Hence, the grid draws current and therefore presents a load to the modulator only on the positive peaks of the modulation cycle. This

---

[1] The transducer power is the power furnished by the current generator or voltage generator in the equivalent circuit of the source. This is the power delivered to the internal resistance of the source in addition to the load.

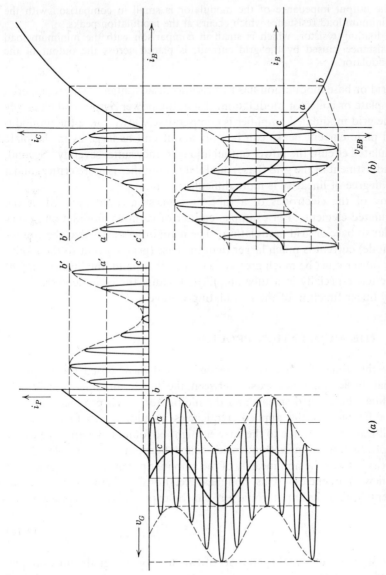

Fig. 14.6. Voltage and current relationships in (a) grid and (b) base-modulated amplifiers.

varying load will cause distortion of the modulation envelope unless one of the following conditions is met:

1. The output impedance of the modulator is small in comparison with the minimum load resistance which occurs at the modulation peaks.
2. A loading resistor, which is small in comparison with the minimum load resistance caused by the grid current, is placed across the output of the modulator.

Grid or base modulation has two serious disadvantages when compared with plate or collector modulation. First, the power output and efficiency of the grid modulated amplifier is comparatively low. Since the unmodulated plate current peaks can be only about half as large as in the plate modulated circuit, the power output and efficiency suffer severely. Second, the adjustment of the grid (base) modulated amplifier is more critical and a high degree of linearity is more difficult to attain.

Any of the electrodes of a tube or transistor could be used as the modulated element. For example, emitter or cathode modulation is very similar to base or grid modulation. The main difference is that the emitter (cathode) current is much larger than the base (grid) current so the modulator power must be much greater. On the other hand, the linearity might be better, especially in a tube amplifier, because the cathode current is a fairly linear function of the modulating voltage.

14.3 THE MODULATION PROCESS

By this time, the inquisitive reader should have posed the question, "What basic difference exists between the linear amplifier which only amplifies the applied signals and the modulator which produces the sum and difference of the applied frequencies in addition to their possible amplification?" A clue to the answer might be found in Chapter 10 where the production of new frequencies called harmonics is considered. In that case, it was the nonlinearity of the amplifier parameters that generated the new frequencies. This nonlinear relationship between the output current i_O and the input voltage v_i can be expressed by the power series

$$i_O = A_0 + A_1 v_i + A_2 v_i^2 + A_3 v_i^3 + \cdots \tag{14.18}$$

Now, if the input signal v_i consists of two sinusoidal signals, for example, a carrier frequency and a modulating frequency, then

$$v_i = A_c \cos \omega_c t + A_m \cos \omega_m t \tag{14.19}$$

Substituting this value of v_i into Eq. 14.18, we have

$$i_O = A_0 + A_1(A_c \cos \omega_c t + A_m \cos \omega_m t) + A_2(A_c \cos \omega_c t + A_m \cos \omega_m t)^2$$
$$+ A_3(A_c \cos \omega_c t + A_m \cos \omega_m t)^3 + \cdots \tag{14.20}$$

If we assume that the nonlinearity is such that the fourth and all higher order terms are negligibly small, Eq. 14.20 can be expanded to

$$i_O = A_0 + A_1 A_c \cos \omega_c t + A_1 A_m \cos \omega_m t + A_2 A_c^2 \cos^2 \omega_c t$$
$$+ A_2 A_m^2 \cos^2 \omega_m t + 2A_2 A_c A_m \cos \omega_c t \cos \omega_m t$$
$$+ A_3 A_c^3 \cos^3 \omega_c t + 3A_3 A_c^2 A_m \cos^2 \omega_c t \cos \omega_m t$$
$$+ 3A_3 A_c A_m^2 \cos \omega_c t \cos^2 \omega_m t + A_3 A_m^3 \cos^3 \omega_m t \tag{14.21}$$

Most of the terms of Eq. 14.21 have a familiar form. As previously discussed, the A_0 term is merely a bias term and the next two terms involving A_1 are the input frequency components which appear in the output current. The next three terms (4th, 5th, and 6th) result from the second-order term of the series. Two of these terms are squared and result in second harmonics of both of the input frequencies, as shown in Chapter 10. The other second-order term is the product term $2A_2 A_c A_m \cos \omega_c t \cos \omega_m t$. Using the trigonometric identity $\cos a \cos b = \frac{1}{2}[\cos(a+b) + \cos(a-b)]$, we see that this term becomes $A_2 A_c A_m[\cos(\omega_c + \omega_m)t + \cos(\omega_c - \omega_m)t]$. In this case the frequencies $(\omega_c + \omega_m)$ and $(\omega_c - \omega_m)$ are the sum and difference frequencies, or the sideband frequencies, of the modulated wave. Thus it is seen that a second-order nonlinearity of amplifier parameters causes modulation.

Continuing the investigation, we see that the remaining four terms of Eq. 14.21 result from the third-order term of the series. If the trigonometric identity $\cos^3 = \frac{3}{4}\cos a + \frac{1}{4}\cos 3a$ is used, it is seen that the cubic cosine terms produce third harmonics of the input frequencies as well as contribute to the fundamental. The remaining two terms of the form $\cos^2 a \cos b$ could be written as $\cos a (\cos a \cos b)$ which, in turn could be written as $(\cos a/2)[\cos(a+b) + \cos(a-b)]$. Using the identities again, we could write this term as $\frac{1}{4}[\cos(2a+b) + \cos b + \cos(2a-b) - \cos b]$. When $\omega_m t$ is substituted for a, and $\omega_c t$ for b, it is seen that sideband frequencies appear at twice the modulating frequency; or, in other words, there is distortion in the modulation components. On the other hand, when $\omega_c t$ is substituted for a, and $\omega_m t$ for b, in the foregoing trigonometric term, it is seen that the second harmonic of the carrier frequency $2\omega_c$ also has sidebands. Therefore, the cubic term of the series produces second harmonic distortion of the modulation envelope, third harmonic distortion of the input frequencies, and sidebands of the $2\omega_c$ term. From the preceding analysis, it should be evident that if the fourth-order term were included in the series, fourth harmonics of the input frequencies and third harmonic distortion terms of the modulation envelope would occur in the amplifier current, and so on.

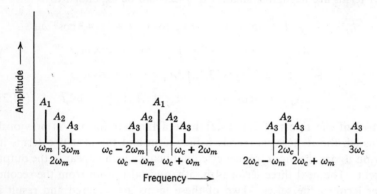

Fig. 14.7. A display of the frequency components which appear in the output current of a nonlinear amplifier which has two frequencies, ω_c and ω_m, applied to its input. Only second- and third-order nonlinearities are considered.

The various frequency components which appear in the output current of the nonlinear amplifier are displayed graphically in Fig. 14.7. The relative magnitudes of these various components depend on the relative magnitudes of the first-order coefficient A_1, the second-order coefficient A_2, and the third-order coefficient A_3, as shown in Fig. 14.7.

If the amplifier has only a second-order nonlinearity and a filter were used to select only the carrier and the side band frequencies, the output of the amplifier would be (from Eq. 14.21 and the trigonometric identities)

$$i_O = A_1A_c \cos \omega_c t + A_2A_cA_m[\cos (\omega_c + \omega_m)t + \cos (\omega_c - \omega_m)t] \quad (14.22)$$

If we write Eq. 14.22 in the form of Eq. 14.3,

$$i_O = A_1A_c\left\{\cos \omega_c t + \frac{A_2A_m}{A_1} [\cos(\omega_c + \omega_m)t + \cos(\omega_c - \omega_m)t]\right\}$$

$$(14.23)$$

By comparison with Eq. 14.3, the modulation index of this second-order or "square-law" modulator is

$$M = \frac{2A_2A_m}{A_1} \quad (14.24)$$

A good "square-law" modulator would then have a large value of A_2, or high degree of second-order nonlinearity, but no higher order of nonlinearity. Unfortunately, this type of device may be difficult to find. However, examples of this type of modulated amplifier appear later in this chapter.

A slight digression at this point may be in order. It should be recalled that in Chapter 10 the objective was to minimize the nonlinearity so that the output waveform would be identical to the input waveform and hence contain the same frequency components in the same relative magnitudes. The harmonics present in the output were used as an index of the degree of nonlinearity of the amplifier. Although the harmonics are a good *index* of the nonlinearity of an audio amplifier, which is used in the reproduction of sound, they *are not* the cause of the dischordant, unpleasant sounds which come from a nonlinear amplifier. The harmonicly related frequencies are harmonious, and although an increased harmonic content will change the timbre of the sound, it will not cause the sound to be unpleasant. It is the modulation terms (sum and difference frequencies) produced by the nonlinearity which cause the dischordant, unpleasant sounds. The sum and difference frequencies may not be harmonious with the original frequencies. Thus a poor sound reproducer may sound acceptable for a solo performance but unacceptable for an ensemble.

PROB. 14.5. A pentode amplifier has $g_m = 4000 + 200\,v_G$ µmhos. The Q point is $V_G = -10$ v. Two sinusoidal signals, each having a maximum amplitude of 5 v are applied to the input. Their frequencies are 150 Hz and 400 Hz. The load is 5 KΩ resistive, and the amplifier is well designed. Assuming the load resistance to be very small in comparison with the plate resistance, determine the amplitude of the sum and difference frequencies and second harmonics in the output. What is the per cent modulation, assuming the 400 Hz frequency to be the carrier? *Answer: fund. = 50 V peak, 2nd Har = 12.5 V peak, Sum = Diff = 25 V peak, % Mod = 100.*

14.4 SINGLE SIDEBAND TRANSMISSION

In a modulated wave the sidebands carry the intelligence. Yet the total sideband power is usually much less than the carrier power. Also, the upper sideband carries the same information as the lower sideband. Therefore, amplitude modulation seems to be an inefficient way to transmit intelligence. To increase the efficiency of transmission, the carrier and one sideband are sometimes eliminated. This type of transmission is known as *single sideband* transmission and results in reduced power and bandwidth requirement for a specific transmission effectiveness. When single sideband transmission is used, the carrier (from a local oscillator) must be inserted in the receiver to recover the intelligence. As will be shown later, the local oscillator which provides the carrier must have very good frequency stability to faithfully reproduce the modulating signal.

One of the problems of single sideband transmission is the separation of one sideband from the other sideband and carrier. If low-frequency components are present in the modulating signal, some side frequencies are very near the carrier frequency. A commonly used circuit which eliminates the carrier and thus reduces the filtering requirement for single

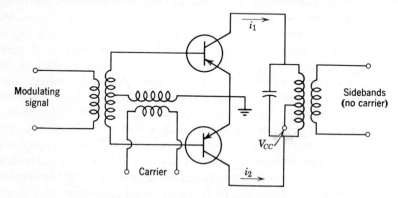

Fig. 14.8. A balanced modulator circuit.

sideband production is the balanced modulator. In a typical balanced modulator circuit such as is shown in Fig. 14.8, the carrier is applied in phase to the inputs of the two transistors while the modulating signal is applied in opposite phase to the two inputs. The amplifiers are operated class *B* so modulation takes place in each amplifier. The carrier is suppressed in the output because the carrier is applied "in phase" to the inputs. The output is tuned to the desired sideband frequency, thus essentially eliminating the modulating signal. Additional filtering is required to eliminate the undesired sideband.

A brief analysis will illustrate this modulation process. It will be assumed that the amplifier is a square law device when biased at cutoff. This is not strictly true, but it is a reasonable approximation when the source impedance is low. Then, assuming the amplifiers to be identical, we see that

$$\left.\begin{aligned} i_1 &= A_0 + A_1 v_{b1} + A_2 v_{b1}{}^2 \\ i_2 &= A_0 + A_1 v_{b2} + A_2 b_{b2}{}^2 \end{aligned}\right\} \tag{14.25}$$

but

$$\left.\begin{aligned} v_{b1} &= V_c \cos \omega_c t + V_m \cos \omega_m t \\ v_{b2} &= V_c \cos \omega_c t - V_m \cos \omega_m t \end{aligned}\right\} \tag{14.26}$$

and

When these values of v_b are substituted into Eq. 14.25,

$$i_1 = A_0 + A_1(V_c \cos \omega_c t + V_m \cos \omega_m t) + A_2(V_c \cos \omega_c t + V_m \cos \omega_m t)^2$$
$$i_2 = A_0 + A_1(V_c \cos \omega_c t - V_m \cos \omega_m t) + A_2(V_c \cos \omega_c t - V_m \cos \omega_m t)^2$$
$$(14.27)$$

Because of the push-pull arrangement, only the components of collector current which are of opposite polarity will be effective in producing an output. Then the effective output current is

$$i_e = i_1 - i_2 = 2A_1 V_m \cos \omega_m t + 4A_2 V_c V_m \cos \omega_c t \cos \omega_m t \quad (14.28)$$

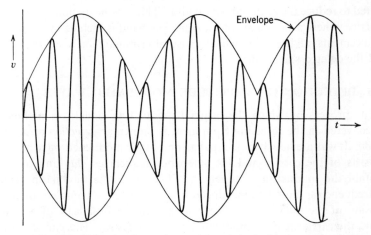

Fig. 14.9. The waveform of a carrier and single side frequency.

The tuned output will eliminate the modulating frequency component, so the effective output voltage is

$$v_0 = B \cos \omega_c t \cos \omega_m t = \frac{B}{2} [\cos (\omega_c + \omega_m)t + \cos (\omega_c t - \omega_m t)]$$
$$(14.29)$$

where the constant B includes the tuned circuit constants in addition to $4A_2 V_c V_m$. It was assumed in Eq. 14.29 that the tuned output circuit accepted each side frequency equally well.

The waveform of the modulation envelope is altered by the removal of one of the sidebands. Figure 14.9 shows the waveform of a single side frequency and a carrier. Note that the envelope is not sinusoidal. This same waveform is produced whenever two signals having nearly the same frequency are mixed or added. The amplitude of the combination then varies as the difference between their two frequencies because of the alternate reinforcement and cancellation of their instantaneous values.

PROB. 14.6. Add the instantaneous values of a 1 volt 9 Hz signal to those of a 1 volt 10 Hz to verify the waveform of Fig. 14.9.

Both sidebands are *not* transmitted with the carrier suppressed because the carrier which must be inserted in the receiver must then maintain the proper phase relationship with the sidebands to have the intelligence properly recovered. This preciseness of oscillator control is practically impossible. At least the required circuit complexity would be prohibitive for the benefit gained. Sometimes the carrier and one sideband are transmitted to reduce the required bandwidth. This is done in modern television practice, where a small part of the other sideband is included to reduce the requirements of the filter which must discriminate between the carrier and the deleted sideband.

14.5 DETECTION OF AMPLITUDE MODULATED WAVES

The process by which the original modulating signal, or intelligence, is recovered in the receiving equipment is known as *detection* or *demodulation*. It was previously noted that an amplitude modulated wave normally consists of the carrier and the sideband frequencies *only* and does not contain the modulating frequencies. Therefore, the modulating signal, or frequencies, must be reproduced in the receiver to complete the transmission of the intelligence. For example, in the broadcast of entertainment, the carrier may be modulated by an orchestra. This carrier with its sidebands are radiated from the transmitting antenna in the form of electromagnetic waves. These waves in turn induce small voltages into the receiving antenna. These voltages are usually amplified by tuned amplifiers with sufficient bandwidth to include the sidebands. If the receiver included only linear amplifiers, the amplified carrier and sidebands would be fed to a loud speaker. However, this would be futile because the loud speaker cannot respond to the carrier or sideband frequencies because they are radio frequencies. Therefore, the receiver must include a detector.

Since each modulating frequency is the difference between a sideband frequency and the carrier frequency, it seems evident that a nonlinear device is needed to recover the modulating frequencies from the modulated wave. The square law device is one possible candidate for a detector. Again, the vacuum tube and transistor are essentially square-law devices when biased near cutoff. Thus, they may be used in this mode to provide detection as illustrated in Fig. 14.10. It may be seen from Fig. 14.10c and 14.10d that the square law detector essentially eliminates one-half the modulated wave. In other words, the detector acts as a rectifier.

It should be observed that the current pulses in the output of the detector vary in amplitude in accordance with the modulation envelope or modulating signal. The capacitor C (referring to Fig. 14.10) is placed in parallel with the load resistance for the purpose of bypassing the carrier and sideband frequencies so that only the recovered modulating signal will appear in the output. In a vacuum tube amplifier, the resistor R_1 permits a fairly constant current to flow through R_K and thus provides a fairly constant self-bias for the tube. This bias will fluctuate somewhat with signal level because the tube current is highly dependent on signal level, but if the bleeder current through R_1 is made large in comparison with the average tube current, the bias may be maintained near cutoff for a wide range of signal levels. The cathode bypass capacitor C_K should be large enough to bypass the detected modulating frequencies.

We assume the detector to have only second-order nonlinearity, the output current i_O is

$$i_O = A_0 + A_1 v_i + A_2 v_i^2 \tag{14.30}$$

If the input voltage is a carrier and two side frequencies which were produced by a sinusoidal modulating signal having the natural frequency ω_m, then from Eq. 14.3,

$$v_i = V_c \cos \omega_c t + \frac{M V_c}{2} \cos (\omega_c + \omega_m)t + \frac{M V_c}{2} \cos (\omega_c - \omega_m)t$$

$$\tag{14.31}$$

Substituting this value of v_i into Eq. 14.30, we have

$$i_O = A_0 + A_1 \left[V_c \cos \omega_c t + \frac{M V_c}{2} \cos (\omega_c + \omega_m)t + \frac{M V_c}{2} \cos (\omega_c - \omega_m)t \right]$$
$$+ A_2 \left[V_c \cos \omega_c t + \frac{M V_c}{2} \cos (\omega_c + \omega_m)t + \frac{M V_c}{2} \cos (\omega_c - \omega_m)t \right]^2$$

$$\tag{14.32}$$

Since the bypass and d-c blocking capacitors in the output eliminate all components of output voltage except those which may result from the squared term of Eq. 14.32, the useful value of output current is

$$i'_o = A_2 \left\{ V_c^2 \cos^2 \omega_c t + M V_c^2 \cos \omega_c t [\cos (\omega_c + \omega_m)t + \cos (\omega_c - \omega_m)t] \right.$$
$$\left. + \left(\frac{M V_c}{2} \right)^2 [\cos (\omega_c + \omega_m)t + \cos (\omega_c - \omega_m)t]^2 \right\} \tag{14.33}$$

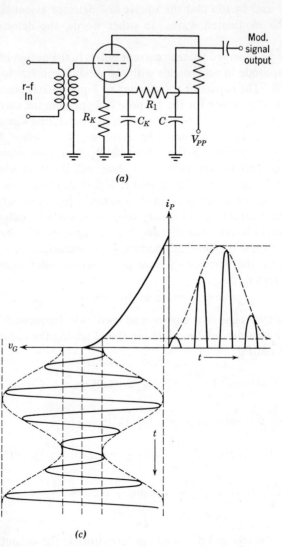

(a)

(c)

Fig. 14.10. (*a*) Vacuum tube detector; (*b*) transistor detector; (*c*) and (*d*) illustration of the detection process by the use of the transfer characteristics.

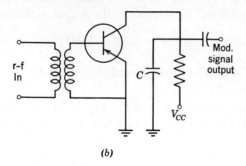

(b)

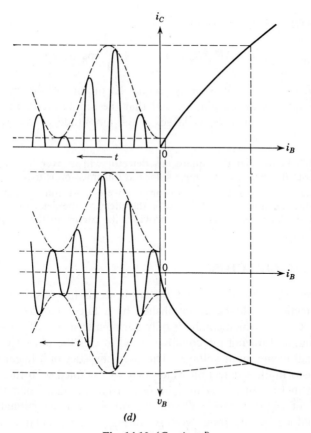

(d)

Fig. 14.10. (Continued)

If we expand Eq. 14.33 and retain only those products which can produce components which will be retained in the output, i'_o becomes

$$i''_o = A_2 M V_c^2 \cos \omega_c t \cos (\omega_c + \omega_m)t + A_2 M V_c^2 \cos \omega_c t \cos (\omega_c - \omega_m)t$$

$$+ \frac{A_2 M^2 V_c^2}{2} \cos (\omega_c + \omega_m)t \cos (\omega_c - \omega_m)t \qquad (14.34)$$

When we replace the product terms of Eq. 14.34 with their trigonometric identities and retain only the terms which will be retained in the output, i''_o becomes

$$i'''_o = \frac{A_2 M V_c^2}{2} \left(\cos \omega_m t + \cos \omega_m t + \frac{M}{2} \cos 2\omega_m t \right) \qquad (14.35)$$

After filtering, the output voltage is

$$v_o = A_2 M V_c^2 R_L \left(\cos \omega_m t + \frac{M}{4} \cos 2\omega_m t \right) \qquad (14.36)$$

Observe from Eq. 14.36 that a second harmonic of the modulating frequency appears in the output, and that the amplitude of this second harmonic is one-fourth M as large as the amplitude of the recovered modulating frequency.

PROB. 14.7. Prove that the square law detector will recover the modulating signal without distortion when single sideband transmission is used.

PROB. 14.8. If single sideband transmission were used and the carrier suppressed at the transmitter, what would be the effect on the detector output frequencies if the local oscillator which provides the carrier in the receiver were tuned to $\omega_c + \Delta\omega$ instead of ω_c?

14.6 LINEAR DETECTORS

In reference to Fig. 14.10c and 14.10d, it seems that distortionless (or linear) detection could be accomplished by a linear rectifier. A linear rectifier is a device which conducts only during alternate half cycles of the input signal, and during the conducting half cycles the output current is proportional to the input voltage. The characteristics of a linear rectifier and the distortionless detection which may be obtained with this rectifier are shown in Fig. 14.11. It may be seen from the figure that the peak amplitude of each current pulse in the output is proportional to the peak amplitude of the input voltage during that particular conducting half cycle. Thus the peak, and therefore the average, values of the output current pulses follow the amplitude of the input voltage precisely during conducting half cycles and have the same waveform as the modulation envelope. Whether the output voltage would approach the peak or average value of the input voltage depends on the type of filter used in the output. If the filter is a bypass capacitor, as previously indicated, and the internal resistance of the rectifier is small in comparison with the load resistance, the output voltage will tend to follow the peaks of the input voltage as explained in Chapter 3. Thus, the capacitor charges essentially to the peak input voltage during the conducting half cycles, but there is not time

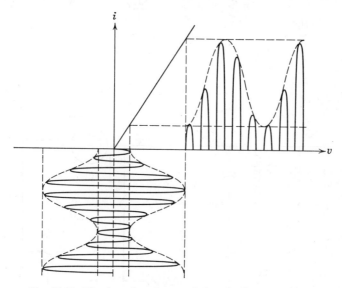

Fig. 14.11. The detection characteristics of a linear rectifier.

for appreciable discharge through the high resistance load during the non-conducting half cycles. If the bypass capacitor is too large, the time constant of the discharge will be so large that the detector output will not be able to follow the modulation envelope when the modulation envelope decreases amplitude rapidly. This situation, which may occur when the modulating frequencies are high, is known as *negative clipping* and will be discussed in more detail later.

As discussed in Chapter 3, the vacuum diode or semiconductor diode has a linear dynamic characteristic when the load resistance is large in comparison with the internal resistance of the diode. The voltage drop across the diode then becomes insignificant in comparison with the load voltage which then closely follows the input voltage. Thus, the properly designed diode detector may be a linear detector. Typical diode detector circuits are shown in Fig. 14.12. In the semiconductor diode circuit, Fig. 14.12a, R_d is the diode load resistor, C_f is the r-f bypass capacitor

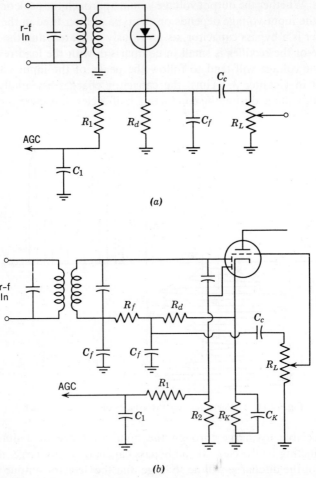

Fig. 14.12. (a) A typical semiconductor diode detector and AGC circuit. (b) A duo-diode triode tube used as a combination detector, AGC, and audio amplifier.

and C_c is the d-c blocking and load-coupling capacitor. R_L represents the actual load on the detector. In this circuit, R_L is a gain control (called a volume control in audio circuits).

In addition to detection, a circuit has been added which is called the *automatic gain control* (AGC). The AGC voltage is the average value of the detector output voltage since R_1 and C_1 act as a filter to remove the modulating signal as well as the r-f from the AGC system. This AGC voltage is therefore proportional to the amplitude of the carrier in a continuous wave system and may be used to automatically control the gain of one or more r-f amplifier stages. For example, if *p-n-p* transistors are used as r-f amplifiers ahead of the detector shown in Fig. 14.12*a* and the diode is connected as shown, the AGC voltage will tend to reverse bias the controlled amplifiers and hence reduce their gain. Thus, for small input signals the r-f amplifier will have high gain, but as the magnitude of the input signal increases, the gain of the r-f amplifier decreases. This effect tends to keep the detector output relatively constant and prevents over-driving the r-f amplifiers. Overdriving an amplifier means to cause its operation to extend into the saturation and cutoff regions. This type of operation in an r-f amplifier changes the waveform of the modulation envelope, thus causing severe distortion.

The circuit of Fig. 14.12*b* has a few added features that are worthy of mention. Double tuning has been used in the input coupling circuit. The popular duo-diode triode tube has been used as a combination detector, AGC and audio amplifier circuit. Since the amplifier section uses cathode bias, the detector load resistor R_d is returned to the cathode rather than to the ground in order to prevent biasing the detector plate as well as the amplifier grid. A π-type r-f filter, consisting of the resistor R_f and the two capacitors C_f, has been used to reduce the r-f in the output. The AGC voltage is obtained from a second diode plate which is coupled to the first by a capacitor. The AGC diode load resistor is R_2 and the AGC filter is R_1 and C_1. This AGC arrangement is known as delayed AGC because the AGC diode is reverse-biased. This reverse bias is provided by the cathode bias resistor since the AGC load resistor returns to ground. Thus no AGC voltage will appear when the peak amplitude of the input signal is less than the bias on the AGC diode plate. Therefore, this type of AGC gives improved r-f gain for very small signals.

Since the diode load resistor develops a d-c voltage which tends to reverse-bias the diode, it may seem that the diode may not conduct during the negative half cycles of the modulation envelope. To investigate this possibility, the relationship between the d-c output voltage and the r-f input voltage is shown in Fig. 14.13 for a typical diode detector. In this figure, it is assumed that the diode load resistor is bypassed for r-f so the d-c load voltage approaches the peak values of the r-f input voltage. However, the d-c load voltage is somewhat less than the peak input voltage because of the internal resistance of the diode and the partial discharge of the r-f bypass capacitor between the input voltage peaks as discussed in Chapter 3. Thus, the d-c load voltage decreases as the load resistance decreases. Simultaneously, the diode current increases, because both the voltage drop across the diode and the discharge between the input peaks increase with decreasing load resistance, as previously discussed.

Since the axes of the plot of Fig. 14.13 are the load voltage and load

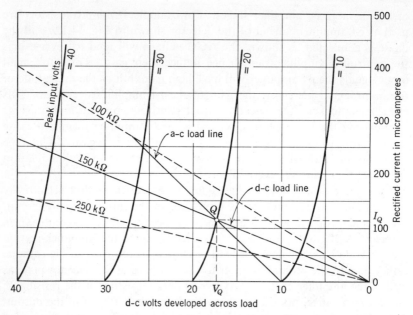

Fig. 14.13. Rectification characteristics of a diode detector.

current, load lines may be drawn on the rectification characteristics as shown. The use of the load line may be most easily explained by an example.

Example 14.2. Consider a 150 KΩ d-c load resistance for the diode of Fig. 14.13. Assuming that the peak carrier voltage at the input of the detector is 20 v, the d-c voltage V_Q across the diode load resistor is about 17.5 v as indicated. So long as the carrier is unmodulated, the d-c voltage across the load resistor will remain constant and the quiescent operating point on the load line will be at point Q. On the other hand, when the carrier is modulated the operating point must move up and down along the d-c load line, since the detector input voltage is continually changing. This condition is true if the d-c load is the *only* load on the detector. When the carrier has 100% modulation, the input voltage must vary between 0 and 40 v peak, so the output voltage will vary between 0 and 36 v peak. Thus, the detection is essentially linear.

As indicated in Fig. 14.12, the detector usually has part of its load isolated from the d-c load resistor by a blocking capacitor. Therefore, the a-c load resistance for the detector is usually smaller than the d-c load resistance. Consequently, an a-c load line should be drawn through the point Q as shown in Fig. 14.13. In this case, the detector operating point moves up and down along the a-c load line as the modulated signal is applied to the input. Thus, a modulation crest causes a greater increase of rectified current than would occur if the d-c load resistor had been the total load. Similarly, the rate of decrease of rectifier current is more rapid during a trough, or negative half cycle, of the modulation than it would be if only the d-c load were present. Notice from Fig. 14.13 that this effect causes the diode current to be reduced to zero before the input voltage is reduced to zero. This is known as negative clipping. Notice that negative clipping occurs only when the percentage of modulation exceeds a certain value. In this example, where the a-c load resistance is one-half the value of the d-c load resistance, the rectifier current is reduced to zero when the input voltage is reduced to one-half the quiescent, or carrier, value. Therefore, negative clipping would occur if the percentage of modulation were to exceed 50%.

A simple relationship exists between the ratio of a-c load resistance to d-c load resistance and the maximum modulation index that can occur without clipping. Referring to Fig. 14.13, we can see that the output voltage which results from the unmodulated carrier is

$$V_Q = I_Q R_{dc} \qquad (14.37)$$

Also, the maximum change in the output voltage which can occur without negative clipping is

$$(\Delta V)_{\max} = I_Q R_{ac} \qquad (14.38)$$

But the maximum modulation index which can occur without negative clipping is the ratio of $(\Delta V)_{\max}$ to V_Q. Then

$$M_{\max} = \frac{(\Delta V)_{\max}}{V_Q} = \frac{I_Q R_{ac}}{I_Q R_{dc}} = \frac{R_{ac}}{R_{dc}} \qquad (14.39)$$

At high modulating frequencies the r-f bypass capacitor may significantly reduce the a-c impedance and thus can cause negative clipping, as previously mentioned. Also, it is apparent that any load which is coupled to the detector through a capacitor must be large in comparison with the d-c load resistance to permit a high percentage of modulation without appreciable distortion.

PROB. 14.9. The detector of Fig. 14.12a has $R_d = 50$ KΩ, $R_1 = 1$ megohm $R_L = 250$ KΩ, $C_f = 500$ pf, and $C_1 = C_c = 0.1$ μf. Determine the maximum percentage of modulation which can be accepted without causing negative clipping. *Answer:* $M_{max} = 80\%$.

It should be observed that a linear detector does not provide distortionless demodulation when only one sideband is present, because the modulation envelope does not have the same shape as the modulating signal when single sideband transmission is used. On the other hand, it may be proven (Prob. 14.7) that a square-law detector provides distortionless demodulation when single sideband transmission is used.

The impression may have been conveyed that tube amplifiers and transistors automatically provide square-law detection when they are biased near cutoff. This is not true. These amplifying types of detectors may provide fairly linear detection if they are properly designed for this purpose. For example, the triode tube may provide linear detection if the load resistance is large in comparison with the plate resistance. Also, the proper adjustment of driving source resistance may provide good linearity for a transistor detector.

In the foregoing paragraphs, the term r-f has sometimes been used to mean the carrier and sidebands whereas *audio* has been used to indicate the modulation. This usage is much too specialized. In some applications, such as automatic control, the carrier may be low frequency of a few hundred Hertz whereas the modulating signal may have a period of several seconds.

The effective input resistance of a detector must be obtained in some manner before the tuned coupling circuit can be properly designed. The effective input resistance may be determined if the average input power can be found in terms of the input voltage. The average input power over one cycle is

$$P = \frac{1}{2\pi} \int_{-\pi}^{\pi} vi \, d\theta \tag{14.40}$$

Assuming the input voltage to be an unmodulated carrier so that $v = V_c \cos \theta$, we see that

$$P = \frac{1}{2\pi} \int_{-\pi}^{\pi} V_c i \cos \theta \, d\theta \tag{14.41}$$

For a biased amplifier type detector or a diode detector which does not have an r-f bypass capacitor, the input current i flows only on alternate half cycles. Then if it is assumed that during these conducting half cycles the input current is

$$i = \frac{V_c \cos \theta}{R_i} \tag{14.42}$$

where R_i is the average input resistance during the conducting half cycle, the average input power is

$$P = \frac{1}{2\pi} \int_{-\pi/2}^{\pi/2} \frac{V_c^2 \cos^2 \theta}{R_i} \tag{14.43}$$

$$P = \frac{1}{2\pi} \left(\frac{\pi V_c^2}{2R_i} \right) = \frac{V_c^2}{4R_i} \tag{14.44}$$

The effective input resistance may be defined as

$$R = \frac{(V_{rms})^2}{P} = \frac{V_c^2/2}{P} = 2R_i \tag{14.45}$$

An accurate value of R_i may be difficult to obtain because of the dependence of R_i on the magnitude of the input voltage in most cases. However, an average value of input resistance which is obtained at an average value of input voltage is sufficiently accurate for good design.

The effective input resistance of a diode detector in which the load resistance is large in comparison with the forward resistance of the diode and an adequate r-f bypass capacitor is connected in parallel with the load resistance may be easily found if we assume that the total input power is dissipated in the load resistor. Since the d-c voltage across the load resistor R_d is approximately equal to V_c, the power dissipated in the load is

$$P = \frac{V_c^{\,2}}{R_d} \tag{14.46}$$

where P is the average power in the load when the carrier is unmodulated. But this power is approximately the same as the r-f input power which may be defined as

$$P = \frac{V_c^{\,2}}{2R_i} = \frac{V_c^{\,2}}{R_d} \tag{14.47}$$

where R_i, again, is the effective input resistance of the detector. Therefore,

$$R_i \simeq \frac{R_d}{2} \tag{14.48}$$

where R_d, as before, is the d-c load resistance. When the carrier is modulated it would at first seem that the a-c load resistance of the diode instead of the d-c resistance R_d should be used to calculate the input resistance because additional power is coupled through the d-c blocking capacitors into the R-C coupled part of the load. However, this additional power comes from the power in the sidebands. Therefore, the effective input resistance remains approximately $R_d/2$ as long as negative clipping does not occur.

14.7 FREQUENCY CONVERTERS

In the preceding paragraphs, it was shown that both modulation and detection involve two basic processes. The first of these processes is the production of sum and difference frequencies by a nonlinear device; the second is the separation of the desired output components from the undesired ones by some type of a filter. In the early days of radio, the idea was conceived that these two processes could be used to change or translate any given frequency to a different frequency. The superheterodyne receiver is based on this principle. This receiver contains an oscillator which is known as a *local oscillator*. The output from this oscillator is mixed with the incoming signal and the combination is applied to a nonlinear device. The output of this nonlinear device is tuned to the difference between the oscialltor frequency and the frequency of the incoming signal. The difference frequency is known as the *intermediate frequency* (i-f). This system has two main advantages when compared with a conventional amplifier. First, higher gain and better stability may be obtained from an amplifier at the lower intermediate frequency. Second, the intermediate frequency may remain constant even though a wide variety of input frequencies may be selected because the local oscillator frequency may be varied in such a manner as to produce a constant difference between the oscillator frequency and the variable input frequency. Therefore, the design of the i-f amplifier may be optimized whereas the design of the r-f amplifier must be a compromise since it is required to operate over a wide range of frequencies.

Example 14.3. The standard broadcast superheterodyne receiver is a good example of the principle of frequency conversion. This receiver is required to tune over the 550 to 1600 KHz frequency range and it should provide essentially constant gain and constant bandwidth over this range. A commonly used intermediate frequency is 455 KHz. To provide this intermediate frequency, the local oscillator must vary from 1005 to 2055 KHz and must always remain 455 KHz above the selected input frequency. This maintenance of a constant difference frequency over the band is known as *tracking*. The local oscillator frequency could be below the input signal frequency, but then its frequency range would have to be 95 to 1145 KHz. This frequency ratio is too high to cover with a single band. When the selected input frequency is 1000 KHz and the sideband frequencies extend from 995 to 1005 KHz, the oscillator frequency is 1455 KHz. Then the frequencies appearing in the output current of the nonlinear device are:

1. The original frequencies   995–1005 KHz
                                                1455 KHz
2. The sum frequencies   2450–2460 KHz
3. The difference frequencies   450–460 KHz
4. Harmonic frequencies   1990 KHz and upwards

When a tuned circuit which has a resonant frequency of 455 KHz and a bandwidth of 10 KHz is placed in the output, the difference frequencies, which include the new 455 KHz carrier with its sideband frequencies, are retained and all the other frequencies are rejected.

The nonlinear device which produces the sum and difference frequencies is frequently called a *mixer*. This term is not very appropriate, however, because it is also used to designate linear devices in which two or more signals are mixed, but in which additional frequencies are not produced. The nonlinear device is more appropriately called a *first detector* or *modulator*. The combination of the first detector and the local oscillator is known as a frequency converter.

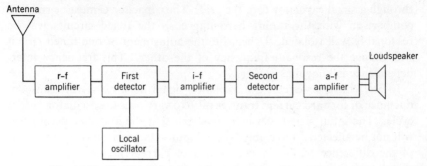

Fig. 14.14. The block diagram of a typical superheterodyne receiver.

The block diagram of a typical superheterodyne receiver is shown in Fig. 14.14. The r-f amplifier shown is frequently omitted in entertainment-type receivers. The advantages of including this r-f amplifier are briefly discussed in a following paragraph.

Some typical converter circuits are shown in Fig. 14.15. In these circuits the oscillators are the tuned grid or base type, although other types could be used. The dashed lines between the input and oscillator tuned circuits indicate that the tuning capacitors are *ganged* so that single knob tuning may be used. In the transistor circuit, the oscillator signal is applied to the emitter; in the tube circuit the oscillator signal is applied

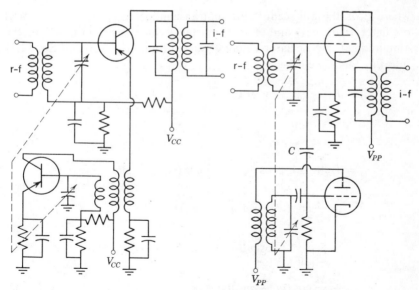

Fig. 14.15. Typical frequency converter circuits.

through a small capacitor C to the grid. The capacitor C must be small in comparison with the tuning capacitance so the tuned circuits will be reasonably well isolated. Otherwise, the adjustment of one tuned circuit will change the resonant frequency of the other. This frequency inter-dependence is known as *pulling*.

In any converter circuit the oscillator signal must cause the transconductance or forward current transfer ratio to vary over the oscillator output cycle. The input signal is usually so small that the amplifier parameters will not be affected appreciably by the input voltage variations. The ratio of the difference frequency component of current in the output to the signal voltage input is known as conversion transconductance. To more fully understand the conversion problem, a special case will be considered in which the input signal is so small that the amplifier parameters are essentially unaffected by the input signal. Then

$$i_O = I_O + g_m v_i \tag{14.49}$$

where v_i is considered to be a sinusoidally modulated carrier.

$$v_i = V_c \left[\cos \omega_c t + \frac{M}{2} \cos (\omega_c + \omega_m)t + \frac{M}{2} \cos (\omega_c - \omega_m)t \right] \tag{14.50}$$

It will be assumed that the transconductance of the amplifier varies linearly with the applied oscillator voltage. This relationship may be expressed by the following equation:

$$g_m = g_0(1 + A \cos \omega_o t) \tag{14.51}$$

where g_0 is the quiescent value of transconductance, ω_o is the natural oscillator frequency, and A is a constant which is proportional to the amplitude of the oscillator voltage. Substituting Eq. 14.50 and Eq. 14.51 into Eq. 14.49, we have

$$i_O = I_O + g_0 V_c \left[\cos \omega_c t + \frac{M}{2} \cos (\omega_c + \omega_m)t \right.$$

$$\left. + \frac{M}{2} \cos (\omega_c - \omega_m)t \right](1 + A \cos \omega_o t) \tag{14.52}$$

$$i_O = I_O + g_0 V_c \left[\cos \omega_c t + \frac{M}{2} \cos (\omega_c + \omega_m)t \right.$$

$$\left. + \frac{M}{2} \cos (\omega_c - \omega_m)t \right] + g_0 A V_c$$

$$\times \left[\cos \omega_c t \cos \omega_o t + \frac{M}{2} \cos (\omega_c + \omega_m)t \cos \omega_o t \right.$$

$$\left. + \frac{M}{2} \cos (\omega_c - \omega_m)t \cos \omega_o t \right] \tag{14.53}$$

Observe that the first bracketed term of Eq. 14.53 contains the carrier and sideband frequencies of the input signal which will be rejected by the filter in the output. The product terms in the second bracket produce sum and difference frequencies when the trigonometric identities are used. The sum frequencies will be rejected by the output filter, assuming that this filter is tuned to the difference frequency, so the only terms of importance in the output are

$$i'_o = \frac{g_0 A V_c}{2}\left[\cos(\omega_c - \omega_o)t + \frac{M}{2}\cos(\omega_c - \omega_o + \omega_m)t\right.$$
$$\left. + \frac{M}{2}\cos(\omega_c - \omega_o - \omega_m)t\right] \quad (14.54)$$

The conversion transconductance is

$$g_c = \frac{|i'_o|}{|v_i|} = \frac{g_0 A V_c}{2 V_c} = \frac{g_0 A}{2} \quad (14.55)$$

Observe from Eq. 14.55 that the conversion transconductance is proportional to the amplitude of the oscillator signal as well as to the quiescent transconductance when the transconductance is proportional to the oscillator signal. It may be seen from Eq. 14.51 that the transconductance would vary from zero to $2g_0$ when $A = 1$. The conversion transconductance would then be $g_0/2$. This is about the maximum attainable conversion transconductance because larger oscillator voltages cause g_m to be zero over an appreciable part of the negative half cycles of oscillator voltage, whereas a saturating or decreasing value of g_m may occur as the grid or base is driven strongly into the forward region. A sensible design procedure may be to bias the amplifier about halfway between the maximum and zero values of g_m and then provide an oscillator signal of sufficient amplitude to vary g_m between the zero and maximum value.

A single amplifier may be used as both the modulator and the oscillator as shown in the circuits of Fig. 14.16. The vacuum tube circuit (a) employs a tube known as a *pentagrid converter*. Grids 1 and 2 serve as the oscillator grid and plate respectively. A Hartley oscillator circuit is used in which one end of the tuned circuit is grounded. Therefore, grid 2, which acts as the oscillator anode, may be at r-f ground potential and serve the additional function of a screen grid. Most of the electrons which pass through the oscillator grid also pass through the oscillator anode and become the space current in the tube. The input signal is applied to grid 3, which controls the space current which passes through the oscillator section. The remaining elements of the tube, grids 4 and 5 and the plate, have the same functions as the screen grid, suppressor grid, and plate of the pentode amplifier. In this converter, the oscillator should operate either class B or

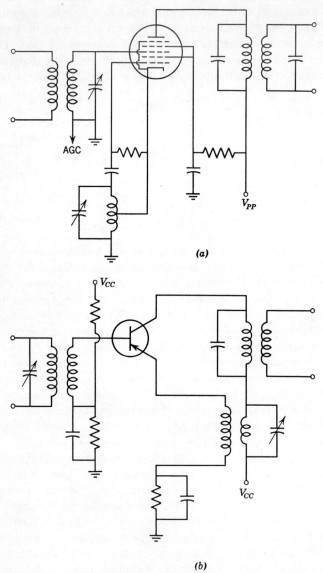

(a)

(b)

Fig. 14.16. Converter circuits which do not use a separate oscillator.

class C so that the tube space current flows through the oscillator section in pulses. The signal grid transconductance is then varied from zero to its maximum value over the oscillator cycle and conversion takes place in the same manner as described for the separate oscillator circuit. The chief advantage of the pentagrid converter circuit lies in the reduction of the number of tubes required. An additional advantage may be the improved isolation between the signal and oscillator-tuned circuits since the mixing of the signals is accomplished in the electron stream of the tube rather than by inductive or capacitive coupling.

The transistor circuit of Fig. 14.16b operates in the same general manner as does the pentagrid converter circuit except that the entire transistor acts as both the oscillator and the detector. The oscillator shown is a tuned collector, common base circuit. The isolation between the oscillator and input signal circuits is not as good in the transistor circuit as it is in the pentagrid converter circuit.

The circuits shown are only representative types. There are several other types of special converter tubes in use, and recommended circuit diagrams are available in tube manuals and other literature. Various types of oscillator circuits, including the crystal-controlled types, may be used in conjunction with a wide variety of detector, or modulator, circuits. Thus, converter circuits may be devised to meet almost any requirement.

Both transistors and vacuum tubes generate more noise at very low frequencies and very high frequencies than they do at moderate radio frequencies. Therefore, the noise in the output of a converter may be greater than the noise in the output of a conventional amplifier because the converter includes a modulator. Hence, the low-frequency noise voltages will modulate the carrier and will cause noise side frequencies which are accepted by the output filter.

The r-f amplifier shown in Fig. 14.14 may improve the signal-to-noise ratio of the superheterodyne receiver because the r-f amplifier is not a good modulator. Thus, the comparatively noise-free amplification ahead of the frequency converter can materially improve the signal-to-noise ratio in the receiver. Also the r-f amplifier improves the selectivity and the sensitivity of the receiver.

Diodes are sometimes used as the nonlinear device in a converter because of their low noise characteristics or because the incoming signal frequency is so high that ordinary amplifiers have practically no gain. The circuit diagram of an ordinary diode converter is given in Fig. 14.17a. This type of converter may be used in the GHz frequency range if the lumped elements are replaced by distributed elements such as wave guides and cavity resonators. Also, a tunnel diode may be used in a converter circuit as shown in Fig. 14.17b. When used in this application,

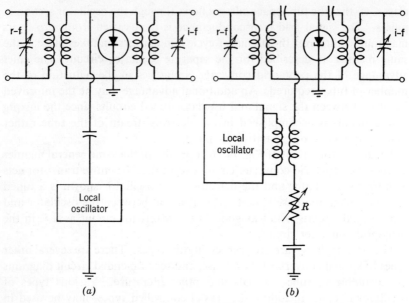

Fig. 14.17. (*a*) A diode converter; (*b*) a tunnel diode converter.

the tunnel diode is biased near the zero conductance point or slightly into the positive conductance region as shown in Fig. 14.18 by point *B*. If the diode is biased at point *A* so the quiescent diode conductance is zero, the local oscillator causes the diode conductance to swing into the positive conductance region during the negative half cycle of oscillator voltage and into the negative conductance region during the positive half cycle. It can be shown that the excursion into the negative conductance region may result in conversion gain. In fact, tunnel diode converters have been constructed which provide conversion gain of more than 20 db and a noise

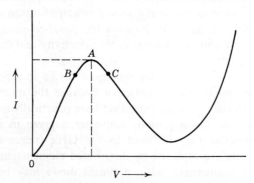

Fig. 14.18. Bias points for a tunnel diode.

figure (decrease of signal-to-noise ratio) of less than 3 db when used to convert 220 MHz to 60 MHz.[2]

The stability of the tunnel diode converter is improved when the bias point is changed from point A (Fig. 14.18) to point B. On the other hand, the circuits may provide self-oscillation if the bias point is moved into the negative conductance region to a point such as C. The separate oscillator may then be eliminated. However, since the diode does not provide isolation between the input, output, and oscillator circuits, it may be difficult to independently control the frequency of oscillation.

PROB. 14.10. A frequency converter is to be used to translate 225 MHz to 60 MHz. What local oscillator frequencies could be used and what would be the frequency components in the output for each local oscillator frequency?

PROB. 14.11. A frequency converter incorporates an amplifier that has $g_m = 2000$ μmhos at the quiescent operating point. The local oscillator signal causes g_m to vary from 1000 to 3000 μmhos. Assuming that g_m is proportional to the oscillator voltage, determine the conversion transconductance of the amplifier.

PROB. 14.12. Draw a circuit diagram for a complete superheterodyne broadcast band receiver (except the power supply). Use vacuum tubes. Component values need not be determined but specify the frequency or frequency range of the tuned circuits.

PROB. 14.13. Repeat Prob. 14.12. using transistors instead of vacuum tubes.

[2] K. K. N. Chang, G. H. Heilmeier, and H. J. Prager, "Low-Noise Tunnel-Diode Down Converter Having Conversion Gain," *Proceedings of IRE*, May 1960; Vol. 48, p. 854.

15

Frequency Modulation

Amplitude modulation was discussed in Chapter 14. Another common method of modulating a carrier signal is known as *frequency modulation*. In this type of modulation the signal frequency is changed in accordance with the amplitude of the modulation as expressed by the following equation:

$$v = A \cos \left[\omega_c t + M_f F_m(t) \right] \qquad (15.1)$$

where $F_m(t)$ is the modulating signal expressed as a function of time and ω_c is the radian frequency of the carrier. The modulation index M_f relates the amplitude of the modulating signal to the variation of the carrier frequency which it produces.

Since the modulating signal can be resolved into frequency components by the Fourier series technique, it will be convenient to assume, as was done in Chapter 14, that the modulating signal is sinusoidal. Then

$$F_m(t) = B \sin \omega_m t \qquad (15.2)$$

When this modulating signal is used, Eq. 15.1 becomes

$$v = A \cos \left(\omega_c t + M_f \sin \omega_m t \right) \qquad (15.3)$$

The modulation index M_f absorbs the amplitude factor B of the modulating signal as will be shown below. Actually, Eq. 15.3 indicates that the term $M_f \sin \omega_m t$ must have the dimensions of an angle θ, not a frequency. Since $\omega = d\theta/dt$, the frequency associated with this angle may be obtained by differentiating the term $M_f \sin \omega_m t$ with respect to time.

$$\frac{d(M_f \sin \omega_m t)}{dt} = M_f \omega_m \cos \omega_m t \qquad (15.4)$$

Then Eq. 15.3 can be written as

$$v = A \cos(\omega_c + M_f \omega_m \cos \omega_m t)t \qquad (15.5)$$

It may be seen from Eq. 15.5 that the maximum frequency deviation is

$$(\Delta\omega)_{max} = M_f \omega_m \qquad (15.6)$$

$$M_f = \frac{(\Delta\omega)_{max}}{\omega_m} = \frac{(\Delta f)_{max}}{f_m} \qquad (15.7)$$

The modulation index M_f is known as the *deviation ratio*, since it is the ratio of the maximum deviation of the signal frequency to the modulating frequency.

15.1 MODULATING CIRCUITS

The characteristics of frequency modulation will be better understood after a few typical modulating circuits have been considered. Probably the simplest way to obtain frequency modulation is to connect a "condenser" (capacitor) microphone across the tuned circuit of an L-C oscillator as shown in Fig. 15.1. The capacitor microphone has a thin metal diaphragm stretched in front of a fixed metal plate. The acoustic pressure in the air causes vibration of the diaphragm and consequently variation of the capacitance between the diaphragm and the plate. This varying capacitance varies the oscillator frequency and thus causes frequency modulation. The capacitor microphone method is not very practical because the oscillator frequency would also depend on the length of the microphone cable, stray capacitance, and so on.

An improved method for controlling the oscillator frequency is shown in Fig. 15.2. In this circuit, a pentode tube is used as a variable reactance to control the frequency of an oscillator. The pentode is made to appear as a reactance by applying phase quadrature voltages at the oscillator frequency to the control grid and plate. The signal component of plate current, being controlled almost completely by the control grid voltage, will then be

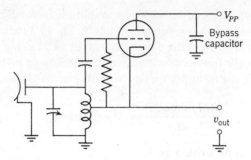

Fig. 15.1. A simple frequency modulation circuit using a capacitor microphone and a Hartley oscillator.

essentially in phase quadrature with the plate voltage and the tube will appear as a reactance when viewed from the plate terminal. In Fig. 15.2 the phase quadrature voltage is obtained by the series R_1C_1 circuit between the plate and ground. The resistance of R_1 must be very large in comparison with the reactance of C_1 at the oscillator frequency so that the current through this circuit I_o will be essentially in phase with the plate voltage V_o. Also the grid resistance which is in parallel with C_1 must be very large so that the impedance between the control grid and ground is essentially a pure reactance. When these conditions are met, the current through the resistor R_1 is

$$I_o = \frac{V_o}{R_1} \tag{15.8}$$

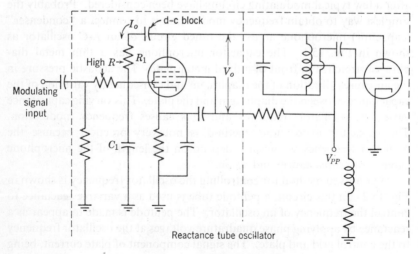

Fig. 15.2. A reactance tube modulator.

The voltage between the grid and ground is

$$V_g \simeq \frac{I_o}{j\omega C_1} = \frac{V_o}{\omega C_1 R_1} \underline{/-90} \tag{15.9}$$

The component of plate current which results from this grid voltage is

$$I_p = g_m V_g \simeq \frac{g_m V_o}{\omega C_1 R_1} \underline{/-90} \tag{15.10}$$

As seen in Eq. 15.10, the plate current I_p lags the plate voltage V_o by approximately 90°; therefore, the tube appears as an inductive reactance when viewed from the output terminals. Using Eq. 15.10, we find that the value of this inductance is

$$L_r = \frac{X_L}{\omega} = \frac{V_o}{\omega I_p} = \frac{R_1 C_1}{g_m} \tag{15.11}$$

The equivalent circuit of the reactance tube is drawn in Fig. 15.3, so that we may investigate it more thoroughly. The oscillator voltage $V_o \underline{/0°}$ which

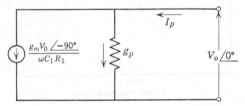

Fig. 15.3. An equivalent circuit of the reactance tube modulator.

is applied to the plate of the reactance tube is used as the reference voltage. In order for the tube to appear as a pure reactance, not only must the control grid and plate voltages be 90° out of the phase but the plate conductance g_p must be zero. This may be seen from the equivalent circuit. If these conditions are not met, the tube will appear as a lossy inductor and will load the oscillator tuned circuit. This loading will reduce the frequency stability of the oscillator and the amplitude of the oscillation. We may minimize the plate conductance g_p by using a pentode tube and confining the operating range to the linear area of the plate characteristics. As mentioned before, the phase angle between the plate voltage and the plate current will approach 90° if the resistance which is in parallel with the capacitance C_1 as well as the resistance in series with this capacitance are very large in comparison with the capacitive reactance of C_1 at the oscillator frequency. This relationship is indicated in Fig. 15.2.

Equation 15.11 shows that the effective inductance of the reactance tube is inversely proportional to the transconductance of the tube. Therefore the transconductance g_m must be a function of the modulating voltage if modulation is to occur. Linear modulation occurs when the frequency deviation is proportional to the modulating voltage as shown in Fig. 15.4. Therefore the derivative of the signal frequency with respect to the modulating voltage is a constant when the modulation is linear.

The signal frequency produced by the oscillator is very nearly

$$\omega = \frac{1}{(LC)^{\frac{1}{2}}} \tag{15.12}$$

where the total effective inductance L is the parallel combination of the fixed inductance of the tuned circuit and the effective inductance of the

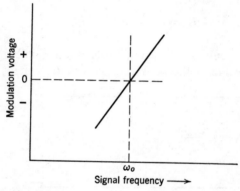

Fig. 15.4. The desired linear relationship between the modulating voltage and the signal frequency.

reactance tube L_r. The reactance tube will be most effective in controlling the frequency of oscillation if the fixed inductance is large in comparison with the effective inductance of the reactance tube. The total inductance would then be essentially L_r. This could be accomplished by using an r-f choke as the fixed inductance. With this simplification, and using the value of L_r from Eq. 15.11, Eq. 15.12 becomes

$$\omega = \frac{g_m^{\frac{1}{2}}}{(R_1 C_1 C_o)^{\frac{1}{2}}} \tag{15.13}$$

where C_o is the capacitance of the tuned circuit.

Equation 15.13 shows that the oscillator frequency can be a linear function of the modulating voltage if the transconductance is proportional to the *square* of the modulating voltage. The transconductance of a typical pentode tube is roughly proportional to the control grid voltage, however, instead of the square of the control grid voltage. By using this proportionality, Eq. 15.13 becomes

$$\omega = \frac{(Kv_g)^{\frac{1}{2}}}{(R_1 C_1 C_o)^{\frac{1}{2}}} \qquad (15.14)$$

The amount of harmonic distortion for a given set of conditions may be obtained if Eq. 15.14 is expanded into a Taylor's Series around the grid bias value V_o.

$$\omega = \frac{(Kv_g)^{\frac{1}{2}}}{(R_1 C_1 C_o)^{\frac{1}{2}}} = A_0 + A_1(v_g - V_o) + A_2(v_g - V_o)^2 + \cdots \quad (15.15)$$

A_0 is found by letting $v_g = V_o$.

$$A_0 = \frac{(KV_o)^{\frac{1}{2}}}{(R_1 C_1 C_o)^{\frac{1}{2}}} \qquad (15.16a)$$

A_1 is found by differentiating both sides of Eq. 15.15 and then letting $v_g = V_o$.

$$A_1 = \frac{K^{\frac{1}{2}} V_o^{-\frac{1}{2}}}{2(R_1 C_1 C_o)^{\frac{1}{2}}} \qquad (15.16b)$$

Similarly, A_2 is obtained by taking the second derivative of both sides of Eq. 15.15, and so on. Thus Eq. 15.15 becomes

$$\omega = \frac{(KV_o)^{\frac{1}{2}}}{(R_1 C_1 C_o)^{\frac{1}{2}}} + \frac{K^{\frac{1}{2}} V_o^{-\frac{1}{2}}}{2(R_1 C_1 C_o)^{\frac{1}{2}}}(v_g - V_o)$$

$$- \frac{K^{\frac{1}{2}} V_o^{-\frac{3}{2}}}{8(R_1 C_1 C_o)^{\frac{1}{2}}}(v_g - V_o)^2 + \cdots \quad (15.17)$$

When a single frequency modulating signal is applied,

$$v_g - V_o = V_m \cos \omega_m t \qquad (15.18)$$

Equation 15.17 then becomes

$$\omega = \frac{(KV_o)^{\frac{1}{2}}}{(R_1 C_1 C_o)^{\frac{1}{2}}} + \frac{K^{\frac{1}{2}} V_o^{-\frac{1}{2}} V_m}{2(R_1 C_1 C_o)^{\frac{1}{2}}} \cos \omega_m t$$

$$- \frac{K^{\frac{1}{2}} V_o^{-\frac{3}{2}} V_m^2}{16(R_1 C_1 C_o)^{\frac{1}{2}}}(1 + \cos 2\omega_m t) \cdots \quad (15.19)$$

Assuming the percentage of second harmonic to be large in comparison with the higher-order harmonics, the percentage of second harmonic is obtained by dividing the magnitude of the second-order term by the magnitude of the fundamental.

$$\text{Per cent } 2^{\text{nd}} \text{ harmonic} = \frac{V_m}{8V_o} \times 100 \qquad (15.20)$$

PROB. 15.1. The oscillator of Fig. 15.2 has $C_o = 10$ pf and very large L. It is modulated by a pentode reactance tube which has $g_m = 5000$ μmhos at the quiescent operating point. g_m is proportional to the grid voltage. The phase-shifting network has $R_1 = 1$ megohm and $C_1 = 20$ pf. What would be the per cent second harmonic distortion when g_m varies sinusoidally 1000 μmhos peak to peak? *Answer: 1.25%.*

PROB. 15.2. What would be the frequency deviation for the conditions given in Prob. 15.1? What would be the modulation index M_f if the modulating voltage is a sinusoid of frequency 1000 Hz?

A transistor could be used instead of a vacuum tube in a reactance type modulator. However, a junction diode will serve the same function if its

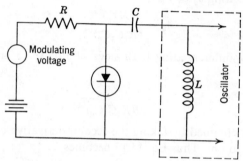

Fig. 15.5. A reactance modulator which utilizes the variable capacitance of a junction diode.

variable capacitance characteristic which was discussed in Chapter 3 is exploited. As shown in Chapter 3, the junction capacitance C_d may be expressed as

$$C_d = K(V_B)^{-\frac{1}{2}} \tag{3.53}$$

A modulating circuit which uses the junction diode as a variable capacitance is shown in Fig. 15.5. In this circuit, a polarizing voltage must be used as indicated to maintain reverse bias across the diode. This bias might be conveniently obtained from the collector circuit of a transistor modulator. The capacitance C should be large in comparison with the diode junction capacitance, but the reactance of C should be large in comparison with the resistance R at the highest essential modulating frequency. Otherwise, these modulating frequency components would be shunted through L. In addition, the resistance of R should be large enough to prevent the modulating circuit from excessively loading the oscillator tuned circuit.

The linearity of the junction diode modulator will now be investigated. The frequency of the oscillator is approximately

$$\omega = \frac{1}{[L(C_o + C_d)]^{\frac{1}{2}}} \tag{15.21}$$

Using Eq. 3.53, we have

$$\omega = [L(C_o + KV_B^{-\frac{1}{2}})]^{-\frac{1}{2}} \qquad (15.22)$$

It can be seen from Eq. 15.22 that the oscillator frequency ω is not a linear function of the modulating voltage V_B. The nonlinear distortion for a given magnitude of V_B may be determined if the right side of Eq. 15.22 is expanded into a Taylor series. Then the techniques of Chapter 10 could be used to determine the harmonic distortion for any given excursion of the modulating voltage. The mathematics is simplified considerably if the diode provides essentially all of the tuning capacitance, or, in other words, C_o may be neglected in comparison with the capacitance of the diode. Then Eq. 15.22 reduces to

$$\omega = \frac{V^{\frac{1}{4}}}{(LK)^{\frac{1}{2}}} \qquad (15.23)$$

using the Taylor series expansion,

$$\frac{V^{\frac{1}{4}}}{(LK)^{\frac{1}{2}}} = \frac{V_o^{\frac{1}{4}}}{(LK)^{\frac{1}{2}}} + \frac{1}{4(LKV_o^{\frac{3}{2}})^{\frac{1}{2}}}(V - V_o) - \frac{3}{16(LKV_o^{\frac{7}{2}})^{\frac{1}{2}}}(V - V_o)^2 + \cdots \qquad (15.24)$$

where V_o is the bias voltage applied to the diode.

When the modulator is adjusted so that the second-order term is small in comparison with the linear term, the third- and higher-order terms may be neglected.

In case the modulating signal is a sinusoid,

$$V - V_o = \Delta V = V_m \sin \omega t \qquad (15.25)$$

$$(V - V_o)^2 = V_m^2 \sin^2 \omega t = \frac{V_m^2}{2}(1 - \cos 2\omega t) \qquad (15.26)$$

Substituting Eqs. 15.26, 15.25, and 15.24 into Eq. 15.23, we obtain an expression for the signal frequency when the modulating voltage is sinusoidal. Neglecting the third- and higher-order terms, we have

$$\omega = \frac{V_o^{\frac{1}{4}}}{(LK)^{\frac{1}{2}}} - \frac{3V_m^2}{32(LKV_o^{\frac{7}{2}})^{\frac{1}{2}}} + \frac{V_m \sin \omega t}{4(LKV_o^{\frac{3}{2}})^{\frac{1}{2}}} + \frac{3V_m^2 \cos 2\omega t}{32(LKV_o^{\frac{7}{2}})^{\frac{1}{2}}} \qquad (15.27)$$

The percentage of the magnitude of the second harmonic to the magnitude of the fundamental is

$$\text{Per cent } 2^{\text{nd}} \text{ harmonic} = \frac{3V_m^2/32(LKV_o^{\frac{7}{2}})^{\frac{1}{2}}}{V_m/4(LKV_o^{\frac{3}{2}})^{\frac{1}{2}}} \times 100 = \frac{3V_m}{8V_o} \times 100 \qquad (15.28)$$

Thus it may be observed from Eq. 15.28 that the second harmonic distortion may be kept within any desired limit by the proper choices of bias voltage V_o and peak modulating voltage V_m.

PROB. 15.3. An abrupt junction diode is used to frequency modulate an oscillator. The junction capacitance is essentially the total tuning capacitance of the oscillator circuit. When 15 v bias is applied to the diode, the oscillator frequency is 5 MHz. Determine the modulation index (deviation ratio) and percentage of second harmonic distortion when the modulating voltage is 2 sin 6280t. Assume the third- and higher-order terms to be negligible. *Answer: $M_f = 178$, % sec = 5.*

PROB. 15.4. The positions of R_1 and C_1 in the circuit of Fig. 15.2 are interchanged. What relative values must R_1 and X_{C1} have to cause the reactance tube to appear as a capacitance? Derive an expression for this capacitance.

The situation may arise where the modulation index is not sufficiently high when the modulating voltage is at the maximum permissible level. Then the modulation index may be increased by multiplying the oscillator frequency by the use of a nonlinear amplifier, as dis-ussed in Chapter 12.

PROB. 15.5. The frequency modulated oscillator signal of Prob. 15.3 is fed into a tripler. What is the carrier frequency and modulation index in the output of the tripler? *Answer: $f_c = 15$ MHz, $M_f = 534$.*

In case the carrier frequency becomes undesirably high because of the multiplication process, the carrier may be reduced to a lower frequency by the use of a heterodyne frequency converter discussed in Chapter 14. This frequency conversion will not affect the modulation index.

15.2 SIDEBANDS OF THE FREQUENCY MODULATED WAVE

When the FM system was first conceived, it was hoped that the bandwidth requirements of this system might be less than that of the AM system discussed in Chapter 14. To investigate the bandwidth requirement, the equation of the frequency-modulated wave is rewritten below.

$$v = A \cos (\omega_c t + M_f \sin \omega_m t) \qquad (15.3)$$

The trigonometric identity for the sum of two angles may be used to give

$$v = A[\cos \omega_c t \cos (M_f \sin \omega_m t) - \sin \omega_c t \sin (M_f \sin \omega_m t)] \quad (15.29)$$

But

$$\cos (M_f \sin \omega_m t) = J_0(M_f) + 2J_2(M_f) \cos 2\omega_m t + 2J_4(M_f) \cos 4\omega_m t + \cdots \qquad (15.30)$$

and

$$\sin (M_f \sin \omega_m t) = 2J_1(M_f) \sin \omega_m t + 2J_3(M_f) \sin 3\omega_m t + \cdots \quad (15.31)$$

where $J_n(M_f)$ is the Bessel function of the first kind having order n and argument M_f. These Bessel functions have been tabulated; that is, they may be obtained from a mathematics table in the same manner as a trigonometric function. Substituting these Bessel function identities into Eq. 15.29, we have

$$v = A\{\cos \omega_c t [J_0(M_f) + 2J_2(M_f) \cos 2\omega_m t$$
$$+ 2J_4(M_f) \cos 4\omega_m t + \cdots] - \sin \omega_c t [2J_1(M_f) \sin \omega_m t$$
$$+ 2J_3(M_f) \sin 3\omega_m t + \cdots]\} \qquad (15.32)$$

Rearranging Eq. 15.32, we see that

$$v = A\{J_0(M_f) \cos \omega_c t - J_1(M_f)(2 \sin \omega_m t \sin \omega_c t)$$
$$+ J_2(M_f)(2 \cos 2\omega_m t \cos \omega_c t) - J_3(M_f)(2 \sin 3\omega_m t \sin \omega_c t)$$
$$+ J_4(M_f)(2 \cos 4\omega_m t \cos \omega_c t) \cdots\} \qquad (15.33)$$

If we use the trigonometric identities, Eq. 15.33 becomes

$$v = A\{J_0(M_f) \cos \omega_c t$$
$$+ J_1(M_f)[\cos (\omega_c + \omega_m)t - \cos (\omega_c - \omega_m)t]$$
$$+ J_2(M_f)[\cos (\omega_c + 2\omega_m)t + \cos (\omega_c - 2\omega_m)t]$$
$$+ J_3(M_f)[\cos (\omega_c + 3\omega_m)t - \cos (\omega_c - 3\omega_m)t]$$
$$+ J_4(M_f)[\cos (\omega_c + 4\omega_m)t + \cos (\omega_c - 4\omega_m)t]$$
$$+ \cdots \cdots \cdots \cdots \cdots \cdots\} \qquad (15.34)$$

Observe from Eq. 15.34 that frequency modulation produces a series of sideband frequency pairs. The number of significant pairs depends on the modulation index M_f, as illustrated by Fig. 15.6. Only the first four Bessel

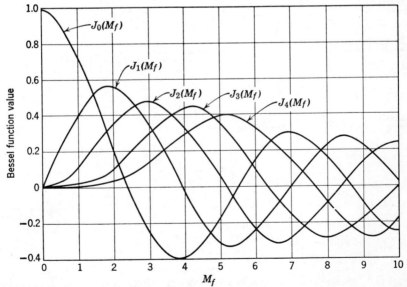

Fig. 15.6. Value of the Bessel Functions as a function of the modulation index M_f.

functions are shown for the sake of clarity. It may be seen from Fig. 15.6 and Eq. 15.34 that when $M_f = 1$, two pair of significant sidebands appear in addition to the carrier. Also it may be seen that when $M_f = 2$, there are three pair of significant sidebands. If the higher order Bessel Functions had been included in Fig. 15.6, it would be evident that the number of pairs of significant sidebands is one greater than the modulation index when integer values of modulation index are considered. This relationship, which may also be observed from the table of Bessel functions given in Appendix IV, is expressed by the following empirical formula.

$$P_s = M_f + 1 \qquad (15.35)$$

where P_s is the number of pairs of significant sidebands.

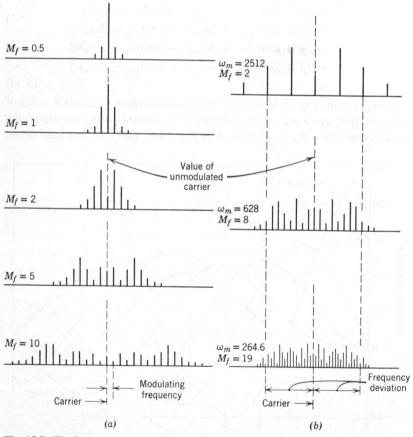

Fig. 15.7. The frequency spectrum of a frequency-modulated wave: (a) as a function of the modulating voltage, and (b) as a function of the modulating frequency.

Unfortunately, the bandwidth requirement for the amplification or transmission of a frequency-modulated wave is much greater than that of an amplitude-modulated wave unless the modulation index M_f is approximately one-half or less. In this case there is only one pair of significant sidebands, as may be seen in Fig. 15.6. At this point in the discussion there is no reason to believe that a modulation index of one-half is not entirely adequate. This problem will be pursued in a following section.

The frequency spectra for a frequency-modulated wave are shown in Fig. 15.7 as a function of both modulation index and modulating frequency. Observe that the bandwidth requirement is essentially proportional to the modulation index, and hence modulating voltage, as previously noted, but is almost independent of the modulating frequency. This behavior is in contrast to the amplitude modulated case where the bandwidth requirement is proportional to the modulating frequency but independent of the modulating voltage.

PROB. 15.6. Verify the number and relative magnitude of the frequency components shown in Fig. 15.7a by the use of a table of Bessel functions.

PROB. 15.7. A 400 Hz modulating frequency has sufficient amplitude to provide a modulation index $M_f = 2$. What bandwidth would be required in order to pass the frequency spectrum of this frequency-modulated wave? What would be the effect on the required bandwidth if the modulating frequency were decreased to 100 Hz and the modulation amplitude remained unchanged? What would be the modulation index? Compare your answers with Fig. 17.5b.

15.3 INTERFERENCE TO FM TRANSMISSION

One of the knottiest problems in radio communication is the interference which undesired signals offer to the desired signal in the radio receiver. These interfering signals may be electromagnetic waves which have frequency components within the pass band of the receiver. They may be coherent signals from radio transmitters or noise signals from electric arcs such as lightning, automotive ignition systems, and other types of arc generating machinery. The amplifiers in the receiver itself also generate interfering noise. Whatever the type of interference, the interfering signal adds vectorially to the desired signal as shown in Fig. 15.8. In this figure the desired carrier voltage v_c is used as the reference. The carrier is

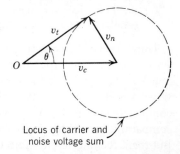

Fig. 15.8. The phasor addition of a desired carrier voltage and an interfering noise in a radio receiver.

assumed to be unmodulated except for the interfering signal which is considered to be noise. The sum of the carrier and noise voltages is v_t.

Figure 15.8 shows that the resultant voltage v_t varies both in phase and amplitude, compared with the carrier voltage, as the interfering signal varies in either phase or amplitude with respect to the desired carrier. In this figure, the amplitude of the interfering signal is assumed to be constant but its relative phase varies with respect to the desired carrier. The locus of all possible values of the resultant voltage v_t forms the dashed circle shown. Observe that the amplitude modulation which results from the noise approaches 100% as the noise voltage magnitude approaches the desired carrier voltage magnitude. On the other hand, the maximum phase deviation θ that can result from the noise voltage will not exceed more than one radian unless the noise voltage becomes essentially equal to or exceeds the desired carrier voltage. As previously noted, the maximum phase deviation is actually equal to the modulation index of a frequency-modulated wave. Therefore, the interfering signal can cause frequency modulation, but the modulation index M_f will not exceed unity unless the interfering voltage becomes essentially equal to or greater than the desired carrier voltage. Consequently, the following conclusions can be drawn:

1. In a communications system which uses amplitude modulation, the modulation caused by interference will approach the modulation produced by the desired intelligence as the magnitude of the interference approaches the magnitude of the desired carrier.
2. In a communication system which uses frequency modulation, the degree of modulation that may be produced by an interfering signal will be small in comparison to the modulation produced by the desired intelligence, providing three conditions are met. These three conditions are:
   (a) the modulation index produced by the desired intelligence must be large in comparison with unity;
   (b) the amplitude of the desired carrier must be larger than the amplitude of the interfering signal;
   (c) the radio receiver must be insensitive to amplitude variations of the resultant signal.

Thus, it may be seen that the frequency-modulation index must be at least 5 or more in order to provide good interference rejection. Consequently, the hope that the frequency spectrum of a frequency-modulated wave would be smaller than that of an amplitude modulated wave has completely dimmed. As previously noted, their frequency spectra are comparable providing the frequency modulation index is small (about 0.5). But then, the interference rejection capabilities of the two systems are also comparable. In fact, the AM system would be slightly superior if a high percentage of modulation could be maintained.

The interference rejecting characteristics of the FM system may be illustrated in the following example. Assume that two communities, which are separated by only a few miles, each have FM broadcasting stations. Also assume that the two stations are operating at the same carrier frequency and their radiated powers are equal. A motorist is listening to the local FM station as he departs from one community on his way to the other. The reception is essentially free of interference until the auto is almost equidistant from the two communities. Then for a very brief time the two programs are heard with essentially equal loudness. After this brief interval, the FM station at the destination will be heard with essentially no interference from the other station. Of course, it has been assumed that both stations maintain a modulation index which is large in comparison with unity and the auto radio is insensitive to amplitude variations.

This interference-rejecting property of the FM system is a great advantage in a communication system. The chief disadvantage of the FM system is the large frequency spectrum produced by a large modulation index. The resulting large bandwidth requirement of the tuned amplifiers in the transmitter and receiver is most easily attained if the carrier frequency is quite high. For example, the frequency spectrum from 88 to 108 MHz has been allotted for commercial FM broadcasting by the Federal Communications Commission. Each station is permitted to use a 150-KHz channel.

PROB. 15.8. An FM broadcasting station modulates with audio frequencies up to 12 KHz and maintains a modulation index $M_f = 5$ at this frequency. What is the required bandwidth of a tuned circuit if none of the significant sidebands are to be excluded? *Answer: B = 144 KHz.*

PROB. 15.9. If the standard AM broadcast band (550 to 1600 KHz) were allotted to FM stations having the standards specified in Prob. 15.8, how many channels could be accommodated in this band? What would be the required Q (approximately) of a single-tuned circuit which would accommodate the frequency spectrum if the carrier frequency were 1 MHz?

15.4 FM DEMODULATORS

The AM demodulator, or detector, will demodulate an FM wave providing that the detector is tuned so that the carrier frequency is on the edge of the pass band instead of in the center of the pass band. The process by which demodulation is accomplished is illustrated in Fig. 15.9. The frequency variations of the FM signal are converted into amplitude variations by the detuned circuit. The AM detector then recovers the waveform of the amplitude variations. This waveform is the same as the waveform of the modulating voltage, providing that there is no distortion in the system. However, there will be some distortion in this demodulator because the sides of the response curve of the tuned circuit are not straight.

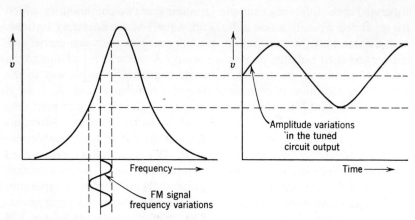

Fig. 15.9. A detuned AM demodulator used as an FM demodulator.

The distortion will be small if the frequency deviation is so small that only a very small portion of the response curve is used. This system is sometimes used to receive *narrow band* FM with an AM receiver. Both the detector and the r-f amplifiers of the receiver are sensitive to amplitude variations, so the conditions required for good interference rejection are not met.

An improved type of demodulator known as a Foster-Seely discriminator is shown in Fig. 15.10. In this circuit the primary voltage across the coil L_1 is applied through the blocking capacitor C to the center tap of the inductively coupled secondary. The relative phase of the secondary current, and hence secondary voltage, changes rapidly with the input frequency because the secondary is tuned to the carrier or center frequency of the input signal. A phasor diagram of the primary voltage V_p, the

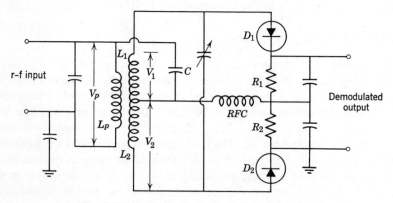

Fig. 15.10. A Foster-Seely discriminator circuit.

primary current I_p, and the voltage V_s induced into the secondary is given in Fig. 15.11a. These phase relationships are easily verified from the basic relationships $V_p = j\omega L_p I_p$ and $V_s = j\omega M I_p$. The secondary current is in phase with the induced secondary voltage V_s when the circuit is in resonance.

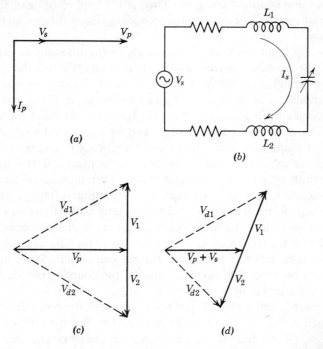

(a)

(b)

(c)

(d)

Fig. 15.11. (a) Phasor relationships of primary voltage, primary current, and induced voltage in the secondary of an inductively coupled circuit. (b) Equivalent circuit of the tuned secondary. (c) Phasor addition of the primary voltage and the voltages across the secondary coils at the resonant frequency. (d) Phasor addition of the primary voltage and the voltages across the secondary coils when the input frequency is above the resonant frequency of the tuned circuit.

As the input frequency deviates above or below the resonant frequency, the secondary current correspondingly lags or leads the induced voltage. This current phase shift may be seen with the aid of the equivalent circuit of Fig. 15.11b. Since the voltages across the secondary coils L_1 and L_2 always lag behind the secondary current by approximately 90°, the voltage across each of these secondary coils is approximately 90° out of phase with the primary voltage when the input frequency is the same as the resonant frequency of the secondary circuit. This situation is illustrated in Fig. 15.11c. The phasor sum of the primary voltage V_p and the voltage V_1

across coil L_1 is applied to the upper diode and its load resistor. This voltage is V_{d1} in Fig. 15.11c. Similarly, the voltage V_{d2} is applied to the lower diode and its load resistor. The output voltage is the algebraic sum of the diode load voltages, but since the current flows in opposite directions through these diode loads, the output voltage is actually the difference between these two load voltages. Thus, if the load resistances are equal, the output voltage is zero when the secondary circuit is tuned to the input frequency.

When the input frequency is raised above the resonant or center frequency, the secondary current and hence the voltage across the secondary coils lag behind their resonant position and the phasor diagram of Fig. 15.11d results. The voltage V_{d1} applied to the upper diode and its load then becomes larger than the voltage V_{d2} applied to the lower diode and its load. The difference between these two voltages produces an output voltage of positive polarity. If the input frequency is decreased from the resonant value, the secondary becomes capacitive and the secondary current shifts phase in a leading direction. Therefore, an output voltage having negative polarity is produced. The output voltage is essentially proportional to the frequency deviation as long as the frequency remains in the flat portion of the frequency response curve of the coupled circuit. As the frequency excursions approach the edge of the pass band, the output wave becomes flattened because of the reduced amplitude of the output voltage. Thus frequency discrimination in the coupling circuit produces waveform distortion in the output voltage.

The linearity and tuning characteristics of the Foster-Seely discriminator are shown in Fig. 15.12. The circuit should be tuned to the carrier frequency ω_o. The edges of the pass band are shown at ω_H and ω_L. As illustrated, the output voltage is essentially a linear function of the input frequency providing that the total frequency deviation does not exceed about 70% of the pass band. This degree of linearity is attained only when the discriminator circuit is double tuned as shown, and when the coefficient of coupling is adjusted so that maximum flatness is obtained in the response curve.

The diode load resistance should be chosen so that the desired circuit Q is attained in the secondary circuit. This problem was discussed in Chapter 14 in conjunction with the AM diode detector. The capacitors in parallel with the diode load resistors bypass the r-f and cause the load voltages to follow the peaks of the r-f voltages applied to the diodes, as discussed in the case of the AM diode detector.

Although the Foster-Seely discriminator may provide good linearity, it is sensitive to amplitude variations and therefore a *limiter* must be included in the r-f amplifier if the interference-rejecting capabilities of FM are to be realized. A limiter is an amplifier which provides a constant amplitude output even though the input amplitude varies. Any amplifier will limit if the input signal is sufficiently large. A limiter, then, has small biases so that it will limit when the values of input signal are comparatively small. For example, the collector supply voltage is reduced and the base or grid bias is reduced in comparison with the conventional amplifier.

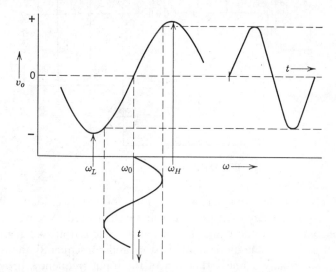

Fig. 15.12. The demodulation characteristics of the Foster-Seely discriminator.

Another type of FM demodulator which operates on the same basic principle as the Foster-Seely discriminator but which is insensitive to amplitude modulation is shown in Fig. 15.13. This demodulator is known as a *ratio detector*. The coupling circuit and the addition of the primary voltage to the center-tap of the secondary coil may be identical to the corresponding portion of the Foster-Seely discriminator. However, in the ratio detector, the two diodes are connected so that their load voltages are additive rather than subtractive. In addition, a large capacitance (perhaps 20 μf to 100 μf) is connected across the series combination of the load resistors. Consequently, the total load voltage cannot follow short-term amplitude variations of the input signal and the circuit is not sensitive to amplitude variations of the input signal. Hence, the limiter previously discussed is *not* required with the ratio detector.[1] However, the individual diode load voltages must be a function of the input frequency as it is for the

---

[1] Limiters are often used in conjunction with a ratio detector to improve the AGC action as well as to reduce the amplitude variations to essentially zero.

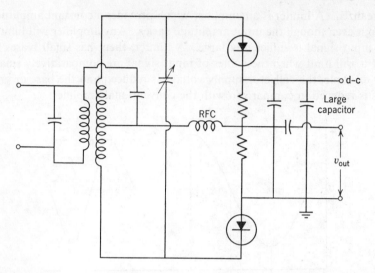

Fig. 15.13. A ratio detector.

Foster-Seely discriminator. Thus, the ratio of the two load voltages changes with frequency even though their sum is forced to remain essentially constant, hence the name *ratio detector*. The output voltage is obtained across one of the diode load resistors and consequently the output voltage is essentially a linear function of the input frequency, providing that the requirements placed on the Foster-Seely discriminator are met. In contrast to the Foster-Seely circuit, the ratio detector has a d-c component in the output even when the carrier is unmodulated and the circuit is properly tuned. This d-c voltage may be used for automatic gain control which may be desirable when limiters are not used.

Several other types of FM demodulators are discussed in the literature.

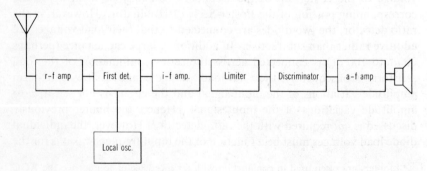

Fig. 15.14. The block diagram of a typical FM receiver.

The examples included here are merely illustrative, not exhaustive. The demodulators which have been included are very commonly used, however.

Figure 15.14 is the block diagram of a typical FM receiver which incorporates a Foster-Seely discriminator.

15.5 PHASE MODULATION

The primary problem in the generation of FM waves is the stability of the carrier frequency. In the AM system, the carrier is generated by a crystal-controlled oscillator which can easily meet the rigorous frequency

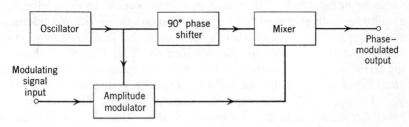

Fig. 15.15. An elementary phase-modulating system.

tolerance requirements of the Federal Communications Commission. In contrast, the reactance modulated oscillator cannot be crystal-controlled because the oscillator would not deviate appreciably from the resonant frequency of the crystal, as discussed in Chapter 13. However, the standard L-C oscillator does not usually meet the frequency stability standards imposed by the Federal Communications Commission. This frequency stability predicament can be resolved by a technique which is known as phase modulation.

The similarity between phase modulation and frequency modulation can be seen from Eq. 15.3, repeated below for convenience.

$$v = A \cos (\omega_c t + M_f \sin \omega_m t) \tag{15.3}$$

As previously mentioned, the term $(M_f \sin \omega_m t)$ has the dimensions of an angle, not a frequency. Therefore, we should suspect that a modulation process could be devised wherein the phase (or relative phase angle) of the wave could be changed rather than the frequency *per se*. One of the simplest systems which may be used to accomplish phase modulation is illustrated by the block diagram of Fig. 15.15. The modulation is accomplished by adding an amplitude-modulated wave to the carrier which has experienced approximately 90° phase shift. The effect of this addition is

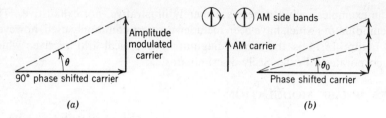

Fig. 15.16. The relative phase shift which is accomplished by the system of Fig. 15.15.

shown by Fig. 15.16a. This figure shows that the relative phase angle θ varies as the amplitude of the modulated carrier varies. In Fig. 15.16b, the amplitude-modulated wave has been resolved into the carrier and sideband components. Only two sidebands have been included, assuming sinusoidal modulation. Since the phase-shifted carrier is used as a reference, the carrier component of the modulated portion remains stationary in the phasor diagram while the sidebands rotate at the relative angular velocity ω_m. The upper sidebands rotate in a counterclockwise direction and the lower sidebands rotate in a clockwise direction. Thus the sideband components alternately add to and subtract from their carrier component as shown, whereas the relative phase varies about the average value, θ_o which is produced by the carrier component of the modulated wave. It may be observed from Fig. 15.16b that the increase of θ during modulation peaks is not as great as the decrease of θ during modulation troughs, if we assume the amplitude modulation to be distortionless. The distortion of the phase modulation θ results because $\tan \theta$ is a nonlinear function of θ.

The distortion of the phase modulation can be reduced for a given variation of θ if the carrier of the modulated wave is removed. In this case θ_o in Fig. 15.16b will be reduced to zero. The balanced modulator which was discussed in Chapter 14 can be used to suppress the carrier of the modulated wave. The block diagram of a system which incorporates a balanced modulator is shown in Fig. 15.17. In this system the output of

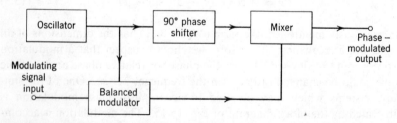

Fig. 15.17. The block diagram of a phase-modulating system which utilizes a balanced modulator.

the balanced modulator was shown in Chapter 14 to be (Eq. 14.29)

$$v_0 = \frac{BM_a}{2} [\cos(\omega_c + \omega_m)t + \cos(\omega_c - \omega_m)t] \qquad (15.36)$$

where M_a is the amplitude modulation index and $BM_a/2$ is the peak amplitude of each sideband, assuming the modulating voltage to be sinusoidal of natural frequency ω_m. The phasor addition of the 90° phase

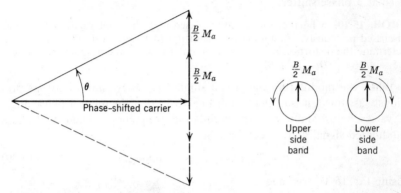

Fig. 15.18. The relative phase shift which is accomplished by the balanced modulator system of Fig. 15.16.

shifted carrier and the output of the balanced modulator is shown in Fig. 15.18. The 90° phase shifted carrier is again used as the reference in this figure. Let the peak amplitude of this carrier be A. As the sideband phasors rotate, the phase modulation angle θ oscillates about the reference carrier vector at the modulation frequency ω_m. Since each sideband has a maximum amplitude $B/2$, they add together twice each modulation cycle to produce a maximum contribution B. The maximum excursion of the phase angle is then

$$\theta_{\max} = \tan^{-1}\frac{BM_a}{A} \qquad (15.37)$$

where A is the maximum amplitude of the phase shifted carrier, as previously stated. But, to obtain distortionless phase modulation, the relative phase angle θ must be proportional to the sideband amplitude $B/2$. The only way this linear relationship can be obtained is by limiting $\theta_{\max}$ to such small angles that the value of the angle is essentially equal to its tangent. With this restriction,

$$\theta_{\max} \simeq \frac{BM_a}{A} \qquad (15.38)$$

The limit which is set on $\theta_{\max}$ will, of course, depend on the tolerable distortion. The limit $\theta_{\max} = 0.5$ radian may be appropriate in some applications. Then assuming the upper limit of the amplitude modulation index M_a to be unity, we could obtain the value of $\theta_{max} = 0.5$ radian by making $A = 2B$. Since A is the peak amplitude of the phase shifted carrier and $B/2$ is the peak amplitude of each sideband, it is evident that the phase shifter must also include amplification. In fact, an amplifier which has a high-output impedance (such as a common base transistor or pentode tube) and a load which is essentially a pure reactance could be used as a phase shifter.

PROB. 15.10. A balanced modulator is used in a phase modulation system as discussed previously. Assuming the distortion to be primarily third harmonic, determine the distortion of the phase modulator when the modulation index is 0.5. *Answer: Dist. = 7.3%.*

When the modulating signal is a single frequency (sinusoidal), as previously assumed, it is evident from Fig. 15.18 that the relative phase angle θ varies sinusoidally at the modulating frequency. Then the phase modulated signal voltage can be written

$$v = V_m \cos (\omega_c t + \theta_m \sin \omega_m t) \tag{15.39}$$

Using Eq. 15.38, we have

$$v = V_m \cos \left(\omega_c t + \frac{B}{A} M_a \sin \omega_m t \right) \tag{15.40}$$

Now, if a phase modulation index $M_p = \dfrac{B}{A} M_a$ is defined,

$$v = V_m \cos (\omega_c t + M_p \sin \omega_m t) \tag{15.41}$$

Since neither A, B, or M_a are functions of the modulating frequency, it is evident that M_p is not a function of the modulating frequency. On the other hand, the frequency modulation index M_f is inversely proportional to frequency, as shown in Eq. 15.7, if we assume the modulating amplitude to be constant. This difference in the character of the modulation indices is the only difference between phase modulation and frequency modulation. Viewing this difference another way, we see that the frequency deviation of the frequency modulated wave is proportional to the modulation amplitude but independent of the modulating frequency whereas the frequency deviation of the phase modulated wave is proportional to the frequency of the modulating voltage as well as to its amplitude.

PROB. 15.11. Prove that the frequency deviation of the phase-modulated wave is proportional to both the frequency and the amplitude of the modulating voltage.

It is clear that the phase-modulating technique could be used to produce frequency-modulated waves, providing that the amplitude of the modulating voltage were inversely proportional to the modulating frequency. This inverse relationship could be obtained by including, in the modulator, an amplifier which has gain inversely proportional to the frequency.

PROB. 15.12. Draw the circuit diagram for an amplifier which has gain inversely proportional to frequency.

One major problem arises when frequency modulation is produced by the phase modulating technique. As previously shown, the maximum

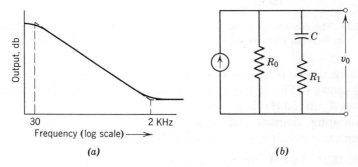

(a)   (b)

Fig. 15.19. The predistortion and compensation characteristics of a phase-modulated system. (a) Predistortion characteristic; (b) a predistorting circuit.

modulation index may be of the order of 0.5. This will then be the acceptable index at the *lowest* modulating frequency. If the modulation is audio-frequency program material as in a commercial broadcast station, this lowest modulating frequency could be 30 Hz. Then, since the modulation index is inversely proportional to frequency, the modulation index at 15 KHz would be $0.5 \times 30/15,000 = 0.001$. As previously mentioned, this modulation index could be increased by frequency multiplication, but to bring this modulation index up to 5, which is considered by the FCC to be an acceptable minimum, the carrier frequency must be multiplied by 5000. The complexity of a circuit which would multiply the frequency by a factor of 5000 would be quite forbidding. Consequently, a compromise is made in phase-modulated transmitters, wherein the modulation index is required to follow the inverse relationship with frequency only up to about 2000 Hz. Above this frequency, the modulation index is permitted to remain independent of frequency. In this case a compensating circuit must be included in the output of the demodulator in the receiver. Otherwise, the frequency response characteristic would be proportional to the frequency for frequencies above 2000 Hz.

The frequency response characteristic of the modulator for a phase-modulated transmitter is shown in Fig. 15.19a. The circuit which produces

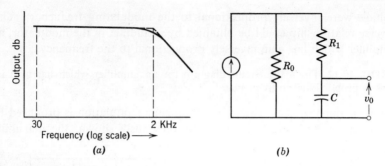

Fig. 15.20. The predistortion and compensation characteristics of a phase-modulated system. (*a*) Receiver compensation characteristic; (*b*) a compensating circuit.

this characteristic is frequently known as a *predistorter*. The simple *R-C* circuit shown in Fig. 15.19*b* could be used as a predistorter. In this circuit $1/\omega C = R_o$ at 30 Hz and $1/\omega C = R_1$ at 2 KHz. Also the receiver compensating characteristic is shown in Fig. 15.20*a* and a typical compensating circuit is given in Fig. 15.20*b*.

PROB. 15.13. An FM transmitter is to have an output carrier of 50 MHz and a modulation index $M_F = 5$ above 2 KHz. The oscillator is phase modulated with a maximum phase deviation of 0.4 radian at 40 Hz. What will be the oscillator frequency if frequency multiplication is used to increase M_F? *Answer: $f_o = 80$ KHz.*

Frequency-controlling crystals are not generally available for frequencies below 100 KHz. Therefore, it may be necessary to utilize frequency conversion to provide an adequate modulation index at frequencies above 2000 Hz. The block diagram of a typical FM transmitter which employs the phase-modulating technique is shown in Fig. 15.21. This

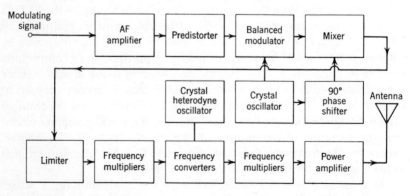

Fig. 15.21. The block diagram of an FM transmitter which uses the Armstrong system.

system is known as the *Armstrong system* of frequency modulation because it was invented by Major E. F. Armstrong. In this diagram, a limiter follows the phase modulator because there is a small amount of amplitude modulation in the output of the phase modulator.

PROB. 15.14. An FM transmitter using the Armstrong system has a modulation index = 5 from 2000 to 12,000 Hz. The initial modulation index is 0.40 radian at 40 Hz. The output carrier frequency is 50 MHz. The signal generating oscillator is crystal-controlled at 200 KHz. Assuming the block diagram of Fig. 15.21 to be used, and further, assuming the frequency multiplication to be equal in the two multipliers, determine both the carrier frequency and the maximum frequency deviation following each of the blocks in the transmitter diagram. Determine the frequency of the crystal oscillator used in the frequency converter.

A vacuum tube device known as a *phasitron* has been developed for the purpose of producing phase modulation.[2] This device requires a three-phase voltage from the crystal-controlled oscillator. Modulation is accomplished by a magnetic field. The phasitron may produce relatively large phase shifts with a given degree of distortion compared with the methods previously discussed. Therefore, considerably less frequency multiplication is needed when the phasitron is used.

15.6 AUTOMATIC FREQUENCY CONTROL (AFC)

One problem which arises in a radio receiver is the detuning which results from changing circuit parameters. For example, the tuning capacitance of a tuned circuit almost always includes the inherent capacitance of the amplifying device. But the transistor junction capacitance is a function of the junction voltage, which in turn may be a function of the temperature. Also the tube interelectrode capacitances are a function of temperature. In addition, the effective capacitance between input and output circuits is a function of the amplifier gain, as previously discussed. Many other causes of detuning exist but will not be mentioned for the sake of brevity. The detuning problem in a superheterodyne-type receiver is accentuated because of the frequency drift in the local oscillator. Of course, the local oscillator can be crystal-controlled, but the receiver cannot then be continuously tunable.

One system which may be conveniently used to maintain a desirable degree of frequency stability in a superheterodyne receiver is known as *automatic frequency control* (AFC). In this system a Foster-Seely-type

[2] For a description of the "phasitron" see Samuel Seely, *Electron Tube Circuits*, McGraw-Hill, New York, 1950.

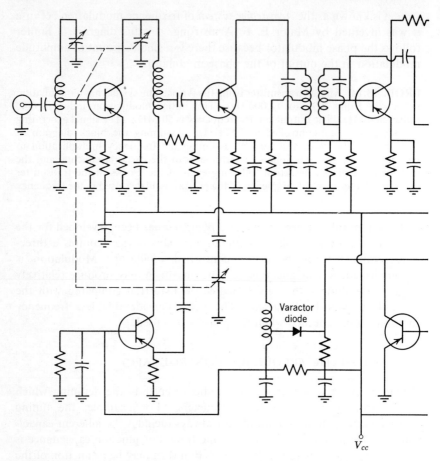

Fig. 15.22. An FM receiver which incorporates automatic frequency control (AFC). A similar circuit with component values listed is available from J. W. Miller Co., 5917 South Main St., Los Angeles, California.

discriminator is used to sense a deviation from the desired intermediate frequency.[3] The rapid variations are filtered from the output voltage of the discriminator and the remaining average voltage is applied to a reactance-type frequency modulator. This reactance modulator changes the frequency of the local oscillator in a direction that will tend to reduce the average discriminator output voltage toward zero. In other words, the intermediate frequency will be changed toward the resonant frequency of the discriminator circuit. Thus, if the discriminator is tuned to the same

[3] The ratio detector circuit may be modified to produce a suitable AFC control voltage. This modification is shown in Fig. 15.22 and is discussed in connection with that figure

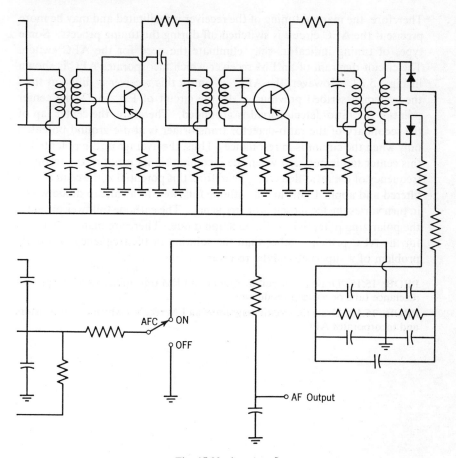

Fig. 15.22. (*continued*).

frequency as the i-f amplifiers, the AFC circuit will continually adjust the local oscillator frequency in a manner that will tend to maintain an intermediate frequency which will be very nearly the resonant frequency of the i-f amplifiers. The preciseness of the frequency control depends on the bandwidth of the discriminator and the sensitivity of the reactance modulator. Also a d-c amplifier could be used to amplify the discriminator output and thus increase the preciseness of control.

Either AM or FM receivers may employ AFC. In the FM receiver the discriminator which recovers the modulation may also provide the control voltage. It may be observed that AFC may compensate for inaccuracy of tuning in a radio receiver. From the standpoint of adjusting the tuning of the receiver, it produces the illusion of greatly increased bandwidth.

Therefore, the manual tuning of the receiver is facilitated and may be more precise if the AFC circuit is switched off during the tuning process. Some types of tuning indicators may eliminate the need for the AFC switch. The circuit diagram of an FM receiver which incorporates AFC is shown in Fig. 15.22. However, the AFC system in this receiver is different than the system described previously. In the circuit of Fig. 15.22, the center point of the ratio-detector load is grounded. Therefore, the center tap of the secondary of the ratio-detector transformer is at d-c ground potential only when the circuit is in resonance. Thus, the average or d-c potential at this center tap is not zero when the incoming signal is not at the resonant frequency of the ratio-detector. Therefore, this potential at the center tap is filtered and applied, through a cathode follower, to a varicap diode which in turn varies the local oscillator frequency. The cathode follower provides the polarizing potential for the junction diode. There are many other uses for the AFC principle other than the solution of the frequency instability problem of a superheterodyne receiver.

PROB. 15.15. Draw the circuit diagram of an FM transmitter which employs a reactance tube or varicap modulator.

PROB. 15.16. Draw the circuit diagram of an FM receiver which uses transistors and incorporates AFC.

16

Switching Circuits

In some applications, tubes and semiconductors are subjected to such large signals that these devices behave as switches. Typically, these devices may be driven beyond cutoff in one direction and to saturation in the other direction. A device which is subjected to such large signals is usually referred to as an *electronic switch*. Switching circuits are used in such diverse fields as bioelectronics, radar, telemetering equipment, television, electronic instrumentation, and digital computers.

16.1 EQUIVALENT CIRCUITS FOR ELECTRONIC SWITCHES

In switching applications, there are three regions in which the devices may operate. These three regions are known as the *cutoff*, *saturation*, and *linear* regions of operation. In the cutoff condition, the input electrode is biased until essentially no output current flows. In the transistor, this condition is achieved when *both* junctions are reverse-biased. The cutoff regions for transistors and vacuum tubes are indicated in Fig. 16.1. In the linear region of operation, the output current is controlled by the input current (or voltage) of the device. This linear region was investigated in the preceding sections of this book and will not be discussed further

593

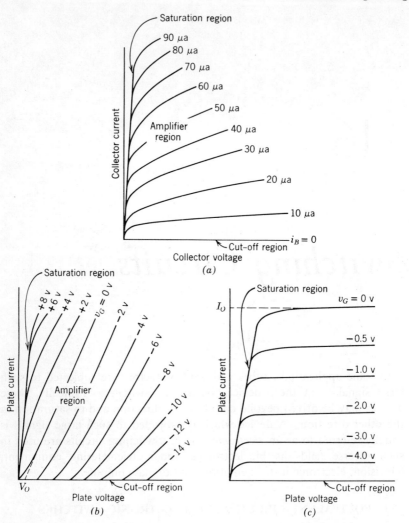

Fig. 16.1. The three basic regions of amplifier devices. (*a*) Transistor; (*b*) triode; (*c*) pentode or beam power tube.

here. The saturation region is reached when an electronic device is passing so much output current that an increase of input current (or voltage) cannot cause a significant increase in output current.

Approximate equivalent circuits can be drawn for the amplifying devices as shown in Fig. 16.2. In the cutoff regions, both the input and output circuits of vacuum tube devices are open circuits. The transistor has an input resistance h_{ie3} and an output admittance h_{oe3}. However, both of these parameters are associated with reverse-bias junctions and can *usually* be considered as *open* circuits.

The circuit for the linear region of the transistor is similar to the small-signal equivalent circuit already described. However, the equivalent circuits desired in this chapter must be valid for d-c conditions. Consequently, since the collector current may not be zero when the base current is zero, the current generator $I_{CO}(h_{FE} + 1)$ is included. Note that i_B may be reversed and become approximately as large as $-I_{CO}$. Then i_C will be essentially zero. The tube circuits must also be altered to account for the fact that the intercept of the idealized $v_G = 0$ v curve does *not* intercept the origin. For example, in Fig. 16.1*b*, the idealized $v_G = 0$ v curve is indicated by the dashed line. This line intercepts the voltage base line at a positive potential V_O. Since the equation for a straight line must give the value of the axis intercept as well as the slope of the line (the slope of $v_G = 0$ is contained in the r_p parameter), a voltage source V_O is included in the equivalent circuit. Note that the voltage axis intercept of the idealized $v_G = -2$ v curve occurs at $(V_O + \mu v_G)$ volts. Since μ is negative and v_G is -2 v, this voltage axis intercept occurs at $(V_O + 2\,|\mu|)$ volts. Thus, we

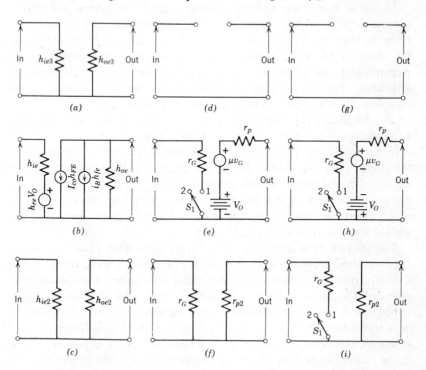

Fig. 16.2. Equivalent circuits for the regions shown in Fig. 16.1.

can summarize:

1. The parameter r_p determines the slope of the idealized curves.
2. The parameter μv_G determines the spacing between the idealized curves.
3. The parameter V_O determines the intercept of the voltage axis and the idealized $v_G = 0$ curve.

The d-c equivalent circuit for the linear region of a pentode (or beam power tube) is quite similar to the d-c equivalent circuit for the triode. However, from Fig. 16.1c we can note that the intercept of the idealized $v_G = 0$ curve (the dashed line) and the voltage axis will occur at a very large negative number. In fact, typical values of V_O may be of the order of -5000 v for a pentode. Since it is usually inconvenient to extend the voltage axis back to the point of intersection with the idealized $v_G = 0$ curve, an alternate method for determining V_O will be given. In this method, the idealized $v_G = 0$ curve is extended until it intersects the current axis. In Fig. 16.1c, the current value of this intersection is noted as I_O. Then, the magnitude of V_O is equal to $I_O r_p$ where r_p is determined by the slope of the idealized $v_G = 0$ curve.

The input signal may be large enough to drive the control grid into its positive region. When this occurs, the positive control grid intercepts electrons from the cathode. In fact, the grid-cathode combination behaves the same as the plate-cathode combination in a high vacuum diode. Accordingly, the resistance r_G (which represents the grid-to-cathode resistance) must be included whenever the control grid is positive. To complete the equivalent circuit, the switch S_1 is included in Figs. 16.2e, 16.2h, and 16.2i. This switch is in position 2 if the control grid is negative and switches to position 1 when the control grid is positive.

In the saturation region, we can find the output resistance by taking the slope of the line which divides the saturation region and the linear region. For the transistor, this resistance ($1/h_{oe2}$) is in the order of a few ohms. The reason for this low value of resistance becomes evident if we observe that the collector-base junction is *forward-biased* whenever v_{CE} is less than v_{BE} as discussed in Chapter 5.

The vacuum tube amplifiers have higher saturation plate resistances, but even these resistances are in the order of a few hundred ohms or less. Consequently, the output impedance under saturation conditions may be considered as approximately zero in many cases. In addition, the input impedance to a saturated amplifier may be that of either a positive grid or a transistor base with a parallel combination of two forward-biased junctions. Under either of these conditions, the input impedance is low in the saturation region. An exception to this low input impedance may occur in the pentode tube or field-effect transistor. If the load resistance is high enough, these devices may enter saturation while the control electrode is reverse-biased.

Circuits which have a low input impedance and large driving signals must be protected from excessive power dissipation. Quite often a resistor in series with the base or grid will provide this protection. In other circuits, a regular diode or a reference diode is placed in parallel with the amplifier input to limit the input-signal amplitude.

PROB. 16.1. Determine the magnitude of the parameters for the three equivalent circuits (Fig. 16.2) of a 6J5 tube. Assume $r_G = 1000\ \Omega$. *Answer:* $\mu = -20$, $r_p = 8\ K\Omega$, $V_0 = 23V$, $r_{p2} = 1{,}333\ \Omega$.

PROB. 16.2. Determine the magnitude of the parameters for the three equivalent circuits (Fig. 16.2) of a 2N1899 transistor. Use the curves given in Appendix III.7 and list any assumptions you had to make.

PROB. 16.3. Determine the magnitude of the parameters for the three equivalent circuits (Fig. 16.2) of a 2N2843 field-effect transistor.

Two examples will be given to illustrate the use of amplifying devices in switching circuits.

Example 16.1. A transistor is connected as shown in Fig. 16.3. The characteristic curves of the transistor are given in Fig. 16.4. If the input signal is a sinusoid as shown, sketch the output voltage as a function of time. Assume I_{CO} is zero. The diode D_1 is placed in the circuit to protect the base from high reverse bias (100 v in this case).

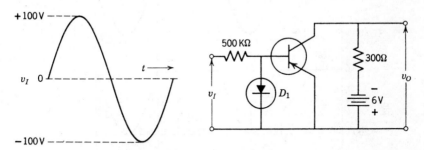

Fig. 16.3. A transistor clipping circuit.

As a first step, the input current i_B for the transistor must be determined. Since the input resistance of the transistor is much less than the 500,000 Ω resistor in series with the input circuit, the base current is

$$i_B \simeq \frac{v_I}{500{,}000} \tag{16.1}$$

when v_I is negative. In contrast, the diode D_1 passes current when v_I is positive.

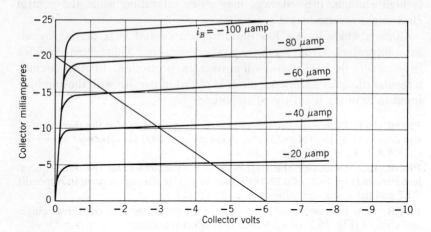

Fig. 16.4. Characteristic curves for the transistor of Fig. 16.3.

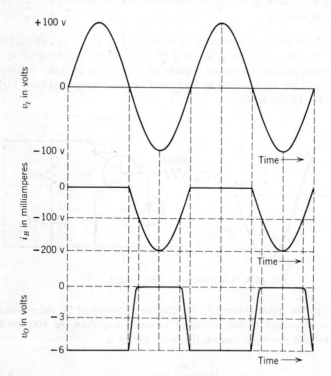

Fig. 16.5. Waveforms for the circuit of Fig 16.3.

(Also, the base-emitter junction of the transistor is reverse-biased.) Therefore

$$i_B \simeq 0 \qquad (16.2)$$

when v_I is positive. Accordingly, the base current of the transistor has the form shown in Fig. 16.5.

With the base current established, the collector current and collector voltage can be found. This collector voltage can be found by using either the equivalent circuits just developed or by graphical methods. In this example, the graphical method is the more simple approach. Accordingly, the voltage output has the form shown in Fig. 16.5. Observe that when the base current reaches -100 μa, the transistor is in the saturation region.

The foregoing example illustrates the operation of the transistor in all three regions. This procedure can obviously be used to predict the output waveform which results from any given input waveform except when the high-frequency limitations must be considered.

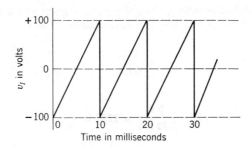

Fig. 16.6. The form of v_I for Prob. 16.4.

PROB. 16.4. The circuit of Fig. 16.3 has an input voltage v_I with the waveform shown in Fig. 16.6 applied to the input terminals. Find the voltage v_O.

A second switching example can be used to indicate the practical use of inductors in pulse circuits.

Example 16.2. A transistor is connected in a circuit as shown in Fig. 16.7. The input signal is a current pulse as shown. The characteristic curves of the transistor are given in Fig. 16.8. Determine the output voltage waveform Assume the internal resistance of the coil L to be negligible.

If I_{CO} is negligible, the transistor will be cut off for time less than t_1. If we assume that all transients have died out, no current will flow through R_L or L just prior to t_1. Accordingly, v_O is -5 v. At t_1, the transistor is suddenly turned ON. Since the waveform of current through an inductor is a continuous function, the current through L is zero at time $t = t_1(+)$. Hence, at time t_1, the load on the transistor is the resistor R_L. Accordingly, the operating point at time $t_1(+)$ is the point A of Fig. 16.8. As the current increases through L, the

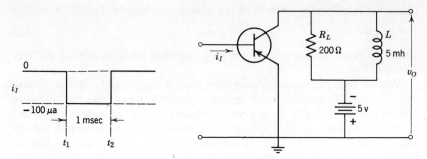

Fig. 16.7. A pulse generator circuit.

operating point shifts from point A toward point B. After a long period of time, all of the current flows through L and the operating point will be at point B of Fig. 16.8. Hence, the transistor can be represented by a circuit with the characteristics of line AB.

Line AB is a straight line with a given slope and a given axis intercept. As already noted, the slope of this line is a conductance. The reciprocal of this conductance is

$$r_{eq} = \frac{\Delta V_C}{\Delta I_C} \qquad (16.3)$$

For our example,

$$r_{eq} = \frac{5 \text{ v}}{2.25 \text{ ma}} \approx 2220 \ \Omega \qquad (16.4)$$

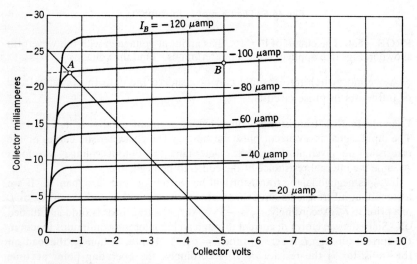

Fig. 16.8. Characteristic curves for the transistor of Fig. 16.7.

The value of the voltage axis intercept is found as

$$-V_O = I_O \times r_{eq} \tag{16.5}$$

where I_O is the value of the current axis intercept. In this example,

$$V_O = -(-22) \times 10^{-3} \times 2.22 \times 10^3 = 48.8 V \tag{16.6}$$

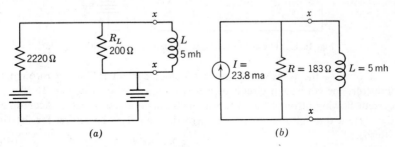

Fig. 16.9. Equivalent circuit for Fig. 16.7. for the period of time between t_1 and t_2. (a) Exact circuit; (b) simplified circuit.

Thus, the equivalent circuit for the transistor becomes a series circuit containing a battery V_O and a resistor r_{eq}. The voltage across this circuit is given by the relationship

$$V_C = V_O + i_C r_{eq} \tag{16.7}$$

For this example,

$$V_C = 48.8 + i_C \times 2.22 \times 10^3 \tag{16.8}$$

Since i_C is a negative term, the voltage along the line AB is given by the previous equation. Consequently, the equivalent circuit at time t_1 is as shown in Fig. 16.9a. Norton's theorem is applied to find an equivalent circuit which will represent all of the circuit to the left of the points $x - x$ in Fig. 16.9a. The admittance of this circuit is the parallel combination of the 2220-Ω output resistance and the 200-Ω load resistor. Therefore, the admittance to the Norton's equivalent circuit is 1/183 mhos. Also, the short-circuit current which would flow in Fig. 16.9a if L were short-circuited is 53/2220 a or 23.8 ma. It should be noted that this current can also be found from Fig. 16.8 as the current which would flow if R_L were zero. In this case, the point B of Fig. 16.8 gives a value of 23.8 ma, which agrees with the value obtained from the equivalent circuit of Fig. 16.9a. The total simplified circuit is shown in Fig. 16.9b.

From Fig. 16.9b, the voltage v_L across the inductor L is

$$v_L = -0.0238 \times 183 e^{-Rt/L} = -4.35 e^{-Rt/L} \tag{16.9}$$

where R is the equivalent resistance of the circuit. In this case, the time constant τ of the circuit is L/R. The total output voltage is $V_{CC} - v_L$ or

$$v_O = -5 + 4.35 e^{-Rt/L} \tag{16.10}$$

A plot of v_O for this period is given in Fig. 16.11 as the plot from t_1 to t_2.

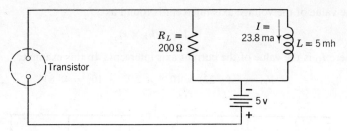

Fig. 16.10. The equivalent circuit for Fig. 16.7 at time $t_2(+)$.

At time t_2, the transistor is cut off. Since current is flowing through the inductor, the equivalent circuit at time $t_2(+)$ is as shown in Fig. 16.10. The current flowing through the inductor must follow a closed path. Accordingly, the current through the inductor returns through R_L. Therefore, for the time after t_2,

$$v_O = -5 - 4.76e^{-R_L t/L} \tag{16.11}$$

A plot of v_o for this period is shown in Fig. 16.11.

Observe that the voltage across the transistor of the foregoing example is nearly twice as large as the V_{CC} supply. Actually, it is possible to develop potentials many times greater than the supply voltage when switching circuits contain inductances. Since the total current through the inductor must also flow through the resistor at the instant when the transistor is cutoff, the higher the value of load resistance, the greater the amplitude of the output voltage pulse. Therefore, great care must be taken in the design of transistor circuits with inductive loads. The vacuum tube is usually more immune to high voltage than is the transistor. However, even in a vacuum tube the high plate voltage must be considered when the cutoff potential is determined.

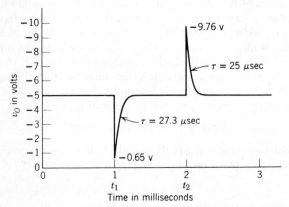

Fig. 16.11. A plot of v_o for Fig. 16.7.

PROB. 16.5. Verify Eqs. 16.9 and 16.11.

PROB. 16.6. Repeat Example 16.2 if all values remain as given except that R_L is changed from 200 to 600 Ω.

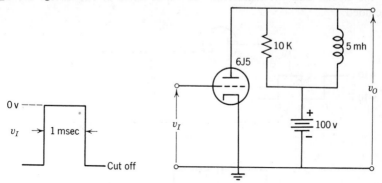

Fig. 16.12. A vacuum tube pulse génerator circuit.

PROB. 16.7. A circuit is connected as shown in Fig. 16.12. Plot the output waveform of this circuit. What is the magnitude of bias voltage required to cut this tube off?

16.2 CAPACITANCE AND CHARGE STORAGE IN DIODE SWITCHING CIRCUITS

In Chapter 3, diodes were used in clipping and clamping circuits. When the voltage waveforms reverse polarity very rapidly, the interelectrode capacitance of the vacuum diode must be taken into account. For example, if a square wave is applied to the clipper circuit shown in Fig. 16.13a, the equivalent circuit of the diode (including interelectrode capacitance) is as shown in Fig. 16.13b. The switch S_1 is in position 1 when the cathode is negative (with respect to the plate) and switches to position 2 as the cathode becomes more positive than the plate. The capacitor C_P couples the input and output circuits in the same manner as an R-C coupling network. However, since C_P is very small (in the order of a few picofarads), the time constant of the circuit is very small and the capacitor is rapidly charged or discharged. Therefore, the voltage output v_O has the form shown in Fig. 16.13b.

Most circuits contain an appreciable amount of stray shunt capacitance. As noted in Chapter 7, the effect of this shunt capacitance is to round off the leading edges of a square wave or pulse signal. Consequently, when the shunt capacitance C_{sh} is also included in the circuit (as in Fig. 16.13c) the spikes on the leading edges of the pulses are considerably reduced. In fact, if the shunt capacitance is large enough, not only will the spikes at the leading edges of the pulses be completely removed, but, in addition, the leading edges of the pulses may also be rounded off. Thus, the exact waveform of the output signal can be found only if the shunt capacitance of the circuit and the interelectrode capacitance of the device are both included.

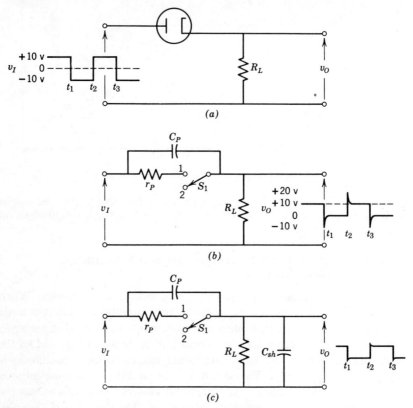

Fig. 16.13. The effect of interelectrode capacitance on the output waveform of a clipper circuit. (a) Actual circuit; (b) equivalent circuit and output when only interelectrode capacitance is included; (c) equivalent circuit and a typical output when interelectrode and stray shunt capacitance is considered.

PROB. 16.8. A diode is connected as shown in Fig. 16.13. (a) Plot the output waveform if, $R_L = 10K\Omega$, $C_P = 10$ pf, and $r_P = 100\Omega$. Assume $C_{sh} = 0$ and $t_2 - t_1 = t_3 - t_2 = 10^{-6}$ sec. (b) Repeat part a if a shunt capacitance $C_{sh} = 10$ pf is present.

Since the semiconductor diode has a junction capacitance, the foregoing analysis should also be applicable to the junction diode. Unfortunately, the junction diode exhibits a more complicated behavior than the simple capacitance-like behavior of the vacuum diode. As already noted in Chapter 3, the junction capacitance is a function of junction voltage.

In addition to the junction capacitance, a second capacitive effect is also present in junction diodes. This new effect is the result of *charge storage* in the diode. The reason for this charge storage can be visualized with the help of Fig. 16.14. In constructing Fig. 16.14, it was assumed that the doping concentration in the *p*-region is $10^{17}/cm^3$ and the doping

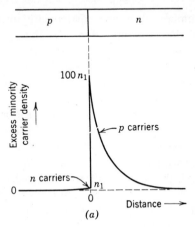

(a)

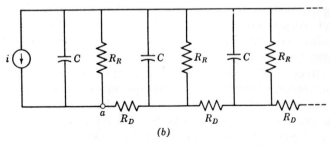

(b)

Fig. 16.14. Minority carrier distribution near a junction. (*a*) Minority carrier distribution; (*b*) equivalent circuit of a section of semiconductor.

concentration in the *n*-region is $10^{15}/cm^3$. If the semiconductor material is germanium, the carrier concentrations far removed from the junction will be

$$n_n \approx 10^{15}/cm^3$$

$$p_p \approx 10^{17}/cm^3$$

$$n_p = \frac{n_i^2}{p_p} = 5.76 \times 10^9/cm^3$$

$$p_n = \frac{n_i^2}{n_n} = 5.76 \times 10^{11}/cm^3$$

When forward bias is applied to the junction, *majority charge carriers* are injected across the junction and become minority carriers in the opposite type material. Since there are 100 times as many *p*-carriers as *n*-carriers, it is logical to assume that 100 *p*-carriers will cross the junction for each *n*-carrier. It can be shown[1] that this condition does, indeed, exist.

Thus, a large number of *p*-type carriers are injected into the *high resistance n*-side of the junction. Some of these carriers are lost by recombination and the others diffuse away from the junctions. This behavior is somewhat analogous to the action of the equivalent circuit shown in Fig. 16.14*b*. When steady state is established in this circuit, the current is injected into junction *a*. Part of this current is lost through R_R (analogous to the recombination loss for our minority carriers) and the rest passes through R_D (analogous to the carrier diffusion) to junction *b*. Again, a given percentage of current is lost through R_R and the remainder is passed through R_D to terminal *c*. When a large number of these sections are used, the current will be found to decrease exponentially. True to the action of the analog, the minority carrier density decreases in a logarithmic manner[2] as the distance from the junction is increased. Thus, minority carrier distribution will be as shown in Fig. 16.14*a*. It may seem that the exponential reduction of *p*-type carries as a function of distance from the junction would cause a corresponding reduction in diffusion current and thus total diode current with distance. Actually, the diffusion current does decrease, but the recombination process produces an electric field which causes a majority carrier drift current. The total diode current, which is continuous throughout the diode, is the sum of the diffusion and drift currents. The excess minority carriers (those in excess of the minority carriers which are present when no current flows) are called stored charges. These stored charges can be considered to be stored in the *C* elements of Fig. 16.14. Note that some minority charges are actually stored in the low resistance side of the junction but the majority of the stored charges are located in the high resistance side of the junction.

When a reverse voltage is applied to the diode, *minority charge carriers* will flow across the junction. Under steady-state conditions, only the thermally generated minority carriers near the junction are available to cause reverse-bias current. However, when current has been flowing in the forward direction, the large concentration of stored minority carriers

---

[1] J. G. Linvill and J. F. Gibbons, *Transistors and Active Circuits*, pp. 19–23, McGraw-Hill, New York, 1961.

[2] A much more exact model for a section of semiconductor material as well as a proof of the logarithmic distribution of carrier density is given in *Models of Transistors and Diodes* by J. G. Linvill, McGraw-Hill, New York, 1963.

shown in Fig. 16.14a exists. These stored carriers will be swept back across the junction. A reverse current will flow until the stored charge has been removed. Of course, recombination will also assist in removing the stored charge. As a result of these two mechanisms, the stored charge is removed (Fig. 16.15). As shown in this diagram, reverse current continues to flow until time t_4, at which time practically all the stored

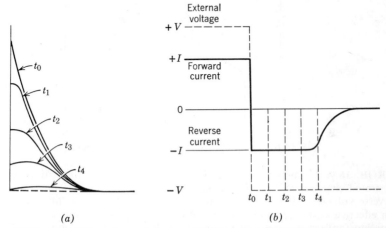

(a)   (b)

Fig. 16.15. The removal of stored charges. (a) Charge density distribution; (b) current waveform.

charges have been removed. The reverse current then decreases to the normal saturation value. Although the external voltage reversed at time t_0, the voltage across the junction does not reverse until time t_4.

From this analysis, it is evident that the following statements apply:

1. The time required to remove the stored charge (*storage time*) increases if the forward diode current (just prior to switching time) is increased.
2. Storage time decreases if the carrier lifetime is decreased.
3. Storage time decreases as the amplitude of reverse current increases.

An *approximate* equivalent circuit which can be used to represent a diode with charge storage is given in Fig. 16.16. Switch S_1 switches to the resistor r_f for forward current conduction and to r_b when the polarity of the diode voltage is reversed. The capacitor C_s holds the stored charge. The capacitance of this capacitor is effectively infinite, since the voltage across the junction remains essentially constant while the stored charge is removed. However, as the last stored charge is removed, the switch S_2 is thrown to the open position. Then, the capacitor C_j (which has a capacitance given by Eq. 3.52) charges as the voltage across the junction increases.

Some manufacturers provide storage times for typical operating conditions of the diodes. If this information is not provided, storage times may be found experimentally. Storage times vary from the order of a millisecond for large current rectifier diodes to a few nanoseconds (10^{-9} seconds) for high-speed switching diodes.

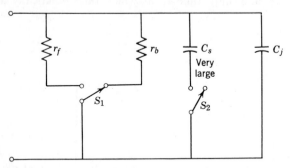

Fig. 16.16. An equivalent circuit for a junction diode.

PROB. 16.9. A junction diode has been conducting in the forward direction. A stored charge of 5×10^{-10} coulombs exists in the diode. At time $t = 0$, a reverse voltage of 10 v is applied to the circuit. The external circuit contains an effective source resistance of 10,000 ohms which is much greater than the internal forward resistance of the diode. If the effective junction capacitance of the diode is 10 pfds, plot the current waveform from the diode. *Answer: Storage time (to t_4 in Fig. 16.15) is 0.5 μsec.*

PROB. 16.10. A junction diode has an external resistance in the circuit such that the forward current flow and reverse current (while the stored charges are removed) are both 10 ma. The time required for the stored charges to be removed is 10 μseconds. The applied voltage is changed so that the forward current flow is 20 ma and the reverse current flow is 10 ma.

(*a*) How long would it take to remove the stored charges under the latter conditions if recombination can be neglected?

(*b*) When recombination is considered, will this storage time be increased or decreased? Explain.

16.3 RESPONSE TIME OF ELECTRONIC SWITCHING CIRCUITS

The rise and fall times of *linear* amplifying type circuits was discussed in Chapter 7. The *rise time* t_r was defined as the time required for the output current or voltage to rise from 10 to 90% of its final value when a rectangular current or voltage signal is applied to the input. This rise time was found to be 2.2 times the effective time constant of the shunt capacitance and shunt resistance of the device. Stated in another way, the rise time or *fall time* t_f can be written as $2.2/\omega_2$, where ω_2 is the high-frequency cutoff of the amplifier in radians per second.

The rise time of a transistor switching circuit can be improved by driving the amplifier into the saturation and cutoff regions. The effect of driving the base into heavy saturation is illustrated in Fig. 16.17. In Fig. 16.17a, the base current is just large enough to barely drive the transistor into saturation. The behavior is identical to that discussed in Chapter 7 for the linear amplifying devices. Thus, t_r is equal to t_f, which is equal to $2.2/\omega_2$. In contrast, the transistor whose current waveforms are

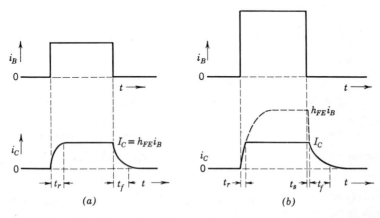

Fig. 16.17. The effect of excess base drive on rise and fall times. (a) Transistor driven to saturation; $i_B = i_C/h_{FE}$; (b) transistor in heavy saturation $i_B = 2i_C/h_{FE}$.

shown in Fig. 16.17b has been driven into heavy saturation. In fact, the base current is twice as large as that required to produce saturation. Consequently, the collector current i_C exponentially increases toward a value twice as large as in Fig. 16.17a. (This behavior is indicated by the dotted curve in Fig. 16.17b.) However, when the collector current has increased to one half this value, saturation occurs and i_C becomes constant. As a result of this action, the rise time (for this example) is reduced to a value less than $0.7/\omega_2$. The fall time is essentially unaffected by the excess base drive. Consequently, the fall time remains approximately equal to $2.2/\omega_2$.

Figure 16.17b indicates one other significant fact. *The collector current does not begin to decrease until a period of time t_s has elapsed after the base current has returned to zero.* This period of time t_s is known as the *storage time* of the transistor and exists only when the transistor has been driven into the saturation region.

The storage time is intimately associated with the stored charge concept already discussed in Section 16.2. In typical transistors, the base has a lower doping concentration than does the emitter. Consequently, when a forward bias is present at the base-emitter junction, a high percentage of the carriers which cross this junction are base minority carriers which are injected into the base region to form an excess density of minority carriers. When the collector-base junction is reverse-biased, most of these minority carriers are swept out of the base region by the collector (Fig. 16.18a). The number of excess minority carriers present in the base under these conditions is known as the "normal" base charge.

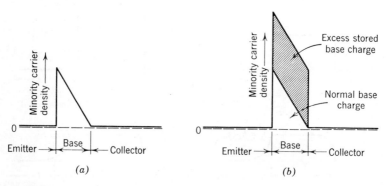

Fig. 16.18. Plots of minority carrier density in the base region of a transistor. (a) Non-saturated; (b) saturated condition.

When the transistor is in saturation, both the emitter-base and collector-base junctions are forward-biased. The charge distribution under these conditions is as shown in Fig. 16.18b. The current injected from the emitter to the base is so large that the collector is unable to collect all of the carriers available in the base. Consequently, the minority carrier density in the base increases until the recombination in the base is able to absorb the additional injected carriers. The excess charge (due to these excess carriers) in the base above the normal base charge is known as *excess stored* charge. The magnitude of stored charge increases as the degree of saturation increases. After the base current is reduced to zero, the collector current cannot decrease from its saturated value until the minority carrier density at the collector junction, and hence the excess stored charge, has been reduced to zero. The time required for this reduction is the storage time t_s (Fig. 16.17b). However, while the excess stored charge is being removed by the collector and also by recombination, the emitter-to-base junction continues to be biased in the forward direction (as noted for the diode) owing to·the excess stored charge. Consequently, additional minority carriers continue to be injected into the base region. Thus, the charge removed by the collector during time

t_s may be several times as large as the excess stored charge present at the beginning of t_s.

The storage and fall times can both be reduced appreciably if reverse voltage is applied to the base terminal (with respect to the emitter terminal) at the beginning of the period t_s. Under these conditions, the excess stored charge in the base is removed by a reverse base current (identical to the reverse diode current of the last section), as well as by recombination

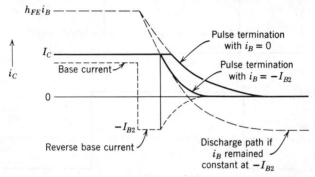

Fig. 16.19. The effect of reverse base current on storage and fall times.

in the base and removal of charge by the collector. The effect of the reverse base current on the storage and fall times is shown in Fig. 16.19.

An equivalent circuit for a transistor, which includes the effect of excess stored charges, is shown in Fig. 16.20. In addition, the various voltage and current waveforms associated with the circuit are also shown. Note that if the base of a transistor is reverse-biased (by a voltage V_{BO}) in order to insure cutoff, a fourth period of time, t_d, is also present. This period of time is known as the *delay time* and is equal to the period of time required for the base current (I_{B1}) to charge the capacitors C_{cb} and C_{eb} sufficiently to allow the base-to-emitter voltage to rise from V_{BO} to the value where conduction can occur. (Actually, by definition, t_d does not end until the collector current has risen to 10% of its final value.)

The behavior of the saturated transistor switch can be summarized by noting the behavior of the transistor as the input signal v_I (Fig. 16.20) is applied to the base B of the equivalent circuit. Originally, switches S_c and S_e are open and a potential V_{BO} exists on the reverse-biased base. When the input voltage pulse is applied, a base current I_{B1} flows. This current changes the charge on C_{cb} and C_{eb} and the base potential of the ideal transistor increases. At the end of the period t_d, the base potential is high enough for collector current to begin to flow. The period t_d can be calculated if I_{B1}, V_{BO}, C_{cb}, and C_{eb} are known. Then,

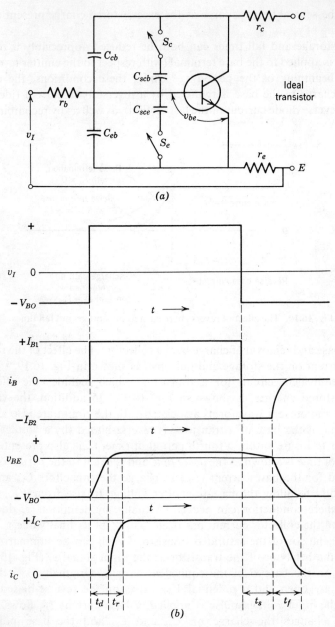

Fig. 16.20. The equivalent circuit and waveform of a saturated transistor when used as a switch. (*a*) Equivalent circuit; (*b*) waveforms.

the change of charge on the two capacitors is

$$\Delta Q = (C_{eb} + C_{cb}) \Delta v_B \tag{16.12}$$

where C_{eb} and C_{cb} are the effective capacitances of these capacitors over the voltage range Δv_B. The voltage Δv_B is equal to the change of potential from V_{BO} to the value where collector current begins to flow. (As a rough approximation, collector current begins to flow in a germanium transistor at 0 base volts and in a silicon transistor when 0.5 volts forward bias exists across the base-emitter junction.) Finally, the delay time is given by the equation

$$t_d = \frac{\Delta Q}{I_{B1}} = \frac{(C_{eb} + C_{cb}) \Delta v_B}{I_{B1}} \tag{16.13}$$

where I_{B1} is the base current which flows while the input pulse is present (see Fig. 16.20).

The capacitors C_{eb} and C_{cb} are usually *not* specified on the transistor data sheet. However, a capacitance C_{ib} (the input capacitance for a common-base configuration) and C_{ob} (the output capacitance for a common-base configuration) may be given. These capacitors are usually slightly larger than C_{eb} and C_{cb}, respectively, but can be used ($C_{eb} \approx C_{ib}$ and $C_{cb} \approx C_{ob}$) to determine fairly accurate values of delay time.

When the potential across the base-emitter junction has reached the proper value, carriers are injected into the base region and collector current begins to flow. Since a very small change of base-emitter voltage occurs between cutoff and saturation, the charging effect of C_{eb} can be ignored during the rise time t_r. Thus, the only capacitor which will experience a substantial change of voltage is C_{cb}. While the exact analysis is somewhat complex, an equation has been developed[3] for rise time which states

$$t_r = \frac{0.9 I_C \left(\dfrac{1}{\omega_r} + C_{cb} R'_C \right)}{I_{B1} - (I_C / 2 h_{FE})} \tag{16.14}$$

where I_C is the final value of collector current while the pulse is applied.

I_{B1} is the base current while the pulse is applied.

R'_C is the Thévenin's equivalent load resistance.

ω_r is the current gain-bandwidth product. (This ω_r is equal to $\beta_o \omega_\beta$ as defined in Chapter 7.)

[3] The development of this equation and a comparison of rise time equations developed by other writers is given in *Motorola High-Speed Switching Transistor Handbook*, pp. 100–104, edited by W. D. Roehr, Motorola Inc., Phoenix, Arizona, 1963.

When the collector current saturates, the two switches S_b and S_c are closed and the excess stored charge is established in the base.

At the end of the pulse duration, reverse voltage is again applied to the base terminal. The stored charge in C_{sb} and C_{sc} is gradually removed from the base region. Until this charge is removed, the base-to-emitter junction remains forward-biased as discussed previously. Thus, collector current continues to flow at the value I_C until the excess stored charge is removed from the base.

An expression often given in the literature[4] can be used to calculate the storage time t_s. This expression is

$$t_s = \tau_x \ln \frac{I_{B1} + I_{B2}}{I_C/h_{FE} + I_{B2}} \tag{16.15}$$

where τ_x is the excess base charge lifetime.

    I_{B2} is the reverse base current which flows immediately after the pulse has been applied.

Although most of the parameters in Eq. 16.15 can be determined readily, the value of τ_x is usually *not* included in the data sheets. However, if the storage time is measured (or given) for one set of conditions, the value of τ_x can be found from Eq. 16.15. Then, this value of τ_x can be used to determine storage times for other conditions. Unfortunately, storage time cannot be predicted very accurately at conditions far removed from a measured point.

At the end of the storage period, the switches S_c and S_b are opened. Then, the charge on capacitor C_{cb} increases as the collector current decreases to zero. Because of the circuit similarity between fall and rise time, it is not surprising to find that the two equations are similar. The equation for fall time is

$$t_f = \frac{0.9I_C\left(\dfrac{1}{\omega_\tau} + R'_c C_{cb}\right)}{I_{B2} + I_C/2h_{FE}} \tag{16.16}$$

An examination of most manufacturer's data sheets leads to a feeling of frustration. Few, if any, manufacturers list all of the data required to accurately predict the switching times. However, most manufacturers do include delay, rise, storage, and fall times for a given input pulse signal. Although extrapolations of these values to other circuit conditions do not produce very accurate results, at least approximate values can be determined which will be of great use in preliminary design work. The effect

---

[4] The derivation of this equation and a comparison with other equations for t_s is given in *Motorola High-Speed Switching Transistor Handbook*, pp. 115–128, edited by W. D. Roehr, Mororola Inc., Phoenix, Arizona, 1963.

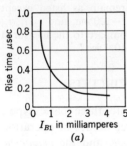 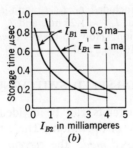 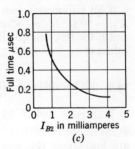

Fig. 16.21. The effect of base current on the switching times of a transistor. (By permission from *Electronic Switching, Timing and Pulse Circuits* by Joseph M. Pettit, Copyright 1959, McGraw-Hill Book Co. Inc.)

of base current on the switching times of a transistor is illustrated in Fig. 16.21.

PROB. 16.11. A germanium switching transistor in a common-emitter configuration is to be used as a pulse amplifier. A pulse is applied to the base at t_o and is terminated at time t_1. Previous to t_o the base has a reverse bias of $V_{BO} = 1.25$ v applied. (Since this is a germanium transistor, assume collector current begins to flow when the base voltage is 0 v.) Determine the values of t_d, t_r, t_s, and t_f for the following conditions:

$$C_{ib} = 3.5 \text{ pfd}$$
$$C_{ob} = 5 \text{ pfd}$$
$$\omega_\tau = 2\pi \times 460 \times 10^6$$
$$R'_C = 50 \ \Omega$$
$$I_{B1} = -5 \text{ ma}$$
$$I_{B2} = +1.25 \text{ ma}$$
$$I_C = -100 \text{ ma}$$
$$h_{FE} = 95$$
$$\tau_x = 20 \times 10^{-9} \text{ sec}$$

Answer: $t_d = 2.125$ ns. $t_r = 12$ nsec.

PROB. 16.12. The following data are listed for a typical 2N964A germanium PNP transistor:

$$C_{ob} = 2.7 \text{ pfd}$$
$$C_{ib} = 2 \text{ pfd}$$
$$f_\tau = 460 \text{ MHz}$$
$$t_d + t_r = 35 \times 10^{-9} \text{ sec}$$
$$R'_C = 300 \ \Omega$$
$$h_{FE} = 80$$
$$I_{B1} = -1 \text{ ma}$$
$$I_{B2} = 0.25 \text{ ma}$$
$$V_{BO} = +1.25 \text{ v}$$
$$I_C = -10 \text{ ma}$$
$$t_s + t_f = 6 \times 10^{-8} \text{ sec}$$

If all parameters (not included t_d, t_r, t_s, and t_f) remain as listed except $R'_C = 50\ \Omega$, $I_{B1} = -5$ ma, $I_{B2} = 1.25$ ma, and $I_C = -100$ ma, find t_d, t_r, t_s, and t_f for this new condition. How do these values compare to the measured values of $t_d + t_r = 30 \times 10^{-9}$ sec and $t_s + t_f = 50 \times 10^{-9}$ sec?

16.4 TRANSISTOR HIGH-SPEED SWITCHING CIRCUITS

Transistor switching circuits can be divided into three basic types, depending on their mode of operation. These three modes of operation are known as the *saturated mode*, the *current mode*, and the *avalanche mode*. The typical regions of operation for each of these modes are shown in Fig. 16.22.

In the saturated mode the transistor switches from cutoff to saturation

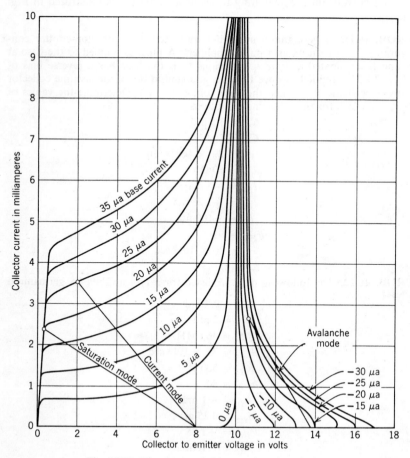

Fig. 16.22. The three switching modes of operation.

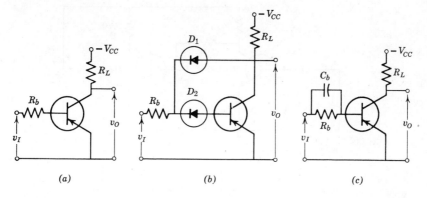

Fig. 16.23. Typical saturated mode circuits. (*a*) Basic circuit; (*b*) baker clamp circuit; (*c*) capacitor-resistor coupling circuit.

as previously discussed. However, as noted in the last section, storage time is present whenever the transistor is driven into saturation. Thus, in high-speed circuits it is desirable to either limit the amount of saturation or at least to neutralize the stored charge as quickly as possible. The amount of saturation can be limited by the Baker[5] clamp circuit shown in Fig. 16.23*b*. In this circuit, the diode D_1 conducts as soon as the base-collector junction becomes forward-biased. If the voltage drops across the forward-biased diodes D_1 and D_2 are identical, the voltage across the base-collector junction will be zero. Thus the stored charge in the transistor is eliminated. Unfortunately, this circuit is not quite as good as it appears at first. The stored charges are not present in the transistor, but they do appear in the diode. However, since storage times of some diodes are very short (the FD-700 diode will recover from 10 ma forward current which switches to 10 ma reverse current in 7×10^{-10} sec), the storage time of the circuit can be considerably reduced by the proper choice of diode.

A more popular method of increasing the switching speed is to use a capacitor in parallel with R_b (or to use conventional capacitive coupling) (Fig. 16.23*c*). In this circuit, the stored charges are removed very rapidly from the base region to the capacitor C_b. With the proper size of C_b, the rise and fall times as well as the delay and storage times can be decreased. In order to have a very short charging time constant for C_b, the output impedance should be small for the circuit which drives the base circuit of Fig. 16.23*c*.

[5] R. H. Baker, "Maximum Efficiency Switching Circuits," *MIT Lincoln Laboratory Report*, TR-110, 1956.

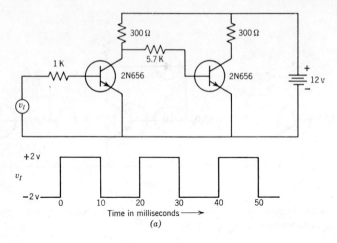

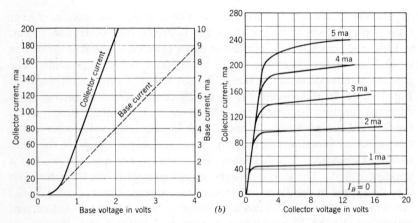

Fig. 16.24. The configuration and characteristic curves for Prob. 16.13. (a) The circuit; (b) characteristic curves.

PROB. 16.13. A circuit is connected as shown in Fig. 16.24. If v_I has the form shown, plot (a) i_{B1}, (b) i_{C1}, (c) i_{B2}, and (d) i_{C2}. *Answer:* $v_I = 2v$, $i_{B1} = 1.1\ ma$, $i_{C1} = 38\ ma$, $i_{B2} = 0\ ma$, $i_{C2} = 0\ ma$.

Storage time can be eliminated completely by not allowing the transistor to go into saturation. The current mode circuit which is shown in Fig. 16.25a can be used to prevent saturation. The action of this circuit can be best explained by considering an example.

Example 16.3. A 2N702 transistor is connected as shown in Fig. 16.25a. The resistor R_L is 3 KΩ and resistor R_E is 5 K ohms. The input signal v_I is a square wave with a maximum value of +2.0 volts and a minimum value of

-2.0 v. The $-V_{EE}$ supply is -12 v and the $+V_{CC}$ supply is 12 v. The conducting diode has a voltage drop of approximately 0.25 v, and h_{ie} is equal to 10,000 ohms.

When the input signal v_I is -2.0 v, the current through R_E is essentially V_{EE}/R_E or 2.4 ma. All of this current flows through the diode D_1 to ground. Since the voltage drop across the forward-biased diode is 0.25 v, the voltage on the emitter of the transistor is also at this potential. With the voltage on the base of this transistor at -2.0 v, the transistor is in the cutoff condition. Thus,

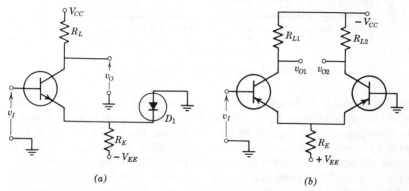

(a)   (b)

Fig. 16.25. Typical current mode circuits. (a) Single transistor; (b) differential output circuit.

no current flows through the transistor or the resistor R_L. Consequently, the output voltage v_O is $+12$ v.

The analysis is more complex when the input signal v_I is $+2.0$ v. Under these conditions, the emitter will be at approximately the same potential as the base since the base-emitter junction is forward-biased. With the emitter positive, the diode D_1 will be reverse-biased. The circuit now becomes very similar to an emitter follower circuit. A load line can be drawn for this circuit as shown in Fig. 16.26 (see line a-b). The value of resistance which determines the slope is $R_L + R_E$ and the voltage axis intercept point (b) is at $(+V_{CC}) - (-V_{EE})$ volts. The point of operation must lie somewhere along this line. The exact operating point can be found by a series of trial and error calculations. (That is, assume a value of collector current and calculate the emitter voltage. Now check to see if the base current which will flow with the assumed base-emitter voltage will produce the required collector current.) An approximate operating point can be found by drawing a second load line (line c-d of Fig. 16.26). This load line has a slope determined by R_L and a voltage axis intercept determined by V_{CC}. The intersection of the two load lines gives the *approximate* operating point. Actually, the exact operating point could be determined by this method if the voltage intercept of the second load line had a value of $V_{CC} - V_E$.

For this example, the approximate operating point is at $i_C = 2.4$ ma. The base current is seen to be slightly less than 100 μ amps. Thus, the base-emitter

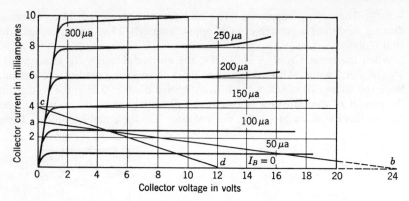

Fig. 16.26. A graphical solution for Fig. 16.25*a*.

voltage is equal to h_{ie} times 10^{-4} or 1 v. Therefore, the emitter is at a potential of +1 v. A load line for $R_L = 3$ KΩ and $V_{CC} = 12 - (+1) = 11$ v establishes an operating collector current of 2.5 ma. Hence, the output voltage is 4.7 v when v_I is +2.0 v. Since saturation does not occur, the storage time for this circuit will be zero. From the data sheet for the 2N702 transistor, $t_d = 8 \times 10^{-9}$ sec, $t_r = 5 \times 10^{-9}$ sec, and $t_f = 5 \times 10^{-9}$ sec when v_B shifts between +1.5 and −1.5 v. These values are extrapolated to produce the waveform shown in Fig. 16.27.

The single transistor current mode circuit of Fig. 16.25*a* can be modified to produce a differential output circuit as shown in Fig. 16.25*b*. In this new circuit, the diode D_1 in the original circuit has been replaced by the base-emitter junction of the second transistor. As observed in Example 16.3, current flows in diode D_1 when the transistor is cutoff and the diode is cutoff when the transistor conducts. Accordingly, one transistor of Fig. 16.25*b* conducts while the other transistor is cutoff and vice versa.

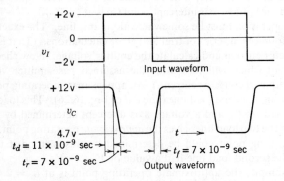

Fig. 16.27. Voltage waveforms for Example 16.3.

Thus, a signal of one polarity can be taken from one output terminal and the complementary (or inverted) signal can be taken from the second output terminal.

The circuit of Fig. 16.25b can also be used to convert a sinusoidal signal (applied at v_I) to a square wave at terminal v_{O2}.

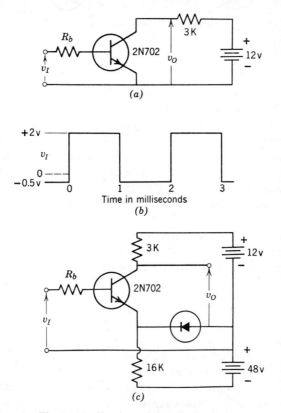

Fig. 16.28. Circuits and data for Prob. 16.14.

PROB. 16.14. A 2N702 transistor is connected in the two configurations shown in Fig. 16.28. Determine the output voltage v_C for both circuits. The input voltage v_I is as shown. The collector characteristics of the 2N702 are given in Fig. 16.26.

PROB. 16.15. A transistor is to be operated in the circuit shown in Fig. 16.29. The characteristics of a 2N656 are given in Fig. 16.24. The voltage v_I is a 500 Hz square wave with a minimum value of -2 v and a maximum value of $+2$ v. Plot i_{B1}, i_{C1}, i_{C2}, v_{C1}, and v_{C2}. *Answer:* $v_I = 2\ v$, $i_{B1} = 1.1\ ma$, $i_{C1} = 40.5\ ma$, $i_{C2} = 0$, $v_{C1} = 7.95\ v$, $v_{C2} = 12\ v$.

Very fast switching is possible by using a transistor in its avalanche

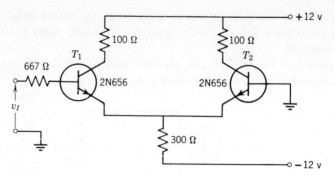

Fig. 16.29. The circuit for Prob. 16.15.

mode. As noted in Section 3.6, avalanche operation in the diode is due to ionizing collisions of thermally generated carriers. The highly reverse biased base-collector junction of a transistor contains not only thermally generated carriers but also carriers which have been injected from the base region. Consequently, as the base-collector junction voltage approaches the avalanche region, the behavior of the transistor should be different than the behavior of the diode.

The characteristics of the transistor in the avalanche region can be calculated rather easily. In Chapter 4, we noted that the collector efficiency of a transistor is given by Eq. 4.20.

$$\delta = \frac{1}{1 - \left(\dfrac{v_{CE}}{V_A}\right)^N} \tag{4.20}$$

The collector current of a transistor which is operating well below the avalanche region is equal to $\alpha I_E + I_{CO}$. The current I_{CO} is the current that flows in the collector-base circuit as a result of thermal electron-hole generation in the base-collector junction. This current is so small that it has been ignored in some of the previous derivations. Nevertheless, this current is always present and becomes important in this derivation. As the base-collector voltage approaches the avalanche voltage, ionizing collisions begin to occur in the base-collector junction. The collector current increases to δ times the collector current without ionizing multiplication. Thus, the collector current in and near the avalanche region is given by the following equation:

$$I_C = \delta(\alpha^* I_E + I_{CO}) \tag{16.17}$$

where α^* is the value of α at low-collector voltage. Thus, from Eq. 4.21, $\alpha = \alpha^* \delta$. Note that I_{CO} is the collector-base charge generation current *excluding multiplication effects* (the multiplication effects are taken into account by δ).

Equation 16.17 can be modified by noting that the emitter current I_E is equal to $I_C + I_B$. When this value is substituted into Eq. 16.17 in place of I_E, the collector current is given by the equation:

$$I_C = \frac{\delta}{1 - \alpha^*\delta}(I_{CO} + \alpha^* I_B) \qquad (16.18)$$

In the avalanche region, the product $\alpha^*\delta$ must be larger than 1. Under these conditions, the term multiplying $(I_{CO} + \alpha I_B)$ in Eq. 16.18 will be negative. However, the current I_{CO} flows the opposite direction to the current I_C. Therefore, if I_C is to be larger than I_{CO}, the current I_B must flow in the reverse direction (with respect to normal base current) in order to satisfy Eq. 16.18. The value of δ from Eq. 4.20 can be substituted into Eq. 16.18 to yield

$$I_C = \frac{I_{CO} + \alpha^* I_B}{1 - \alpha^* - \left(\dfrac{v_{CE}}{V_A}\right)^N} \qquad (16.19)$$

Equation 16.19 can be solved for v_{CE} with the following equation as the result:

$$v_{CE} = V_A\left[1 - \alpha^* - \alpha^*\left(\frac{I_B}{I_C} + \frac{I_{CO}}{\alpha^* I_C}\right)\right]^{1/N} \qquad (16.20)$$

A plot of the relationship given by Eqs. 16.19 and 16.20 is plotted in Fig. 16.30. The characteristics of actual transistors in the avalanche

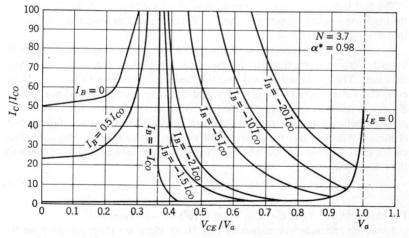

Fig. 16.30. Theoretical plot of transistor output characteristics in the avalanche region. Courtesy of Motorola Semiconductor Products Inc., Phoenix, Ariz.)

region are very similar to the theoretical curve. However, some difference between actual and theoretical curves does exist because the values of both α^* and N depend on the current density in the device. A comparison of Figs. 16.30 and 16.32 indicates the similarity of the actual and theoretical curves.

An example will be used to illustrate the use of a transistor operated in its avalanche mode.

Example 16.4. A 2N709 transistor is connected as shown in Fig. 16.31. The current input waveform is also shown. If the characteristics of the transistor are given in Fig. 16.32, find the output signal v_O of this transistor.

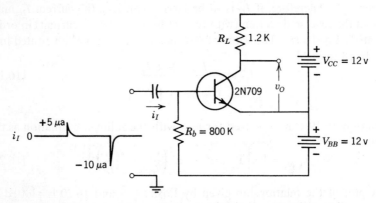

Fig. 16.31. A transistor switch operating in the saturation mode.

The first step in the solution is to determine the load line. For an R_L of 1.2 K, the load line would be located as shown. We note that this load line extends well into the avalanche region.

In order to determine the operating point, the base bias current must be known. We observe that the base-emitter junction is *biased* in the *reverse direction*. Thus, we may suspect that the base current is essentially zero. However, the voltage source V_{BB} is 12 v and the base-emitter breakdown voltage BV_{EBO} is listed in the transistor characteristics as 4.0 v. Thus, the base-emitter junction behaves as a zener diode and can be considered as a constant voltage element. Accordingly, the base circuit can be represented by the equivalent circuit shown in Fig. 16.33. The bias current I_B will have a magnitude given by the relationship

$$I_B = \frac{V_{BB} - BV_{EB0}}{R_b} \tag{16.21}$$

For this example, I_B is $(-12 + 4)/(8 \times 10^5) = -10$ μamp.

From the characteristic curves of Fig. 16.32, there are three positions on the load line where the $I_B = -10$ μamp crosses. However, one of these positions (the center one) represents an unstable point of operation. This instability is

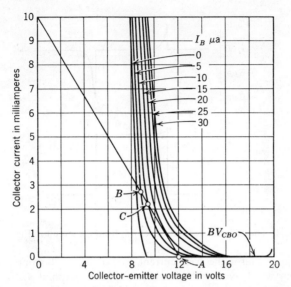

Fig. 16.32. Output characteristics of a 2N709 transistor in the avalanche region.

due to the fact that the negative resistance of the transistor ($1/h_{oe}$) is greater than the positive resistance of the load R_L. Thus, we are left with two stable operating points. When the circuit is first turned "on," the base current will be -10 μamp and the operating point will shift from the origin out to the point marked A. Since point A is a stable operating point, the transistor will remain at this point until either an increase of collector voltage or a decrease of base-current magnitude occurs. In this example, a decrease of 5 μamp base current occurs at time t_1. Thus, at t_1 the base current drops to -5 μamp. Since the $I_B = -5$ μamp only crosses the load line at one position (point B), the operating point shifts very rapidly to point B. As the base trigger pulse decays back to -10 μamp, the operating point shifts along the load line from point B to point C. Since point C is a stable operating condition, the transistor will remain in this condition until the next pulse is applied at time t_2.

The pulse at time t_2 has a magnitude of -10 μamp and when added to

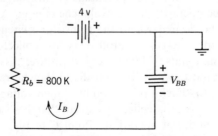

Fig. 16.33. The equivalent circuit for the base circuit of Fig. 16.31.

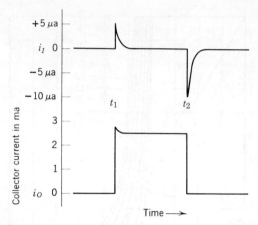

Fig. 16.34. The collector current waveform from the circuit in Fig. 16.31.

$I_B = -10$ μamp causes the base current to become -20 μamp. The $I_B = -20$ μamp curve only crosses the load line at one point (point A). Thus, operation is rapidly shifted back to point A. Since the $I_B = -20$ μamp and the $I_B = -10$ μamp approximately coincide, there is essentially no change in operating point as the trigger pulse slowly decays.

From the foregoing analysis, the collector current waveform will have the shape indicated by Fig. 16.34. There is one additional item that should be checked. The power dissipation should be investigated while the transistor is operating at point C. For our particular example, the base circuit has -10 μamp $\times (-4$ v$) = 40$ μwatts dissipation and the collector circuit has 2.5 ma $\times 9$ v $= 22.5$ mw dissipation. Since the total power dissipation should not exceed 300 mw for this transistor, we can safely operate in the region indicated.

The foregoing example indicates how the avalanche region of operation can be used for switching applications. In addition, this example can also serve to indicate a hazard which the switching circuit designer must remember. The characteristics of the 2N709 list maximum collector-to-base voltage of 15 v. If supply potentials of this magnitude are used, the transistor may be operating in the avalanche region. A saturated mode of operation may be desired where the transistor switches from saturation (very low collector voltage) to cutoff (very low collector current). Either of these operating points will have very low power dissipation. However, if the transistor must switch through the avalanche region, it is possible for the transistor to "latch-up" at a point of high voltage and high current. Latch-up occurs when the collector current "latches" at the higher value of two possible modes of operation. Point C in Fig. 16.32 illustrates the latched condition for this circuit. The power dissipation may be high enough to destroy the transistor in a very short period of time. The characteristics of the 2N709 indicate that if the maximum base-to-emitter voltage does not exceed BV_{EBO} (-4 v), or if the maximum collector-to-emitter voltage does not exceed 8.0 v, the transistor will not be operating in the avalanche region and latch-up cannot occur.

The foregoing material implies that switching in the avalanche mode occurs at a very fast rate. The characteristic curves in the avalanche region (Fig. 16.32) can be used to indicate why the switching speed is so fast. The curves in the avalanche region have a negative slope (an *increase* of voltage causes a *decrease* of current). Consequently, the internal resistance of the transistor is negative in the avalanche region. In addition, the stored charge in the reverse biased base-emitter junction acts as if a *negative* capacitance is present. (An increase of voltage causes a decrease in stored charge.) As a result of the negative internal resistance and negative internal capacitance, the time constant for the avalanche mode circuit is lower than the time constant in the current mode circuit. Thus, the avalanche mode is the fastest configuration considered in this section.

PROB. 16.16. A 2N702 transistor is connected as shown in Fig. 16.35. The characteristic curves of the 2N709 are given in Fig. 16.32. Plot i_B, i_C, and v_C for this transistor when v_I has the form indicated.

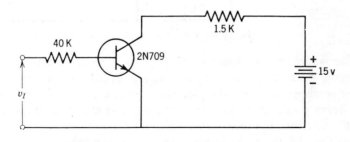

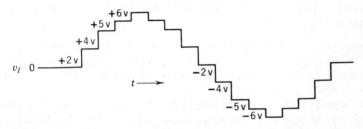

Fig. 16.35. The circuit and input voltage waveform for Prob. 16.16.

16.5 THE BISTABLE AND MONOSTABLE MULTIVIBRATOR

Multivibrators are an interesting group of electronic switching circuits. They are formed by coupling two amplifiers in a cascade (the output of one amplifier is coupled to the input of the second amplifier) configuration. Then, the output of the second stage is coupled back into the input of the first stage. Thus, a multivibrator is a two-stage amplifier with 100% *positive* feedback. This configuration is very unstable in the linear region

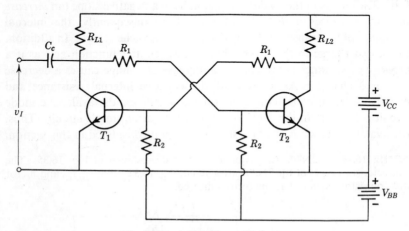

Fig. 16.36. A bistable multivibrator.

(as the reader has no doubt surmised). As a result of this instability, whenever both amplifiers are conducting equally the slightest signal (noise perhaps) can upset the precarious balance and drive one amplifier into heavy conduction (usually saturation) and the other amplifier into cutoff. The circuit is then stable under these latter conditions.

One form of the multivibrator (known as a *bistable multivibrator*) is shown in Fig. 16.36. For proper operation, the values of R_1 and R_2 are chosen so that when one transistor is conducting, the second transistor will be cutoff. If silicon transistors are used, the supply V_{BB} is not required. An example will be used to illustrate the behavior of the circuit in Fig. 16.36.

Example 16.5. Two 2N702 transistors are connected as shown in Fig. 16.36. The collector characteristic curve for the 2N702 is given in Fig. 16.37. The parameters in the circuit are: $R_L = 1.67\,\mathrm{K\Omega}$, $R_1 = 20\,\mathrm{K\Omega}$, $R_2 = 100\,\mathrm{K\Omega}$, $V_{CC} = 10\,\mathrm{v}$, $V_{BB} = -10\,\mathrm{v}$.

To begin the analysis, assume transistor T_2 is cutoff. Then, the equivalent circuit for the base of T_1 will be as shown in Fig. 16.38a. This circuit can be simplified by finding a Thévenin's equivalent circuit which can replace all of

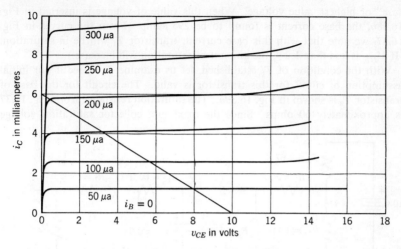

Fig. 16.37. Collector characteristics of the 2N702 transistor.

the external circuit of Fig. 16.38a. Then, the circuit is reduced to that shown in Fig. 16.38b. The equivalent Thévenin's impedance is

$$R_{eq} = \frac{(R_1 + R_L)R_2}{R_1 + R_L + R_2} \qquad (16.22)$$

For this example, $R_{eq} = 17.8$ K. In addition, the Thévenin's equivalent voltage will be

$$V_{eq} = V_{BB} + R_2 \left(\frac{V_{CC} - V_{BB}}{R_L + R_1 + R_2} \right) \qquad (16.23)$$

(The voltage on the base is equal to $V_{BB} + IR_2$ for this circuit.) Since V_{BB} is -10 v, the value of V_{eq} is $+6.45$ v. The manufacturer's data indicate the *maximum* base-to-emitter voltage V_{BE} for a collector current of 10 ma is 1.2 v. Since our maximum collector current is 6 ma, this voltage is certainiy a "*worst*

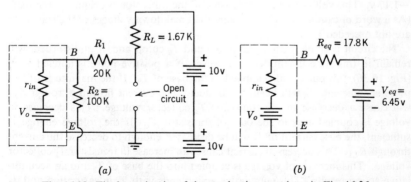

Fig. 16.38. The base circuits of the conducting transistor in Fig. 16.36.

case" or highest value voltage. When this value of voltage is inserted in Fig. 16.38b, the base current is found to be 295 μamp. From the curves in Fig. 16.37, we note that with this base current, transistor T_1 will be in saturation. (If V_{BE} is less than 1.2 v, the amount of saturation will increase.)

With the condition of T_1 established, let us examine T_2 to see if our initial assumption of cutoff for this transistor is valid. The circuit for the base of transistor T_2 is shown in Fig. 16.39a. The saturation resistance from Fig. 16.37 is approximately 60 ohms. Since the maximum collector saturation voltage

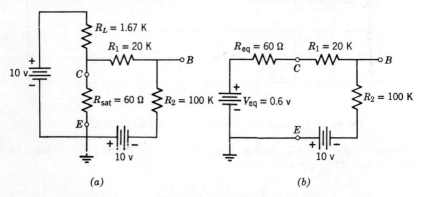

Fig. 16.39. The base circuits of the cutoff transistor in Fig. 16.36.

for $i_C = 10$ ma is 0.6 v (manufacturer's data), the equivalent circuit (for worst possible conditions) is simplified by Thévenin's theorem to that shown in Fig. 16.39b. A d-c analysis of this circuit indicates v_B is:

$$v_B = V_{BB} - \frac{V_{eq} - V_{BB}}{R_1 + R_2 + R_{eq}} R_2 \qquad (16.24)$$

where R_{eq} and V_{eq} are the equivalent Thévenin's resistance and the equivalent Thévenin's voltage from collector to emitter of the conducting transistor. For our example, $V_{eq} = 0.6$ v and $V_{BB} = -10$ v. Then, the base voltage will be -1.17 v. This voltage is sufficient to cut off the transistor as originally assumed. (As a word of caution, check to be sure the breakdown voltages of the transistor are not exceeded.)

The circuit is stable with T_1 saturated and T_2 cutoff and, if undisturbed, will remain in this state indefinitely. However, if a positive pulse is applied at v_I (Fig. 16.36), this pulse is also applied to the base of T_2. If the magnitude of this pulse is sufficient, T_2 will begin to conduct. The current flowing through R_{L2} will cause a decrease in the transistor T_2 collector voltage. This decrease in voltage is coupled over to the base of transistor T_1. If the voltage change is sufficient, the base current of T_1 will be decreased enough to decrease the current through R_{L1}. This decreased current causes an increase in transistor T_1 collector voltage. This increase of voltage is coupled into the base of T_2 and an accumulative action results. This cumulative action ends with T_2 in saturation and T_1

cutoff. Again, the circuit will be stable until either a positive pulse is applied to the base of transistor T_1 or a negative pulse is applied at v_I.

From the foregoing description, it is easy to see why the circuit is described as a *bistable* multivibrator. In order to insure proper operation and also as a means of decreasing the switching time, the circuit is usually connected as shown in Fig. 16.40. In this circuit, only one input terminal is required. Each input pulse will initiate a switching action in the circuit with two input pulses required to complete one full cycle of operation.

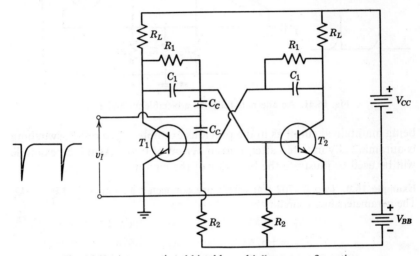

Fig. 16.40. A conventional bistable multivibrator configuration.

PROB. 16.17. A circuit is connected as in Example 16.5. What is the range of values R_2 can have and still insure proper action? Assume all other components are as listed. *Answer: 22.6 KΩ to 333 KΩ.*

PROB. 16.18. A circuit is connected as shown in Fig. 16.40. Assume that T_1 is conducting and T_2 is cutoff. Prove that the charges on the capacitors C_1 will produce switching even if the input pulse v_I is large enough to produce cutoff in both transistors instantaneously. (Assume that the input pulse duration is very short compared to the time constants associated with the capacitors C_1. Also assume that $C_1 \gg C_c$.)

PROB. 16.19. When only one voltage source is available, self-bias can be used to insure transistor cutoff. A circuit which accomplishes this objective is shown in Fig. 16.41. Determine the limits of R_1 for proper operation if $R_L = 3K\Omega$, $R_K = 2K\Omega$, and $R_2 = 50K\Omega$. Assume $V_{CC} = 10$ v and the two transistors are type 2N702.

A slight modification in the bistable multivibrator configuration can produce a *monostable* multivibrator (Fig. 16.42). In this configuration, the base of T_2 is permitted to return to a conducting state rather than

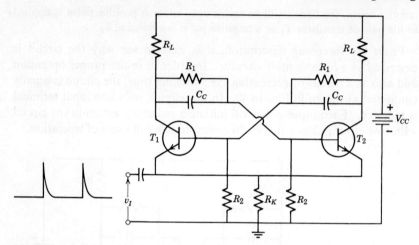

Fig. 16.41. An alternate form for a bistable multivibrator.

being maintained cutoff as in the previous example. As a result, switching is automatically initiated after a given period of time. Again, an example will be used to illustrate the behavior of the circuit.

Example 16.6. Two 2N702 transistors are connected as shown in Fig. 16.42. The parameters in the circuit are:

$$R_1 = 20 \ K\Omega \qquad\qquad R_2 = 100K\Omega$$
$$R_{L2} = 1.67K\Omega \qquad\qquad R_{L1} = 1.67K\Omega$$
$$R_b = 20K\Omega \qquad\qquad C_{c1} = 0.1 \ \mu\text{fd}$$
$$V_{BB} = -10 \ \text{v} \qquad\qquad V_{CC} = +10 \ \text{v}$$

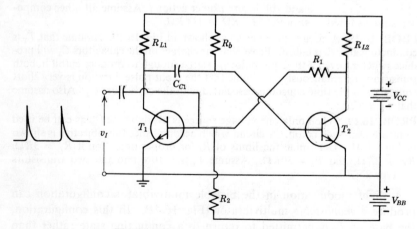

Fig. 16.42. A monostable multivibrator.

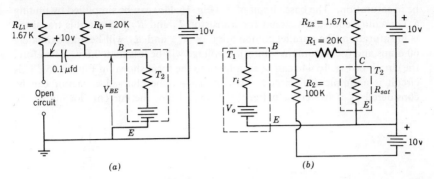

Fig. 16.43. The equivalent base circuits for the transistors in Fig. 16.42 for steady-state conditions.

To begin the analysis, assume T_1 is cutoff and T_2 is conducting. If the circuit has been in this condition for a period of time, the charges on the capacitors will have formed and the current through these capacitors will be zero. Thus, the capacitors can be treated as open circuits.

Under these conditions, the equivalent base circuit for transistor T_2 will be as shown in Fig. 16.43a and the equivalent base circuit for transistor T_1 will be as shown in Fig. 16.43b. If we take worst case conditions and assume V_{BE} in Fig. 16.43 is 1.2 v, the base current will be $(10 - 1.2)/20K\Omega = 440\ \mu\mathrm{amp}$. This magnitude of base current is great enough to saturate transistor T_2 (see Fig. 16.37 for the load line of $1.67K\Omega$ on a 2N702 transistor). Since Fig. 16.43b is the same as Fig. 16.39a, the base voltage of T_1 is -1.17 v and T_1 is cutoff. Thus, our initial assumptions are valid and the circuit will be stable under these conditions.

If a positive pulse is applied at time t_0 to the input circuit, transistor T_1 will begin to conduct and transistor T_2 will be cutoff. Under these conditions, the base circuits (immediately after switching) will be as shown in Fig. 16.44. The circuit for the base of T_1 (Fig. 16.44b) is essentially the same as the one in Fig. 16.38a. Hence, the base current will be approximately 295 μamp and T_1 will

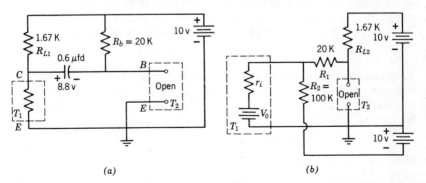

Fig. 16.44. The equivalent base circuits for Fig. 16.42 at time $t_0(+)$.

be in saturation. The base circuit of T_2 (Fig. 16.44a) can be simplified by finding a Thévenin's equivalent circuit for transistor T_1 and R_{L1}. Since this transistor is in saturation, the parallel combination of R_{sat} and R_L will be approximately 60 ohms and the maximum saturation voltage will be less than 0.6 v. Therefore, the circuit of Fig. 16.44a can be simplified to the form shown in Fig. 16.45. This circuit is a simple R-C circuit. At time $t_0(+)$, the charged capacitor can be considered as if it were a battery of 8.8 v. Then, the current flowing in the

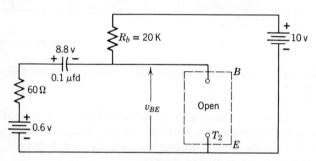

Fig. 16.45. A simplified version of Fig. 16.44a.

circuit at this instant will be $(10 + 8.8 - 0.6)/(20K + 25)$ or 0.91 ma. The voltage v_{BE} will be $0.6 + (0.9 \times 10^{-3} \times 25) - 8.8$ v or -8.2 v and T_2 will be cutoff. It is a good idea to check the maximum voltage ratings of the transistor at this point. The collector-to-base voltage is 18.2 v and the base-to-emitter is -8.2 v. For this transistor (2N702), the emitter-to-base breakdown voltage *does* exceed the manufacturer's minimum breakdown rating of -5 v. When the ratings have been exceeded, diodes must be placed in series with the base for protection. The modified circuit that accomplishes this result is shown in Fig. 16.46. Of course, the voltage ratings of the diode must be high enough to withstand the reverse voltages it will encounter.

The base of transistor T_2 (or the diode-base combination) will be at -8.2 v at $t_0(+)$, but will not remain at this value. From Fig. 16.45 we note that v_{BE} will charge toward $+10$ v with a time constant of $\tau = RC$. For this circuit, $\tau \approx 2.0 \times 10^4 \times 1 \times 10^{-7} = 2 \times 10^{-3}$ or 2 msec. Then, the equation for v_{BE} will be

$$v_{BE} = 10 - 18.2e^{-t_1/(2 \times 10^{-3})} \tag{16.25}$$

Since these transistors are silicon, collector current can be assumed to begin to flow when the base-emitter voltage has reached $+0.5$ v. (Germanium transistors can usually be assumed to begin conduction when the base-emitter voltage is zero.) Thus, collector current begins to flow in T_2 at the time t_1.

$$0.5 = 10 - 18.2e^{-t_1/(2 \times 10^{-3})} \tag{16.26}$$

or

$$\frac{9.5}{18.2} = e^{-t_1/(2 \times 10^{-3})} \tag{16.27}$$

and

$$\frac{18.2}{9.5} = 1.916 = e^{t_1/(2 \times 10^{-3})} \qquad (16.28)$$

Finally

$$\ln 1.916 = \frac{t_1}{2 \times 10^{-3}} = 0.65 \qquad (16.29)$$

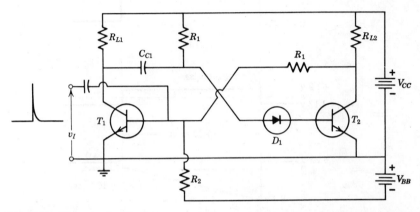

Fig. 16.46. The use of a diode to prevent the reverse breakdown voltage of transistor T_2.

This equation can be solved for t_1 to yield the value $t_1 = 1.30$ msec. At this time, transistor T_2 begins to conduct and the collector voltage of T_2 decreases. This decrease of voltage is coupled over to transistor T_1 and the switching action is initiated. From this description of the transistor behavior, the voltage waveforms on the two transistors will be as shown in Fig. 16.47.

The monostable multivibrator is able to generate one output pulse with a given duration for each trigger pulse which is applied. The duration of the output pulse can be adjusted by modifying the values of C_{c1} and R_b. For proper operation of the circuit, the trigger pulse duration should be short compared to the time constant τ ($\tau \approx C_{c1}R_b$).

PROB. 16.20. Two 2N702 transistors are connected as shown in Fig. 16.46. The parameters in the circuit are:

$$R_1 = 20K\Omega \qquad\qquad R_2 = 100K\Omega$$
$$R_{L1} = 2K\Omega \qquad\qquad R_{L2} = 1.67K\Omega$$
$$R_b = 30K\Omega \qquad\qquad C_{c1} = 1\ \mu\text{fd}$$
$$V_{BB} = -10\ \text{v} \qquad\qquad V_{CC} = +10\ \text{v}$$

Plot the four output waveforms v_{C1}, v_{B1}, v_{C2}, and v_{B2}.

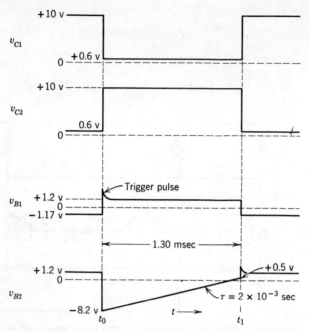

Fig. 16.47. The voltage waveforms for the circuit in Fig. 16.42.

16.6   THE ASTABLE MULTIVIBRATOR

When both base circuits are connected so that they can return to a value where conduction can occur, a *free-running* or *astable* multivibrator results. An example of an astable multivibrator circuit is shown in Fig. 16.48. In this circuit, spontaneous switching occurs in both transistors. Thus, the transistors are alternately switched OFF and ON. The collector

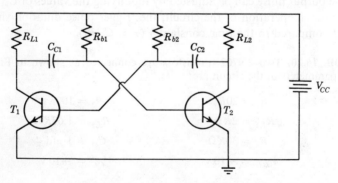

Fig. 16.48. An astable multivibrator.

voltage is a series of identical equally spaced pulses (or a square wave if the circuit is symmetrical). An example will be solved to illustrate the analysis procedure.

Example 16.7. Two 2N656 transistors are connected as shown in Fig. 16.48. $R_{L1} = R_{L2} = 300 \ \Omega$; $R_{b1} = R_{b2} = 6K\Omega$; $C_{c1} = C_{c2} = 0.01 \ \mu f$; $V_{CC} = 12$ v. Plot the voltage waveforms on the two collectors and also on the two bases in this circuit. For convenience, the characteristics of the 2N656 are repeated in Fig. 16.49. In addition, the manufacturer's data sheet states that typical parameters are:

$$h_{IE} = 300 \text{ ohms}$$

$$h_{FE} = 43$$

$$R_{cs} = 9 \text{ ohms saturation resistance}$$

$$t_f = 1 \ \mu\text{sec}$$

$$t_d + t_r = 0.8 \ \mu \text{ sec}$$

$$t_s = 0.5 \ \mu\text{sec}$$

In order to have a starting point, assume transistor T_1 is in full conduction and transistor T_2 has been cutoff but has just reached the condition where it is ready to begin conducting. (The validity of this assumption will be checked later.) Under these conditions, the load line for the transistors will be as shown in Fig. 16.49b. Since transistor T_1 will be operating somewhere along this load line, the operating point will be determined if the base current is known. Since h_{IE} is known, the base current of transistor T_1 can be found by using the equivalent base circuit. However, in order to illustrate a different approach, a graphical method will be used. The input characteristics of the 2N656 are given in Fig. 16.49a. The base current is determined by the input characteristics of the transistor, the $6K\Omega$ resistor R_{b1}, and the 12-v power supply. Thus, a $6K\Omega$ load line for the 12-v power supply is drawn on the input characteristics. (Note, that the voltage coordinate had to be extended to locate the $I_B = 0$ and $V_{BB} = 12$-v point. Also note that the base-current coordinate is printed along the right side of the input characteristics.) The intersection of the input characteristic curve and the $6K\Omega$ load line (Point A, Fig. 16.49a) indicates the base current will be about 1.7 ma and the base voltage will be about 1.12 v. With the base current known, the collector current and the collector voltage of transistor T_1 are found from the output characteristics (Point B, Fig. 16.49b) to be about 38 ma and 0.35 v, respectively.

Transistor T_2 is in the cutoff condition so the collector voltage will be 12 v and the collector current will be near zero. From the input characteristics in Fig. 16.49, the transistor will begin to conduct if the base voltage becomes greater than about 0.3 v. Thus, at the instant before switching occurs, transistor T_2 will have a base voltage of 0.3 v and a base current of 0 ma. The collector and base voltages of both transistors at the instant before switching is shown in Fig. 16.50 just before time $t = t_1$.

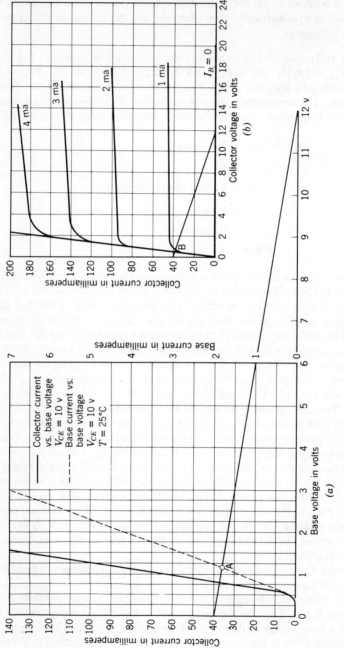

Fig. 16.49. Characteristic curves of the 2N656. (Courtesy of Texas Instruments.)

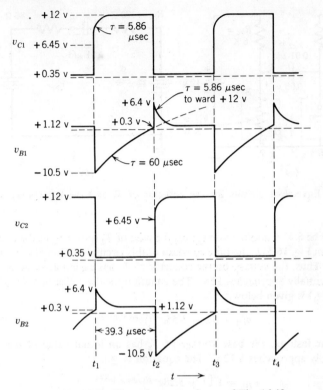

Fig. 16.50. The voltage waveforms of Fig. 16.48.

Switching occurs at time t_1 with transistor T_1 switching to the "off" condition and transistor T_2 switching to the "on" condition. With transistor T_1 in the "off" condition, the equivalent circuit for the collector of T_1 and the base of T_2 will be as shown in Fig. 16.51a. Since the voltage on the collector of T_1 was 0.35 v and the base voltage of T_2 was 0.3 v just previous to time t_1, the voltage across C_{C2} was 0.05 v. The voltage on the capacitor cannot change instantly. Thus, this same potential appears in Fig. 15.51a, which represents the circuit at time $t_1(+)$. This circuit can be simplified by finding the equivalent Thévenin's circuit for the components on the right of the points x-x. The equivalent Thévenin's impedance will be equal to the parallel combination of R_{b2} and h_{IE2}. For this example, the equivalent resistance is about 286 ohms. The open circuit d-c voltage has already been calculated for this circuit (the graphical solution for the voltage on the base of T_1) and found to be 1.12 v. Hence, the equivalent circuit of Fig. 16.51a can be represented by the simplified circuit of Fig. 16.51b.

A d-c analysis can be made of the circuit in Fig. 16.51b to determine the potentials and currents at time $t_1(+)$. Capacitor C_{C2} is replaced by a battery of 0.05 v for the d-c solution. The voltage on the collector of T_1 (point C_1 in the circuit)

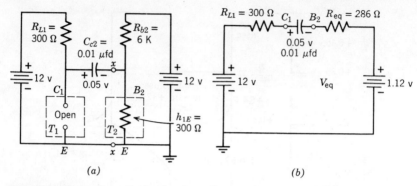

Fig. 16.51. Equivalent circuits for the collector of T_1 and the base of T_2 at time $t_1(+)$.

is found to be 6.45 v and the voltage on the base of T_2 (point B_2 in the circuit) is 6.4 v. From Fig. 16.51b, the time constant of this circuit is $RC = 586 \times 10^{-8} = 5.86 \ \mu\text{sec}$. Thus, the voltage on the collector of T_1 has an initial value of 6.45 v and exponentially approaches 12 v. The equation for the collector voltage of T_1 (after time t_1) is given below.

$$v_{C1} = 12 - 5.55e^{-t/(5.86 \times 10^{-6})} \tag{16.30}$$

In a similar fashion, the base voltage of T_2 has an initial value of 6.4 v and exponentially approaches 1.12 v. The equation is

$$v_{B1} = 1.12 + 5.28e^{-t/(5.86 \times 10^{-6})} \tag{16.31}$$

The voltages, according to Eqs. 16.30 and 16.31, are plotted in Fig. 16.50.

An equivalent circuit can also be drawn for the collector circuit of T_2 and the base circuit of T_1. This equivalent circuit is shown in Fig. 16.52a. At time $t_1(-)$,

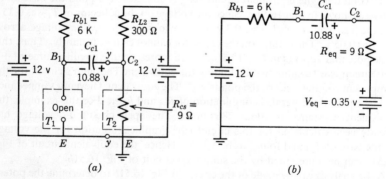

Fig. 16.52. The equivalent circuits for the collector of T_2 and the base of T_1 at time $t_1(+)$.

the voltage on the base of T_1 was 1.12 v and the voltage on the collector of T_2 was 12 v. Thus, at $t_1(+)$ the voltage across the capacitor will be 10.88 v (Fig. 16.52a). This equivalent circuit can be simplified by finding the Thévenin's equivalent circuit for the portion of the circuit to the right of the points y-y of Fig. 16.52a. The equivalent Thévenin's impedance is the parallel combination of the transistor saturation resistance R_{cs} and the load resistance R_{L2}. In this example, the equivalent impedance is approximately 9 ohms. We have already determined the magnitude of the open circuit voltage (from the graphical solution on the collector curves in Fig. 16.49) to be 0.35 v. Thus, the new simplified equivalent circuit will be as shown in Fig. 16.52b.

A d-c analysis of Fig. 16.52b (with C_{C1} treated as if it were a 10.88 v battery) leads to 0.28 v on the collector of T_2 (point C_2 in the circuit) and -10.50 v on the base of T_1 (point B_1 in the circuit). The time constant of this circuit is RC or $6 \times 10^3 \times 10^{-8} = 6 \times 10^{-5}$ sec $= 60$ μsec. The collector voltage of T_2 changes exponentially from 0.38 v to 0.35 v and therefore is essentially a constant value as shown in Fig. 16.50. In contrast, the base voltage of T_1 changes exponentially from -10.50 v toward $+12.0$ v. The equation which represents this voltage is given as follows.

$$v_{B1} = 12 - 22.5e^{-t/(6 \times 10^{-5})} \tag{16.32}$$

This voltage excursion is not completed since the circuit will switch as soon as the base of T_1 reaches the conducting condition. From Fig. 16.49a, conduction begins as soon as the base reaches 0.3 v. The length of time (after t_1) until v_{B1} is 0.3 v can be found by using Eq. 16.32. Thus,

$$0.3 = 12 - 22.50e^{-t/(6 \times 10^{-5})} \tag{16.33}$$

and

$$\frac{22.5}{11.7} = 1.922 = e^{-t/(6 \times 10^{-5})} \tag{16.34}$$

or

$$\ln 1.923 = 0.655 = t/(6 \times 10^{-5}) \tag{16.35}$$

and finally

$$t = 39.3 \ \mu\text{sec}$$

Therefore, transistor T_2 conducts for 39.3 μsec. (The period from t_1 to t_2.) At the end of this period, transistor T_2 has the same potentials as transistor T_1 had at time $t_1(-)$ and transistor T_1 has the same potentials as transistor T_2 had at time $t_1(-)$. Hence, the circuit switches and T_1 begins to conduct. Because of the symmetry of the circuit, the equivalent circuits in Fig. 16.51 and Fig. 16.52 are again applicable if the subscripts 1 and 2 are interchanged. Thus the response of this circuit is as shown in Fig. 16.50.

Before leaving this example, the breakdown voltages of the transistors should be considered. The breakdown potential between collector and base (BV_{CBO}) is 60 v and between collector and emitter (BV_{CEO}) is 60 v. The transistors are certainly safe as far as these two potentials are concerned. However, the breakdown potential between base and emitter (VB_{EBO}) is only 8 v and this value is exceeded in this circuit. Consequently, the circuit should be modified by placing diodes in the base circuits as shown in Fig. 16.53.

When the circuit of Fig. 16.53 was connected, the actual output waveforms were as shown in Fig. 16.54. The diodes have modified the amount of overshoot and the components used had ±10% tolerance. Even so, the expected wave-form (Fig. 16.50) and the actual waveforms agree very closely.

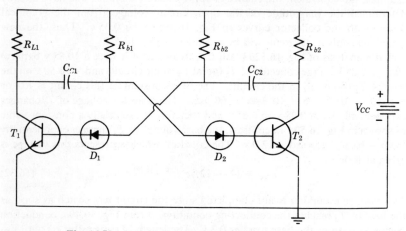

Fig. 16.53. A multivibrator circuit with protective diodes.

In this example, infinitely fast switching has been assumed. However, we noted at the beginning of this section that $t_f = 1$ μsec, $t_d + t_r = 0.8$ μsec, and $t_s = 0.5$ μsec. It may appear that a noticeable switching time is present. However, from Fig. 16.39b we find that the output impedance of the saturated transistor is only 9 ohms. This low output impedance in conjunction with the relatively large coupling capacitor produces almost instant charging (or discharging) of the internal capacitors in the transistor. Consequently, the actual switching time in this circuit would probably be a small fraction of a microsecond and could be assumed negligible for this example.

The foregoing example illustrates the typical waveform of a multivibrator. In this example, the length of the pulse is equal to the time between pulses and the circuit is referred to as a symmetrical multivibrator. Many applications require pulse widths that are greater or smaller than the time between pulses. Such waveforms can be obtained from the conventional multivibrator by making one $R_b C_c$ time constant different from the other $R_b C_c$ time constant. Such a circuit is known as a *nonsymmetrical circuit*. In the nonsymmetrical circuit, four equivalent circuits are required for the solution of the problem rather than the two circuits of the foregoing example.

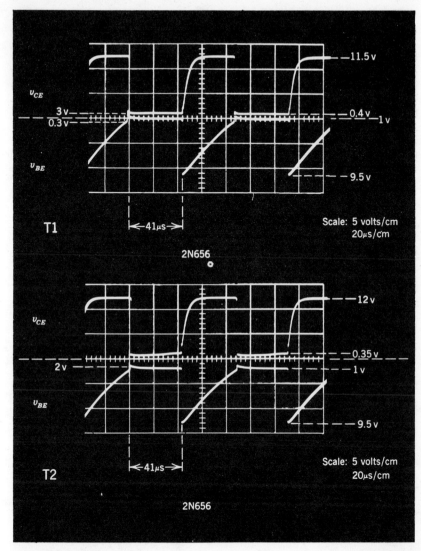

Fig. 16.54. Measured waveforms from the circuit of Fig. 16.53 when connected as noted in Example 16.7.

Vacuum tube multivibrator circuits can be analyzed in a similar manner. There is one point which must be remembered, however. The control grid of the vacuum tube version will be driven positive. Whenever this occurs, an equivalent resistance (usually $1 K\Omega$ or less) must be included to simulate the cathode-grid resistance. When this resistance is included, the behavior of the circuit can be accurately predicted.

The foregoing circuits are indicative of a large group of switching circuits. Many modifications and refinements are noted in the literature.[5]

PROB. 16.21. Repeat Example 16.7 if $R_{b1} = R_{b2} = 50K\Omega$.

PROB. 16.22. In Example 16.7, if V_{CC} is reduced, the protective diodes of Fig. 16.53 may not be required. How large can V_{CC} be without permitting the base voltage to exceed BV_{EBO}?

PROB. 16.23. Two 2N656 transistors are connected as shown in Fig. 16.53. $R_{L1} = R_{L2} = 200\ \Omega$, $R_{b1} = 5K\Omega$, $R_{b2} = 50K\Omega$, $C_{c1} = 0.01\ \mu$fd, $C_{c2} = 0.1\ \mu$fd, and $V_{CC} = 20$ v. Determine the voltage waveform on the two bases and the two collectors for this circuit.

[5] For example, see the following books:

1. *Selected Semiconductor Circuits Handbook*, edited by S. Schwartz, Wiley, New York, 1960.

2. *Motorola Transistor Handbook*, edited by W. D. Roehr, Motorola, Phoenix, Arizona, 1963.

3. *Pulse Circuits: Switching and Shaping*, by D. S. Babb, Prentice-Hall, Englewood Cliffs, N.J., 1964.

4. *Pulse Electronics* by R. Littauer, McGraw-Hill, New York, 1965.

5. *Pulse and Digital Circuits*, by J. Millman and H. Taub, McGraw-Hill, New York, 1965.

6. *Electronic Switching, Timing, and Pulse Circuits*, by J. M. Pettit, McGraw-Hill, New York, 1959.

17

Power Supplies

Essentially all of the electronic devices discussed in the preceding chapters of this book require a d-c power source for their operation. Up to this point, little attention has been given to the problem of obtaining this d-c power. In fact, the inference may have been made that one or more batteries will supply adequate power for any device. This is possible, but in most instances the battery is neither the most convenient nor the most economical means of obtaining d-c power. It is usually much more convenient and economical to obtain, by the use of rectifiers and appropriate filters, d-c power from the a-c power line. Some of the commonly used rectifying and filtering systems are discussed in this chapter.

The requirements of a power supply differ widely among the various electronic devices. The primary characteristics which need to be considered in the design of a power supply follow.

1. The d-c voltage or voltages required by the device, which is known as the load on the supply, is of primary importance.
2. The power supply must be able to furnish the maximum current requirement of the load.
3. The variation of the d-c output voltage with change in load current may be important. The voltage regulation of a power supply is defined as the change in output voltage, when the current is changed from no load to full load,

divided by the full load voltage. The voltage regulation is expressed as a per cent, as shown in the following equation:

$$\% \text{ regulation} = \frac{\text{no load voltage} - \text{full load voltage}}{\text{full load voltage}} \times 100 \qquad (17.1)$$

4. The rapid variations of the output voltage which result from imperfect filtering must be considered. These voltage variations have a fundamental frequency which is related to the a-c power line frequency and are called ripple voltage or simply *ripple*. The ripple is defined as the ratio of the rms value of the ripple voltage to full load d-c voltage. This ripple is usually expressed in per cent as indicated below:

$$\% \text{ ripple} = \frac{\text{rms ripple voltage}}{\text{full load d-c voltage}} \times 100 \qquad (17.2)$$

Power supply characteristics in addition to those listed are also considered in power supply design. These characteristics will be considered as the need arises.

17.1 CAPACITOR INPUT FILTERS

Some basic rectifier circuits were considered in Chapter 3. These circuits included both half-wave and full-wave rectifiers using either solid state or electron tube diodes. Also, the capacitor was considered as a filtering element in Chapter 3. Whenever the filter capacitor immediately follows the rectifier, the filter is known as a capacitor input filter. Three basic rectifier circuits are shown in Fig. 17.1. The half-wave circuit of Fig. 17.1a and the full-wave circuit of Fig. 17.1b were considered in Chapter 3. The circuit shown in Fig. 17.1c provides full-wave rectification without the use of a center tapped transformer. This circuit is known as a bridge rectifier circuit. The current path for this circuit is shown for the half cycle in which the upper end of the transformer is positive with respect to the lower end. Note that two of the diodes pass current during this half cycle. During the next half cycle, current is passed by the other two diodes. Observe that the current through the load is always in the same direction.

The output voltage waveforms of half-wave and full-wave rectifiers with capacitor filters are shown in Fig. 17.2. As discussed in Chapter 3, the capacitor charges to a maximum voltage $V_{\max}$, which is equal to the peak value of the supply voltage minus the voltage drop across the rectifier (or rectifiers). When junction diodes are used, the forward voltage drop is usually less than one volt and may be neglected in case the supply voltage is large in comparison with one volt. When gas tubes are used as rectifiers, their forward drop is essentially constant and known, so $V_{\max}$ may be obtained by subtracting the tube drop from the maximum supply

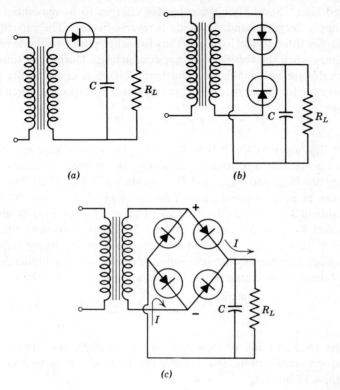

Fig. 17.1. Typical rectifier circuits incorporating a single capacitor filter. (*a*) Half-wave rectifier; (*b*) full-wave rectifier using a tapped transformer; (*c*) a bridge rectifier circuit.

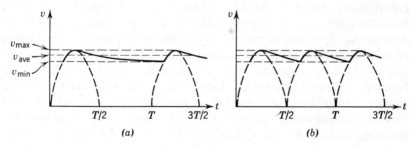

Fig. 17.2. Output voltage waveforms for (*a*) half-wave and (*b*) full-wave rectifiers with capacitor filters.

voltage. The vacuum diode presents a special problem and will be considered later. Soon after the capacitor charges to its maximum voltage the supply decreases and the diode is reverse-biased. The capacitor then discharges through the load and thus furnishes power to the load during the times when the rectifiers are not conducting. During the times when the diodes are not conducting, the load voltage is equal to the product of the capacitor discharge current and the load resistance R_L. Then the load voltage is

$$V_L = V_1 e^{-t/R_L C} \qquad (17.3)$$

where V_1 is given by Eq. 3.91 or Fig. 3.37. The load voltage may be found from Eq. 17.3 at any time t. However, the interesting values of load voltage are V_{max} and V_{min}, and V_{ave}, as shown in Fig. 17.2. The value of V_{min} can be easily determined with the aid of Fig. 3.37. After determining the value of V_{min}, the d-c load voltage V_{ave} can be obtained by averaging V_{max} and V_{min}, as discussed in Chapter 3. The peak-to-peak ripple voltage is $V_{max} - V_{min}$. Although the waveform of the ripple is far from sinusoidal, a sufficiently accurate value of ripple for most applications may be obtained by assuming the waveform to be sinusoidal. Then

$$\% \text{ ripple} \simeq \frac{0.707(V_{max} - V_{min})}{2V_{ave}} = \frac{0.707(V_{max} - V_{ave})}{V_{ave}} \qquad (17.4)$$

As the load current is increased (R_L decreased), the filter capacitor discharges more rapidly, thus causing the d-c load voltage to decrease and the ripple to increase.

The foregoing discussion, and Chapter 3 as well, assumes that the maximum supply voltage V_{max} is known. Then the d-c load voltage V_{ave} may be calculated for a specific value of load current and given filter capacitance. However, the desired load voltage at a specific current is usually known, and the required value of a-c input voltage needs to be determined. To eliminate the tedious calculations required for the solution of this problem, the rectifier manufacturers have produced charts and graphs which correlate the d-c load voltage and a-c input voltage as a function of filter capacitance. These charts naturally account for the rectifier voltage drop. A typical chart for a full-wave rectifier using the 5U4 vacuum duo-diode is given in Fig. 17.3. Observe that the permissible operating area for the tube is clearly marked. When the filter capacitance becomes large, the maximum permissible d-c load current must be reduced to limit the peak tube currents to an acceptable value. The peak diode current increases as the filter capacitance is increased because the conduction time (or angle) decreases as the discharge time constant is increased, assuming that the load current remains constant. The chart does not give ripple information, but after determining the required a-c input voltage the percentage ripple can be calculated by the methods of Chapter 3 and Eq. 17.4. The chart is developed for 60 Hz input power frequency.

In case the percentage ripple is unacceptably high, an additional filter section may be used as shown in Fig. 17.4. The d-c voltage and ripple

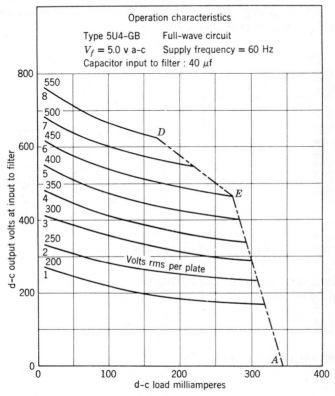

Fig. 17.3. Rectifier characteristics of the 5U4 duo-diode. (Courtesy of the Radio Corporation of America.)

voltage V_{r1} across the filter capacitor C_1 are essentially unaffected by the addition of the L-C filter, providing that the ohmic resistance of the inductor is small in comparison with the load resistance, as it should be. This observation follows from the fact that the discharge rate of the capacitor C_1 is determined essentially by the load resistance, since the current is continuous through the inductor, and in this case the inductance offers no opposition to direct current. Also, the capacitor charging circuit has been unaltered. Therefore, V_{r1} is essentially the ripple voltage of the single capacitor filter previously discussed. The ripple (a-c) component of current I_r which flows through the inductance L is

$$I_r = \frac{V_{r1}}{R_c + j\omega L + 1/(G_L + j\omega C_2)} \tag{17.5}$$

where R_c is the ohmic resistance of the choke and G_L is the conductance of the load. But R_c is negligible in comparison with ωL when a suitable inductor (known as a filter choke) is used. Also, the reactance of the choke

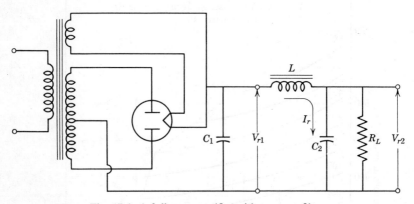

Fig. 17.4. A full-wave rectifier with a π-type filter.

must be large in comparison with the reactance of the filter capacitor C_2 if the L-C filter is to be effective in reducing the ripple. Then

$$I_r \simeq \frac{V_{r1}}{j\omega L} \tag{17.6}$$

The ripple voltage across the load is

$$V_{r2} = \frac{I_r}{G_L + j\omega C_2} \tag{17.7}$$

But if C_2 is to be effective as a filter capacitor, ωC_2 must be large in comparison with G_L. Then

$$V_{r2} \simeq \frac{I_r}{j\omega C_2} = \frac{V_{r1}}{(j\omega L)(j\omega C_2)} = \frac{V_{r1}}{-\omega^2 L C_2} \tag{17.8}$$

The negative sign in Eq. 17.8 indicates that the ripple voltage across the load has reversed polarity compared with the ripple voltage across C_1. Again the ripple voltage V_{r1} has been assumed sinusoidal in the equations above. Note that in the case of a full-wave rectifier the ripple frequency is twice the frequency of the input power source.

The d-c load voltage is reduced by the $I_{dc}R_c$ drop across the filter choke. Therefore, the rectifier input voltage must be increased to compensate for this voltage drop. The power supply regulation and efficiency are also deteriorated as a result of the d-c voltage drop across the choke. Consequently, the ohmic resistance of the choke should be small but must be weighed against the cost of the choke. Sometimes, when the initial cost of the power supply is the dominant factor, the filter choke is replaced by a resistor.

PROB. 17.1. A 5U4 tube is used in the circuit of Fig. 17.4, where $C_1 = 40\ \mu f$, $L = 10$ h and $C_2 = 40\ \mu f$. The resistance of the choke is 100 Ω. The desired load voltage is 300 v at the full load current of 200 ma. Determine the required rms input voltage for each half of the power transformer high voltage secondary. The frequency of the power source is 60 Hz. *Answer: 305 v.*

PROB. 17.2. Determine the regulation of the power supply of Prob. 17.1.

PROB. 17.3. Determine (approximately) the percentage ripple of the power supply of Prob. 17.1 at full load. *Answer: 0.16%.*

PROB. 17.4. What maximum value of rms volts could be used in the power supply of Prob. 17.1 without exceeding the peak current rating of the 5U4?

PROB. 17.5. What is the peak inverse voltage across the diodes of the power supply of Prob. 17.1? *Answer: 860 v at no load.*

PROB. 17.6. Could the chart of Fig. 17.3 be used when the input power frequency is 400 Hz? What changes would need to be made to use the chart at this frequency?

17.2 ACTIVE FILTERS

In transistor circuits, the voltages are low and the currents are frequently high compared with the vacuum tube counterparts. Thus the impedance levels of transistor circuits are frequently low and large values of capacitance, of the order of millifarads, are often needed for adequate filtering. For example, in the conventional R-C filter circuit of Fig. 17.5a, the resistance R may be only a few ohms if the current is of the order of an ampere and only a few volts drop can be tolerated across R. But if the filter is to be effective, the time constant RC_2 must be long in comparison with the period of the lowest frequency ripple component to be filtered. Therefore C_2 may be very large if this lowest ripple frequency is small.

The required filter capacitance can be greatly reduced if a transistor is included in the filter circuit as shown in Fig. 17.5b. In this circuit, which is known as an *active filter*, the load current flows in the emitter but only the forward-biasing base current flows through the filter resistor R'. If v_{EB} is assumed small in comparison with v_{CB}, as usual, then the voltage drop across R' may be approximately equal to the voltage drop across R in the conventional filter. But the current through R' is reduced by the factor $(h_{fe} + 1)$ compared with the current through R. Therefore $R' \simeq (h_{fe} + 1)R$ and if the time constants of the two filter circuits are the same, $C'_2 \simeq C_2/(h_{fe} + 1)$. The space requirement of the active filter is usually much less than the conventional filter and the cost may also be less. The active filter technique cannot be used to reduce the capacitance of C_1 in the circuit shown because C_1 must supply current to the load from its stored charge during the time the rectifier is not conducting.

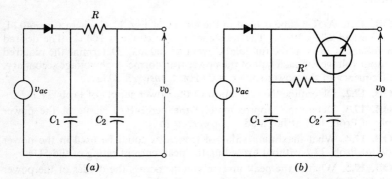

Fig. 17.5. An active filter (b) compared with a conventional filter (a).

PROB. 17.7. (a) In the circuit of Fig. 17.5a, the primary power source is 24 V, 60 Hz. The load draws 100 ma and the tolerable drop across R is 3 v. Determine values of R and C_2 which will reduce the fundamental component of ripple voltage by a factor of approximately 20.

(b) If a 2N2712 transistor is used in the filter circuit of 17.5b, determine the values of R' and C'_2 which will provide approximately the same voltage drop and filtering effectiveness specified in a. *Answer:* (a) $R = 30 \, \Omega$, $C_2 = 1770 \, \mu fd$, (b) $R' = 25h_{fe}$, $C'_2 = (2120/h_{fe}) \, \mu f$.

17.3   CHOKE INPUT FILTERS

It should be observed from the preceding discussion and problems that voltage regulation of a power supply is poor when a capacitor input filter is used. Poor voltage regulation is not necessarily bad. For example, when the load draws a relatively constant current, as in a class A amplifier, power supply regulation is unimportant. Then ripple, cost, and efficiency may be the only characteristics which need to be considered in the selection of a power supply. On the other hand, many devices such as class B or class C amplifiers require varying amounts of current, since the current depends on the input signal, amplifier tuning, load impedance, and so on. For these devices it may be highly desirable to have a power supply which maintains fairly constant output voltage under varying load conditions, or, in other words, has good regulation. Consequently, other filtering systems should be investigated in the hope of obtaining a power supply with better regulation.

The inductor will next be investigated as a filtering element. Since the filter should pass direct current with minimum attenuation but provide high attenuation for the ripple frequency components, a low-pass filter is needed. The half-wave rectifier with a low-pass L-R filter as shown in

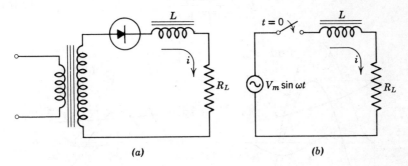

(a) (b)

Fig. 17.6. (a) A half-wave rectifier with L-R filter. (b) The equivalent circuit of a.

Fig. 17.6 will first be considered. The equivalent circuit of 17.6b will be used to find i. The switch is closed at $t = 0$. Then

$$L\frac{di}{dt} + R_L i = V_m \sin \omega t \qquad (17.9)$$

If R_L is written as R, the Laplace transform of Eq. 17.9 is

$$sLI + RI = \frac{V_m \omega}{s^2 + \omega^2} \qquad (17.10)$$

$$I = \frac{V_m \omega}{(sL + R)(s^2 + \omega^2)} = \frac{A}{sL + R} + \frac{Bs + C}{s^2 + \omega^2} \qquad (17.11)$$

where

$$A(s^2 + \omega^2) + (Bs + C)(sL + R) = \omega V_m \qquad (17.12)$$

Equating the coefficients of equal powers of s on each side of Eq. 17.12, we have

$$A + BL = 0$$

$$BR^2 + CL = 0 \qquad (17.13)$$

$$A\omega^2 + CR = \omega V_m$$

Solving Eqs. 17.13 simultaneously, we have

$$A = \frac{\omega L^2 V_m}{\omega^2 L^2 + R^2} \tag{17.14}$$

$$B = -\frac{\omega L V_m}{\omega^2 L^2 + R^2} \tag{17.15}$$

$$C = \frac{\omega R V_m}{\omega^2 L^2 + R^2} \tag{17.16}$$

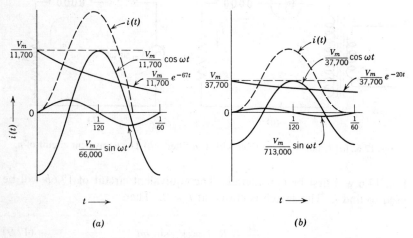

Fig. 17.7. A sketch of $i(t)$ and its components when $\omega = 377$ and (a) $L = 30$ h, $R = 2$ KΩ, (b) $L = 100$ h, $R = 2$ KΩ.

Substituting the values of A, B, and C above into Eq. 17.11, we have

$$I = \frac{\omega V_m}{\omega^2 L^2 + R^2} \left(\frac{L}{s + (R/L)} - \frac{Ls}{s^2 + \omega^2} + \frac{R}{s^2 + \omega^2} \right) \tag{17.17}$$

The inverse transform of Eq. 17.17 is

$$i = \frac{\omega V_m}{\omega^2 L^2 + R^2} \left[L(e^{-Rt/L} - \cos \omega t) + \frac{R}{\omega} \sin \omega t \right] \tag{17.18}$$

The time-varying current i and its components are sketched in Fig. 17.7 for two cases. In the first case, $L = 30$ h and $R_L = 2$ KΩ. In the second case, $L = 100$ h and $R_L = 2$ KΩ. In each case, $\omega = 377$. In the second case where $L = 100$, the scale is larger than in the first case where $L = 30$. Otherwise, the current components would be difficult to visualize.

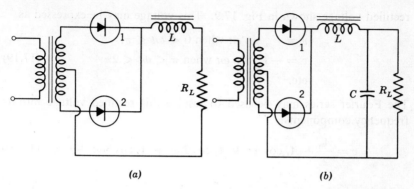

Fig. 17.8. Full-wave rectifier circuits with choke input filters. (*a*) Without filter capacitor; and (*b*) with filter capacitor.

Observe that in each case the current *i* flows for *more* than one-half of the input cycle. The current *i* cannot extend below the $i = 0$ axis because of the rectifier in the circuit. Therefore, the current completely stops each cycle and thus every cycle is just like the first cycle sketched in Fig. 17.7.

Since the series inductor in the half-wave rectifier circuit reduces the load current but does not succeed in smoothing it, the preceding analysis may appear to be a waste of time. However, the extension of the current flow for a time greater than that of one-half of the input cycle shows great promise for the inductor as a smoothing element in a full-wave rectifier circuit. For example, consider the circuits of Fig. 17.8. Because of the inductor, diode 1 is still conducting when diode 2 becomes forward-biased and vice-versa. The current then switches instantly from one diode to the other and continuous current may be maintained through the inductor and the load. Consequently, the circuit current can be found by steady-state techniques after the power switch has been closed for a few cycles. The equivalent circuits of Fig. 17.9 will be used to analyze the full-wave circuits of Fig. 17.8. The voltage applied to these circuits is the full-wave

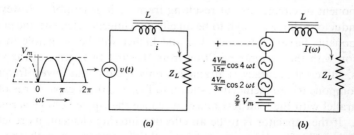

Fig. 17.9. Equivalent circuits of the power supplies of Fig. 17.8*a*.

rectified voltage shown in Fig. 17.9. This voltage may be expressed as

$$v = V_m \sin \omega t \text{ when } 0 < \omega t < \pi,$$
$$v = -V_m \sin \omega t \text{ when } \pi < \omega t < 2\pi \qquad (17.19)$$
$$\text{etc.}$$

The Fourier series may be used to resolve this rectified voltage into its frequency components.

$$v = \frac{A_0}{2} + A_1 \cos \omega t + A_2 \cos 2\omega t + A_3 \cos 3\omega t + \cdots \qquad (17.20)$$

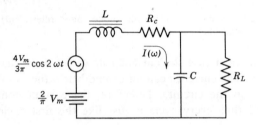

Fig. 17.10. An equivalent circuit for the full-wave rectifier with a choke input L-type filter.

Sine terms do not appear in the series since the function is even. Solving for the coefficients

$$A_n = \frac{V_m}{\pi}\left[\int_0^\pi \sin \omega t \cos n\omega t \, d(\omega t) - \int_\pi^{2\pi} \sin \omega t \cos n\omega t \, d\omega t\right] \qquad (17.21)$$

we have

$$v = V_m\left(\frac{2}{\pi} - \frac{4}{3\pi}\cos 2\omega t - \frac{4}{15\pi}\cos 4\omega t \cdots\right) \qquad (17.22)$$

The voltage source in Fig. 17.9a can be replaced by a series of generators, each one representing one of the Fourier series terms as shown in Fig. 17.9b. The superposition theorem can then be used to solve for each component of circuit current resulting from each generator. However, if the inductor is large enough to be an effective filtering element, the current components having frequency $4\omega t$ and higher will be negligible in comparison with the currents resulting from the first two terms of the series. Thus, sufficient accuracy is attained if only the d-c and lowest frequency a-c components are included as shown in Fig. 17.10. A capacitor is placed in parallel with the load resistance to reduce the ripple voltage across the load. If the capacitor is to be an effective filtering element, its reactance at the ripple frequency must be small in comparison with the load resistance. Then it may be seen from Fig. 17.10 that the direct current is

$$I_{dc} \simeq \frac{(2/\pi)V_m}{R_c + R_L} \tag{17.23}$$

where R_c is the ohmic resistance of the choke.

$$V_{O(dc)} = I_{dc}R_L = \frac{2}{\pi} V_m \frac{R_L}{R_c + R_L} \tag{17.24}$$

Observe from Eq. 17.24 that the d-c output voltage could be independent of the load resistance except for the ohmic resistance of the choke. However, V_m, the maximum voltage applied to the filter and load, is the maximum power source voltage minus the drop across the rectifier. In case the rectifiers are junction diodes with negligible voltage drop or gas diodes with essentially constant voltage drop, the choke input filter can provide excellent voltage regulation. This follows from the fact that the d-c load voltage is then essentially the average value of the input voltage.

The *rms* ripple current which results from the lowest frequency a-c voltage component may be determined from Fig. 17.10.

$$|I_r| \simeq \frac{4V_m}{3\pi(2)^{1/2}(2\omega)L} \tag{17.25}$$

Since the reactance of the filter capacitance is small in comparison with R_L, the ripple voltage across the parallel combination of C and R_L is approximately

$$|V_r| = \frac{4V_m}{3\pi(2)^{1/2}(2\omega)L} \frac{1}{(2\omega)C} = \frac{V_m}{3(2)^{1/2}\pi\omega^2 LC} \tag{17.26}$$

Neglecting the ohmic resistance of the choke, we have

$$\% \text{ ripple} = \frac{V_r}{V_{dc}} \times 100 = \frac{\dfrac{V_m}{3(2)^{1/2}\pi\omega^2 LC} \times 100}{\dfrac{2}{\pi} V_m} = \frac{100}{6(2)^{1/2}\omega^2 LC} \tag{17.27}$$

From Eq. 17.27 we see that the percentage ripple is inversely proportional to the product of L and C. In case the percentage ripple is not sufficiently small when practical values of L and C are used, an additional L-C filter section may be added, as was suggested for the capacitor input filter. Then, using Eq. 17.8 and Eq. 17.27, we see that

$$\% \text{ ripple} = \frac{100}{6(2)^{1/2}\omega^2 L_1 C_1} \frac{1}{(2\omega)^2 L_2 C_2} = \frac{100}{24(2)^{1/2}\omega^4 L_1 L_2 C_1 C_2} \tag{17.28}$$

where ω is the angular frequency of the input power.

PROB. 17.8. Two junction diodes are to be used in a full-wave choke input circuit. The load requires 200 v at 300 ma. The available choke has $L = 10$ h and $R_c = 33 \; \Omega$. What must be the approximate rms voltage of the power source for each half of the secondary?

PROB. 17.9. What will be the percentage ripple of the power supply of Prob. 17.8 if the filter capacitor is 40 μf? *Answer: 2.1%.*

PROB. 17.10. What would be the percentage ripple if an additional *L-C* filter with $L = 10$ h and $C = 40$ μf were added to the power supply of Prob. 17.9?

The preceding discussion of the full-wave rectifier with choke input filter was based on the assumption that the current through the choke is

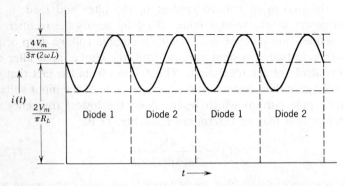

Fig. 17.11. The inductor current of a choke input filter.

continuous. If the current were to cease for a part of each cycle, the preceding analysis would not hold. The waveform of the current through the input choke is sketched in Fig. 17.11. The d-c and a-c components are indicated. Also, the current provided by each diode is shown. The ohmic resistance of the choke and the reactance of the filter capacitor have been neglected. From Fig. 17.11 we can see that the current through the choke is continuous as long as the d-c component is equal to or exceeds the maximum value of the a-c component. The limiting condition is then $I_{ac} = I_{dc}$. Therefore,

$$\frac{4V_m}{6\pi\omega L} = \frac{2V_m}{\pi R_{L(\text{max})}} \tag{17.29}$$

where $R_{L(\text{max})}$ is the maximum value of load resistance which can be used without causing the current through the choke to be discontinuous. Then

$$R_{L(\text{max})} = \frac{12\pi L\omega V_m}{4\pi V_m} = 3\omega L \tag{17.30}$$

When the primary power frequency is 60 Hz, $\omega = 377$ and

$$R_{L(\text{max})} = 1131L \tag{17.31}$$

Again, this is the maximum value of resistance the load can present if good voltage regulation is to be maintained, assuming the inductor L to be fixed. More frequently, the maximum value of load resistance is fixed. Then the required value of inductance required to provide good regulation may be found by rearranging Eqs. 17.30 or 17.31.

$$L_{min} = \frac{R_{L(max)}}{3\omega} \qquad (17.32)$$

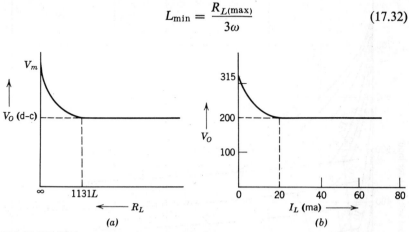

Fig. 17.12. (a) D-c output voltage as a function of R_L, neglecting R_c and rectifier drop; (b) d-c output voltage as a function of load current with $L = 10$ h, $R_c = 50 \, \Omega$, $V_m = 315$ v and negligible rectifier drop.

If L is less than this minimum value, the filter capacitor will charge through the choke during part of the input cycle and discharge through the load during the times the current through the input choke is zero. This situation is similar to that of the capacitor input filter. When the load resistance rises to infinity, the capacitor cannot discharge and therefore rises to the maximum value of the input voltage. Figure 17.12a is a sketch of the d-c output voltage as a function of R_L, neglecting the ohmic resistance of the choke and the drop across the rectifier. Figure 17.12b is a sketch of the d-c load voltage as a function of load current for a power supply which has $L = 10$ h, choke resistance $R_c = 50 \, \Omega$, peak input voltage $= 315$ v (for $\frac{1}{2}$ secondary), and negligible rectifier drop.

When vacuum diodes are used as rectifiers, the full-wave rectifier with choke input filter does not provide nearly as good regulation as when gas tubes or junction diodes are used. This follows because the vacuum diode has an appreciable voltage drop which is a function of the load current. Since the internal resistance of the vacuum diode is a function of the load current, the diode characteristics are needed for an accurate determination of regulation. However, the tube manufacturers provide charts which give the average voltage into the filter as a function of rms input volts, load current, and filter inductance. Such a chart is shown in Fig. 17.13.

The swinging choke is a choke especially designed for use as the input choke in a filter. This choke has practically no air gaps in its magnetic

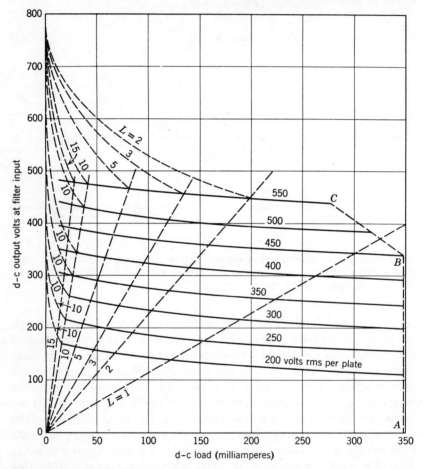

Fig. 17.13. Voltage regulation curves for the 5U4 rectifier with choke input filter. (Courtesy of Radio Corporation of America.)

circuit and therefore has high inductance when the load current is small. Therefore, good regulation is maintained to high values of load resistance without using excessive turns of wire which increase resistance and deteriorate regulation. As the load current increases, the inductance of the swinging choke decreases because the magnetic core of the choke approaches saturation. Consequently, the ripple increases somewhat with load, but good regulation is maintained over a wide range of load currents with a minimum cost choke.

There is one way good regulation can be assured from a choke input supply even when the minimum load current is not known. This is accomplished by connecting a bleeder resistor which has the value determined by Eq. 17.30 across the output of the power supply. A bleeder resistance also provides a discharge path for the filter capacitors. This feature increases the life expectancy of repairmen who assume the high voltage to be zero when the power switch is in the OFF position.

PROB. 17.11. A power supply with a single L section choke input filter is to provide 250 v direct current at 200 ma. A 12 h 225 ma (rated) choke having 40-Ω resistance is to be used. Calculate the value of bleeder resistance which will insure good voltage regulation ($f = 60$ Hz). *Answer: 13.6 KΩ.*

PROB. 17.12. Determine the percentage voltage regulation for the power supply of Prob. 17.11 if the rectifiers are junction diodes or gas diodes.

PROB. 17.13. Determine the percentage voltage regulation of the power supply of Prob. 17.11 if a 5U4 is used as the rectifier. *Answer: 20%.*

PROB. 17.14 What is the peak inverse voltage applied to the rectifiers of Prob. 17.11?

17.4 POLYPHASE RECTIFIERS

Many industrial concerns and transportation companies (electric railroads) require large amounts of d-c power. These users derive their d-c power from three-phase (in some cases six-phase or higher) a-c power lines. In addition, most large electronic installations such as radio and TV transmitters, large computers, etc. use three-phase power supplies. The advantages and characteristics of these polyphase power supplies will now be considered.

A circuit is connected as shown in Fig. 17.14. This circuit is known as a three-phase half-wave rectifier circuit. If R_L is pure resistance, the relationship between voltage and current for the three rectifier tubes is shown in Fig. 17.15. Each tube conducts for that portion of the cycle while its plate is more positive than the plate of either of the other two tubes. Consequently, each tube conducts for $120°$ of the input cycle. Since the voltage across the load is equal to $i_L R_L$, this load voltage has the same form as the current of Fig. 17.15.

A visual inspection of the three-phase half-wave output current indicates the ripple voltage is much lower than in the single phase full-wave rectifier circuit. In fact, when the waveform of Fig. 17.15 is analyzed the rms value of the fundamental ripple voltage is found to be 0.18 V_{ave}. As before, V_{ave} is the average d-c load voltage. If rectifier losses are ignored,

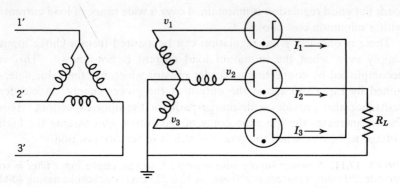

Fig. 17.14. A three-phase half-wave rectifier circuit.

V_{ave} is 0.828 V_{max} where V_{max} is the peak value of the voltage applied to the rectifier circuit. In addition, the frequency of the fundamental component of the ripple voltage is three times the input frequency. As a consequence, the size of the filter components for the three-phase circuit can be much smaller than the corresponding filter for a single-phase circuit. An additional advantage is noted when the efficiency of rectification is found. For the circuit of Fig. 17.14 this efficiency is found to be 96.5% if rectifier and transformer losses are neglected.

PROB. 7.15. Prove the ripple voltage of the three phase half-wave rectifier is as given previously.

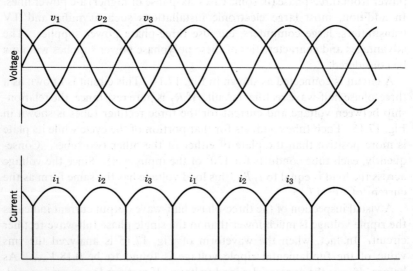

Fig. 17.15. The voltage and current relationship of the circuit shown in Fig. 17.14.

PROB. 7.16. What is the peak inverse voltage across one of the tubes in Fig. 17.14? (*Answer: 2.09 V_{ave}*)

The ripple can be further reduced by a three-phase full-wave rectifier circuit, connected as shown in Fig. 17.16. In this circuit, the voltages and currents are related as shown in Fig. 17.17. In this figure, the voltage listed as V_{21} is equal to $-V_{12}$, etc., where the double subscript indicates the voltage from the first subscript to the second subscript.

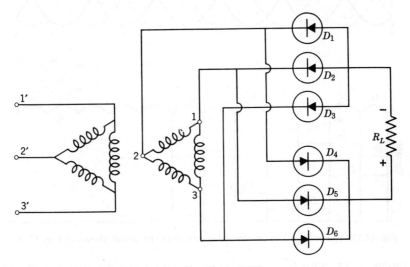

Fig. 17.16. A three-phase full-wave rectifier circuit.

The current i_1 occurs when V_{32} is maximum positive. This current flows through D_4, R_L, and D_3. Similarly, i_2 flows through D_4, R_L, and D_2 and i_3 flows through D_6, R_L, and D_2. The current i_4 flows through D_6, R_L, and D_1 and i_5 flows through D_5, R_L, and D_1. Finally, the current i_6 flows through D_5, R_L, and D_3. From this analysis, current flows through each diode for 120° per cycle of input voltage. However, the current flows through a given combination of diodes for only 60° of one input cycle.

Again, if the load is purely resistive, the load voltage has the same waveform as the load current. In this case, the rms value of the fundamental component of ripple voltage is only $0.042V_{ave}$. In addition, the fundamental component of ripple voltage has a frequency *six* times the frequency of the line voltage. Also, the average d-c output potential is $0.95V_{max}$. As a further advantage, the efficiency of rectification is 99.8% when rectifier and transformer losses are neglected.

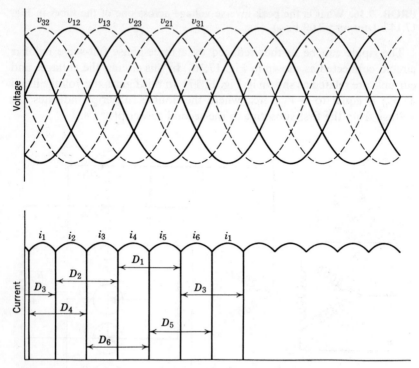

Fig. 17.17. The voltage and current relationship of the circuit shown in Fig. 17.16.

PROB. 17.17. What is the peak inverse voltage across the rectifier diodes in Fig. 17.16? *Answer: 1.05 V_{ave}.*

The foregoing circuits are indicative of the type encountered in polyphase rectifiers. Since many additional configurations can be used, the reader is referred to handbooks for additional circuits. In addition to the three-phase circuits considered, six-phase, twelve-phase, etc., circuits are used. From the foregoing analysis, several generalizations can be made for an *n*-phase system.

In half-wave circuits, one rectifier (or one plate) is required for each phase. Hence an *n*-phase system requires *n* rectifiers. Also, the lowest frequency component in the *n*-phase system is *n* times the frequency of the supply voltage. As *n* increases, the average rectified d-c voltage increases for a given applied a-c voltage. In addition, as *n* increases the percentage of ripple voltage decreases. A full-wave rectifier circuit in an *n*-phase system has the same characteristics as a half-wave rectifier in a 2*n*-phase system.

The values of d-c output voltage and amount of ripple can be readily

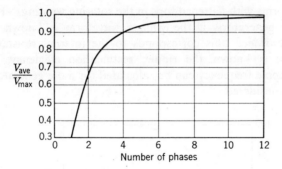

Fig. 17.18. A plot of d-c output voltage for polyphase rectifier circuits with resistive loads.

calculated for a given polyphase system. However, for ease of design, Fig. 17.18 gives the d-c output voltage for a given number of phases. Also, Fig. 17.19 indicates the variation of ripple for polyphase systems. In addition, Fig. 17.20 is a plot of rectification efficiency (if rectifier and transformer losses are ignored) vs the number of phases used.

To keep rectification losses to a minimum, semiconductor diodes are usually preferred. High vacuum diodes have high internal impedance and are seldom used if large d-c currents are required.

An interesting application of polyphase rectifiers is found in the standard d-c generator. The d-c generator can be considered as a polyphase generator with a polyphase full-wave mechanical rectifier. This mechanical rectifier is called a commutator. In effect, the commutator of a d-c generator connects the load to the generator winding while the peak voltage is present. As the next winding approaches its peak voltage, this winding is connected to the load. This action is seen to be identical with that of a rectifier. Therefore, a d-c generator with an n-section commutator can be considered as an $n/2$ phase full-wave rectifier. To reduce the output ripple, some generators have the magnetic fields designed to generate

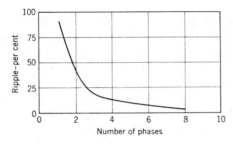

Fig. 17.19. A plot of ripple voltage for polyphase rectifier circuits with resistive loads.

voltage waveforms with flattened tops in the rotating windings. However, even in these generators, if the voltage waveform is known and the *commutator resistance* (this corresponds to the internal resistance of a diode rectifier) is known, the ripple, rectification efficiency, average, voltage, and ripple frequency can be calculated for a d-c generator by the methods just considered.

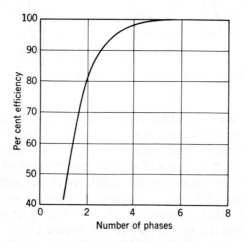

Fig. 17.20. A plot of rectification efficiency for polyphase rectifier circuits with resistive loads (ignoring losses of the rectifiers and transformers).

PROB. 17.18. A d-c generator has thirty-six windings on the rotor. Each winding generates a sinusoidal voltage with a peak value of 200 v as the rotor revolves at 600 rpm. A commutator of thirty-six sections is used to convert the output to a d-c voltage. An external load of 50 Ω resistance is connected to the generator. If the commutator resistance and resistance of the winding is ignored find: (*a*) average d-c voltage across the load; (*b*) rms value of the ripple voltage; (*c*) fundamental frequency of the ripple voltage; (*d*) rectification efficiency.

17.5 ADJUSTABLE OUTPUT VOLTAGE RECTIFIERS

In many instances a power supply which can deliver an adjustable output voltage is highly desirable. One of the simplest circuits of this type (although not inexpensive) is shown in Fig. 17.21. This circuit is a simple full-wave rectifier circuit with an adjustable voltage applied to the plates of the rectifier tubes.

The transformer T_1 supplies filament voltage to the rectifier tubes and must *not* be part of transformer T_2 in this circuit. The transformer T_2 is a center tapped plate transformer. The transformer T_3 is a power type of adjustable auto-transformer (Variac, Powerstat, Adjust-A-Volt, etc.).

The adjustment of T_3 adjusts the voltage to T_2 which furnishes voltage to the rectifier plates. The circuit from the rectifier to the output terminals is a conventional full-wave rectifier and π section capacitor input filter. The output voltage of this circuit can be adjusted from the full peak voltage rating of transformer T_2 (ignoring transformer and rectifier losses) to zero.

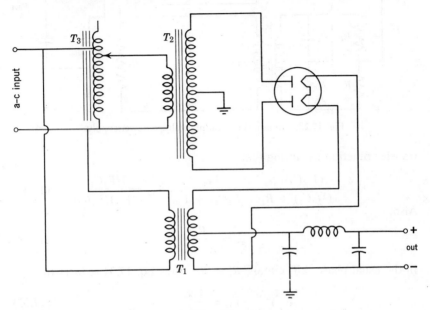

Fig. 17.21. A simple adjustable voltage power supply.

In addition, the efficiencies of the transformers are very high so the losses in the circuit are low. The primary disadvantage of this type of circuit is the bulk and cost of the components.

A more popular type of adjustable power supply is shown in Fig. 17.22. This is a power supply of a type very similar to the controlled rectifier circuit already described in Section 6.10 (Example 6.4). However, this circuit incorporates a full-wave rectifier, and the current can be adjusted over a much greater range. The silicon controlled rectifiers may be replaced by thyratron tubes if desired.

The circuit composed of R_1, C_1, R_2, and R_3 is a phase-shifting circuit. The adjustment of R_1 determines when the controlled rectifiers fire, which in turn determines the magnitude of output voltage. The operation of the phase shift circuit can be found from Fig. 17.23. In this circuit, the transfer function of V_{34}/V_{12} must be determined. We may find this

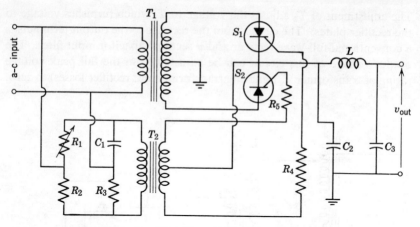

Fig. 17.22. An adjustable output voltage power supply.

transfer function by noting that

$$V_{32} = \frac{(1/sC_1)V_{12}}{(1/sC_1) + R_1} = \frac{V_{12}}{R_1C_1s + 1} = V_{12}\frac{1/R_1C_1}{s + (1/R_1C_1)} \qquad (17.33)$$

Also,

$$V_{42} = \frac{R_2 V_{12}}{R_2 + R_3} \qquad (17.34)$$

In the usual phase shift circuit, $R_2 = R_3$; thus Eq. 17.34 reduces to

$$V_{42} = \frac{V_{12}}{2} \qquad (17.35)$$

Since $V_{34} = V_{32} + V_{24}$ or $V_{34} = V_{32} - V_{42}$,

$$V_{34} = V_{12}\frac{1/R_1C_1}{s + (1/R_1C_1)} - \frac{V_{12}}{2} \qquad (17.36)$$

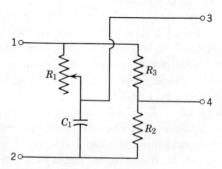

Fig. 17.23. A phase-shift circuit.

Then

$$V_{34} = V_{12} \left[\frac{1/R_1C_1}{s + (1/R_1C_1)} - \frac{1}{2} \right] \tag{17.37}$$

or

$$\frac{V_{34}}{V_{12}} = \frac{1/R_1C_1}{s + (1/R_1C_1)} - \frac{1}{2} \tag{17.38}$$

Since the phase shift circuit is intended to operate at a given frequency, Eq. 17.38 can be written as

$$\frac{V_{34}}{V_{12}} = \frac{1/R_1C_1}{j\omega + 1/R_1C_1} - \frac{1}{2} = \frac{1}{j\omega C_1 R_1 + 1} - \frac{1}{2} \tag{17.39}$$

Reducing to a common denominator, we have

$$\frac{V_{34}}{V_{12}} = \frac{2 - 1 - j\omega C_1 R_1}{2(1 + j\omega C_1 R_1)} \tag{17.40}$$

or

$$\frac{V_{34}}{V_{12}} = \frac{1}{2} \frac{1 - j\omega C_1 R_1}{1 + j\omega C_1 R_1} \tag{17.41}$$

Equation 17.41 can be rewritten as

$$\frac{V_{34}}{V_{12}} = \frac{1}{2} \frac{|\sqrt{1^2 + (\omega C_1 R_1)^2}| \underline{/-\psi}}{|\sqrt{1^2 + (\omega C_1 R_1)^2}| \underline{/+\psi}} = \frac{1}{2} \frac{1 \underline{/-\psi}}{1 \underline{/+\psi}} \tag{17.42}$$

where

$$\psi = \tan^{-1}(\omega C_1 R_1) \tag{17.43}$$

Equation 17.42 can be written as

$$\frac{V_{34}}{V_{12}} = \frac{1}{2} 1^{\underline{/-2\psi}} \tag{17.44}$$

Thus V_{34} is always equal to $(\frac{1}{2})V_{12}$ in magnitude, but V_{34} can lag V_{12} from $0°$ when R_1 is zero to $-180°$ when R_1 approaches an infinite value. (In some circuits, R_1 is fixed and C_1 is adjusted.) A plot of V_{34}/V_{12} (as R is adjusted) is shown in Fig. 17.24.

Of course, in actual circuits R_L cannot be adjusted all the way to ∞. However, if R_1 is much greater than $1/\omega C_1$, a shift of nearly $180°$ can be obtained.

If the gates of the controlled rectifiers in Fig. 17.22 are negative, the rectifiers will remain cut off even though the anodes are positive. Hence, if V_{34} lags V_{12} by a phase angle of $120°$, each controlled rectifier will only fire for $60°$ of the total cycle. This typical condition is shown in Fig. 17.25. The filter removes the ripple component to produce essentially a pure d-c

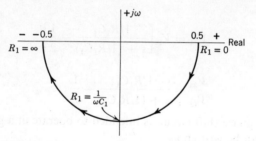

Fig. 17.24. A plot of V_{34}/V_{12} as R_1 is adjusted in Fig. 17.23.

voltage. Thus the circuit shown in Fig. 17.22 can be used to adjust the d-c output potential between zero and the peak value of anode potential. (If large currents are drawn, some voltage loss will be present in the transformer, rectifiers, and wiring. Hence the maximum voltage will be somewhat less than the peak a-c anode voltage.) The resistors R_4 and R_5 are used to limit the gate currents to a safe value.

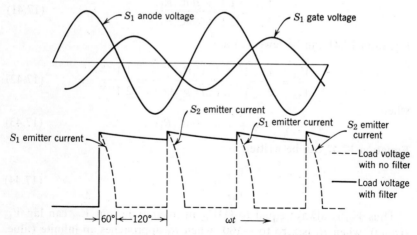

Fig. 17.25. Voltage relationships in the circuit of Fig. 17.22.

PROB. 17.19. Find the transfer function V_{34}/V_{12} of Fig. 17.23 if (a) $R_1 = 1/10 \ \omega C_1$ (b) $R_1 = 1/\omega C_1$ (c) $R_1 = 10/\omega C_1$. *Answer:* (a) $0.5 \underline{/-11.4°}$, (b) $0.5 \underline{/-90°}$, (c) $0.5 \underline{/-168.8}$.

PROB. 17.20. Two 3A200 controlled rectifiers are connected as shown in Fig. 17.22. (The characteristics of a 3A200 switch are given in Example 6.4.) The a-c input signal is 110 v rms 60 Hz. The number of turns on the primary winding of transformer T_1 is equal to the total number of turns on the center-tapped secondary winding. If R_2 is 10,000 Ω and C_1 is 0.25 μf, find the values of all other circuit components (except the d-c filter) including the turns ratio of transformer T_2 for proper operation.

17.6 REGULATED POWER SUPPLIES

In many electronic systems, the voltage regulation of the previously discussed power supplies is not adequate. Also, the fluctuations of the primary supply voltage may cause intolerable variations of the output voltage in some applications. Therefore, circuits have been developed which provide essentially constant output voltage, even though the output

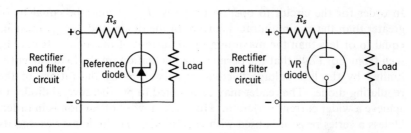

Fig. 17.26. Power supply regulating circuits which employ voltage-regulating diodes.

current and the input voltage vary widely. Power supplies which employ these voltage-regulating circuits are known as *regulated power supplies*.

The simplest means of regulating the output voltage of a power supply is by the use of reference (zener) diodes or voltage-regulating (gas) diodes. These devices were discussed in Chapter 3. The manner in which the reference or regulating diode is used to improve the voltage regulation of the power supply is illustrated in Fig. 17.26. In these circuits the internal resistance of the power supply and filter should be included in R_s.

The circuits of Fig. 17.26 have definite limitations. For example, if the power line potential fluctuates, the open circuit voltage out of the power supply filter may vary between V_{max} as a maximum value and V_{min} as a minimum value. In addition, the load current may vary between $I_{L(max)}$ as a maximum value and $I_{L(min)}$ as a minimum value. Now, if V_L is the voltage across the load, and the maximum supply voltage occurs at a time when the load current is minimum, then

$$V_{max} - V_L = (I_{L(min)} + I_{D(max)})R_s \qquad (17.45)$$

where $I_{D(max)}$ is the maximum current through the diode. On the other hand, if the maximum load current occurs at a time when the supply voltage is minimum,

$$V_{min} - V_L = (I_{L(max)} + I_{D(min)})R_s \qquad (17.46)$$

where $I_{D(\min)}$ is the minimum current through the diode. Subtracting Eq. 17.46 from Eq. 17.45, we have

$$V_{\max} - V_{\min} = (I_{D(\max)} - I_{D(\min)})R_s - (I_{L(\max)} - I_{L(\min)})R_s \quad (17.47)$$

Then

$$I_{L(\max)} - I_{L(\min)} = I_{D(\max)} - I_{D(\min)} - \frac{V_{\max} - V_{\min}}{R_s} \quad (17.48)$$

In order for the circuit to operate properly, $I_{D(\min)}$ must be equal to or greater than the minimum rated current of the diode, and $I_{D(\max)}$ must be equal to or less than the maximum rated current of the diode. It may be seen from Eq. 17.48 that the permissible fluctuation on the load current is limited by the line voltage fluctuation as well as by the ratings of the regulating diode. The reader may be tempted to parallel several diodes to achieve a wider current variation. However, a word of caution is in order. Unless a series resistor is used with each diode, one diode may exceed its maximum rating while the other diodes pass little or no current because the breakdown voltages of the diodes differ slightly. However, the use of a series resistor decreases the regulation of the device since the output voltage will then be dependent on the current through the diode-resistor combination.

PROB. 17.21. A reference diode (1N468) has an average voltage of 5 v and a maximum power dissipation rating of 500 mw. (Assume 1 ma is the minimum diode current.) The open circuit potential of the power supply is 10 v and R_s (Fig. 17.25a), is 100 Ω. Over what range of resistance can the load resistor vary and still maintain proper regulation? *Answer: From 102 Ω to ∞ Ω.*

PROB. 17.22. A power supply has 10 v output and an internal impedance of 10 Ω. A 1N468 reference diode (Prob. 17.21) is used to obtain a 5-v regulated output. The current through the load will vary between 100 and 150 ma. (*a*) Design a circuit to give the proper operation. (*b*) Over what range can the voltage of the 10-v supply vary without causing improper operation of your regulating circuit?

PROB. 17.23. An OA2 gas diode maintains 105 v across itself for diode currents of 5 to 30 ma. If a circuit is connected as shown in Fig. 17.26b, what value must R_s have if the regulator input voltage varies between 290 and 310 v with an average load current of 200 ma. Over what values can the load current vary and still maintain 105 v output? *Answer: $R_s = 900 Ω$, 2.8 ma variation.*

PROB. 17.24. Repeat Prob. 17.23 when the regulator input voltage varies between 280 and 320 v.

The permissible fluctuation of load current can be greatly increased if a transistor is included in the regulating circuit as shown in Fig. 17.27a. This regulator, which is sometimes known as an *emitter follower regulator*, is very similar to the active filter, the essential difference being that the filter capacitance has been replaced by the reference diode. The load voltage is the reference diode voltage minus v_{BE}. In this circuit, the maximum variation of the reference diode current is equal to the maximum variation of base current. Since the output current is the emitter current, the output current variation can be $(h_{fe} + 1)$ times the permissible reference diode variation, providing that the voltage from the rectifier

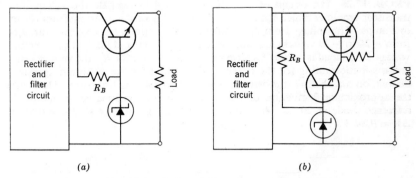

(a)   (b)

Fig. 17.27. Emitter follower type regulators.

and filter circuit remains constant. If this voltage is not constant, a derivation similar to that of Eq. 17.48 will show that the change in reference diode current is

$$I_{D\max} - I_{D\min} = \frac{I_{L\max} - I_{L\min}}{h_{fe} + 1} + \frac{V_{\max} - V_{\min}}{R_s} \qquad (17.49)$$

The output resistance of this regulator is approximately that of an emitter follower with the reference diode dynamic resistance r_d as its base circuit resistance. Thus, from Eq. 7.134

$$R_o \simeq \frac{h_{ie} + r_d}{h_{fe} + 1} \qquad (17.50)$$

Since r_d and R_B are essentially in series so far as a-c components are concerned, any fluctuations in output voltage from the rectifier and filter, including ripple, will be reduced by the ratio r_d/R_B approximately.

The ratio of load current variation to reference diode current variation can be further increased by the Darlington arrangement of Fig. 17.27b. This circuit is often useful when the load currents are in the range of amperes. In either of the emitter follower-type circuits, the minimum instantaneous voltage from the rectifier and filter circuit must be at least a volt or so greater than the output voltage to cause proper operation of the transistors. Also the power dissipation in each transistor, as well as in each diode, needs to be estimated so that adequate cooling can be provided. However, the emitter follower type regulator is much more efficient than the simple reference diode regulator because the regulating transistor may have a small voltage drop across it though it has a large current through it, whereas the reference diode may have a large voltage across it but a small current through it.

PROB. 17.25. The circuit of Fig. 17.27a is used to regulate the voltage to a transistor amplifier which requires -20 v V_{CC} at a variable current from 100 ma to 2 amps. The voltage from the rectifier and filter circuit has a voltage variation from -24 to -29 v, including fluctuations due to line and load. The maximum voltage at full load is -26 v. Determine a suitable value for R_B, the voltage rating and dissipation rating for the reference diode, and for the maximum transistor dissipation if a 2N2147 transistor is used as the regulating transistor. Determine the approximate fluctuation of load voltage if the dynamic resistance of the reference diode is 20 Ω.   *Answer: $R_B = 270\ \Omega$, $V_D = 20.4\ V$, $P_D = 0.66\ W$, $\Delta V = 0.84\ V$.*

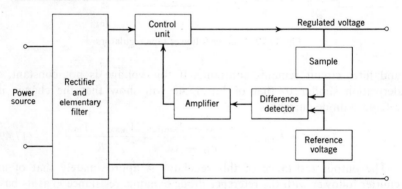

Fig. 17.28. A block diagram of a regulated power supply.

More elaborate regulators may provide better voltage regulation, lower output impedance, and less ripple than the regulators previously considered. These voltage regulators are a type of automatic control system and can be analyzed from the control system approach. In block form, a voltage control system can be represented as shown in Fig. 17.28. In this system, a constant reference potential is maintained. In addition, a sample of the voltage to be regulated is required. The sample of regulated voltage is compared to the reference potential. Any difference in the sample and the reference potential is detected by a difference detector. This difference voltage or *error signal* is then amplified and used to activate a control unit which changes the regulated voltage in a direction which will reduce the error signal. Hence, the system attempts to correct any variations in the regulated voltage. Although the foregoing analysis has been concerned with voltage regulation, this basic concept can be used to control temperature, position, velocity, and so on.

A basic vacuum tube voltage regulator is shown in Fig. 17.29. In this simplified circuit, the voltage regulating diode V_3 maintains a constant voltage which is used as the reference voltage. The resistors R_1, R_2, and R_3 are connected as a voltage divider. Any fluctuations in the regulated output voltage appear (reduced in magnitude because of the voltage

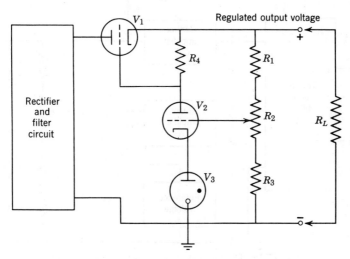

Fig. 17.29. A vacuum tube voltage regulator circuit.

divider action) on the control grid of V_2. Therefore, the resistors R_1, R_2, and R_3 (Fig. 17.29) form the sampling circuit of Fig. 17.28. Since any voltage difference between the grid and cathode of V_2 is amplified in the plate circuit, V_2 acts as the difference detector and also as the amplifier. The tube V_1 of Fig. 17.29 acts as the control unit of Fig. 17.28.

We can illustrate the manner in which the circuit of Fig. 17.29 regulates the output voltage by assuming that the output voltage suddenly decreases because of either an increased load current or a decreased supply voltage. This decreased output voltage causes a decrease of potential on the grid of V_2. Since the grid of V_2 becomes more negative with respect to the cathode, which is held at constant potential, the plate current through V_2 and hence the voltage drop across R_4 decreases. Therefore, the potential on the grid of the control tube V_1 becomes more positive and consequently the plate-to-cathode voltage of the regulator tube V_1 decreases, thus compensating for the assumed reduction in output voltage.

The improvement in voltage regulation which results from the regulator circuit may be determined with the aid of the block diagram of Fig. 17.30. First, it will be assumed that the regulator input voltage V_I changes by an amount ΔV_I for some reason. This change of input voltage causes an output voltage change ΔV_O. Since a fraction K of the output voltage V_O is applied to the input of the error amplifier, the change in error voltage is $K \Delta V_O$. Because the voltage between the plate and cathode (or collector

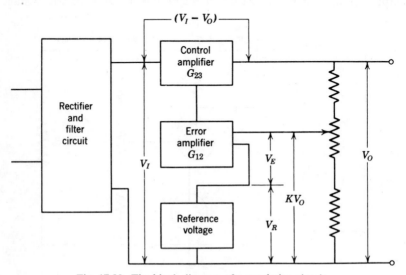

Fig. 17.30. The block diagram of a regulating circuit.

and emitter) of the control amplifier is $V_I - V_O$, and also because the control amplifier and error amplifier are in cascade, the following relationship holds.

$$\Delta(V_I - V_O) = K \Delta V_O G_{12} G_{23} \tag{17.51}$$

where G_{12} is the voltage transfer function or gain of the error amplifier and G_{23} is the voltage transfer function of the control amplifier. Re-arranging Eq. 17.51, we have

$$\Delta V_I = \Delta V_O(1 + KG_{12}G_{23}) \tag{17.52}$$

$$\Delta V_O = \frac{\Delta V_I}{1 + KG_{12}G_{23}} \tag{17.53}$$

It may be seen from Eq. 17.53 that insofar as variations of the input voltage V_I are concerned, the regulator improves the output stability by a factor equal to the total loop gain $KG_{12}G_{23}$ of the control system.

An appropriate way to specify the regulation of a power supply is by specifying its dynamic output impedance $Z_o = \Delta V_O/\Delta I_L$. In this case, the change of output voltage ΔV_O is assumed to be caused by the change of load current ΔI_L rather than by a change of primary power voltage. However, the change of load current ΔI_L will cause a change of input voltage ΔV_I. Then, dividing both sides of Eq. 17.53 by ΔI_L, we have

$$\frac{\Delta V_O}{\Delta I_L} = \frac{\Delta V_I / \Delta I_L}{1 + K G_{12} G_{23}} \tag{17.54}$$

$$Z_o = \frac{Z_o'}{1 + K G_{12} G_{23}} \tag{17.55}$$

where Z_o is the output impedance of the regulator and $Z'_o = \Delta V_I / \Delta I_L$ is the output impedance of the rectifier and filter without the regulator. Again, note that the regulator reduces the output impedance and hence the voltage regulation by a factor equal to the total loop gain of the control system.

PROB. 17.26. A regulating circuit similar to Fig. 17.30 has $K = 0.5$, $G_{12} = -200$, and $G_{23} = -10$. What will be the voltage change of the regulated output when the voltage applied to the input of the regulator is changed by 10 v?

PROB. 17.27. The output voltage of a specific power supply decreases 20 v when the load current is increased from 20 to 100 ma. What is the dynamic output impedance of this power supply? The regulator circuit of Prob. 17.26 is added to this power supply. What is the dynamic output impedance after regulation? *Answer:* $R'_s = 250 \ \Omega$, $R_s = 0.25 \ \Omega$.

From the preceding development and problems it is evident that high loop gain is desirable in the regulator circuit. Consequently, the error amplifier must be a high-gain amplifier in order to realize good regulation. Also, high-voltage gain would be desirable in the control amplifier. However, the control amplifier must be capable of carrying the maximum load current. Therefore, the current and power dissipation ratings of the control amplifier may take precedence over the voltage amplifying capabilities of this amplifier. It should be mentioned in passing that the voltage amplification of the control amplifier is a function of the load resistance which is connected to the output of the regulator. Consequently, the ripple and voltage regulation are functions of the load current.

The circuit diagram of a typical vacuum tube regulator is shown in Fig. 17.31. This circuit incorporates several improvements over the basic circuit of Fig. 17.29. For example, the pentode error amplifier V_1 may have much higher gain than the triode amplifier in the basic circuit. A negative potential is supplied by the solid state rectifier and the filter $R_4 C_3$. This potential, which is regulated by the two voltage regulating diodes, is used for two purposes. First, it provides an adjustable bias source through the potentiometer R_{p2}. Second, the positive V_{PP} (or $B+$) output voltage may be adjusted downward to 0 volts because the potential of the cathode of the difference amplifier V_1 is negative with respect to the common terminal.

Consequently, as the slider on the potentiometer R_{p1} is moved upward toward the V_{PP} output terminal, the V_{PP} output voltage is reduced toward this negative VR_1 cathode potential. The resistance of R_1 should be such that the V_{PP} voltage just reduces to zero as the potentiometer slider reaches the end of its travel. The resistor R_1 may also be a potentiometer. As the slider of potentiometer R_{p1} is moved toward resistor R_2, the V_{PP} output voltage increases toward its maximum value. The maximum

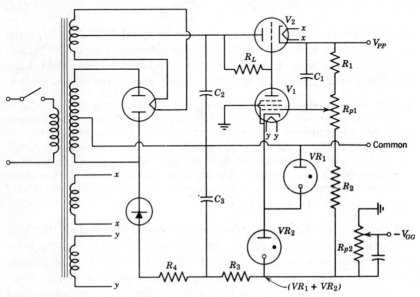

Fig. 17.31. A typical regulated power supply.

attainable regulated voltage is the voltage across the filter capacitor C_2 minus the plate-cathode drop across the control tube. This voltage drop across the control tube may be determined from its plate characteristic curves as shown in Fig. 17.32. Of course, the control tube voltage drop and the voltage across the filter capacitor C_2 must both be determined at the maximum (full load) current. The resistance of R_2 should be adjusted so that the V_{PP} output voltage cannot rise above the maximum attainable full load voltage, even though the adjustment is made at no load. Otherwise, the regulator will fail to regulate properly at the maximum voltage setting. Again, the resistor R_2 may be a potentiometer. The capacitor C_1 bypasses the resistance between the V_{PP} output terminal and the control grid of the difference amplifier. Thus the rapid fluctuations of the output voltage are applied to this control grid with little attenuation. Consequently the a-c loop gain of the control system is increased and the ripple and dynamic output impedance decreased as a result. The difference amplifier and control amplifier tubes must be heated by separate transformer windings as indicated, because the heater-cathode voltage ratings of the tubes would be exceeded if a single filament winding were used.

The control tube V_2 may actually be several tubes connected in parallel to provide the required current and power dissipation characteristics. Theoretically, it would be advantageous to use beam power tubes in the

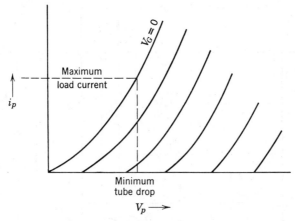

Fig. 17.32. A method of obtaining the minimum tube drop at maximum load current.

control amplifier because of the high power gain of these tubes. However, a suitable screen grid voltage source may be difficult to obtain. Of course, beam power tubes may be triode connected for this application.

Voltage regulators may employ transistor amplifiers. Usually the transistor-regulated supplies have lower voltage and higher current ratings than their vacuum tube counterparts. The transistor circuits could be very much like the vacuum tube circuits previously considered. However, many different types could be and have been devised.[1] Therefore, two transistor types which do not closely resemble the tube types previously considered will be examined. A regulated transistor power supply, whose output voltage is adjustable over a narrow range, is illustrated in Fig 17.33. In this circuit, the potential at the slider on the potentiometer R_p must be very nearly equal to the potential of the base of transistor T_2, which is controlled by the reference (zener) diode D_2. Resistor R_5 permits several milliamperes of current to flow through this reference diode, so the

[1] For some variations of the circuit of Fig 17.33 see "Design of Transistor Regulated Power Supplies," by R. D. Middlebrook, *Proc. IRE*, Vol. 45, No. 11, pp. 1502–1509, November 1957. Also see "Designing Transistorized Voltage Regulators," by Earl Wilson, *Electronics*, Vol. 33, No. 39, pp. 62–65, September 23, 1960.

base current variations of transistor T_2 are negligible by comparison. The collector supply voltage of transistor T_1 is more negative than the emitter of the control transistor T_5 by the amount of the voltage across the reference diode D_1. This additional negative voltage is necessary to forward-bias the transistors T_3, T_4, and T_5.

The basic operation of the circuit of Fig. 17.33 may be illustrated by assuming that the output voltage increases for some reason, thus causing

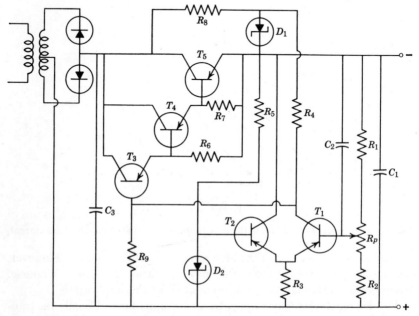

Fig. 17.33. A transistor-regulated power supply.

the potential at the slider of potentiometer R_p to become more negative with respect to the positive terminal. This increased forward-bias increases the collector current of transistor T_1, thus causing the collector of T_1 to become more positive. As the collector of T_1 becomes more positive, the forward-bias of transistors T_3, T_4, and T_5 is decreased, thus causing a greater voltage drop across the control transistor T_5. This increased voltage drop compensates for the assumed increase of the output voltage. The transistors T_3, T_4, and T_5 are in the Darlington connection, so the input impedance of transistor T_3 is very high and, therefore, the voltage gain of transistor T_1 may be very high. The resistors R_6 and R_7 improve the temperature stability of the Darlington connection as previously discussed in Chapter 9. Since audio transistors are commonly used in the regulator circuit, the voltage gain decreases and hence the output impedance increases with frequency when the frequency is above a few kilocycles per second. Therefore, the capacitor C_1 is connected across the output to maintain low output impedance at high frequencies.

The transistor regulator circuit shown in Fig. 17.34 has two features which are not incorporated in the circuit of Fig. 17.33. First, the output voltage may be adjusted from zero to the maximum capability of the supply. Second, automatic current limiting is provided for the protection of the power supply. This current-limiting feature is very important because transistors usually burn out more quickly than fuses when overloads occur. Therefore, although fuses will usually protect vacuum tube circuits, fuses do not provide adequate protection for transistors.

In the circuit of Fig. 17.34, the reference diode D_1 maintains a constant voltage between the base of transistor T_1 and the common terminal. Since the emitter-base voltages of transistors T_1 and T_2 are comparatively small, the voltage across resistor R_2 is essentially equal to the voltage across the reference diode D_1. Hence, the current through resistor R_2 must be essentially constant. Since this current through R_2 may be large in comparison with the base current of transistor T_2, the current through potentiometer R_p is essentially equal to the current through resistor R_2 and, therefore, this current is essentially constant. Thus the voltage across the potentiometer R_p is proportional to the resistance of R_p. Observe that this voltage is the regulated output voltage, neglecting the emitter-base voltage of transistor T_2.

To understand the operation of the regulating circuit of Fig. 17.34, it will be assumed that the current through potentiometer R_p is decreased, either because of a decrease in output voltage or an increase in the resistance of R_p. Then, since the current through resistor R_2 must be constant, additional current must flow into the base of transistor T_2. This additional base current will cause additional collector current flow in transistor T_2 and thus will cause the base potential of transistor T_3 to become more positive. This reduced forward bias of transistor T_3 will decrease the collector current of transistor T_3 and thus increase the base current in transistor T_4. Since transistors T_4 and T_5 are in the Darlington connection, an increase of base current in transistor T_4 will tend to increase the current through, and decrease the voltage across, the control transistor T_5. This decreased voltage across transistor T_5 tends to compensate for the assumed decreased output voltage which was initially assumed. Since there are five transistors in the amplifier, the voltage gain and current gain of this amplifier may be very high, thus producing very good voltage regulation and low output impedance.

In the foregoing discussion, we saw that the potential of the base of transistor T_3 must become more positive to increase the current through

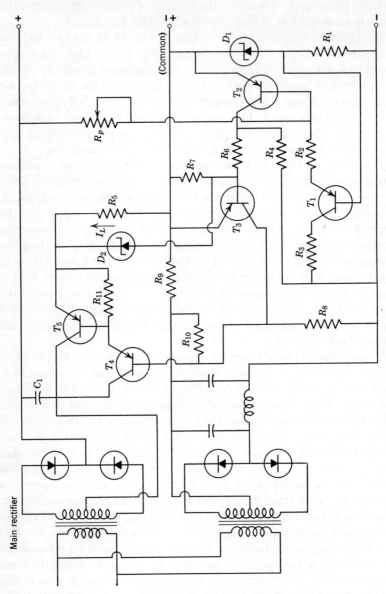

Fig. 17.34. A transistor-regulated supply with current limiting.

the control transistor T_5. But the diode D_2 will not permit the base potential of transistor T_3 to become appreciably positive with respect to the emitter potential of the control transistor T_5, since diode D_1 would then be forward-biased. Now the resistor R_5 is placed in series with the emitter of transistor T_5 so the load current must flow through resistor R_5. As the load current increases, the emitter potential of control transistor T_5 becomes more negative until the diode D_2 is forward-biased and, therefore, conducts current. At this point, the potential of the base of transistor T_3 cannot increase in the positive direction and the current through the control transistor cannot increase. Thus the load current is limited by the voltage drop across resistor R_5. Therefore, the maximum value of load current is determined by the resistance of R_5. When R_5 is either a potentiometer or a switch-resistor combination which increases resistance in discrete steps, the current limit may be set to a value which will protect the load as well as the regulator. The diode D_2 should be a silicon diode so it is essentially nonconducting until its forward bias approaches $\frac{1}{2}$v or more. Since the voltage drop across resistor R_5 must be equal to the sum of this minimum forward-bias voltage of diode D_2 plus the emitter-base voltage of transistor T_3 before current limiting will occur, the voltage across R_5 will normally be of the order of 0.7 v when current limiting occurs. These assumed voltages are based on an ambient temperature of the order of 25°C.

The maximum current and voltage capabilities of the regulated supply of Fig. 17.34 depend, of course, on the current, voltage, and power dissipation ratings of the main rectifier and filter as well as on the ratings of the control transistor T_5. Also, an adequate heat sink must be supplied for this control transistor. Several refinements may be made on the circuit of Fig. 17.34. For example, the output impedance may be reduced if a capacitor is placed in parallel with the potentiometer R_p. Also, a large capacitance should be placed across the output to insure low output impedance at high frequencies.[2]

PROB. 17.28. The regulated power supply of Fig. 17.34 is capable of delivering 30 v at 2 amp. If potentiometer R_p is 5000 Ω and the reference diode D_1 is 7.0 v, what should be the value of resistor R_2? Should R_2 be adjustable? Could the positive output terminal become negative with respect to the common terminal?

PROB. 17.29. Referring to Fig. 17.34, the voltage across the filter capacitor C_1 is 35 v when 2 amp are being drawn by the load. What must be the power dissipation capability of the control transistor T_5 if the power supply is to be capable of delivering 2 amp at any voltage between 0 and 30 v?

[2] The circuit of Fig. 17.34 is a modification and simplification of a circuit used by the Hewlett Packard Co. of Palo Alto, California, in their regulated transistor power supply Model 721A. The instruction manual for this power supply has additional refinements not included in the circuit of Fig. 17.34.

Appendix
I

Consider the configuration shown in Fig. I.1. A small element of volume has dimension of Δx, Δy, and Δz. An electric field, denoted by $\mathscr{E}$, passes through this cube. The electric field vector can be resolved into three components $\mathscr{E}_x$, $\mathscr{E}_y$, $\mathscr{E}_z$. When this has been done, the flux into the back face of the cube is equal to the component of flux density normal to that face times the area of the face.

$$\text{Flux into back face} = \epsilon \mathscr{E}_x \, \Delta y \, \Delta z \tag{I.1}$$

where ϵ is the dielectric constant of the medium. The dielectric constant is equal to the product of the relative dielectric constant[1] ϵ_r and the dielectric constant of free space ϵ_v

$$\epsilon = \epsilon_r \epsilon_v \tag{I.2}$$

where ϵ_r is determined by the ratio of electric flux lines in the given medium to the number of flux lines in free space for the same electric field intensity. The dielectric constant of free space ϵ_v is 8.85×10^{-12} f/m.

The flux out of the front face of the cube of Fig. I.1 is equal to the sum of the flux into the back face plus the change of flux in the cube. The change of the x component of flux in the cube is equal to the rate of change of

---

[1] The factor ϵ_r can be determined for a material by the ratio of the capacity of a capacitor using the material as a dielectric to the capacity of a capacitor with identical measurements but with free space (vacuum) as a dielectric. Measurements of ϵ_r for many different materials have been made and are given in most electrical engineering handbooks.

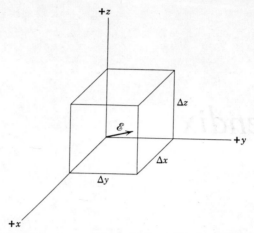

Fig. I.1. Configuration used in derivation of Laplace's Equation.

this flux with distance times the distance Δx. Therefore,

$$\text{Flux out of front face} = \epsilon \left(\mathcal{E}_x + \frac{\partial \mathcal{E}_x}{\partial x} \Delta x \right) \Delta y \, \Delta z \qquad \text{(I.3)}$$

The net flux flowing out of the cube is equal to the flux flowing out minus the flux flowing in. The net x component of flux is found by subtracting Eq. I.1 from Eq. I.3.

$$\text{Net flux out of the back and the front of the cube} = \epsilon \frac{\partial \mathcal{E}_x}{\partial x} \Delta x \, \Delta y \, \Delta z$$

$$\text{(I.4)}$$

A similar treatment of the two sides of the cube reveals the

$$\text{Net flux out of the side faces of the cube} = \epsilon \frac{\partial \mathcal{E}_y}{\partial y} \Delta x \, \Delta y \, \Delta z \qquad \text{(I.5)}$$

Similarly, the

$$\text{Net flux from the top and the bottom of the cube} = \epsilon \frac{\partial \mathcal{E}_z}{\partial z} \Delta x \, \Delta y \, \Delta z$$

$$\text{(I.6)}$$

When Eq. I.4, I.5, and I.6 are added together, the net flux flowing out of the cube is obtained. Using Coulombs law, we see that this total outward flux is equal to the total charge contained in the cube. Therefore,

$$\epsilon \left(\frac{\partial \mathcal{E}_x}{\partial x} + \frac{\partial \mathcal{E}_y}{\partial y} + \frac{\partial \mathcal{E}_z}{\partial z} \right) \Delta x \, \Delta y \, \Delta z = \rho \, \Delta x \, \Delta y \, \Delta z \qquad \text{(I.7)}$$

where ρ is the volume charge density which is assumed to be constant throughout the small volume. This equation can be reduced to the simpler form

$$\frac{\partial \mathscr{E}_x}{\partial x} + \frac{\partial \mathscr{E}_y}{\partial y} + \frac{\partial \mathscr{E}_z}{\partial z} = \frac{\rho}{\epsilon} \qquad (I.8)$$

Now, since

$$\mathscr{E}_x = -\frac{\partial V_x}{\partial x}, \mathscr{E}_y = -\frac{\partial V_y}{\partial y}, \quad \text{and} \quad \mathscr{E}_z = -\frac{\partial V_z}{\partial z},$$

Equation I.8 can be written as

$$\frac{\partial^2 V_x}{\partial x^2} + \frac{\partial^2 V_y}{\partial y} + \frac{\partial^2 V_z}{\partial z^2} = -\frac{\rho}{\epsilon} \qquad (I.9)$$

This equation is known as Poisson's equation. When no charge is present in the volume, the charge density is zero. In this case, Eq. I.9 becomes

$$\frac{\partial^2 V_x}{\partial x^2} + \frac{\partial^2 V_y}{\partial y^2} + \frac{\partial^2 V_z}{\partial z^2} = 0 \qquad (I.10)$$

This equation is known as Laplace's equation. In terms of vector notation, Poisson's Equation (Eq. I.9) can be written as

$$\nabla^2 \mathbf{V} = -\frac{\rho}{\epsilon} \qquad (I.11)$$

and Laplace's equation (Eq. I.10) can be written as

$$\nabla^2 \mathbf{V} = 0 \qquad (I.12)$$

Appendix
II

Feedback circuits have the general configuration shown in Fig. II.1. As indicated in Section 11.1, the transfer function G_{13} for this type of circuit can be written as

$$G_{13} = \frac{G_{23}}{1 + G_{23}G_{34}} \tag{11.6}$$

The feedback is known as negative when the denominator of the total transfer function G_{13} contains a plus sign as in the case of Eq. 11.6. On

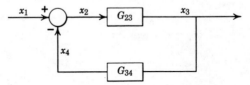

Fig. II.1. The block diagram of a feedback system.

the other hand, when the feedback is positive, the polarities of the signals x_1 and x_4 of Fig. II.1 are alike and the total transfer function becomes

$$G_{13} = \frac{G_{23}}{1 - G_{23}G_{34}} \tag{II.1}$$

In the general case, the transfer functions G_{23} and G_{34} are complex functions of s. Accordingly, the transfer functions, G_{23} and G_{34} can be written as

$$G_{23} = H_1 \frac{P_1(s)}{Q_1(s)} \tag{II.2}$$

and

$$G_{34} = H_2 \frac{P_2(s)}{Q_2(s)} \tag{II.3}$$

where H_1 and H_2 are constants and $P_1(s)$, $P_2(s)$, $Q_1(s)$, and $Q_2(s)$ are polynomials of s. Therefore, Eqs. 11.6 and II.1 become

$$G_{13} = \frac{H_1 \dfrac{P_1(s)}{Q_1(s)}}{1 \pm H_1 H_2 \dfrac{P_1(s)P_2(s)}{Q_1(s)Q_2(s)}} \tag{II.4}$$

Usually the product $H_1 H_2$ is written as K. Simplifying, Eq. II.4 becomes

$$G_{13} = H_1 \frac{\dfrac{P_1(s)}{Q_1(s)}}{\dfrac{Q_1(s)Q_2(s) \pm KP_1(s)P_2(s)}{Q_1(s)Q_2(s)}} \tag{II.5}$$

or

$$G_{13} = H_1 \frac{P_1(s)Q_2(s)}{Q_1(s)Q_2(s) \pm KP_1(s)P_2(s)} \tag{II.6}$$

To determine the time response of this transfer function to a specific excitation, the denominator of Eq. II.6 must be factored. In other words, the roots of the denominator or poles of the transfer function must be found. The zeros of the complete transfer function (Eq. II.6) are known because the numerator is normally in factored form.[1]

A different set of poles of the complete transfer function exists for each different value of K. For example, inspection of Eq. II.6 shows that if K approaches zero, the roots or poles of G_{13} approach the roots of $Q_1(s)Q_2(s)$ which are the poles of the open-loop transfer function $G_{23}G_{34}$. In contrast, as K becomes very large the roots or poles of G_{13} approach the roots of $P_1(s)P_2(s)$ which are the zeros of $G_{23}G_{24}$. The root-locus plot is, as the name implies, a plot of the loci of all the possible poles of G_{13} as K is varied from 0 to ∞.

To obtain the root-locus plot, Eq. II.4 is rewritten as

$$G_{13} = H \frac{\dfrac{(P_{1c}s)}{Q_1(s)}}{1 \pm KF(s)} \tag{II.7}$$

[1] The reader should be careful to preserve the known zeros by writing the polynomials as

$$P = (s + a)(s_1 + a_2) \cdots$$

and not lose the identity of these known zeros by writing the polynomial as

$$P = s^n + b_1 s^{n-1} + b_2 s^{n-2} + \cdots b$$

where

$$F(s) = \frac{P_1(s)P_2(s)}{Q_1(s)Q(s)} \tag{II.8}$$

The root locus is a plot of

$$KF(s) = \mp 1 \tag{II.9a}$$

Therefore,

$$F(s) = \mp 1/K \tag{II.9b}$$

A set of rules has been developed to simplify the plotting of Eq. II.9. Since the proof of these rules is given in the literature,[2] the rules (with no proof) will be given in this Appendix.

1. A pole-zero plot is made of the function $F(s)$ of Eq. II.8.
2. Each root-locus branch departs from a pole of $F(s)$ as K increases from zero and terminates at a zero of $F(s)$ as K approaches infinity.
3. The number of individual paths or branches is equal to the number of poles of $F(s)$. (In all actual circuits, the number of poles is equal to or greater than the number of zeros.)
4. Since poles only occur on the real axis or as conjugate pairs, the root-locus plot will be symmetrical with respect to the real axis.
5. If the number of finite poles of $F(s)$ is n and the number of finite zeros of $F(s)$ is m, $n - m$ branches will extend to ∞ as K approaches ∞. (In addition, it is possible for a branch to extend through ∞ in going from a finite pole to a finite zero.)
6. (a) For a positive feedback, the portions of the real axis to the right of all finite poles and zeros and to the left of an even number of poles and zeros are branches of the root locus. (b) For negative feedback, the portions of the real axis to the left of an odd number of finite poles and zeros are branches of the root locus.

The foregoing six rules (and other rules to follow) are illustrated by Fig. II.2.

7. As the infinite-seeking branches become far removed from the finite poles and zeros of the function $F(s)$, these infinite-seeking branches approach asymptotes that intersect on the real axis. To facilitate the root-locus plots, these asymptotes must be found. $F(s)$ is of the form

$$F(s) = \frac{(s + z_1)(s + z_2)(s + z_3) \cdots (s + z_m)}{(s + p_1)(s + p_2)(s + p_3) \cdots (s + p_n)} \tag{II.10}$$

The asympotes will intersect on the real axis at a value A where

$$A = \frac{\displaystyle\sum_{m=1}^{m=m} z_m - \sum_{n=1}^{n=n} p_n}{n - m} \tag{II.11}$$

[2] See L. Dale Harris, *Introduction to Feedback Systems*, John Wiley and Sons, New York, 1961.

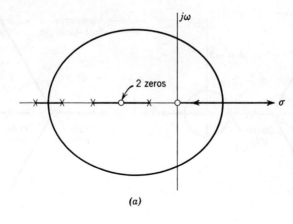

(a)

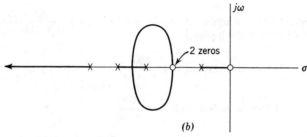

(b)

Fig. II.2. A root-locus plot for $F(s) = \dfrac{s(s+2)^2}{(s+1)(s+3)(s+4)(s+5)}$. (a) Positive feedback; (b) negative feedback.

8. As noted in rule five, the number of infinite-seeking branches is $n - m$. The angles of the asymptotes for these branches are found in the following manner;

(a) For positive feedback, the angles of the asymptotes are:

$$1\text{st angle} = 0° \tag{II.12}$$

$$2\text{nd angle} = \frac{360°}{n - m}$$

$$3\text{rd angle} = 2\frac{360°}{n - m}$$

$$k\text{th angle} = (k - 1)\frac{360°}{n - m} \tag{II.13}$$

(b) For negative feedback, the angles of the asymptotes are:

$$1\text{st angle} = \frac{360°}{2(n - m)} \tag{II.14}$$

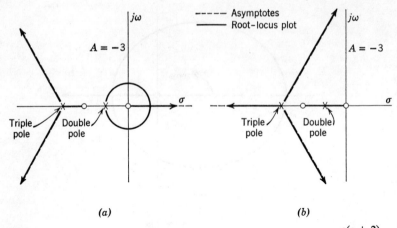

Fig. II.3. The asymptotes for the infinite-seeking branches of $F(s) + \dfrac{s(s + 2)}{(s + 1)^2(s + 3)^3}$. (a) Positive feedback; (b) negative feedback.

$$2\text{nd angle} = 1\text{st angle} + \frac{360°}{n - m}$$

$$3\text{rd angle} = 2\text{nd angle} + \frac{360°}{n - m}$$

$$k\text{th angle} = (k - 1)\text{th angle} + \frac{360°}{n - m} \tag{II.15}$$

The rules seven and eight are illustrated in Fig. II.3, where $n - m = 3$ and in Fig. II.4 where $n - m = 4$.

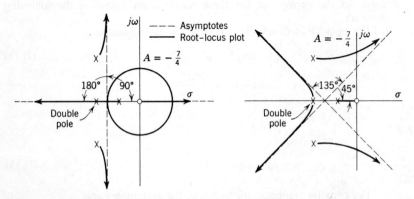

Fig. II.4. The asymptotes for the infinite seeking branches of

$$F(s) = \frac{s}{(s + 1)(s + 2)^2(s + 2 + j2)(s + 2 - j2)}.$$

9. When there are at least *two* more poles than zeros in the function $F(s)$, the sum of the roots (poles of G_{13}) for a given value of K are equal to a constant which is independent of K. This constant is equal to the sum of the poles of $F(s)$. Hence, as one locus moves to the right with increasing K, one or more other branches must move to the left as shown in Fig. II.5. Also note that as one locus increases in the $+j\omega$ direction, another locus increases in the $-j\omega$ direction (rule 4).

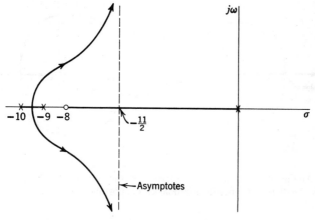

Fig. II.5. A root-locus plot for negative feedback where $F(s) = \dfrac{s + 8}{s(s + 9)(s + 10)}$.

The angle at which a branch approaches or leaves a pole or zero can also be found. These angles are known as departure angles and will be considered next.

10. The departure angle from *single* poles or zeros on the real axis will always be along the real axis. Rule 6 determines the direction of departure.
11. The departure angle from *double* poles or zeros on the real axis will either lie along the real axis or be at right angles to the real axis. Again, rule 6 will determine the direction.
12. When a third-order or triple pole (or zero) lies on the real axis, one root-locus branch will always depart from this triple pole along the real axis. The other two branches will depart at 120° angles from this real axis branch. Rule 6 determines the direction of departure along the real axis. In general, there will be as many departing branches as there are poles or zeros at the given location. In addition, if there are k poles or zeros, the angle between adjacent directions of departure will be $360°/k$. Rule 6 will determine the directions of departure along the real axis. In any case, the directions of departures will be symmetrical with respect to the real axis (rule 4). Rules 10, 11, and 12 are illustrated in Fig. II.6.
13. The departure angle from poles not on the real axis can be found by using Eq. II.10.

$$F(s) = \frac{(s + z_1)(s + z_2)(s + z_3) \cdots (s + z_m)}{(s + p_1)(s + p_2)(s + p_3) \cdots (s + p_n)} \tag{II.10}$$

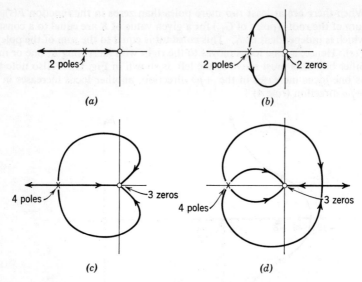

Fig. II.6. An illustration of departure angles from the real axis. (*a*) Negative feedback; (*b*) negative feedback; (*c*) negative feedback; (*d*) positive feedback.

Now, assume the required departure is from pole p_2. Let s approach $-p_2$ and rewrite Eq. II.10 as

$$F(-p_2) = \frac{(-p_2 + z_1)(-p_2 + z_2)(-p_2 + z_3) \cdots (-p_2 + z_m)}{(-p_2 + p_1)\delta/\underline{\psi}(-p_2 + p_3) \cdots (-p_2 + p_n)} \quad \text{(II.16)}$$

where $\delta/\underline{\psi}$ is the distance and direction from a point on the locus to p_2. Convert each of the terms $(-p_2 + z_m)$ and $(-p_2 + p_n)$ etc. to the polar form. Then Eq. II.16 becomes

$$F(-p_2) = \frac{Z_1 {}^{/\underline{\phi_1}} Z_2 {}^{/\underline{\phi_2}} Z_3 {}^{/\underline{\phi_3}} \cdots Z_m {}^{/\underline{\phi_m}}}{P_1 {}^{/\underline{\theta_1}} \delta {}^{/\underline{\psi}} P_3 {}^{/\underline{\theta_3}} \cdots P_n {}^{/\underline{\theta_n}}} \quad \text{(II.17)}$$

For positive feedback,

$$\phi_1 + \phi_2 + \phi_3 + \cdots + \phi_m - \theta_1 - \psi - \theta_3 - \cdots - \theta_n = 0° \quad \text{(II.18)}$$

For negative feedback,

$$\phi_1 + \phi_2 + \phi_3 + \cdots + \phi_m - \theta_m - \theta_1 - \psi - \theta_3 - \cdots - \theta_n = 180° \quad \text{(II.19)}$$

All of the angles in Eq, II.18 and Eq. II.19 are known except ψ. The angle ψ is the departure angle from p_2. The same approach is used to determine the departure angles from zeros not on the real axis. However, in this case, Eq. II.18 becomes

$$\phi_1 + \psi + \phi_3 + \cdots \phi_m - \theta_1 - \theta_2 - \theta_3 - \cdots - \theta_n = 0° \quad \text{(II.20)}$$

and Eq. II.19 becomes

$$\phi_1 + \psi + \phi_3 + \cdots \phi_m - \theta_1 - \theta_2 - \theta_3 - \cdots - \theta_n = 180° \quad \text{(II.21)}$$

14. When two branches cross the real axis or depart from the real axis, the departure angle is always 90°. The point of departure from the real axis can be found by trial and error from the following procedure:

(a) Assume a point of departure from the real axis.

(b) Transpose any singularities not on the real axis to an equivalent location on the real axis by the following procedure:

1. Draw a straight line (L_1) from the singularity to be transposed to the assumed departure point.

2. Draw a straight line (L_2) through the singularity and normal to the line L_1.

3. The intersection of line L_2 and the real axis is the required equivalent location for the singularity.

(c) After transposing all of the singularities to their equivalent location on the real axis, apply the rule

$$\sum \frac{1}{P_{\ell i}} + \sum \frac{1}{Z_{rj}} = \sum \frac{1}{P_{ri}} + \sum \frac{1}{Z_{\ell j}} \quad \text{(II.22)}$$

where $P_{\ell i}$ is the distance from the ith pole (left of the departure point) to the assumed departure point.

P_{ri} is the distance from the ith pole (right of the departure point) to the departure point.

Z_{rj} is the distance from the jth zero (right of the departure point) to the assumed departure point.

$Z_{\ell j}$ is the distance from the jth zero (left of the departure point) to the assumed departure point.

(d) If the assumed point of departure does not satisfy Eq. II.22, a second trial point must be selected and the foregoing steps repeated. Fortunately, good initial trial points can be made by an experienced root-locus plotter.

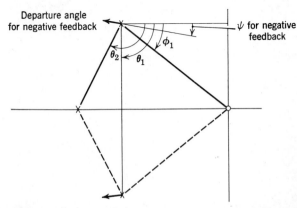

Fig. II.7. An illustration of the departure angle from a pole not on the real axis.

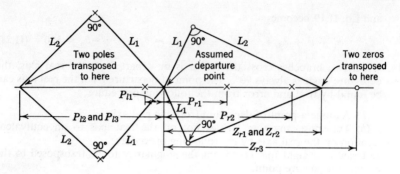

Negative feedback

Fig. II.8. A method of determining the point of departure from the real axis.

Fig. II.8 will help clarify the foregoing procedure.

The foregoing list of rules will help the uninitiated reader in simple root-locus plots. A device known as a *spirule* can be used to speed up the plotting process when accurate plots are required. However, in most situations a rough sketch is sufficient to obtain a fairly good idea of how the given feedback circuit will perform. In these cases, the foregoing rules can quickly be applied to obtain the rough sketch.

Appendix III

Transistor and Tube Characteristics

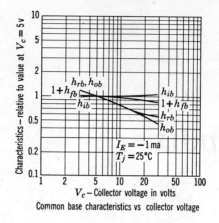

Common base characteristics vs collector voltage

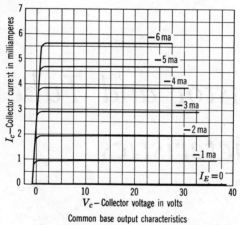

Common base output characteristics

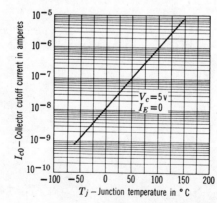

Collector cutoff current vs junction temperature

Fig. III.1. Characteristics of the 2N117 transistor. (Courtesy of Texas Instruments Inc.)

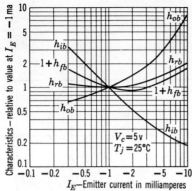

Common base characteristics vs emitter current

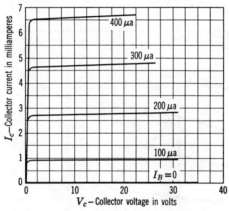

Common emitter output characteristics

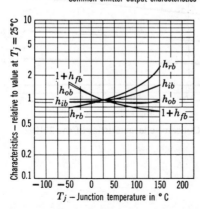

Common base characteristics vs junction temperature

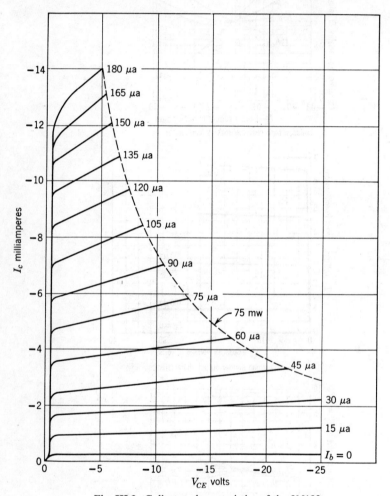

Fig. III.2. Collector characteristics of the 2N192.

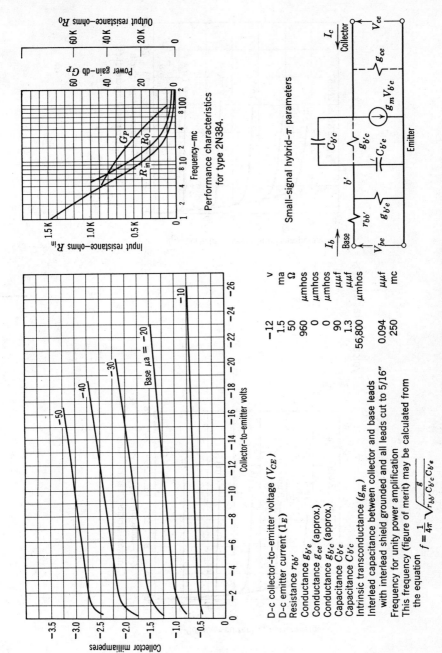

D-c collector-to-emitter voltage (V_{CE}) −12 v
D-c emitter current (I_E) 1.5 ma
Resistance $r_{bb'}$ 50 Ω
Conductance $g_{b'e}$ 960 μmhos
Conductance g_{ce} (approx.) 0 μmhos
Conductance $g_{b'c}$ (approx.) 0 μmhos
Capacitance $C_{b'e}$ 90 μμf
Capacitance $C_{b'c}$ 1.3 μμf
Intrinsic transconductance (g_m) 56,800 μmhos
Interlead capacitance between collector and base leads
  with interlead shield grounded and all leads cut to 5/16″ 0.094 μμf
Frequency for unity power amplification 250 mc
This frequency (figure of merit) may be calculated from
the equation $f = \dfrac{1}{4\pi} \sqrt{\dfrac{g}{r_{bb'} C_{b'c} C_{b'e}}}$

Fig. III.3. Characteristics of the 2N384 transistor. (Courtesy of Radio Corporation of America.)

Typical Characteristics

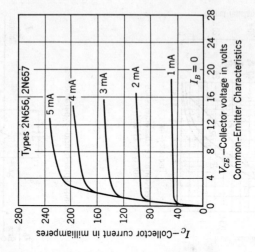

Types 2N656, 2N657

Common–Emitter Characteristics
V_{CE} –Collector voltage in volts
I_C –Collector current in milliamperes

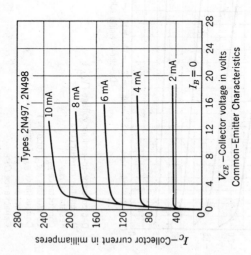

Types 2N497, 2N498

Common–Emitter Characteristics
V_{CE} –Collector voltage in volts
I_C –Collector current in milliamperes

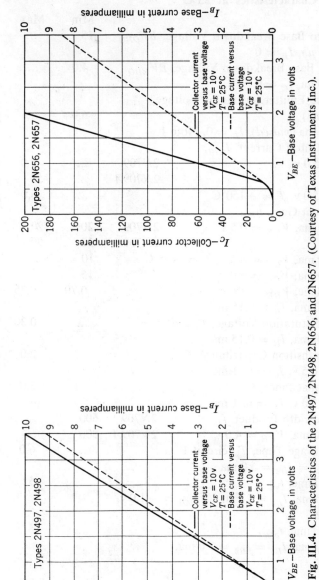

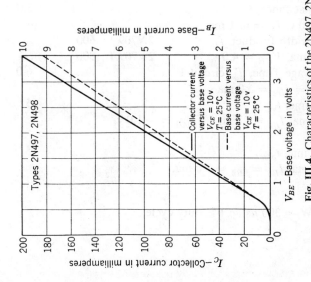

Fig. III.4. Characteristics of the 2N497, 2N498, 2N656, and 2N657. (Courtesy of Texas Instruments Inc.).

Electrical Characteristics at 25°C

		Min	Max	Unit
Collector to Base Breakdown Voltage, BV_{CBO}		15	...	volts
$I_C = 10\ \mu a,\ I_E = 0$				
Emitter to Base Breakdown Voltage, BV_{EBO}		4.0	...	volts
$I_E = 10\ \mu a,\ I_C = 0$				
Collector to Emitter Sustaining Voltage,				
$\quad V_{CEO}(sust)$		6.0	...	volts
$I_C = 10\ ma\ (pulsed),\ I_B = 0$, Note 1				
Collector Cutoff Current, I_{CBO}				
$\quad V_{CB} = 5.0\ v$	2N709	...	5.0	na
	2N709A	...	50	na
$\quad V_{CB} = 5.0\ v,\ T = +150°C$		...	5.0	μa
D.C. Current Gain, h_{FE}				
$\quad I_C = 10\ ma,\ V_{CE} = 0.5\ v$	2N709	20	120	
	2N709A	30	90	
$\quad I_C = 10\ ma,\ V_{CE} = 0.5\ v,\ T = -55°C$		10	...	
$\quad I_C = 30\ ma,\ V_{CE} = 1.0\ v$		15	...	
Input Voltage, V_{BE}		0.70	0.85	volts
$\quad I_C = 3.0\ ma,\ I_B = 0.15\ ma$				
Collector Saturation Voltage, $V_{CE}sat$		...	0.30	volts
$\quad I_C = 3.0\ ma,\ I_B = 0.15\ ma$				
Emitter Transition Capacitance, C_{TE}		...	2.0	pf
$\quad V_{EB} = 0.5\ v,\ I_C = 0,\ 1\ mc$				
Output Capacitance, C_{ob}		...	3.0	pf
$\quad V_{CB} = 5.0\ v,\ I_E = 0,\ 1\ mc$				
Gain Bandwidth Product, f_t	2N709	600	...	MHz
$\quad I_C = 5.0\ ma,\ V_{CE} = 4.0\ v$	2N709A	800	...	MHz
Charge Storage Time, T_s, circuit 1		...	6.0	nsec
$\quad I_C = I_{B1} = I_{B2} = 5.0\ ma$				
Turn On Time, t_{on}		...	15	nsec
$\quad I_C = 10\ ma,\ I_{B1} = 2\ ma,\ V_{BE(O)} = -1.0\ v,$				
$\quad circuit\ 2$				
Turn Off Time, t_{off}		...	15	nsec
$\quad I_C = 10\ ma,\ I_{B1} = I_{B2} = 1.0\ ma,$				
$\quad circuit\ 2$				

Note 1. PW = 300 μs @ 1% duty cycle.

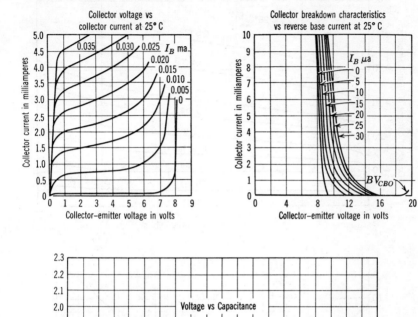

Fig. III.5. Characteristics of the 2N709 and 2N709A. (Courtesy of Sylvania Electric Products.)

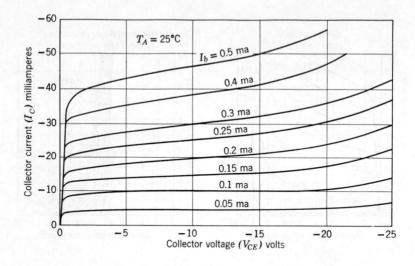

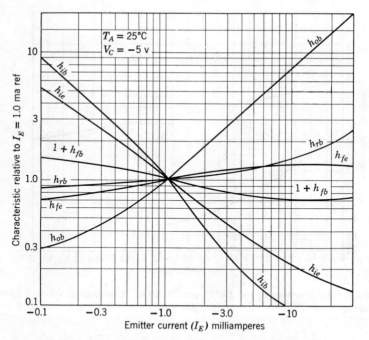

Fig. III.6. Characteristics of the 2N1415. (Courtesy of General Electric Co.)

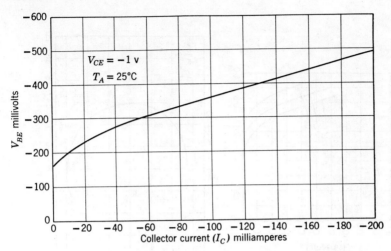

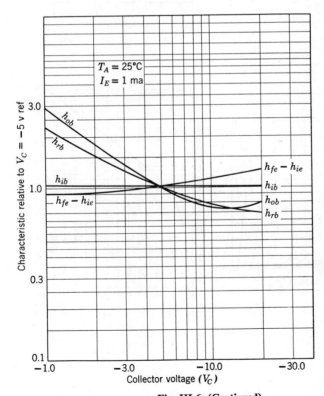

Fig. III.6. (Continued)

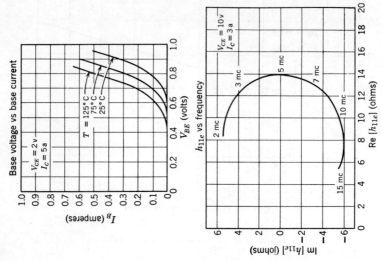

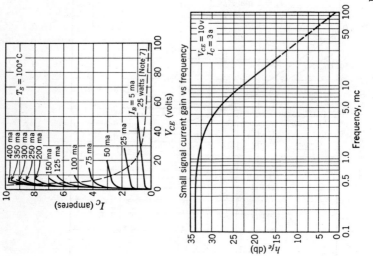

Fig. III.7.

ELECTRICAL CHARACTERISTICS (25°C Stud Temperature unless Otherwise Noted)

Symbol	Characteristics	Test Conditions	Min	Typical	Max	Unit
I_{CBO}	Collector Cut-off Current	$V_{CBO} = 60$ V, $T = 125°C$		20	120	mA
		$= 60$ V,		15		mA
		$= 140$ V		38	250	mA
I_{CER}	Collector Cut-off Current	$V_{CER} = 100$ V, $R = 10\ \Omega$		36	250	mA
V_{EBO}	Emitter-Base Voltage	$I_{EBO} = 100$ mA	5	7.2		Volts
$V_{CE}(\text{sat})$	Collector Saturation Voltage	$I_C = 10$ A, $I_B = 1$ A		0.5	2	Volts
$V_{BE}(\text{sat})$	Base Saturation Voltage	$I_C = 10$ A, $I_B = 1$ A		1.0	2.5	Volts
h_{FE}	DC Current Gain	$V_{CE} = 2$ V, $I_C = 10$ A	10	21		
h_{FE}	Pulsed DC Current Gain (Note 2)	$V_{CE} = 5$ V, $I_C = 10$ A		37		
h_{fe}	Small Signal Current Gain	$V_{CE} = 10$ V, $I_C = 3$ A, $f = 10$ mc		10		
$h_{fe} \cdot f_{hfe}$	Current Gain—Bandwidth Product (Note 3)	$V_{CB} = 10$ V, $I_C = 3$ A	50			mc
C_{ob}	Collector-Base Capacitance	$V_{CR} = 10$ V, $I_E = 0$		0.0006		μf

Fig. III.7. Characteristics of the 2N1899 (similar to the 2N1937). (Courtesy of Pacific Semiconductors, Inc.)

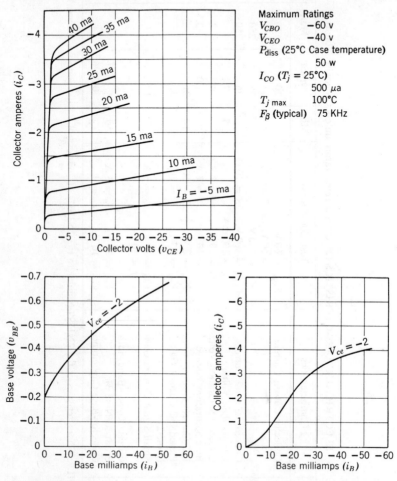

Maximum Ratings
V_{CBO} -60 v
V_{CEO} -40 v
P_{diss} (25°C Case temperature)
                50 w
I_{CO} ($T_j = 25$°C)
                500 μa
$T_{j\ max}$ 100°C
F_β (typical)   75 KHz

Fig. III.8. Characteristics of the 2N1905 transistor. (Courtesy of RCA.)

MAXIMUM RATINGS

Collector-to-Base Voltage.............................	−75 max	volts
Collector-to-Emitter Voltage	−50 max	volts
Emitter-to-Base Voltage	−1.5 max	volts
Collector Current...................................	−5 max	amperes
Base Current.......................................	−1 max	ampere
Emitter Current	5 max	amperes

Transistor Dissipation:

At mounting-flange temperatures up to 81°C..........	12.5 max	watts
At mounting-flange temperatures above 81°C..........	Derate 0.66 watt/°C	

Temperature Range:

Operating (junction) and Storage	−65 to 100	°C
Lead Temperature (for 10 seconds maximum)	255 max	°C

CHARACTERISTICS

Collector-to-Base Breakdown Voltage (with collector ma = −10 and emitter current = 0)......................	−75 min	volts
Collector-to-Emitter Breakdown Voltage (with collector ma = −100 and base current = 0)..................	−50 min	volts
Base-to-Emitter Voltage (with collector-to-emitter volts = −10 and collector ma = −50)	−0.24	volt
Collector-Cutoff Current (with collector-to-base volts = −40 and emitter current = 0)......................	−1 max	ma
Collector-Cutoff Saturation Current (with collector-to-base volt = −0.5 and emitter current = 0)	−70 max	μa
Emitter-Cutoff Current (with emitter-to-base volts = −1.5 and collector current = 0)	−2.5 max	ma

Thermal Resistance:

Junction-to-case	1.5 max °C/watt	

In Common-Emitter Circuit

DC Forward Current-Transfer Ratio (with collector-to-emitter volts = −1 and collector ma = −1000)	150	
Gain-Bandwidth Product (with collector-to-emitter volts = −5 and collector ma = −500)	4	Mc

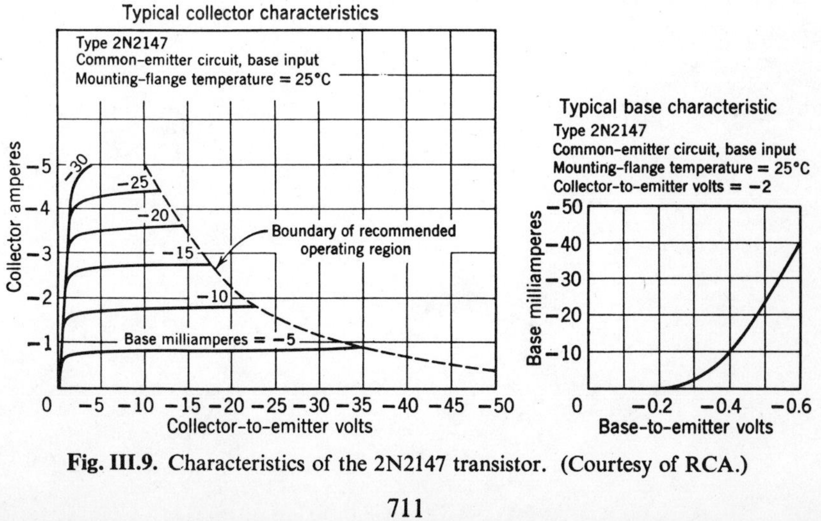

Fig. III.9. Characteristics of the 2N2147 transistor. (Courtesy of RCA.)

I. *Absolute Maximum Ratings* (25°)

  A. Voltage

    V_{CEO} 18 v

    V_{BEO} 5 v

    V_{CBO} 18 v

  B. Current

    I_C 100 ma

  C. Dissipation

    P_t (25°C free air)   200 mw

    P_t (55°C free air)   120 mw

II. *Electrical Characteristics* (*DC*) (25°C *unless otherwise specified*)

  A. D-C Characteristics

    I_{CO} 0.5 μa (max)

    h_{fe} 225 (max)

    h_{ie} (large sig)   = 222

  B. Small-Signal Characteristics (common emitter $V_{CE} = 5$ v $I = 2$ ma $F = 455$ KHz)

    h_{ce} $169/\!-42°$

    h_{ie} $2580/\!-41°$

    h_{re} $0.071/48°$

    h_{oe} $4770/48°$

  C. Other Data

    Collector cap.   12 pf (max)

    Noise figure   2.8 db

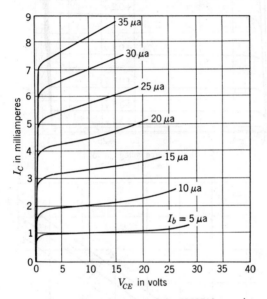

Fig. III.10. Characteristics of the 2N2712 transistor.

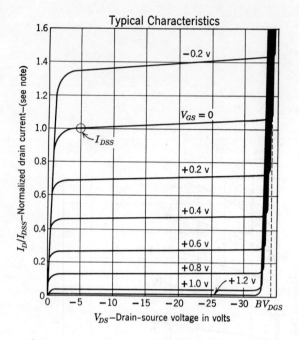

Typical Characteristics

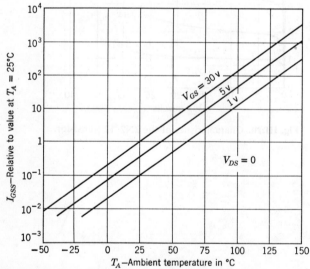

Fig. III.11. Characteristics of the 2N2841-2-3-4 field effect transistors. (Courtesy of Siliconix Incorporated.) *Note:* Drain-current scale has been normalized. To obtain curves for specific device, use the following scale factor:

Type	Multiply Current Scale by:
2N2841	$-56\,\mu a$
2N2842	$-170\,\mu a$
2N2843	$-500\,\mu a$
2N2844	$-1100\,\mu a$

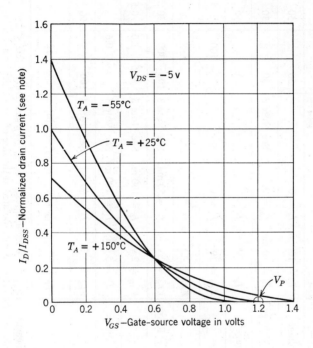

electrical characteristics at 25°C free-air temperature

Parameter	Test Conditions	2N3704 Min	2N3704 Max	2N3705 Min	2N3705 Max	2N3706 Min	2N3706 Max	Unit
$V_{(BR)CBO}$ Collector-Base Breakdown Voltage	$I_C = 100\ \mu a,\ I_E = 0$	50		50		40		v
$V_{(BR)CEO}$ Collector-Emitter Breakdown Voltage	$I_C = 10$ ma, $I_B = 0$, See Note 3	30		30		20		v
$V_{(BR)EBO}$ Emitter-Base Breakdown Voltage	$I_E = 100\ \mu a,\ I_C = 0$	5		5		5		v
I_{CBO} Collector Cutoff Current	$V_{CB} = 20$ v, $I_E = 0$		100		100		100	na
I_{EBO} Emitter Cutoff Current	$V_{EB} = 3$ v, $I_C = 0$		100		100		100	na
h_{FE} Static Forward Current Transfer Ratio	$V_{CE} = 2$ v, $I_C = 50$ ma, See Note 3	100	300	50	150	30	600	
V_{BE} Base-Emitter Voltage	$V_{CE} = 2$ v, $I_C = 100$ ma, See Note 3	0.5	1.0	0.5	1.0	0.5	1.0	v
$V_{CE(sat)}$ Collector-Emitter Saturation Voltage	$I_B = 5$ ma, $I_C = 100$ ma, See Note 3		0.6		0.8		1.0	v
f_T Transition Frequency	$V_{CE} = 2$ v, $I_C = 50$ ma, See Note 4	100		100		100		Mc
C_{obo} Common-Base Open-Circuit Output Capacitance	$V_{CB} = 10$ v, $I_E = 0$, $f = 1$ Mc		12		12		12	pf

NOTES: 3. These parameters must be measured using pulse techniques. PW = 300 μsec. Duty Cycle $\leq 2\%$.
4. To obtain f_T, the $|h_{fe}|$ response with frequency is extrapolated at the rate of -6 db per octave from $f = 20$ Mc to the frequency at which $|h_{fe}| = 1$.

TYPICAL CHARACTERISTICS

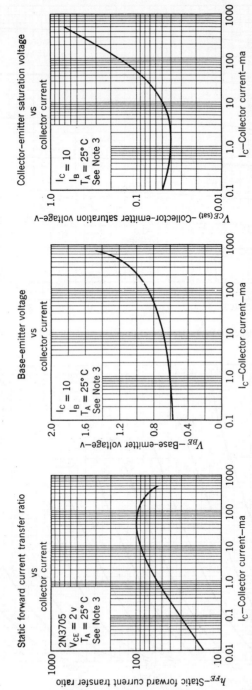

Fig. III.12. Characteristics of the 2N3704, 2N3705 and 2N3706 transistors. The 2N3703 is simliar to the 2N3705 and the 2N3702 is similar to the 2N3706 except they are pnp. (Courtesy of Texas Instruments Inc, Dallas, Texas.)

717

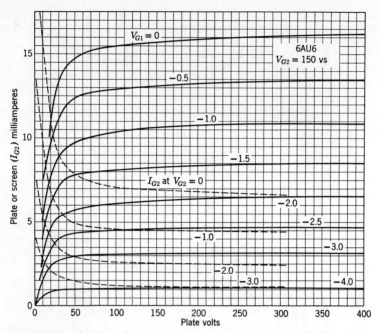

Fig. III.13. Characteristics of the 6AU6 tube. (Courtesy of the Radio Corporation of America.)

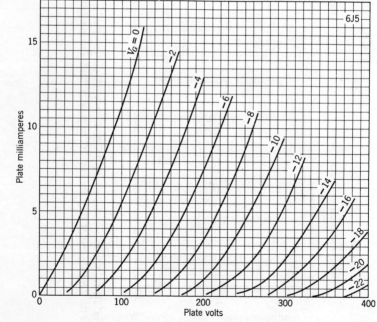

Fig. III.14. Characteristics of the 6J5 tube. (Courtesy of Radio Corporation of America.)

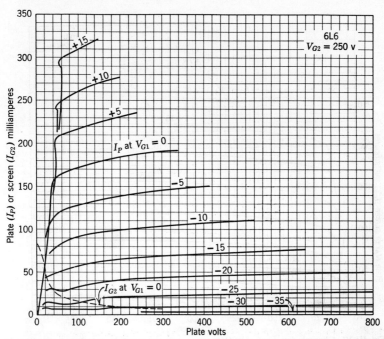

Fig. III.15. Characteristics of the 6L6 Beam Power tube. (Courtesy of Radio Corporation of America.)

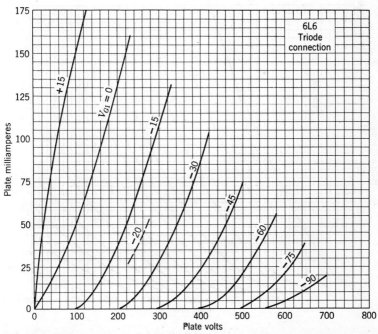

Fig. III.16. Characteristics of the 6L6 triode connected. (Courtesy of Radio Corporation of America.)

719

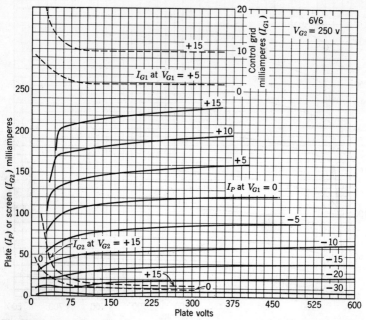

Fig. III.17. Characteristics of the 6V6 tube. (Courtesy of Radio Corporation of America.)

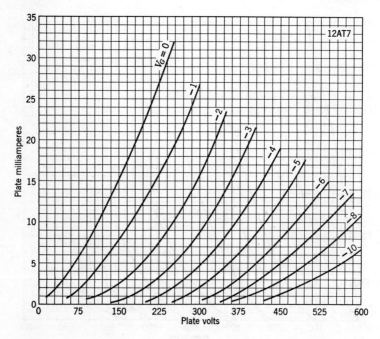

Fig. III.18. Characteristics of the 12AT7 tube. (Courtesy of Radio Corporation of America.)

720

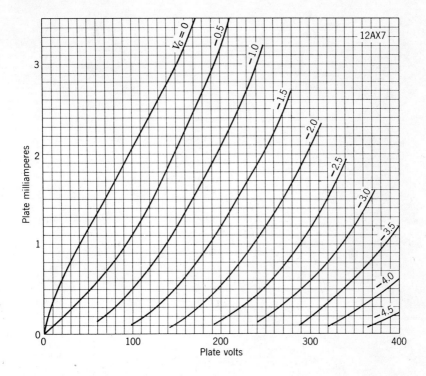

Fig. III.19. Characteristics of the 12AX7 tube. (Courtesy of Radio Corporation of America.)

Appendix
IV

p	$J_P(1)$	$J_P(2)$	$J_P(3)$	$J_P(4)$	$J_P(5)$	$J_P(6)$	$J_P(7)$	$J_P(8)$	$J_P(9)$	$J_P(10)$	$J_P(11)$	$J_P(12)$	$J_P(13)$	$J_P(14)$
0	+.7652	+.2239	−.2601	−.3971	−.1776	+.1506	+.3001	+.1717	−.09033	−.2459	−.1712	+.04769	+.2069	+.1711
0.5	+.6714	+.5130	+.06501	−.3019	−.3422	−.09102	+.1981	+.2791	+.1096	−.1373	−.2406	−.1236	+.09298	+.2112
1.0	+.4401	+.5767	+.3391	−.06604	−.3276	−.2767	$-.0^2 4683$	+.2346	+.2453	+.04347	−.1768	−.2234	−.07032	−.1334
1.5	+.2403	+.4913	+.4777	+.1853	−.1697	−.3279	−.1991	$+.0^2 7593$	+.2545	+.1980	−.02293	−.2047	−.1937	−.01407
2.0	+.1149	+.3528	+.4861	+.3641	+.04657	−.2429	−.3014	−.1130	+.1448	+.2546	+.1390	−.08493	−.2177	−.1520
2.5	+.04950	+.2239	+.4127	+.4409	+.2404	−.07295	−.2834	−.2506	$-.0^2 2477$	+.1967	+.2343	+.07242	−.1377	−.2143
3.0	+.01956	+.1289	+.3091	+.4302	+.3648	+.1148	−.1676	−.2911	−.1809	+.05838	+.2273	+.1951	$+.0^3 3320$	−.1768
3.5	$+.0^2 7186$	+.06852	+.2101	+.3658	+.4100	+.2671	$-.0^2 3403$	−.2326	−.2683	−.09965	+.1294	+.2348	+.1407	−.06245
4.0	$+.0^2 2477$	+.03400	+.1320	+.2811	+.3912	+.3576	+.1578	−.1054	−.2655	−.2196	−.01504	+.1825	+.2193	+.07624
4.5	$+.0^3 807$	+.01589	+.07760	+.1993	+.3337	+.3846	+.2800	$+.0^2 4712$	−.1839	−.2664	−.1519	+.06457	+.2134	+.1830
5.0	$+.0^3 2498$	$+.0^2 7040$	+.04303	+.1321	+.2611	+.3621	+.3479	+.1858	−.05504	−.2341	−.2383	−.07347	+.1316	+.2204
5.5	$+.0^4 74$	$+.0^2 2973$	+.02266	+.08261	+.1906	+.3098	+.3634	+.2856	$-.0^2 8439$	−.1401	−.2538	−.1864	$+.0^2 7055$	+.1801
6.0	$+.0^4 2094$	$+.0^2 1202$	+.01139	+.04909	+.1310	+.2458	+.3392	+.3376	+.2043	−.01446	−.2016	−.2437	−.1180	+.08117
6.5	$+.0^5 6$	$+.0^3 467$	$+.0^2 5493$	+.02787	+.08558	+.1833	+.2911	+.3456	+.2870	+.1123	−.1018	−.2354	−.2075	−.04151
7.0	$+.0^5 1502$	$+.0^3 1749$	$+.0^2 2547$	+.01518	+.05338	+.1296	+.2336	+.3206	+.3275	+.2167	+.01838	−.1703	−.2406	−.1508
7.5	—	—	—	—	—	+.08741	+.1772	+.2759	+.3302	+.2861	+.1334	−.06865	−.2145	−.2187
8.0	$+.0^7 9422$	$+.0^4 2218$	$+.0^3 4934$	$+.0^2 4029$	+.01841	+.05653	+.1280	+.2235	+.3051	+.3179	+.2250	+.04510	−.1410	−.2320
8.5	—	—	—	—	—	+.03520	+.08854	+.1718	+.2633	+.3169	+.2838	+.1496	−.04006	−.1928
9.0	$+.0^8 5249$	$+.0^5 2492$	$+.0^4 8440$	$+.0^3 9386$	$+.0^2 5520$	+.02117	+.05892	+.1263	+.2149	+.2919	+.3089	+.2304	+.06698	−.1143
9.5	—	—	—	—	—	+.01232	+.03785	+.08921	+.1672	+.2526	+.3051	+.2806	+.1621	−.01541
10.0	$+.0^9 2631$	$+.0^6 2515$	$+.0^4 1293$	$+.0^3 1950$	$+.0^2 1468$	$+.0^2 6964$	+.02354	+.06077	+.1247	+.2075	+.2804	+.3005	+.2338	+.08501

Note: $.0^2 7186$ = .007186 and $.0^3 807$ = .000807.

Index

725